W9-CNN-642

THE DRAWINGS OF
PAUL CÉZANNE

A CATALOGUE RAISONNÉ

VOLUME I

THE DRAWINGS

OF PAUL

CÉZANNE

A Catalogue Raisonné

by ADRIEN CHAPPUIS

VOLUME I

INTRODUCTION AND CATALOGUE

NEW YORK GRAPHIC SOCIETY LTD.

GREENWICH, CONNECTICUT

Translated from the French:

Introduction by Paul Constable and M. and Mme Jacques Féjoz

Catalogue by Barbara Marchutz

Edited by Betty Morrison Childs

Designed by Philip Grushkin

International Standard Book Number 0-8212-0427-0
Library of Congress Catalog Card Number 72-187143

130913

© 1973 by Adrien Chappuis
First published 1973 by New York Graphic Society Ltd.,
140 Greenwich Ave., Greenwich, Conn., 06830
First printing 1973

Set in Monophoto Baskerville by Reproof Ltd., London, England
Lithographed by The Murray Printing Company, Forge Village, Massachusetts
Bound by A. Horowitz and Son, Clifton, New Jersey

Manufactured in the U.S.A.

CONTENTS

THE DRAWINGS OF

PAUL CÉZANNE

A CATALOGUE RAISONNÉ

VOLUME I

INTRODUCTION

1. *The catalogue and its antecedents*

In this catalogue of the drawings of Paul Cézanne, most of the artist's drawings known to us at the present time are reproduced and described. A few wash and pastel works have been included with the drawings, but—with negligible exceptions—the watercolored drawings are not to be found here: these will be classified with the watercolors in the catalogue of Cézanne's paintings and watercolors that John Rewald is now preparing. How can one, in fact, establish a sharp distinction between the watercolored drawings and the watercolors, which nearly all include some pencil work?[1]

This catalogue is preceded, of course, by that of Lionello Venturi, or more precisely, by that part of his work dealing with the drawings. But here we must dispel a misunderstanding that is all too likely to arise. This Italian scholar devoted the last years of his life to preparing a new edition of his catalogue of Cézanne's paintings and watercolors, but from it *he intended to exclude the drawings.* He wrote to me in 1958: "I have finished preparing the second edition of my Cézanne catalogue, but I do not know when it will be published. In any event it will include no drawings. So I will be delighted if you publish the catalogue of the Basel drawings."[2]

The catalogue of the Basel drawings appeared in 1961, the year of Lionello Venturi's death. Reassured by the encouragements I received from many sources, I decided to get this present catalogue underway.

It goes without saying that Venturi's work, published in 1936, was the starting point. However, I felt that I must locate and assemble the numerous drawings that had escaped Venturi's work. Moreover, it was necessary to incorporate into the overall classification all the drawings in the seven sketchbooks; Venturi had treated these sketchbooks as units, giving approximate dates for each notebook as a whole. Last, I had to take into consideration the information furnished by the historical and critical studies since 1936, especially John Rewald's catalogue of the five *carnets*, 1951, and Gertrude Berthold's book on Cézanne's copies of works of art, published in 1957.[3]

Lionello Venturi's heirs, as well as his colleague, Signor Nello Ponente of the University of Rome, very kindly gave me access to the records in their custody, allowing me to consult the documents and photographs concerning Cézanne's drawings. In October 1968, in Rome, I was able to study the bulky files that Lionello Venturi had compiled on the drawings over the years. These files contained notes on journeys, exhibition catalogues, documents and photographs. The fact that he intended to exclude the drawings from the new edition had not stopped Venturi from gathering photographs. A number had been, in fact, submitted for his appraisal and for publication. I am personally very pleased that by reproducing these drawings at this time I can fulfill the wishes of those collectors who had been in contact with this great scholar. From Rome I brought back photographs of twenty-seven drawings hitherto unpublished and unknown to me, as well as about a hundred photographs of better quality than the prints I already possessed.

2. *The contents of the catalogue*

In the present catalogue 1242 drawings by Cézanne are reproduced and classified. There are 1223 numbers, plus 19 *bis* or *ter* numbers for entries added after the initial classification. This total seems rather modest when one thinks of the number of paintings and watercolors that the artist—*Pictor semper virens*—executed, or at least started.[4] I am convinced that many of the drawings, no doubt more than half, were destroyed or lost. Those who witnessed Cézanne working have said that the artist seemed to set no store by most of his pencil studies, and it is well known that he was often very careless or capricious with his works.[5] Others claim that he drew a great deal.[6] A historian as knowledgeable as John Rewald supports this assertion, one, moreover, that is not so much challenged as unknown.[7]

3. *The appreciation of Cézanne's drawings*

When one reads of the great sums of money paid today for any work by Cézanne, one would think that after the artist's death in 1906 every rough sketch, every page of his sketchbooks, every large sheet bearing one or several drawings (and he often used both sides), would have been carefully collected and preserved. This is far from the truth. At the time of his death things were seen differently: nearly everyone was convinced that *Cézanne could not draw*. There were few who could see, and grasp, the beauty in a Cézanne drawing, few who were capable of understanding the significance of the pencil strokes that most of the experts considered rough, ill-formed jottings.

Even those close to the artist treated the drawings with a hint of indulgence. Although he had thirty-six paintings by Cézanne, the collector Victor Chocquet, friend and dauntless defender of the artist, owned not a single one of his drawings. But a number of painters justly appreciated, and loved, his drawings—Camille Pissarro, Edgar Degas, Claude Monet, Auguste Renoir, Georges Rivière, Maurice Denis, to mention the most important. Others confined their admiration to his academic studies from the nude, to the small portraits done in pencil, to the compositional studies, or even to the watercolored drawings, for Cézanne was reputed to be a good colorist. The compositional studies were of interest because of the paintings, which were already increasing in value in spite of reproaches for *dessin défaillant*. It had been the custom for at least two centuries to praise or criticize in every picture that *very important part: the drawing*. Now Cézanne instinctively sought beauty in the visual sensations, controlled by the intellect, that he experienced when looking at nature. He was not looking for Ideal Beauty, defined intellectually as perfect drawing; thus he was abandoning the Renaissance tradition that preached the laws of scientific perspective and the great care needed for strictly defined contours. Much as he wished to be classic, he intended to achieve it through nature.

Other artists abandoned tradition at the same time as he, but more discreetly, so that it was Cézanne who was later given the credit for having opened the way to modern art. The title of the work published by Fritz Novotny in 1938, *Cézanne und das Ende der wissenschaftlichen Perspektive* (Cézanne and the End of Scientific Perspective), sums up the situation. Cézanne's drawings were not always "correct" by the standards of classical perspective, nor were they *line* drawings. He was a born colorist, vigorously and harmoniously contrasting the black, gray, and white parts in his drawings; in other words, he used contours much less than values.[8] This does not mean that values are neglected in drawings with strictly defined outlines, like those of Ingres; values can be obtained by closing up details, backgrounds, etc. . . . Nor does this mean that outlines play no part in Cézanne's drawings—only that the outlines are not defined by a single stroke, but by several strokes close together. To this unusual technique was added the artist's original way of seeing—this new characteristic in art that was *la beauté cézannienne*. This character was lost upon his contemporaries. Rarely has there been better witness to Baudelaire's sentence, *"Le public est, relativement au génie, une horloge qui retarde"* (When it comes to genius, the general public is like a clock running slow.)[9]

The public was quite incapable of reading this Provençal painter's graphic writing. And if Diderot in his time would have given *"dix Watteau pour un Teniers,"* there were many art critics at the turn of the century who would have given ten Cézannes for a single Cabanel. Even today the general public has not completely lost this hostile attitude.

But to return to the end of the nineteenth century: Cézanne had hidden himself away from a world that had insulted him or ignored him. His paintings were not exhibited, hence even more reason for not displaying his drawings. A few people would go to see his paintings in Tanguy's shop in the rue Clauzel, but there was never any question of showing a drawing at Tanguy's. There is no point in quoting the testimonies of the various biographies, but I will cite the following statement, less familiar, by Roger Fry, a man who was quick to recognize the value of Cézanne's work. Fry said of the painter, "He faded out so completely from the general artistic consciousness of his day that the present writer, when he was an art student in Paris in the nineties—a very ignorant and helpless, but still an inquisitive student—never once heard the name of the recluse of Aix."[10]

Nevertheless, in 1898 Ambroise Vollard reproduced a drawing to decorate the invitation-catalogue of his Cézanne exhibition (May–June 1898). This drawing (our No. 514) was a compositional study for *Les Baigneuses*; there are several versions of the subject in oils—for example Venturi No. 547, which Vollard had exhibited in December 1896. Our drawing No. 938, studies of the artist's son in Harlequin costume, was reproduced by Théodore Duret in his *Histoire des Peintres impressionnistes*, Paris, 1906. Duret had this reproduction printed in the tone of sanguine, possibly to suggest a link with Watteau drawings. In 1907 the *Gazette des Beaux-Arts* reproduced the same drawing, but in black and white, in its review of Duret's book. Later, Ambroise Vollard introduced more than sixty drawings in his 1914 volume. Meier-Graefe, in Munich, repeated a fair number of these reproductions,[11] and to his credit, in 1918 and 1921 he reproduced in facsimile, in "Cézanne und seine Ahnen" (a *Mappe der Marées-Gesellschaft*), our Nos. 109, 491, 493, 510, 611, 880, 897, 962, 999.

Gradually a few collectors were beginning to take an interest in the drawings, while the oil paintings and certain watercolors had been sought after for a good time. Some drawings were exhibited in Berlin, others auctioned in Paris, but most of them remained in the possession of the artist's son, had been put away in Ambroise Vollard's cupboards, or were in the hands of Cézanne's friends—who kept them, if I am not mistaken, more as souvenirs than as masterpieces. From about 1931 onwards, Cézanne's drawings were exhibited for sale in a few Paris galleries. After 1930 the severe economic crisis lowered the price of art works, and the shortage of cash made the sale of major works very difficult. Prices had fallen and working capital was frozen. Cézanne's drawings were therefore good material for the dealers: they were new objects and the dealers did not already have unsold stocks of them; moreover, they were small articles and had the guarantee of a great name. And public taste had evolved under the influence of Derain, Matisse, Braque, Picasso, all artists who had taken much from the art of Cézanne.

The principal owners, Paul Cézanne *fils* and Ambroise Vollard, sold the drawings, Cézanne's son in small groups or in *carnets*, Vollard in minuscule numbers at the same time as the watercolors. The Basel museum, with the help of private collectors, bought up large batches in 1934 and 1935.[12] At the same time the drawings that had entered Central European collections (thanks to Meier-Graefe and to the galleries of Paul Cassirer and Alfred Flechtheim) began to flow back to the Paris galleries. Nevertheless, most dealers were still skeptical of their artistic value. They sold them with not a little undertone of irony. So they were surprised to see, in 1936, many of the drawings that had passed through their hands displayed in the Orangerie Museum during the great Cézanne exhibition organized by the National Museums on the occasion of the thirtieth anniversary of the artist's death. In the foreword to the catalogue, "*Les Techniques de Cézanne,*" Jacques-Emile Blanche expressed the reservations generally put forward by the world of the Hôtel Drouot and the art exhibitions: "The drawing alone is an incomplete expression of the artist." However, René Huyghe and Charles Sterling, whom Henri Verne, Directeur des Musées Nationaux, had put in charge of collecting the exhibits, clearly appreciated the true value of the drawings. The catalogue groups the drawings under twenty-six numbers, and the exhibition opened many people's eyes. In the same year, 1936, another Cézanne exhibition was held in Basel with sixty-nine drawings. Finally, still in 1936, Lionello Venturi's Cézanne catalogue appeared, and in it were reproduced a group of paintings, watercolors, and drawings never seen before. This work permitted a sounder judgment of Cézanne's role in his century, and—to return to our own subject—of the meaning and value of his drawings. The drawings were equally well represented in the San Francisco exhibition of 1937, and in 1939 at the exhibitions in Lyons at the Palais Saint-Pierre, in Paris at the Rétrospective du Centenaire des Indépendants, and in London at the Wildenstein Gallery. Then the war came, followed by great changes in collections. The drawings that Vollard (who died in 1939) had collected were dispersed; of the five *carnets* that went from Maurice Renou to a collector in Lyons, four were sold to American collectors and one entered the Cabinet des Dessins of the Louvre (as the gift of Sam Salz).

4. *Aims and methods*

Our catalogue is richer in drawings than Venturi's, but even so, are we able to claim that it contains all Cézanne's drawings known to us? I am careful to make no such assertion. First of all, let us consider the initial contribution made by that part of the Venturi catalogue dealing with drawings. There, 375 drawings are reproduced, each with a separate number. Furthermore, Venturi makes reference to other drawings that are not reproduced, and consequently are recorded without numbers. The 375 drawings that Venturi reproduced appear in our catalogue under 360 numbers; this difference of fifteen numbers is explained by the fact that several of Venturi's numbers are classed under a single number here, Venturi having followed Vollard's book of 1914 in reproducing separately some sketches that had originally been on the same sheet. Other drawings have since been classified among the watercolors, or excluded. Our catalogue reproduces 1242 drawings, hence about 882 additional. As for the drawings Venturi mentioned but did not reproduce, I have done my best to find these *unpublished works*; most of them are here, but not all. Some of those that Venturi described as belonging to the Paul Gachet or Kenneth Clark collections, for example, have eluded my investigations.

I have often been asked if my catalogue will be complete, and I have always replied in the negative. It goes without saying that a catalogue should be as complete as possible; however, it seems to me that this requirement is imposed as a working discipline rather than as a moral exigency or artistic ideal. My real goal has been to assemble the drawings and to classify them in such a way that the evolution of Cézanne's art and style becomes abundantly clear. That certain sketches have eluded me or have been deliberately withheld from me does not distress me overmuch.

In accepting or rejecting works, I have judged their authenticity according to my personal convictions, hence according to a subjective criterion. In doubtful cases, where this decision has at times been most difficult, I have consulted other lovers of Cézanne's art. Thus John Rewald, Léo Marchutz, and Robert W. Ratcliffe have constantly afforded me most judicious opinions. In the end, however, the final decision has always been based on my own feelings. I willingly admit the possibility of my being mistaken and that among the considerable number of rejected drawings there may be some authentic ones. May I be accused, on the other hand, of having reproduced some non-authentic works? When convincing evidence of such a case is presented, I shall willingly accede.

Finally, several sketches ascribed to the artist's youth seemed so ambiguous as to leave me in doubt; not knowing whether I should credit them to Cézanne or to one of his friends, I finally rejected them. It was only from about 1866 that Cézanne acquired a truly personal stroke, and even then this can be clearly discerned only in the more spontaneous, non-academic and non-applied drawings. The biographers never fail to mention the second prize obtained by Cézanne in 1859 at the *Ecole Spéciale de Dessin*. The work that merited this distinction is not known to us—a great pity, because it would shed some light on the darkness that covers the artist's early efforts. As a biographical document we reproduce the label certifying the attribution of the prize (Fig. 1).

5. *The order*

I have chosen to classify the drawings—*grosso modo*—in chronological order. I felt also that like subjects needed to be grouped together. It is interesting to see a number of these consecutively, as in this way the evolution of Cézanne's style in a given period becomes clear. To divide such drawings up would impede comparison. In order to limit such series in time, however, it has been necessary to place some caesuras, but these are not uniform and periods covering between five and ten years often overlap. In this field there is no single framework that always holds good, and each method has both drawbacks and advantages. In grouping those drawings related by their subject—and certain disparate sketches that had to be included somewhere—I have trusted my own taste and sensibility. In some cases I have renounced the principle of grouping by subject, preferring to classify the pages according to the similarity of graphic technique.

There are, on the other hand, some sketches, more or less elaborated, that denote the essentials of some *vision* of the artist, a portrait, a landscape, an arrangement of clothing; these pages can look alike in spite of having been executed at different times. It is not at all easy to date them. These pages do, however, illustrate how certain spontaneous graphic devices were used by Cézanne from about 1866, and in particular from 1879, until the very end. Those art historians who wish to reduce everything to rational processes will reproach me here, and in general in my classification of the drawings, for giving preference to my own feelings and intuition when judging values, rather than following a systematically logical approach. In fact, what interests me essentially is *art*, and I feel more at ease in the atmosphere of an artist's studio than in that of some laboratory of artistic, chronological, morphological and topographical analyses, equipped with an annex for sexual pathology. I do not despise systematic methods, but when dealing with art one must not try to completely eliminate the irrational. The precious essence of Cézanne's art is, and will remain, irrational. Possibly this fact is a little too elusive for those to whom Cézanne's art is essentially a problem of structure, and who believe that their task is finished once they have analyzed its logic and technique (especially where the former leads to cubism).

6. *Characteristics of Cézanne's drawings*

We have pointed out that Cézanne's drawings have a distinctive character. Before taking a closer look at their singularities, let us rapidly review the more noteworthy publications on the subject. The articles by André Salmon, Waldemar George, and Maurice Denis[13] show an appreciation of Cézanne's drawing that was exceptional in their time. They lack depth, however, so I mention them only in passing. Lionello Venturi appreciated Cézanne's drawings but preferred to dwell on the paintings and on the various problems arising from them. The characteristics of the drawings were studied by Fritz Novotny in his book of 1938, *Cézanne und das Ende der wissenschaftlichen Perspektive*, and in his article of 1950, *Cézanne als Zeichner*,[14] which enlarges upon what the author had succinctly stated in 1938. But before approaching Novotny's argument, I feel obliged to repeat here a few lines from my own book of 1938, *Dessins de Paul Cézanne*, in which forty-eight drawings were carefully reproduced. Tired of hearing criticism aimed at the Master's distortions and incompetence, I wrote in the preface: "There is a derogatory sense attached to the word distortion that opposes a drawing so described to an accurate, non-distorted drawing, implying that the latter alone is capable of providing beauty and satisfaction. The error lies in believing that a drawing exists in absolute form and that this form will always and necessarily be "truer" than another; in reality, we have, on the one hand, traditional nineteenth-century drawing, which our eyes are accustomed to, and on the other, Cézanne's drawing, slightly different but equally satisfying, if not more so, to the eye that has learned to see it as it is. Cézanne's adversaries were unable to look at his drawings without mentally comparing them with the *dessin académique* they were familiar with. Naturally Cézanne's drawings appeared inaccurate to them and therefore less beautiful, less "true." Their obsession with the *style académique* obscured their vision, so that instead of discovering nature in Cézanne's works, they saw only clumsiness."

The discussion was put on another level by Novotny's study of 1950. We can give here only a fragmentary view of this article, which is exemplary for its logic and probity. Novotny begins by quoting Cézanne: *"Line and modeling do not exist.*" He thinks that by this statement Cézanne meant that he refuted the elementary device of line to represent things and their shapes. The author continues: "What do we see when a painter who makes such a statement and who paints the way Cézanne does, starts to draw?" He then states that the second part of the sentence, *"drawing is a relationship of contrasts or simply the relationship between two tones, black and white,"* conse-crates the fact that in nature a line is produced where two colored surfaces meet.

That painting can do without line, Novotny says, was not a new observation, but Cézanne applied it in a new way. He "devalued" the line, or, to use a more neutral expression, he transmuted it. In his drawings line is weakened, reduced. "The result is a certain rigidity and awkwardness, and a strangely cold quality in the treat-ment of line that strikes everyone approaching Cézanne's art. . . . His drawings and watercolors are essentially of the same nature as his oil paintings. The characteristic form of the drawings especially is as close to painterly form as one could possibly imagine, given the technical means of graphic expression. . . . He obtains this effect by depriving line of that power of expression that describes figures and objects and situates them in space. It can be said that the result of the various treatments he employs is rather negative. . . . In the drawings, line remains essentially a limit between colors. This, of course, constitutes a seeming paradox: in the absence of colors, line designates only the place where they meet. . . . The nature of his drawings is singularly ambiguous: line is in fact used, but from an artistic viewpoint it is denied." These few passages from Novotny's article placed consecutively and no doubt oversimplified communicate the essential idea. Obviously this calls for certain observations from me, but first I think it would be useful to note two sentences from John Rewald's introduction to the catalogue of five sketchbooks published in 1951, and to mention Gertrude Berthold's *Cézanne und die alten Meister*, 1957, in which the author discusses various prevalent and conflicting opinions. This will enlarge the debate.

John Rewald speaks at considerable length of the drawing in the artist's paintings and of his pencil drawings. Concerning line and perspective, his views are similar to Novotny's but much more flexible. We must confine our attention to the following passages, leaving aside a large number of pertinent observations that affect the matter less directly. "Cézanne never spoke of drawing without also mentioning color. Drawing, according to him, is a form of logic, though a hybrid logic between arithmetic, geometry, and color. . . . Since line and modeling did not exist for Cézanne, drawing was basically a relationship of contrasts. However, all these definitions have been supplied by Cézanne the painter, for it appears that the artist did not consider himself a draftsman. He enjoyed using line, as he liked to admit, but he nonetheless reproached the great draftsmen of the past—Raphael, Holbein, Clouet, or Ingres—for having 'nothing but line. . . .' Cézanne did a great deal of sketching but always for his own purposes. . . ."

Let us now turn to Gertrude Berthold's book. In the introduction she quotes the passage previously cited from my book of 1938, for in her opinion this sentence constitutes the best point of departure. She writes: "When studying Cézanne's drawings, one must accept the idea that there are many methods of drawing and that Cézanne's is only one of them; that it is new and peculiar to him." Having examined John Rewald's 1951 intro-duction, Berthold concludes: "Rewald does not succeed in defining the essential and distinctive merit of Cézanne's drawings, mainly because his starting point is the definition of *line* in Cézanne's paintings. It is true that he assigns a 'new significance' to it, but given his point of departure, the author can consider line in the drawings only as an inferior means of expression compared to its role in the paintings." In theory this is a valid criticism; however, it is badly aimed, since John Rewald has always valued Cézanne's drawings highly, and in his writings does not treat them as inferior productions. Berthold then proceeds to Novotny's study and underscores the importance he attributes to Cézanne's phrase, *Line and modeling do not exist.* She places the accent on the second part of the statement: *Drawing is a relationship of contrasts or simply the relation between two tones, black and white.* "Cézanne," says Berthold, "thus makes a clear distinction between *line* and *drawing,* and defines drawing as the relation bet-ween two tones, black and white. When this relation is respected in drawing, line—that is, an unbroken outline —is nonexistent. In this case the relationship can be said to be 'transversal' to the lines of the contour, between the black stroke and the white paper beside it. This is why Cézanne sketches with short, staccato strokes, often doubled or tripled."

The tone of this criticism directed at Novotny is unduly aggressive, but one senses that the author is primarily interested in defending Cézanne, not in asserting herself. And finally, Berthold reproaches Novotny for consider-ing line a natural phenomenon instead of a historical one linked to the intellect, and for relating line as it occurs in art to that which exists in nature. She says, "Novotny thinks that the outline of a leaf, a twig, or a tree trunk conveys in a half-objective, half-subjective manner something of its plant life and growth. If this were the case, the artist would find himself confronted with contours and his role would be not to reproduce their lines but to minimize them in some way and suppress some of them." Against this view, Berthold suggests that in nature there are only forms, and the artist has the choice of representing them by lines or otherwise. In a drawing, lines used to represent an object are *a priori* an artistic device and should be differentiated from what actually exists, even when the edges of a flat surface one is looking at create a linear effect. She also accuses Novotny of obstinately clinging to the traditional concept of line, a concept handed down from the Renaissance.

Berthold then proceeds directly to the study of the drawings made after a great variety of works of art, examines their techniques and arranges them chronologically in nine groups. We will take this up shortly, but let us first conclude the discussion concerning line. Setting aside the old philosophical controversy of antimonies linked to sense perception (subject-object relationships), it seems difficult, in my opinion, to deny that we frequently perceive linear appearances around us. On the other hand, I quite agree that drawn lines are symbolic and conventional. In nature I see contours suggesting lines whenever I look at a half-opened door, at houses, at the sea, at cobwebs reaching from one rosebush to another in my garden. Why then did Cézanne so categorically deny their very existence? Simply in self-defense against the partisans of linear drawing. All of the Master's expressed opinions on art are defensive reasoning. He was not an intellectual painter; he drew and painted without a theoretical plan. It was only afterwards, when his drawings were being subjected to traditional modes of interpretation, that he sought to justify them by theory.[15] It is meaningless to try to build a system on Cézanne's "maxims." R. W. Ratcliffe has shown that he often gave his young friends advice taken directly from Thomas Couture's *Propos d'Atelier*. Without going back to the controversy of the Rubenists and Poussinists, to Jacques-Louis David and Ingres, let us consider the ideas Cézanne opposed in his precepts. The following passage is from Charles Blanc's *Ecole espagnole* (1869), the volume containing engravings copied by Cézanne (see Nos. 244, 726, 731, 821): "The more elevated the painting, the less is color vital to it, and where the human figure dominates, the work tends to become sculptural, since drawing is the means of expression par excellence. Innermost feelings can well be expressed by drawing alone, but inanimate objects cannot be properly imitated without the use of color." Evidently we must interpret the word "drawing" here as drawing by means of linear contours, and accept that the profiles of flat surfaces and of sculptural surfaces are alike. Delacroix had already taken a stand against those who saw beauty only in line.[16] By saying that line did not exist, Cézanne wished to make clear that line in drawing was a conventional technique and one that he was not compelled to use. He maintained that he was free to choose his colorist's techniques and to ignore the academic tradition's disregard for color. This did not deter him from saying, on other occasions: "I'm no stupider than the next person, and I can take pleasure in line when I want to." The sentence shows that he was defending himself against charges of being ignorant or incompetent. Novotny is well aware of the fact that Cézanne was not ignorant. He is simply amazed at the way Cézanne was able to reject linear drawing and still obtain such worthwhile results. "Is it not clear," wrote Novotny in 1938 (p. 74), "that the character of Cézanne's lines, apparently inexplicit, somewhat indefinite—the lack of drawing for which he was reproached by his contemporaries—does not disperse the elements of the painting, but on the contrary, strengthens their cohesion in a particular way? And as I have already suggested, this strengthened cohesion is the result of a play between space and surface, play which could not sustain more pronounced lines, which even tends to repudiate line." Berthold is wrong to accuse Novotny of remaining a prisoner to the academic tradition, for his writings on the drawings of van Gogh, Kokoschka, and others reveal how very receptive Novotny is to modern art, especially where linear drawing is used.

We may find a parallel to this kind of predisposition in music, where some ears are more attuned to melody than to the riches of chords, more receptive to the song of a flute than to an Aeolian harp. With art, it is in man's nature to be receptive to outline drawing, as proven by prehistoric and other ancient drawings. Line defines objects and the limits of space, the contour captures expression and can render volume by vanishing points or receding planes. Color added to an outline drawing cannot possibly produce a colorist's drawing. The latter made its appearance rather late in the history of painting; in Europe, the use of chalk and pastels, introduced after 1500, favored the colorist drawing—after Dürer, for example, and after the period of the prestige of pure line in Italy. Drawing by means of contrasting tones, although rarer than linear drawing, is not an inferior genre; far from it! An observation made by Kenneth Clark suggests that it is evidence of a certain mastery. Speaking of Leonardo da Vinci and Michelangelo, he says: "Both have learnt in old age to avoid outlines and to present their subject through interior modelling, suggested by mysterious blots and blurs. This is what Cézanne meant when he praised a picture by saying that it was *dessiné dans la forme*."[17] We must note that most of us seem predisposed to linear drawing; most children draw by contours. The errors we see in children's work prove that distortions are easily accepted when they are represented by a firm outline. Linear drawing is generally used in works that bear distinctly the stamp of their era, for it lends itself to virtuosity, caricature, and to technical design intended to be understood by all. The colorist's drawing, on the other hand, indicates a personal disposition. Here any distortion is frowned upon.

7. *Observations and descriptions*

Novotny does not deal with the body of drawings we know, but concerns himself with a limited number of characteristic works from the artist's mature period, for example Nos. 932, 1026, 1027, 1028, 1037, 1058, 1090, 1154, 1165, 1171, 1177, 1188, to name only a few. But there are other drawings of a very different nature. It cannot be denied that the pencil strokes sometimes become lines; to refute this would be unreasonable. The fact is that it seems impossible to find a single formula covering the general character of all Cézanne's drawings from beginning to end. At most one can say that it is light which provides their unity, and that certain graphic treatments persist throughout the stylistic transformations, notably the hatching, the rendering of angles, the spirals, and the repetition of contours. And yet, slowly, after adequate reflection, we come to recognize Cézanne's hand, at least after 1866. Otherwise it would be impossible to separate the wheat from the tares; impossible to compile a catalogue. Roger Fry was struck by an indefinable yet distinctive trait of Cézanne's: ". . . in the last resort we cannot in the least explain why the smallest product of his hand arouses the impression of being a revelation."[18] Like Novotny, many have described only a portion of the drawings in seeking to explain their general characteristics. Using this approach myself in 1957 I wrote: "On the paper, the play of blacks or whites organizes itself into forms with remarkable clarity and grace. . . . Often the drawing emphasizes abrupt changes where light and shadows meet, giving the impression of an infinitely flexible mosaic, of a fluid partitioning suggested by angles and curves. . . . Abandoning the calm play of planes arranged according to classical taste, many of the sketches whirl with baroque motion. There are thrusts curling forward, the pencil depicting volume by flecks of shadow and velvety halftones, the lines writhing and vanishing in spirals."[19]

Gertrude Berthold did the most thorough job of analysis in assembling the copies and grouping them. I will make no attempt to give a résumé of her analysis nor try to be even more thorough, for verbal descriptions of graphism remain vastly inferior to visual perception. Maurice Denis said: *"Mais être précis au sujet de Cézanne, quelle difficulté!"*[20] However, I shall note some of Berthold's observations about certain curves and their rendering in the drawings done after classical marbles. We are dealing here with the artist's mature style: "The resemblance between various categories of forms is due to the use of certain forms of curves. The solidity of stance and of the human frame is achieved by arches identically incurved in relation to the vertical and the horizontal." To characterize the style of old age: "While in the preceding group the device of curves, employed constantly and almost exclusively, dominated the style of the drawings, henceforth this technique will no longer be preponderant. Cézanne will use it freely where he needs it. It was the principle of a solid construction that offered at the same time plasticity and a unified ornamental shape which had given rise to its use. From now on this principle will dominate all technical means: the appearance of a curve will express the principle and so create a stronger effect than in the preceding period; for example, in the copies after Rubens [our Nos. 1128, 1140, 1209] and likewise when large wigs appear in the model [our Nos. 1207, 1212]."

I should like to cite some other observations at random. Kurt Badt, who emphasizes that Cézanne always composed by placing the shadows first, says: "The technique of the drawings proves that he proceeded in accordance with what he had said. He draws shadows, draws what is black, using strokes in such a way that their intensity corresponds to the darkness of reality . . . thus making a careful distinction between shadows with a sharp edge and those which fade softly."[21] Theodore Reff, speaking of the motif of the subject drawn, says: "The motif, then, is an integration of separately perceived parts into a system of construction, as he himself explained to Gasquet by locking together the fingers of both hands (Gasquet, pp. 130–31). . . . He thus perceives primarily in terms of relations, not objects; hence his relative indifference to their unique qualities of substance, surface and content."[22] Alfred Neumeyer: "Even in his youthful, passionate jottings one perceives a relationship to a larger entity. In the later drawings the emphasis on the compositional context yields to an inherent adjustment to underlying form structures, such as the famous cone, sphere and cylinder, or to the directional orientation."[23] Kenneth Clark: *"He saw in depth and pattern at once. . . .* Drawings always increase our intimacy with an artist, and sometimes intimacy leads to disillusion; but with Cézanne the more we grow familiar with the large, noble, characteristic movements of his hand, the more we become confident in his greatness."[24]

8. *Chronology*[25]

Let us now consider the different periods that can be distinguished in the Master's drawing. When we define and set limits on Cézanne's periods, we are really dealing with transitions and not with barriers strictly observed. Furthermore, I am not sure that the dates indicated are always accurate, for this is difficult to prove. On the other hand, I feel more certain about the order in which the dated pages are arranged. In other words, I am more concerned with the sequence of the drawings than with the exactness of each date. Few dates seem to me to be incontestable, with the exception of those determined by external evidence and therefore independent of style. Berthold, in her book on the copies, distinguished nine groups which follow each other chronologically. Her method consists of looking for stylistic changes and also for chronological clues furnished by the models: dates of acquisition or exhibition of sculptures for example. Her observations do not contradict mine, but they cover a special area and are often linked to the outside evidence. In the chronological summary which follows I shall give Berthold's indications in parenthesis.

The date assigned to our first drawing is around 1858. (We reproduce as Fig. 1 the label of a second prize awarded Cézanne in 1859—for "*peinture*," but we may assume that at the *Ecole Spéciale de Dessin* the word would refer equally to colored drawing.) The first step that shows an evolution is situated around 1862, the year of Cézanne's return to Paris. (Berthold's first group: 1858–60.) A second threshold is situated about 1866; the artist was then twenty-seven years old and his drawing acquired a more personal character. It was the era of good friendships, solitary study, erotic violence, and dramatized landscapes. (Berthold notes some progress around 1866–67; roughly speaking, her second group comprises the drawings of the decade 1860–70.) From 1872 on, the influence of Pissarro and the birth of a son to the artist strengthens his work, and we begin to see drawings universally attributed to Cézanne. (Berthold designates the copies done after 1872 as the core of the third group.) The years 1878–87 brought about what is commonly referred to as the artist's *style constructif,* with clarity and technique gradually emerging. His style rids itself of impressionistic influences. Even while staying close to nature he tends towards a classical vision. It seems probable to me that the reproductions in *Le Magasin Pittoresque, Le Musée des Familles,* and Charles Blanc's books, and also the engravings of Marcantonio Raimondi, influenced the taste of the young Aixois, and that we find this taste, transformed and adapted, in the drawings executed around 1880. (Berthold places her fourth group after 1876–77 and even up until 1882; her fifth between 1880 and 1883.) As early as 1882, but especially after 1883, there are attempts at a freer form, with trials of new techniques and a return, mainly around 1885, to a certain solidity and sobriety. (Berthold designates a sixth group: 1883–86.) The studies for *Mardi Gras* (around 1888) betray a classical tendency, recalling nonetheless certain aspects of Rubens and Pierre Puget; the latter is present in the *Scènes de Carnaval.* A few landscapes portray trees with similar rhythms. (Berthold's seventh group begins in 1886 and is characterized by the use of arched strokes. It extends beyond 1890 and becomes in part transformed into the first phase of the eighth group.) Around 1890 the drawings acquire a new clarity; there is mastery in the easy flow of the stroke, whether it be deliberate or swift. Shortly after 1895 the style of old age finally emerges: impatient, very free in appearance, but grasping the subject both in surface and depth. True, the subject is not always easily deciphered; the details are cursory. (Berthold finds the indications for her eighth group in 1894 and 1895. After 1895 we can follow the copies of busts with large wigs. Her ninth group is situated around 1899, date of Vollard's portrait, our No. 1194. The exhibition of busts from the Comédie Française at the Louvre in 1900 does not, however, furnish the evidence Berthold claims to find there.) Unfortunately there are few drawings left that were done around 1900 or after—just a few sketches for watercolors, a few pages in the sketchbooks, and what else? After Cézanne's death, his heirs probably considered these late sketches confused, unintelligible, and bad. They no doubt believed they were serving the artist's reputation by not preserving these evidences of his failing power. As for me, these are the very pages that move me most.

To conclude this summary, let us recall the four periods in Cézanne's evolution distinguished by Venturi:

FIG. 1. Label of a second prize awarded Cézanne in 1859. (Photographed in 1964 by R. W. Ratcliffe in the Lauves workshop, Aix-en-Provence. It disappeared from there in the late sixties.)

1.	Academic and romantic period	1858–1871
2.	Impressionistic period	1872–1877
3.	Constructive period	1878–1887
4.	Synthetic period	1888–1906

Venturi's dates often need reviewing but it is still convenient to use his definitions of the periods, which have been widely accepted.

9. *The different types of figures*

In a good many of the bather drawings, the same poses recur so often that we come to speak of typical postures or simply of Cézanne types. Some of these poses are derived from statues, paintings, or drawings copied by the artist, for example, from the marble statue of *The Roman Orator* in the Louvre, seen front view or from the back; see Nos. 1050 and 421, 423, 424, 430. Another example: Signorelli's drawing *Standing Man*, Fig. 121; see Nos. 996–998. Let us also enumerate figures he copied without any intention-of using them in his compositions; for example, those of *Bellona, The Genius of Health*, the *Naiads*, of Rubens; *Hercule au repos, Milo of Crotona*, the *Atlantes* of Puget; and finally, a number of busts. We may wonder why the artist went to draw at the Louvre and elsewhere; it was merely his way of familiarizing himself with the art forms of the past.[28] By rendering according to his own vision what others had created, he developed his style—like a composer of music, whose originality does not prevent him from playing, replaying, and interpreting the works of the repertoire. Some of Cézanne's copies are variations. Bernard Dorival wrote: ". . . a habitual visitor to the Louvre, to the sculpture rooms where his eye fell on the *Borghese Mars* as well as on Michelangelo's *Slaves* and Puget's *Milo of Crotona*, Cézanne was attracted by the masters for whom art was construction; he felt he was one of them and by their contact he fortified his natural inclinations."[29]

But let us reconsider the *types* used by the artist in his paintings. A few have their origin in the poses of live models, nude or clothed, for Cézanne had drawn from models at the Académie Suisse from 1861 until 1870 or so, and also from time to time after 1870 at the Ecole des Beaux-Arts in Aix-en-Provence. Furthermore, nothing prevented his hiring models whenever he was in Paris. Addresses of models—male and female—are noted in the sketchbooks. In Paris, even before 1870, there was Hortense Fiquet, who had first been his model. Generally speaking, in Paris he could always go and draw at an academy. Legend has it that he was so afraid of female models that he never did. I only half believe this. That fear was present, but it was relative. Cézanne undoubtedly contributed to this legend by being secretive about all his activities in this domain. It was a way of defending himself. Naturally shy, he was always on the defensive. His parents had never taught him how to act in society. To compensate, he took the offensive in painting and in front of nature. No doubt he was suspicious of women because he feared being distrubed by them in his work. After having had certain experiences, which are fortunately shrouded with mystery, he resolved to sacrifice the practice of love to his vocation as a painter. "In Cézanne's case, the artist triumphed over the male."[30] It is the key to his alleged madness and his authentic phobias. As Georg Schmidt observed in a more general manner: "The objectivity and serenity of his art in maturity are the fruits of a magnificent victory over the temptation to base his art on the avowal of personal problems."[31] The narrow provincial atmosphere prevalent in Aix and elsewhere, a total, aggressive incomprehension of the artist, must be understood in order to fully grasp the life Cézanne lived in his beloved native city. Hiring women for posing was socially impossible. In this connection, two of the artist's personal reasons should be mentioned. First of all, he felt watched by his sister, Marie, a spinster devoted to the Jesuits and disapproving of nudity.[32] Second, a scandal had broken out in the town when some respectable gentlemen who had photographed nude women were convicted by the courts. Cézanne had every reason to keep quiet, then, for in the eyes of the gossips what difference could there be between a man who photographs nudes and one who draws them?

Among the bathers we can distinguish several types: the *Bather walking away towards the background* (Nos. 510, 511, 963, 964, etc.); the *Bather drying herself* (Nos. 514, 518, 521, etc.). Among the males, the *Seated bather* (Nos. 422, 431, 432, 433, etc.) figuring at the left of the paintings; the *Bather going down into the water* (Nos. 526, 528, 962, etc.) recalling the pose of Alonso Cano's *Christ* (see fig. 74); the *Bather with his hands on his hips* (Nos. 946, 947); and the *Bather with outstretched arms*. Among all these, it is the last that raises a specifically "Cézannien" problem, and we must therefore discuss it. (See Nos. 630, 631.)

10. *The bather with outstretched arms*

The bather with outstretched arms appears in the painter's work only between 1875 and 1885. The figure is always isolated, and generally this bather is related to the landscape of L'Estaque. Our catalogue reproduces twelve drawings and Venturi reproduces three paintings showing this pose: Nos. 259, 262, 271. The *Bather with outstretched arms* has a sort of pendant in the *Bather with his hands on his hips*. This figure also is characteristic, but it appears in groups with other bathers, which renders it less singular. Theodore Reff attempts to throw light on the problem by means of psychoanalysis.[33] Briefly summed up, Reff's article contends that through these bathers, Cézanne depicts the slow and painful struggle he waged against masturbation and a guilt complex. The uplifted arms are supposed to be a symbol of the male sex organ.[34] We shall not go into the details of his argument, which is often subtle, and we shall avoid any judgment on the soundness of his conclusions from a psychological viewpoint. His article about this and other bathers, however, necessitates a general comment on his methods. In order to analyze Cézanne's art and his psychological problems, the author in various places adopts a strictly positivist Freudian attitude, intended to be objective. His psychoanalysis approaches the artistic life, and life in general, on a scientific basis, objective, free of prejudice, where there is no morality, no discretion, no propriety, and no real artistic value. The usual attitude of the art critic, the historian, or the connoisseur is abandoned in favor of an attitude that is above good and evil; beyond beauty or disgust. Other authors, notably Wayne V. Andersen, Sara Lichtenstein, and Meyer Schapiro, followed this same path in writing about Cézanne. Kurt Badt studied the hidden meaning in the drawing No. 37 in particular, but employed a different technique. It should be noted that the three authors previously cited were earnest in their desire to reveal the primary motives that drove the artist to execute certain rather erotic or violent drawings, but it must be noted also that these authors are not professional psychiatrists. The latter are usually more cautious in their judgments; they confine themselves to generalities unless citing clinical cases. Concerning Cézanne, there is no opinion generally accepted by professionals at the present time. In their articles these authors emphasize the erotic, anguished, and tortured aspects of a number of drawings and paintings, and explore the artist's life, especially his youth—the least interesting period from an artistic point of view. They search for repressed desires, peculiarities susceptible to being considered symbols of deviations or sexual distress. They then interpret these symbols, and because scientific methods rarely lead beyond general conclusions, they interpret subjectively. In their legitimate desire to say something new about Cézanne they boldly penetrate the redoubtable arsenal of Freudian associations.[35] The conclusions resulting from this type of investigation are worthwhile only if they are considered as a whole with the man and his artistic evolution. Without discussing the content of these articles, I shall say that they are at variance with my general view insofar as they ignore that in Cézanne, *the artist triumphed over the male*. These authors do not share my point of view. For them, the crises are of primary importance throughout.

11. *General criticism of method*

It is not the authors and their articles that trouble me so deeply; it is their methods, their claims to being objective, medically scientific and positivist towards art. Drawing or painting is treated as some strictly functional phenomenon; and more often than not, this activity is considered as an effect of sexual disorders that need to be cured. Man is a physio-psychic mechanism functioning more or less correctly. The ideal being would function without sexual disorders, guilt complexes, etc. . . . If this idea is followed through to its conclusion, logically we should admire the perfection in the simplest living cells that multiply by splitting in two. As yet they have no particular shape, no difference of sex, no back or front to cause problems. And consequently there is no art. But let us not stop there—what concerns us is establishing that the scientific rationalist attitude, having tolerated art for a long time by declaring it irrational, virtually meaningless for the scholar, incapable of being assimilated into any rational conception of nature, now wishes to devalue it, that is, scientific rationalism seeks to destroy art on the pretext of de-mythifying and integrating it. This attitude attacks not only art, but also all spheres of the soul and spirit. For modern man, it is said, nothing must escape the ascendancy of scientific systems. All that is not justified by objective methods appropriate to exact sciences comes under attack: religion, art, love, virtues, customs, traditional ceremonies, and attachment to one's country. And so it goes for everything, except, perhaps, egalitarianism and the progress that is believed to be inherent in what is new. At the time of the Renaissance, the defenders of religion tried to stifle the scientific spirit and the blossoming of its applications. One has only to think of Galileo's trial. Nowadays it is science putting religion on trial, and also, in the way we have seen, art. Let us not be misunderstood: we are not here condemning the methods employed by those scholars who act as psychiatrists, putting Freudian theories and their developments to the test. Rather, we are asking if all other methods should give theirs precedence. Is there not a multiplicity of methods on which to draw for differing values and subjects? The *unity of science* constitutes an act of faith for many scholars. But the unity of science and the system of the absolute seem to me to be no more than working hypotheses belied by the facts.[36] The sciences are constantly evolving, but are they heading towards unity? There are, I agree, certain scientific principles which are of universal value: first and foremost, that of intellectual integrity and skepticism in the face of contradictions. The systems containing no internal contradictions are of preëminent interest for demonstrative purposes. They may not, however, demonstrate the whole of the truth because the *fundamental premises* vary according to the subject and spiritual values. When positivist language speaks of art and religion as *non-integrated superstructures*, it forgets that these superstructures actually unite *infrastructures*. A new ethic of knowledge is being sought to replace the human values which science has maltreated; I hope it will be the answer to man's needs. However, if it means to be scientific, it will be continually changing. My belief is rather that cybernetics, once it has succeeded in integrating not only quantities, but also qualities, will confirm the existence of artistic and spiritual values, and will show up the contradictions raised by their elimination. Once the whole universe has been examined, cybernetics will perhaps lead the most enlightened of scholars to conceive of a spirituality springing from some hidden and permanent fund, and thence to the recognition of an art whose source is not so narrowly linked to sexuality; an art that can also exist without being mechanized. We are still a long way from that. In fact, once one adopts the strictly positivist Freudian point of view, the criticism of art and the appreciation of works of art become useless. We have a state of incompatibility. The art critic turns psychiater, and in so doing, saws through the branch on which he is sitting. Painting becomes a sign of disorder, and be it beautiful or bad, it is no longer of any consequence.

We hasten to point out that we are in no way trying to exclude psychoanalysis from art criticism. It makes many things more comprehensible. In certain treatments prescribed for the mentally ill, painting and drawing can be used as a diagnostic aid. Often people express themselves better through a picture than through speech; they discover their true identity making spontaneous sketches. Through the patient's drawings, more or less confused, the source of a particular trauma may be revealed; the diagnosis is determined and the specific medical treatment is given. The searchings of an artist curing himself (I am not speaking of someone who is truly ill) come usually during periods of lack of balance, during crises when the artist doubts his own value, thus making him lose all courage. It is in such moments that sometimes quite strange searchings enable him to find his way again, to rid himself of whatever was for him an obstacle. These searchings are the means by which he can free himself from the prejudices of his time, and by which, alone in his workshop, he can find out what is at his very depths and become aware of his true nature. In this way, drawing and painting can be used curatively. But whereas psychoanalysis reveals the events that passed in the man's heart, artistic value is measured by the artist's genius expressed in his works. Here let us quote two sentences from Cézanne: *"Je me remonte moi-même,"* and *"L'artiste éprouve de la joie à pouvoir communiquer aux autres âmes son enthousiasme devant le chef-d'oeuvre de la nature dont il croit posséder le mystère."* ("I recover my spirits by myself," and "The artist takes joy in his ability to communicate to other souls the enthusiasm he feels before the masterpiece of nature, whose mystery he believes he possesses."[37]) The difference between the rationalist attitude, which seems to us to be quite incompatible with art criticism, and the second attitude, is characterized by the fact that the latter places the origins of art outside of sexuality, although taking it into account. It was not sexual traumatisms, feelings of guilt towards his father, or repressed sentiments of love alone that made Cézanne draw and paint; there is no closed circle between sexuality and art. (Such a circle seems to be suggested in Meyer Schapiro's article, "The Apples of Cézanne"[38]; reading it, one cannot escape the feeling that the artist *had* to paint apples because repressed sentiments of love were relentlessly forcing him to.) Art is an irrational reality whose origins remain a mystery. Art must not be confused with religion, but the poetry in great art goes, more often than not, side by side with religion. Pushed by some dominating instinct, the artist creates and expresses. Psychoanalysis can be useful in bringing to light the nature of the problems tormenting the artist, and which he seeks to overcome with his singular purpose of mind. There are many painters who evolve exclusively with the problems of their time; they are its illustrators. It is only the greatest creators, who, after going through a critical and decisive period in order to *"toucher le fond,"* do find their vocation; and their originality rises far above the ordinary level of the time. Each must seek the truth that is sleeping in the depths of the well. The artist who is aware of the *catabasis* hears a kind of voice, that of his *vocation.* Cézanne certainly went through a crisis of this kind, and then through several other crises of which we know almost nothing, but from which his art emerged spiritually heightened. Most of the articles quoted here seem to assume that Cézanne never emerged from the anguish and crises that certain drawings from his youth bear witness to—pictures such as the *Temptation of Saint Anthony,* etc. . . . People are only too happy to show you a Cézanne who is more or less mad, tormented by his flesh, enslaved by his misogyny, always seized by fear at the thought of a woman undressing. We find him described as an unsavory provincial, groveling under the weight of his repressed desires. And alongside that, as if by some miracle, his genius, a flash of inspiration, enabling him to throw masterpieces on to canvases that nowadays realize fabulous prices. Somehow this image does not seem the right one to me, in spite of extravagant gestures toward certain people who offended the sensibility of this man living secluded in his own subjective atmosphere. As far as I am concerned, the interior conflicts and crises the artist undergoes are part of the process leading to the liberation of his art. Crises and anguish can, indeed, be fertile, as long as they are overcome and do not finish as in Zola's novel, *L'Oeuvre: "Claude s'était pendu à la grande échelle, en face de son oeuvre manquée."*[39] Cézanne overcame these crises, thanks to his obstinate courage, to his *"tempérament, id est, la force initiale."*[40] He did not give in to the flesh, for the flesh would have prevented the opening out of the spirit in his painting. This is what he meant when writing to Vollard: *"L'Art serait-il, en effet, un sacerdoce qui demande des purs qui lui appartiennent tout entiers?"* ("Isn't Art, in fact, something sacerdotal, requiring those who are pure, who give themselves up to it completely?"[41]) This seems hardly ever understood nowadays.

The belief now is that the vegetative irresponsibility of the flesh opens up the way. But with Cézanne, this would have suppressed all that was most elusive, and at the same time, universal, in his art. The universal goes beyond the individual and his problems. Cézanne's canvases, and also, more and more, his drawings, possess a universal value, or—what is really the same thing—have an apparently enduring normative force. This art acts on the forms of our time and on its taste; but unfortunately, that which is most inimitable in what Cézanne communicated is seen and felt by too limited a number. Leaving aside the erotic scenes and the tormented canvases, how many of his paintings, serious perhaps, but radiant, communicate the joy of a vision that shares in the divine harmony glimpsed by the artist? This is a personal experience, it cannot be proved; one must see it oneself, one must feel it oneself.

12. *The sketchbooks and their dates*

The dates assigned to Cézanne's drawings and paintings have always given rise to discussion. It therefore seems necessary to consider the *methods* used to establish these dates and the criticisms that can be made of them, especially as far as our drawings are concerned.

First of all, there are some drawings from the artist's youth that he himself dated—these are the sketches illustrating the letters, Nos. 17, 27, 37, 38, 150, 151, 152. Then come a few studies from the nude, Nos. 75, 76, 77, 78. Fig. 2 reproduces the signature and date on the back of No. 78; these I consider to be authentic, but I must admit that the same kind of signature and date can be seen on the backs of several studies from the nude that have been excluded from the catalogue, all drawn from the same models at the *Ecole* in Aix, and in which Cézanne's touch is rarely found. It is true that at that time there was much resemblance between Cézanne's studies from the nude and those of his friends. However, in drawing a leg, for example, or the way in which the thighs join the human crossroads of the buttocks, Cézanne shows himself gifted with a sense of volumes and a true instinct for stability that none of his fellow students could match. The objection has been raised that certain signatures seem authentic—I do not contradict this, but what decision can one reach about a male nude study, a rather weak drawing, that on the front bears *Coste's* signature, and on the reverse, Cézanne's? (Numa Coste, see *Corr.* letter XV.) We can date certain other pencil studies because they relate to works that the author himself dated (Nos. 199, 200, and Nos. 248, 249, 250); or because they have been dated by other means: from information we have been given by Paul Cézanne *fils* (Nos. 938–941), or from the testimony of Ambroise Vollard (Nos. 1193, 1194). When places where the artist stayed at various times can be recognized in his pictures (No. 1173), they also offer some indication of dates. Similarly, there are certain subjects that Cézanne is known to have treated for only a few years; the works depicting these subjects are easily grouped into periods of time. (This last remark concerns the paintings more than the drawings.) Often points of reference and limiting factors are provided by certain events, such as the death of the artist's father (1886), or by small facts, such as the exhibition on a certain date of a sculpture in the Louvre or of a cast in the Musée de Sculpture comparée du Trocadéro. Sometimes the verso of a drawing can offer a *terminus post quem*: see Nos. 361, 460, 461. Above, we talked about groups composed of similar subjects, and one is tempted, in dealing with the drawings, to look for such groups within the bounds of each of the sketchbooks. For many artists this undoubtedly gives interesting results; for Cézanne, however, this method does not lead very far, and it is better to base one's judgment on the style of each drawing rather than on its coming from a particular sketchbook. But faced with the difficulties and uncertainties which arise from stylistic analysis based on a piecemeal method, authors start to lose patience.[42]

It must be pointed out that none of the experts has ever undertaken a comprehensive study of the known drawings; they have preferred dealing with fairly limited selections, working either by subject or within the bounds of a single sketchbook. When, with all the drawings in front of me, I found they were so many, I felt an initial sorting out to be necessary: this I did according to style. The order thus obtained followed the chronological evolution in a general way. My idea of putting those pieces depicting the same subject into groups modified this order somewhat, without, however, upsetting the time sequence very much. I fully share the conviction that as far as possible it is preferable to date the drawings according to external criteria, irrespective of style. On the other hand, I cannot agree with those who mistrust all judgments based on style, criticizing them in terms such as "stylistical guesswork." W. V. Andersen, after studying the sketchbook in the Art Institute of Chicago, wrote: "Realizing both the hazard and the futility of attempting to establish the sequence of the sketches in this book on a stylistic study, I have reduced the book to a topographical analysis."[43] With Cézanne's drawings, as with literature, music, or architecture, one succeeds, after lengthy study, in quite clearly distinguishing the particular style.[44] Mistrust of stylistical analysis is often accompanied by an overconfident acceptance of the results that can be obtained from certain non-artistic investigations—investigations that, in fact, have all the marks of police inquiries: an account of movements, witnesses, identifications, letters and notes, railway timetables, medical examinations, addresses—everything has to come under the microscope. But reliable infor-

FIG. 2. Cézanne signature and date on back of drawing No. 78.

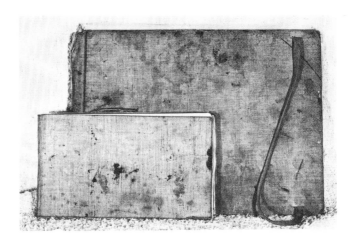

FIG. 3. Two Cézanne carnets (Chappuis I, the smaller; and Chappuis IV).

mation at our disposal is fairly rare, and in most cases has already been well investigated. Thus, those doing research in this field are forced, if they wish to reach any conclusions, to insert reasonable guesses into their chains of argument. It seems to me that if one refuses to acknowledge the value of stylistical analysis, it is necessary, in historical inquiries, to establish the facts in such a way that they can successfully bear examination at all levels by serious historical criticism. Now this is not always the case. I shall not amuse the reader here with an enumeration of passages taken from articles that claim to date the drawings by scientific means and that appeal to the goodwill of the reader to accept the links in the suppositions. I shall limit myself to returning to the conjecture that the sketchbooks can be used as frameworks allowing one to date the pages they contain with more exactitude. In order to examine this idea with the prudence it imposes, it will be useful to begin by describing the sketchbooks known to us.

First of all, let us remember that the word *carnet* means, truly speaking, a small account book that is higher than it is wide. When the leaves are bound by their shorter side one should use the word *album*. However, it has become the habit to speak of *"un carnet de Cézanne."* We shall start with the sketchbooks from the artist's youth. The measurements of these are generally in centimeters, which is the course we shall adopt.

1. Pages from an early album in the Bezalel National Museum in Jerusalem. It was sold by Jean-Pierre Cézanne, the artist's grandson, to the important New York collectors Mr. and Mrs. Henry Pearlman, who donated the drawings by Cézanne's hand to the Bezalel National Museum (1962). On its pages, measuring 17,4 × 24,1 cm., are also a few sketches by Marie Cézanne, Paul's elder sister. Dates: 1857–60. (Let us also mention for the record another sketchbook from the artist's youth that one hears about in Aix-en-Provence. I saw a few of its pages, but the rest was not visible. This carnet seems to me to be of no interest.)

2. Carnet from the artist's youth *(Carnet de jeunesse)* in the Cabinet des Dessins of the Louvre, RF 29949. Acquired by the Musées Nationaux from Pierre Berès in 1953, this sketchbook was first deposited in the studio of Les Lauves in Aix-en-Provence and later transferred to the Cabinet des Dessins. Dimensions of the pages: 15 × 23 cm.

3. Carnet cited as the 10,3 × 17 cm. sketchbook. This sketchbook has long since been broken up and very few of its pages are known to us. The Basel catalogue included ten of its sheets, bearing nineteen drawings. No others have been found.

4. Carnet cited as the 18 × 24 cm. sketchbook. Its pages have been totally dispersed. Dimensions: between 17,7 × 23 cm. and 18 × 24 cm. Our catalogue contains 68 numbers that we believe come from this sketchbook. The Basel catalogue gave 54, but several of these pages were later found to come from other sources, as can be seen from their dimensions, for example, or from their being on laid paper.

Now we come to the seven sketchbooks mentioned by Venturi:

5. Carnet cited as Chappuis I (CP I); Venturi Nos. 1267–82; see Fig. 3. It was bought by the author in 1934, a short time after the death of Paul Guillaume. As with the six others in the Venturi catalogue, Maurice Renou and Paul Guillaume acquired it from Paul Cézanne *fils*. The leaves measure 19,5 × 12 cm., and sometimes 19,4 × 11,8 cm. A relatively small sketchbook, easily carried in one's pocket, its spine was so worn that it could hardly keep the sheets bound together. It has now been broken up, for reasons I shall explain below.

6. Carnet cited as Chappuis II (CP II); Venturi Nos. 1283–1300. It was bought at the same time as the sketchbook CP I. Leaves measure between 21,5 × 12,6 cm. and 21,7 × 12,5 cm. Was incomplete at time of purchase; now broken up.

7. The carnet cited as Album, Paul Mellon Collection. Venturi Nos. 1301–15. Bought from Paul Guillaume in 1933 (same source as the preceding ones). It was acquired by Mr. and Mrs. Paul Mellon in 1967. Leaves measure 15,2 × 23,7 cm. In 1966 it was reproduced in facsimile by Daniel Jacomet, Paris.

8. Carnet cited as Chappuis IV (CP IV). Venturi Nos. 1316–22. See Fig. 3. It was bought in 1933 from Paul Guillaume (same source as the preceding ones). Leaves measure between 27,3 × 21 cm. and 25,5 × 21,1 cm. Very incomplete at the time of purchase, the spine worn out; it must have contained many watercolors.

Now we come to the three Basel Museum carnets:

9. Carnet I (BS I) in the Department of Engravings (Kupferstichkabinett der oeffentlichen Kunstsammlung Basel). Venturi Nos. 1323–1357. Leaves measure between 13 × 21,8 cm. and 13,1 × 21,4 cm. In many cases the leaves have been trimmed. Bought by the dealer Werner Feuz after the death of Paul Guillaume (same source as the preceding ones). All the leaves are detached from the binding. Those acquired by the Basel Museum are reproduced in the *Beschreibender Katalog der Zeichnungen von Paul Cézanne* (Catalogue of the Basel Drawings).

10. Carnet II (BS II), same place as above. Venturi Nos. 1358–97. Leaves measure between 12,5 × 21,5 cm. and 12,2 × 20,9 cm. Bought, broken up, and sold by the dealer Werner Feuz in the same way as the preceding one. The leaves acquired by the Basel Museum are reproduced in the Catalogue of the Basel Drawings.

11. Carnet III (BS III), same place as above. Venturi Nos. 1398–1436. Leaves measure between 20,7 × 12,5 cm. and 19,3 × 12,4 cm. Bought, broken up, and sold in the same way as the preceding two. The leaves acquired by the Basel Museum are reproduced in the Catalogue of the Basel Drawings.

Five sketchbooks now follow which were catalogued by John Rewald in 1951, but none of which is mentioned by Venturi. This batch of five comes from: Cézanne *fils*, Paris; Maurice Renou, Paris; Poyet, Lyons; Maurice Renou, Paris; Sam Salz, New York. From this last source they went to their various present owners.

12. First carnet belonging to Mrs. Enid A. Haupt, New York; Rewald Carnets: C I. Leaves measure 11,6 × 18,2 cm. The leaves have all been detached and framed, and together with those from Mrs. Haupt's second carnet are displayed on the walls of her house with most remarkable effect. John Rewald reproduces a few of them together with others selected from the five carnets catalogued in 1951.

13. Carnet belonging to the Art Institute of Chicago, cited here as A.I.C. sketchbook; Rewald Carnets: C II. Leaves measure 12,4 × 21,7 cm. Sketchbook intact; has been reproduced in facsimile with a catalogue by Carl O. Schniewind (New York: Curt Valentin, 1951).

14. Carnet from the Cabinet des Dessins of the Louvre. (Donated by Sam Salz.) Cited here as sketchbook ML (RF 29933); Rewald Carnets: C III. Leaves measure 13,7 × 21,6 cm. Sketchbook intact.

15. Second carnet belonging to Mrs. Enid A. Haupt, New York. Cited here as: Second sketchbook Mrs. Enid A. Haupt; Rewald Carnets: C IV. Leaves measure 12,7 × 21,6 cm. Sketchbook not intact.

16. Carnet belonging to Mr. and Mrs. Leigh Block, Chicago. Cited here as: sketchbook Leigh Block; Rewald Carnets: C V. Leaves measure 12,6 × 21,7 cm. When the old binding was replaced, the leaves were bound in a different order and paged in arabic numerals. We deal with the old pagination as it was noted by John Rewald.

17. Carnet known as the *violet moiré*, belonging to Mlle. Edmée Maus, Geneva. A carnet in the true sense of the word, being higher than it is wide, but very small; cited here as: violet moiré sketchbook. Leaves measure between 11,7 × 6,7 cm. and 10,2 × 6,8 cm. Source: Jean-Pierre Cézanne, the artist's grandson. Originally it was kept inside the flap of a leather wallet, one that is still in the family's possession. It was exhibited at Bernheim-Jeune in 1956, in a glass case, amidst a marvelous display of watercolors. A short time afterwards Daniel Jacomet published it privately in a facsimile edition. The outside cover of these facsimile reproductions is mauve-pink moiré cloth.

18. Finally, there are a few rare leaves done in the artist's youth that would seem to come from two sketchbooks otherwise unknown. Dimensions 12,5 × 20,8 cm. or 12 × 20,5 cm., and 11,5 × 20,3 cm. It is possible that all these may all come from the same sketchbook.

In trying to discover, amidst the whole mass of Cézanne's drawings, certain groups that might help to circumscribe the dates of the artist's works, Th. Reff and W. V. Andersen have tried to delimit the periods in which the painter used one or other of his sketchbooks. Thus, on the Album, Paul Mellon Collection, Th. Reff writes ". . . it seems more reasonable to suppose a usage within one decade than over a span of 25 years."[45] He thinks that most of the drawings in the Album were done about 1895. W. V. Andersen, for his part, has studied the 18 × 24 carnet; the one in the Art Institute of Chicago; and the *violet moiré* carnet. He estimates that the 18 × 24 carnet was used for ten years, from 1866 to 1876, whereas in the Basel catalogue I had presumed the dates to extend from 1858 to 1880.[46] However, we should point out that the date 1858 applies only to one short, undated rhyme, which John Rewald *(Corr.)* classifies at the end of 1858 as No. VII bis (our No. 179). The 1880 limit is set by one page dated 1870–80, and another 1873–80 (our Nos. 119, 174). The drawings have been dated from 1864 on. In this present catalogue the dates given for the works done in the 18 × 24 sketchbook extend from 1864 to 1875, with one exception: No. 476 is dated 1876–78. This exception I make on stylistic grounds, and to date this drawing as early as the year 1875 simply to keep things in nice order is something I refuse to do. Here I am asserting the artist's right, should the occasion arise, to take up a sketchbook he has not used for years and sketch in a scene from life, as here, with this drawing of a dog. We must make clear that it is a question of method, or principle, which takes precedence over treating this sketch in the way that would be most convenient. It is a question of the artist's freedom—whether he is to be allowed to do things as he pleases, in generous disorder, or whether he is to be made to comply with university discipline and its yearly periods of work. Had he followed the latter, Cézanne ought to have used the same sketchbook until it was full, then to have started a new one and kept to it. But, from what we know, Cézanne made use of several sketchbooks at one time, and filled them up without regard to page order. We should not forget that he generally had at least two places of work, one in Aix, the other in Paris, L'Estaque, Fontainebleau, or elsewhere. When moving around he might well have left one or two sketchbooks in the Jas de Bouffan, another in the Château Noir, or he might have bought a new one in Paris. The sketchbook CP IV was bought in Barbizon, at Bodmer's (cf. note 57). The apartments where Hortense lived with young Paul were in Aix or Paris. Cézanne could have done many of his sketches in the evening amidst his family. Could he not quite easily have left one of his sketchbooks in a drawer in his wife's home? In short, it does not seem reasonable to insist on reducing the dates during which Cézanne might have used any one sketchbook to as short a period as possible. One should never date any page of a sketchbook simply to make it comply with previously decided time limits, saying that a certain page belongs to a group, and that the group is situated in a certain period of time. One must take into account works done at isolated times, early or late. To cite another example of disputed dating of a carnet, W. V. Andersen thinks the Art Institute of Chicago sketchbook was used between 1876 and 1885[43]; Rewald had indicated 1875–85; our catalogue 1870–85. Again: according to W. V. Andersen, the sketchbook in the Cabinet des Dessins dates from the years 1888–90[47]; Rewald had indicated 1880–81, and also partly 1888–95; our catalogue gives 1888–99.

13. *Is it imperative to keep the sketchbooks intact?*

I must be frank and say that personally, I do not regret that the sketchbooks are no longer all intact. It seems sufficient to know from what sketchbook any one page comes. I agree, of course, that holding one of Cézanne's sketchbooks that has been kept intact is a moving experience, and that glancing through it is gratifying to the curiosity, for it brings one into contact with the man and his skill. But upon reflection one realizes that what one wants most, and what is important, is to see and to appreciate the drawings contained in that small album with its gray cloth binding, stained with specks of color and dirt. It is seeing the splendor of certain pages, the lighter, more gracious notes of others; it is grasping the shape of a series of human figures, or objects; it is being admitted to the seductions of a landscape. The sketchbook itself is comparable to a musical manuscript: the manuscript is interesting in itself, but how much more interesting it is to hear the actual music! My thirty-five years' experience has taught me that a drawing by Cézanne assumes its full importance only when it is presented in isolation, in a suitable, not overcrowded, setting. I will even go so far as to say that one cannot judge its effect fully until it has thus been seen set off to best advantage. This is sometimes the way to discovering something new.

There are also other disadvantages in leaving the drawings in the sketchbooks. In order to keep the bindings and leaves in a good state of preservation, the drawings must not be shown too often over the years, and never to more than two or three people at a time. When looking at a sketchbook, one has constantly to pick it up and turn it in all directions, as the sketches are often inverted; public collections would find this extremely inconvenient. When the pages are bound in a sketchbook, it is impossible to juxtapose two studies for comparison, and to look at any one sketch it is necessary to pick up and thumb through the whole album. In addition, and contrary to what is generally thought, one soon tires when looking at a complete Cézanne sketchbook, possibly because it takes a lot of concentration to grasp the significance of so many sketches crammed unpretentiously together in an unassuming sketchbook. There is also the appeal of novelty—one is so impatient to turn to the next page that he forgets what he has just seen. It is like eating cherries from a cherry tree: the eye is always looking for the one to come.

14. *The presentation of the catalogue*

For the reader's convenience, the drawings are reproduced in a separate volume, thus allowing comparisons to be made between the drawings and the models that inspired the artist, the latter being reproduced in the text volume.

Some readers may find it regrettable that the reproduction volume has some pages in lengthwise format and that it is therefore occasionally necessary to put the volume flat on a table and rotate it in order to turn from a lengthwise page to an upright page. There are, however, reasons for this presentation. Above all it was necessary to make sure that the drawings were well reproduced, and this requirement took precedence over the convenience of thumbing through a volume without having to turn it. It was also necessary to keep the cost of the book within reasonable limits, for this catalogue is not a luxury work, but an instrument for general use. And finally, it was necessary for the reproduction volume to be easy to handle. To have presented all the pages lengthwise would have required a considerably greater number of pages, and moreover, many of the lengthwise drawings would have had to have been reproduced in an even smaller format. Experience has shown that these drawings are far better on a page of lengthwise format.

In any case, in a work such as this, it is impossible to reproduce the drawings and to keep the proportions of the original leaves. The aim of a catalogue is to put reproductions at the public's disposal, thus enabling one to identify the drawings without error; this is as important as putting the drawings into chronological sequence. Thus, in order to present the works clearly, it has often been necessary to suppress a part of the white page. This was done notably in series of small sketches drawn on one large leaf. There are also pages with a head sketched at the top; here it was necessary to leave enough blank space to maintain the rhythm of the whole. This leads us to note a difference between reproducing several paintings on the same page of a book and reproducing several drawings similarly. The colors of the paintings are transposed into black and white, and as a rule the resulting tones, reduced to darkish grays, fill the rectangle. With drawings, the transposition is less complete, the pencil strokes remaining gray, the whites remaining light. This creates a different rhythm, the background of the drawings tending to merge with the white of the book page; it is less a question of assembling smaller darkish rectangles within the rectangular shape of a page, as with groups of paintings, than of harmoniously juxtaposing drawings of various appearances. The whites have a part to play—they space the drawings out and bear the pencil strokes—and it is necessary to take this into consideration. This is why it is more difficult to place reproductions of drawings rather than of paintings on a page "*à la française*" (an upright page). Having said that, even when one has the very best reproductions before one's eyes, it must not be forgotten that they cannot equal the originals. To obtain an overall view an exhibition would be needed for which several hundred of the Master's best drawings would be selected—no doubt a chimerical project, but one that for me is marvelously seductive.

15. *Acknowledgments*

I would like to express my sincere thanks to all those, collectors, dealers, connoisseurs, and friends who have helped in compiling this catalogue. My gratitude goes first to John Rewald, Barbara and Léo Marchutz, Robert Ratcliffe, Fritz Novotny, and Gertrude Berthold. To Professors Theodore Reff, Wayne V. Andersen, Chuji Ikegami, as well as to Helmut Ripperger in New York and Paule Cailac in Paris, I am grateful for their effective help in gathering together little-known drawings. Of the museums who lent me assistance, I would like to cite first the Cabinet des Dessins of the Louvre and its Director, Maurice Sérullaz, and the Kupferstichkabinett Basel; and also The Art Institute of Chicago. The eminent collectors Lord Clark of London, Mr. and Mrs. Paul Mellon of Upperville, Virginia, Mr. and Mrs. Leigh Block of Chicago, and Mrs. Enid A. Haupt of New York have been most generous. I am grateful for the kind coöperation of collectors who furnished me with photographs of their precious drawings; the reader will find their names (with the exception of those who preferred the simple mention "Private collection") under the heading "Collections" in the catalogue texts. I wish to express my gratitude also to Dr. Silberstein, a high official of the administration of the art collections of the U.S.S.R., who has been kind enough to ascertain whether the Russian museums or the private collections possess any Cézanne drawings in addition to their great number of paintings by the artist: there are no drawings to be recorded. And finally, I would like to stress the great contribution of those who translated this work from French into English. The Introduction was undertaken by Paul Constable and Mr. and Mrs. Jacques Féjoz of Chambéry, in collaboration; the catalogue texts were translated, reviewed with much care, and transcribed by Barbara Marchutz, aided by her husband, Léo. They carried out this work, which called for a genuine love of the Master's art, in Aix-en-Provence, on the Route de Cézanne, from a site where one's eye is drawn naturally toward the crest of Sainte-Victoire.

ADDENDUM TO THE INTRODUCTION
Mes Confidences, an unpublished biographical document

Mes Confidences is an 8-page booklet, $3\frac{3}{4} \times 5$ inches (104×135 mm). It was given by Joachim Gasquet in 1911 or 1912 to M. and Mme Ladislas Rohozinski of Aix-en-Provence, for their daughter Lili, Gasquet's godchild. In all probability the album came from Joachim Gasquet's father, Henri, a well-known baker in Aix and an old schoolmate of Cezanne's. Some lines the painter wrote to Henri Gasquet on December 23, 1898, testify to their long friendship:

. . . that rue Suffren that was our cradle. It is impossible to think without emotion of those wonderful days, of that atmosphere that one breathed without ever doubting oneself . . .

(J. Rewald, *Cézanne, Geffroy et Gasquet*, p. 37)

Ladislas Rohozinski, a musician, was twenty when he met the poet Joachim Gasquet at the literary salon of Juliette Adam, in Paris in 1908. They formed a lasting friendship, Rohozinski going to live in Aix-en-Provence. In the same salon Rohozinski met the woman he would marry, Mlle Nouryé de Châteauneuf, daughter of the minister to the Ottoman sultan, Abdul Hamid II. Mlle de Châteauneuf was a close friend of the writer Pierre Loti, a frequent visitor to her parents' home in Istanbul, who painted a glamorous picture of Parisian literary circles to her. When she came to Paris, the young woman was introduced to the salon of Juliette Adam, where her beauty and naïve charm caught the attention of the well-known writers and artists gathered there. Thus it was to her and to her husband that Jo Gasquet gave the little album. In turn, Mme Rohozinski gave it to her daughter and son-in-law, M. and Mme Cecil Michaelis, after having kept it secretly for forty years. In October 1971, finally, the album was entrusted to me, with the mission of photographing and publishing it. By this time the present catalogue was already in press, but in view of its interest, the document demanded prompt and accessible publication; as it supported some views expressed in the Introduction, it seemed appropriate to add it here.

Mes Confidences probably dates from the years 1866-69. In my view this album constitutes an authentic personality test.

On the cover Cézanne indicated the place where he was writing his answers: on the second floor, at 30 rue St. Louis. This was in Aix, evidently, not in Paris,

and I can not say at whose home, but rue Suffren, mentioned in the letter cited above, was adjacent.

Let us examine the questions and answers on the pages following:

1. *Q:* What is your favorite color?
   A: General harmony.
The response indicated that the artist had already discussed the question with his friends, and that, even at this time, the harmony of the ensemble seemed to him the prime factor.

2. *Q:* What is your favorite smell?
   A: The smell of the fields.
This is the answer of a landscapist, devoted to the earth and to the early morning.

3. *Q:* What is your favorite flower?
   A: Scabiosa.
To understand that, one must look at scabiosa growing in the meadows.

4. *Q:* What animal is most appealing to you?
   A: (No reply)
According to Louis Aurenche, *"il parlait amicalement aux animaux."*

(J. Rewald, *Cézanne, Geffroy et Gasquet*, p. 62).

5. *Q:* What color eyes and hair do you prefer?
   A: (No reply)

6. *Q:* What do you consider the most estimable virtue?
   A: Friendship.
To be worthwhile, friendship must be disinterested.

7. *Q:* What vice do you detest most?
   A: (No reply)

8. *Q:* What work do you prefer?
   A: Painting.

9. *Q:* What leisure activity do you enjoy most?
   A: Swimming.
Thus the "Bathers." A swimmer is difficult to paint. Water is an element of nature, like the smell of the fields.

10. *Q:* What seems to you the ideal of earthly happiness?
    A: To have *une belle formule.*
This reply should be compared to No. 8, "Painting."

To have a personal style, beautiful and valid in general. In the language of Cézanne, to realize. See *Correspondance*, letter CLXXXIII (1905): "The Louvre is the book in which we learn to read. We must not, however, be satisfied with retaining *les belles formules* of our great predecessors."

11. *Q:* What seems the worst fate to you?
    A: To be destitute.

If he had had to earn his living, Cézanne would not have been able to do what he did. His friends used to say, "Without money, Cézanne would be dead." He knew it.

12. *Q:* May we ask how old you are?
    A: (No reply—to our regret.)

13. *Q:* What Christian name would you have taken if you had the choice?
    A: My own.

Remember that the artist's mother thought the name "Paul" augured well for a painter.

14. *Q:* What was the finest moment of your life?
    A: (No reply)

15. *Q:* What was the most painful?
    A: (No reply)

16. *Q:* What is your greatest aspiration?
    A: Certainty.

Magnificent response, recalling Blaise Pascal. An intellectual equivalent of "la belle formule," certainty should spring from intuition controlled by reason and métier.

17. *Q:* Do you believe in friendship?
    A: Yes.

18. *Q:* What moment of the day do you find most agreeable?
    A: The morning.

For the impatient artist, painting began at daybreak. It is said that he got up during the night to see if the sky promised good light for painting.

19. *Q:* What historical personage are you most drawn to?
    A: Napoleon.

Great Mediterranean figure.

20. *Q:* What character from literature or the theater?
    A: Frenhoffer *(sic)*.

New confirmation of his attraction to the type of artist-painter defined by Balzac in *Le Chef-d'Oeuvre inconnu*. One should add that the teachings of Rembrandt as they are reported by Samuel van Hoogstraaten include much of what Balzac has ascribed to Frenhofer.

21. *Q:* In what region would you like to live?
    A: Provence and Paris.

He might have answered: Provence and the Ile-de-France, but Paris was the artistic center.

22. *Q:* What writer do you admire most?
    A: Racine.

French genius, endowed with a passionate sensibility that follows nature without disowning reason. Like Cézanne.

23. *Q:* What painter?
    A: Rubens.

24. *Q:* What musician?
    A: Weber.

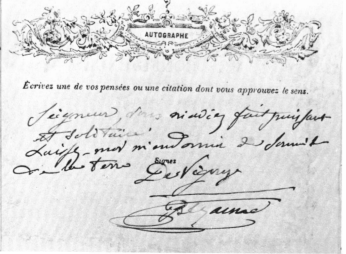

QUESTIONS

1. Quelle est la couleur que vous préférez ?
2. Quelle est votre odeur favorite ?
3. Quelle fleur trouvez-vous la plus belle ?
4. Quel animal vous est le plus sympathique ?
5. Quelle couleur d'yeux et de cheveux préférez-vous ?
6. Quelle est, selon vous, la plus estimable vertu ?
7. Quel vice détestez-vous le plus ?
8. Quelle est votre occupation préférée ?
9. Quel délassement vous est le plus agréable ?
10. Quel est, selon vous, l'idéal du bonheur terrestre ?

RÉPONSES

1 L'harmonie générale
2 L'odeur des champs
3 ...
4
5
6 L'amitié
7
8 Peindre
9 La natation
10 Avoir une belle formule -

QUESTIONS

11. Quel sort vous paraît le plus à plaindre ?
12. Peut-on vous demander l'âge que vous avez ?
13. Quel prénom auriez-vous pris, si vous l'aviez choisi ?
14. Quel a été le plus beau moment de votre vie ?
15. Quel en a été le plus pénible ?
16. Quelle est votre principale espérance ?
17. Croyez-vous à l'amitié ?
18. Quel est, pour vous, le plus agréable moment de la journée ?
19. Quel personnage historique vous est le plus sympathique ?
20. Quel personnage de roman ou de théâtre ?

RÉPONSES

11 Être dénué
12
13 Le mien
14
15
16 La certitude
17 oui
18 Le matin
19 ...
20 ...

QUESTIONS

21. Quel pays habiteriez-vous de préférence ?
22. Quel écrivain préférez-vous ?
23. Quel peintre ?
24. Quel musicien ?
25. Quelle devise prendriez-vous si vous deviez en avoir une ?
26. Quel est, selon vous, le chef-d'œuvre de la nature ?
27. De quel site avez-vous gardé le plus agréable souvenir ?
28. Quel est votre mets de prédilection ?
29. Préférez-vous un coucher dur ou tendre ?
30. Quel peuple étranger vous est le plus sympathique ?

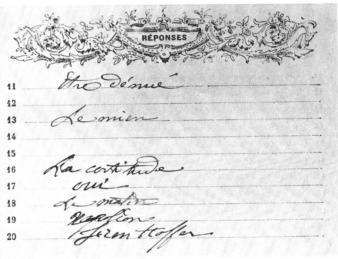

RÉPONSES

21 La Provence et Paris.
22 Racine
23 Rubens
24 Weber
25
26 La diversité infinie -
27 Les autels de St Marc
28 Les pommes de terre à l'huile
29 Entre les deux.
30 Aucun.

Gerstle Mack writes: "Madame Marie Gasquet, widow of Joachim Gasquet, has told me that Cézanne sometimes asked her to play the piano for him—preferably selections from *Oberon* or *Der Freischütz*..." (*Paul Cézanne*, 1935, p. 23). In Paris, Cézanne seems to have attended the opera occasionally. Louis Aurenche relates that he sang some choruses with him (J. Rewald, *Cézanne, Geffroy et Gasquet*, p. 63).

25. *Q:* What motto would you take if you had to have one?
    A: (No reply)

26. *Q:* What do you consider nature's masterpiece?
    A: Her infinite diversity.

To be related to the reply to the first question: "General harmony." It is in this frame of reference that "infinite diversity" belongs. Cézanne guarded against being overwhelmed by the richness of what he observed, while his art was based on this richness.

27. *Q:* Of what place have you retained the pleasantest memory?
    A: The hills of St. Marc.

St. Marc-Jaumegarde is located a few kilometers northeast by east of Aix-en-Provence.

28. *Q:* What is your favorite dish?
    A: Les pommes de terre à l'huile.

Potatoes boiled, peeled, sliced crosswise, and sprinkled with olive oil. Provence produces a savory olive oil.

29. *Q:* Do you like a hard bed or a soft one?
    A: In-between.

30. *Q:* To the people of which foreign country are you most drawn?
    A: To none.

Autograph. Write one of your own thoughts or a quotation that you agree with.

> Lord, you have made me strong and solitary
> Let me sleep the sleep of the earth.
>
> —De Vigny

The quotation is from the poem "Moïse" by Alfred de Vigny (1797–1863). These lines appear in it four times, the first line in a slightly different form each time.

The quotation and signature were reproduced by Joachim Gasquet on page 208 of his book, so this detail is not unpublished. Gasquet used "Mes Confidences" as a source, putting several of the replies in Cézanne's mouth, but their meaning is drowned in poetical conversation.

Taken together, the replies of Cézanne show that even at this time, when he was between 27 and 30 years old, he saw clearly the path he would follow. The personal problems, the difficulties of realization, the criticisms, would be surmounted. However, one must not confuse the responses concerning the man with those concerning the painter on painting.

Much remains to be said, but it is not my intention to exhaust the subject; it is enough to have made this extraordinary document available.

NOTES TO THE INTRODUCTION AND CATALOGUE RAISONNÉ

1. The etchings and lithographs have not been included here, as they do not proceed directly from the artist's hand. Coming from presses, the numerous examples vary slightly in their condition; thus, although the graphics are undoubtedly of interest in themselves, this factor makes them different from the drawings.

2. Handwritten letter dated: Siena, 19 luglio 1958.

3. Wayne V. Andersen's *Cézanne's Portrait Drawings*, Cambridge, Massachusetts: M.I.T. Press, 1970, appeared just as the drafting and translation of our text was completed. To my great regret, I have not been able to incorporate the information and teachings of this important book in the catalogue.

4. *Pictor semper virens:* painter constantly full of life. See near the signature on the rough copy of a letter: *Corr.* LVII, our No. 378, and *Corr.* letter XXVI.

5. See, for example, Vollard 1914, p. 93; Borély, *Art Vivant*, July 1, 1926; Gasquet, pp. 103, 117; Rivière, 1923, p. 83.

6. Gasquet, p. 55; Rivière, 1923, p. 183.

7. Rewald, *Carnets*, p. II.

8. Léo Larquier, *Le Dimanche avec Paul Cézanne*, Paris, 1925, p.136, XXX: *"Contrastes et rapports de tons, voilà tout le secret du dessin du modelé."* Rewald, *History of Impressionism*, 1961, p. 62 and note 32: "According to Monet, Cézanne was in the habit of putting a black hat and a white handkerchief next to the model in order to fix the two poles between which to establish his values."

9. Charles Baudelaire, *L'Oeuvre et la vie d'Eugène Delacroix*, p. 13, in *L'Art Romantique*, Paris: Garnier, 1931.

10. Roger Fry, *Cézanne*, London, 1927, p. 38.

11. Meier-Graefe, *Cézanne und sein Kreis*, Munich, 1922.

12. The description given on pages 12 and 13 in the introduction to the Basel catalogue is accurate, but is incomplete inasmuch as it passes over the fact that the loose leaves went directly from Cézanne *fils* to the dealer Werner Feuz, whereas the three carnets were sold to this dealer through Madame Paul Guillaume.

13. Waldemar George, *Le Dessin Français de David à Cézanne*, Paris, 1929—André Salmon, Dessins inédits de Cézanne, *Cahiers d'Art* I, 1926.—Maurice Denis, Le Dessin de Cézanne, *L'Amour de l'Art*, 1924, 2.

14. Fritz Novotny, Cézanne als Zeichner, *Wiener Jahrbuch für Kunstgeschichte*, vol. XIV (XVII), 1950. Reproduced in *Ueber das Elementare in der Kunstgeschichte und andere Aufsätze von Fritz Novotny*, Vienna: Rosenbaum, 1968.

15. *"Redoutant des critiques trop justifiées, j'avais résolu de travailler dans le silence, jusqu'au jour où je me serai senti capable de défendre théoriquement le résultat de mes essais."* Letter of Nov. 25, 1889, to Octave Maus. *Corr.* CXV.

16. Eugène Delacroix, letter to Peisse, July 15, 1849. Addressing himself to Chopin, Delacroix made (according to George Sand) a statement which can not well be translated without losing its character: *"Pourtant, si vous êtes coloriste vous viendrez à bout avec le simple trait à faire comprendre que j'ai un relief, une épaisseur, un corps. Comment en viendrez-vous à bout? En n'arrêtant pas également partout ce contour, en le faisant très délié, presque interrompu en certains endroits, en l'accusant en d'autres endroits au moyen d'un second trait et, s'il le faut, d'un troisième ou encore au moyen d'un trait élargi, engraissé, qui se gardera bien d'être un fil de fer, car partout où j'ai vu un relief (...) il n'y a pas d'opacité au contour qui l'indique; ni la lumière qui frappe le contour, ni l'ombre qui glisse dessus n'ont de point d'arrêt saisissable."* (See Raymond Escholier, *Eugène Delacroix*, Vol. I, p. 146.)

17. Kenneth Clark, *Leonardo da Vinci*, Penguin Books, 1958, p. 142.

18. Roger Fry, *Cézanne*, London, 1927, p. 88.

19. *Dessins*, 1957, pp. 66, 67.

20. Maurice Denis, Cézanne, *L'Occident*, Sept. 1907. Reprinted in *Théories*, Paris: Hermann, 1964, p. 156.

21. Kurt Badt, *Die Kunst Cézannes*, Munich, 1956, p. 169.

22. Theodore Reff, *Studies in the Drawings of Cézanne*, a Thesis presented by Theodore Franklin Reff to the Department of Fine Arts, Harvard University, Cambridge, Massachusetts, May, 1958, p. 177.

23. Neumeyer, 1958, p. 17.

24. Kenneth Clark, in the Introduction to the catalogue *Paul Cézanne, an Exhibition of Watercolours*, The Arts Council of Great Britain, 1946.

25. *Various markings accompanying the drawings:* On a certain number of drawings we find notes in pencil, blue pencil, or ink. These marks, it is true, are rarely visible on the reproductions in this book because it has been necessary to reduce the white margins around the drawings. Some of these inscriptions are in Cézanne's own hand; these are treated in the catalogue and will not be considered here. We refer now only to marks attributable to other sources. Certain drawings have notes in one corner, such as 5D, 2E, etc.; these are undoubtedly prices inscribed by dealers according to personal codes. There are words such as *"tel"* or *"tel ensemble,"* crosses, the word *"réduire,"* etc., and figures. In *Dessins de Cézanne*, 1957, and in the catalogue of Cézanne's drawings at the Basel museum, I put forth the hypothesis that the *tel* accompanied by a cross had been placed there by Cézanne himself, indicating that the sketches could be used as they were for future pictures. Theodore Reff (see Note 26), then Douglas Cooper (see Note 27), contested the validity of these suppositions. These markings, according to them, were made by Ambroise Vollard, or others, who wished to reproduce the drawings so marked. I now agree with them; these are signs commonly used by platemakers, particularly by those who use the offset process. The crosses indicate how many blocks (or plates) are to be made. The word *"tel"* next to a drawing (sometimes on the back) means that the platemaker will use the original drawing and not its photograph to make the plate. If we accept this, the other inscriptions are easily explained. The figures, such as "30 × 23," generally indicate the dimensions of the photographic plates or films used. Finally, there are the indications jotted down casually by picture framers.

26. Th. Reff, *BurlM*, August, 1963, p. 376.

27. Douglas Cooper, *Master Drawings*, vol. 1, Winter 1963, p. 56.

28. See Gasquet, 1926, p. 171.

29. Bernard Dorival, *Cézanne*, Paris, 1948, p. 69.

30. François Lehel, *Notre art dément*, Paris: Jonquières & Cie., 1926, p. 83: *"C'est l'artiste qui l'a emporté sur le mâle."* The only sentence worth remembering in this work.

31. Georg Schmidt, *Aquarelle von Paul Cézanne*, Basel, 1952; French edition, 1953, p. 9.

32. Quelques souvenirs sur Paul Cézanne, by one of the artist's nieces, in *GBA* 1960, p. 298: "Louis-Auguste avait coutume de dire: *Paul se laissera manger par la peinture, et Marie par les Jésuites.*"

33. Th. Reff, Cézanne's Bather with outstretched arms, *GBA*, March, 1962, p. 173.

34. Th. Reff refers to Paul Schilder's book *The Image and Appearance of the Human Body* (New York: International University Press, 1950). Speaking about hysteria, the author says: "The protruding parts of the body may become symbols of the male sex organ." (pp. 171/72) Apart from this observation I have found nothing in this medical book which can be directly applied to the case in question.

35. Let us give three examples, taken from articles on Cézanne, where the details have been interpreted in a way somewhat removed from art.

1: The rhyme *Songe d' Annibal, Annibalis somnium*, composed by Cézanne at the age of 19 (*Corr.* Letter VI), describes a drinking bout, a *"festin dans lequel on avait fait trop fréquent usage du rhum et du cognac. . . . Sur la nappe le vin s'épandit à grands flots. . . ."* Th. Reff likens the spilt liquids to scattered sperm, and refers once again to the feelings of guilt linked to masturbation. (Th. Reff, Cézanne's Dream of Hannibal, *AB*, 1963, p. 149.)

2: Sara Lichenstein says about drawing No. 37: "Beheading may be coupled with emasculation in Cézanne's early *Ugolino* drawing." (*Master Drawings*, Vol. 5, No. 2, 1967, p. 187, note 17.) The emasculation in this case is undoubtedly that of the artist's father, whose skull (according to Kurt Badt) is being devoured.

3: Meyer Schapiro, in his article, The Apples of Cézanne (*Art News Annual*, XXXIV, 1968, p. 51, note 30), speaks about the painting, Venturi No. 1520A: "In a drawing which may be a sketch for Venturi No. 115, are two nude women on one bank and a clothed fisherman on the opposite bank with a rod extending across the river to the women." It is my opinion that, with this small canvas (not a drawing), the man may be looking at the bathers, but he is displaying far more interest in his fishing than in assaulting the women. Instead of suggesting that he is bursting with repressed desires, one can say that he is curbing the will of the flesh in favor of his primary interest (in Cézanne's case, painting). Moreover, his fishing rod deliberately passes by the side of the bathers. If one is committed to considering the fishing rod as symbol of the erect sex organ, one should logically also interpret our drawing No. 260 (Venturi No. 1213) in this way. Meyer Schapiro has refrained from so doing; might it be for fear of ridicule? And finally, considering these interpretations solely from the point of view of methodology, I find many analogies between them and astrological ones. Astrology also aspires to a rigorously scientific determinism. And in establishing a horoscope one mainly gives individual interpretations to information which is considered true only in its general form.

36. Scientific hypotheses sometimes link up with myths.

37. J. Rewald, *Thèse*, p. 125: *"Je n'ai pas besoin d'excitant, je me remonte moi-même."* Léo Larguier, *Le Dimanche avec Paul Cézanne*, Paris, 1925, p. 132, X.

38. Meyer Schapiro, The Apples of Cézanne, *Art News Annual*, XXXIV, 1968, pp. 35 ff.

39. Emile Zola, *L'Oeuvre*, Oeuvres complètes, Paris, 1928, p. 385.

40. Larguier, *op. cit.*, quotation pp. 88, 94; and *Corr.*, letter CLX: *"Avant tout, il n'y a que le tempérament, id est, la force initiale, qui puisse porter quelqu'un au but qu'il doit atteindre."*

41. Letter to Vollard, Jan. 9, 1903. *Corr.* CLIX.

42. Th. Reff, Album de Paul Cézanne, *BurlM*, vol. CIX, Nov., 1967, p. 653.

43. W. V. Andersen, Cézanne's Sketchbook in The Art Institute of Chicago, *BurlM*, May, 1962.

44. I exposed myself to much criticism when writing, in *Dessins*, 1957, dates such as 1870–90. Twenty years is obviously too long, when taken literally. But, in fact, what this dating really meant was no more than, *"Que les historiens de l'art me pardonnent: la date exacte m'intéresse peu, je regarde le dessin. Cherchez la date si le dessin ne vous dit rien tel que vous le voyez."* For me, art itself has always taken precedence over the history of art, and the drawing itself has always meant more than all that could be written to fix the date on which it was done. My attitude about dating changed once I started to classify the Basel museum drawings, about 1959. It was necessary to put the drawings in an order corresponding to the artist's evolution, and hence to consider dates. With this present catalogue the necessity of establishing dates became even more important. I accept the sarcasm and censorship that my past attitude has aroused—and will continue to arouse—without wincing. As for my earlier years of unconcern—those were the days!

45. Th. Reff, *Album de Paul Cézanne*, quotation p. 652.

46. W. V. Andersen, Cézanne's Portrait Drawings from the 1860's, *Master Drawings*, vol. 5, No. 3, 1967, p. 279, note 9.

47. W. V. Andersen, Cézanne's Carnet violet moiré, *BurlM*, June, 1965, note 19.

48. In the Basel catalogue, No. 67, I had accepted the reading *ideme* (sic), taking it for a fantasy of southern French pronunciation. But the fantasy is in the handwriting. See my commentary in the text of No. 461.

49. R. W. Ratcliffe and another connoisseur preferring to remain anonymous are of the opinion that this drawing is not by Cézanne.

50. Ambroise Vollard, *En écoutant Cézanne, Degas, Renoir*, Paris, 1938, p. 215.

51. La Bodinière was the name of a room used by the art dealer Le Barc de Bouteville for an exhibition, in which Cézanne was to participate.

52. For this information I am indebted to Herr Hans Schedelman, of Salzburg, erudite expert on armor, who adds that it is impossible to decide whether this suit was antique or was one of the numerous copies manufactured in the nineteenth century.

53. Record of the sale at the Hôtel Drouot, auctioneer Me Chevalier, on March 9 and the days following, 1903.

54. In the Basel catalogue (No. 104) our No. 553 is dated 1880–82. The date raised much controversy, as did those of No. 552 (Basel catalogue, No. 105, dated 1885–1900) and No. 554 (Basel catalogue, No. 106, dated 1882–92). Th. Reff (*Burlington Magazine*, August 1963, p. 376) considered the date 1880–82 incorrect, but whereas Neumeyer (1958) had suggested 1894–1900, Reff proposed 1895–1900. Douglas Cooper (*Master Drawings*, 1963, Vol. 1, No. 4, p. 56) indicated 1896 for all three drawings: our Nos. 552, 553, 554. I would therefore like to give my reasons for maintaining the date 1881–84 here for all three. If we compare

the *Still Life with Candlestick* with a drawing done between 1895 and 1900, for example our No. 1135, we are at first struck by the resemblance in treatment of details: the circular strokes, the vertical contours, even the hatching indicating shadows. The studied horizontal lines in the lower center of both drawings are very much alike, yet after thoroughly examining *the whole*, one is aware of a real and striking difference of rhythm and feeling. The *Still Life with Candlestick* renders a more naturalistic vision; each object maintains its individual form and weight, the rounded and vertical volumes appear heavy, the hatching is done in several directions; there is no "taking wing." Admittedly, the rising movement of the candlestick base is rendered by multiple serpentine strokes. But compare the chair back of No. 1135, or even better, the decorative flowers on the panel; compare also Nos. 1106, 1186, and, in No. 1056, the underarm and abdomen especially. The drawing of the candlestick belongs to an earlier period, a period when the rhythmic ordonnance of the surface (the details arranged in a certain order) was still patiently studied, worked out with a conscious search for balance—in short, constructed. Between 1895 and 1900 the decorative rhythm established in a drawing is less conscious; the pencil no longer needs to search, the stroke is instantly found. The drawing palpitates, and even the stability demanded by the subject suggests movement. The circular strokes acquire a nervous eloquence and the hatching blends without the least insistence. Surface and depth, volumes and linear rhythms, are mysteriously allied. The still lifes Nos. 552, 553, 554 are certainly very fine drawings, but their quality is of a different kind; it consists in a kind of fixity, the ransom of a monumental intention. To justify the date he proposes, Mr. Reff puts forward two reasons (the other critics offer none): the arrangements of the objects, and the very low viewpoint chosen. He writes: "No. 104 (of the Basel catalogue), *Nature morte au bougeoir*, given as 1880–82, clearly belongs, like all the comparable still lifes cited by M. Chappuis (V. 1493, 1541, etc.) to the later 1890's—a date also supported by the radical overlapping and cutting of objects and by the extremely low viewpoint."

The scientific enunciation of these reasons should create no illusion as to their fragility, since it is easy to find similar arrangements and viewpoints in periods other than 1895–1900. See for example Venturi Nos. 357, 430, 594, 597, 598, for the objects; Venturi Nos. 12, 59, 69, etc., for the low angle of vision. It will be objected that there are various ways of seeing. This is true, but here, as on other occasions, the main point is to be clear about one's methods. The dating of Cézanne's drawings allows only small room for the kind of systematic reasoning we find in Euclidean geometry. The problems raised generally involve some probabilities. The various ways of seeing, for instance, embody probabilities. Instead of trying to build a rational system by the means of deductions and amplifying inductions, the scholar who is anxious to state his case in a most scientific way should not hesitate to apply the probability calculus.

55. *Les Incas*. Paris and Limoges, 1850, chez Martial Ardent Frères. There is a slight possibility that the name was added by the son of the artist.

56. The date of execution of this drawing has been much disputed. Venturi dates it 1872–77, the Basel catalogue 1886–96. In their reviews, Th. Reff (*BurlM*, Aug. 1963, p. 376) and Douglas Cooper (*Master Drawings*, Vol. 1, No. 4, 1963, p. 56) both agree (exceptionally) with Venturi, the first giving the date as 1872–77, the second as 1873–75. But the stroke is freer and at the same time more stylized than at that period. Douglas Cooper relates this drawing to the paintings Venturi Nos. 231, 234, and to the drawing Venturi No. 1228 (our No. 319). Venturi No. 231 and our drawings Nos. 251 and 252, which are contemporaneous, and also our No. 319, seem to me less closely related to it than the painting Venturi No. 234, *Déjeuner sur l'herbe*. In the first place, however, stress should be laid on the affinity of Venturi No. 234 to the watercolors Venturi Nos. 875, 876, and especially to the wash drawing Venturi No. 1225 (our No. 356); probably also our No. 654 (b), although this is less certain. The group of figures in the lower half of No. 356 is a preliminary study for the oil. The present drawing, *Spectators,* should therefore be compared to our No. 356 and the watercolors Venturi Nos. 875, 876. I repeat my conviction that, despite certain analogies of detail to earlier works, the rendering of the whole is in Cézanne's more mature style.

57. The name Bodmer was jotted down by Cézanne in his Carnet violet moiré on the verso of our No. 972. I read: *Bodmer 43 fr 70.* Most probably the artist had bought some materials for painting at Bodmer's little shop. In *BurlM*, June, 1965, p. 317, Wayne Andersen gives another interpretation of the handwritten notation (which he reproduces, fig. 48). See page III verso: *Bodmer/le 3ʰ 10.* Andersen writes (note 28): "Bodmer could be Barthélémy-Marc Bodmer (1848–1904), a romantic landscape painter who lived in Geneva and painted in the Geneva–Annecy region.... The notation probably refers to a *rendez-vous.*" Now, since the stamp relates the name of Bodmer to Barbizon, one might remember Karl Bodmer, painter, engraver and lithographer, who was born near Zurich in 1809 and died at Barbizon October 30, 1893. Having acquired French nationality, he settled in Barbizon; there J.-F. Millet painted his portrait. I can not ascertain, however, who really managed the shop, because there were other Bodmers on the spot, for instance, one Frédéric-Adolphe, draughtsman and engraver, born at Barbizon, known to have exhibited a picture at the Salon of 1878.

INTRODUCTION

1. *Le catalogue et ses antécédents*

Ce catalogue des dessins de Paul Cézanne reproduit et décrit la plus grande part des dessins de l'artiste aujourd'hui connus. Quelques lavis et quelques pastels ont été assimilés aux dessins, en revanche les dessins aquarellés n'ont pas, à d'insignifiantes exceptions près, trouvé leur place ici : ils seront classés avec les aquarelles dans le catalogue des peintures et des aquarelles de Cézanne que prépare John Rewald. Comment, en effet, tracer une limite raisonnable entre les dessins aquarellés d'une part, et d'autre part les aquarelles qui presque toutes comportent du crayon ?[1]

Notre catalogue a été précédé, on le sait, par le catalogue de Lionello Venturi, ou plus exactement par la partie du catalogue réservée aux dessins. A ce sujet il importe de dissiper une équivoque qui pourrait s'imposer. Le savant italien avait consacré les dernières années de sa vie à une nouvelle édition de son catalogue des peintures et des aquarelles de Cézanne, mais il en avait *délibérément exclu les dessins*. Il m'écrivait en 1958 : "Ma deuxième édition du Cézanne est préparée, mais je ne sais quand elle sera publiée. En tout cas elle ne contiendra aucun dessin. Je serai donc ravi si vous écrivez le catalogue des dessins de Bâle."[2]

Après avoir publié le Catalogue des dessins de Bâle et après la mort de Lionello Venturi en 1961, je décidai, rassuré par des encouragements venus des quartiers les plus divers, à mettre en chantier le présent catalogue.

Il va sans dire que l'ouvrage de Venturi publié en 1936 demeurait la base de départ de ce que j'allais entreprendre. Cependant il m'imcombait de recenser, après les avoir repérés, les nombreux dessins qui s'étaient dérobés à l'emprise de Venturi ; il fallait en outre incorporer dans le classement général les croquis des sept carnets que Venturi avait enregistrés en bloc, avec des dates approximatives se rapportant à l'ensemble de chaque carnet. Il fallait enfin tenir compte de ce qu'ont apporté les nouvelles études critiques et historiques depuis 1936, le catalogue de cinq carnets par John Rewald, en 1951, ainsi que celui des copies d'après des oeuvres d'art par Gertrude Berthold, en 1957.[3]

Les héritiers de Lionello Venturi, ainsi que son collègue, M. Nello Ponente, professeur à l'Université de Rome, ont bien voulu m'ouvrir les archives dont ils ont la garde, me permettant de consulter des documents écrits et photographiés concernant les dessins de Cézanne. En octobre 1968 j'ai pu étudier à Rome les volumineux dossiers qu'au cours des années Lionello Venturi avait constitués sur les dessins. Ces dossiers contenaient des notes de voyage, des catalogues d'exposition, des documents et des photographies. D'avoir exclu les dessins de la nouvelle édition projetée du catalogue ne devait aucunement empêcher Venturi de rassembler des photographies. Un certain nombre de celles-ci lui furent d'ailleurs soumises pour expertise et afin qu'il les publie. On sait qu'il n'en fit rien. Je suis heureux, pour ma part, qu'en les reproduisant aujourd'hui je puisse répondre aux voeux des collectionneurs qui s'étaient adressés au savant disparu. De Rome je pus rapporter vingt-sept photographies de dessins inédits, nouveaux pour moi, ainsi qu'une centaine de photographies de qualité supérieures à celles que je possédais déjà.

2. *Le contenu du catalogue*

Le présent catalogue classe et reproduit 1242 dessins de Cézanne. Il y a 1223 numéros et 19 numéros *bis* ou *ter*, ceux-ci furent insérés après-coup. Ce chiffre parait modeste si l'on songe au nombre des peintures et des aquarelles que l'artiste—*Pictor semper virens*—a exécutées ou simplement commencées.[4] Je suis persuadé que beaucoup de dessins, plus de la moitié sans doute, furent détruits ou perdus. Les témoins rapportent que Cézanne ne semblait faire aucun cas de la plupart de ses études au crayon et on sait qu'il était souvent négligent ou capricieux à l'égard de ses oeuvres.[5] D'autres attestent que Cézanne dessinait beaucoup.[6] Un historien aussi avisé que John Rewald confirme cette vue, d'ailleurs plus souvent ignorée que contestée.[7]

3. *L'appréciation du dessin de Cézanne*

Lorsqu'on voit les prix élevés payés aujourd'hui pour tout ce qui est de la main de Cézanne, on est porté à croire qu'après la mort de l'artiste, survenue en 1906, toutes les esquisses, toutes les pages de ses carnets de croquis, les grandes feuilles portant un ou plusieurs dessins, souvent au recto et au verso, furent recueillies avec respect et conservées. Cette idée correspond mal aux faits. A l'époque, les choses se présentaient autrement: presque tout le monde demeurait convaincu que *Cézanne ne savait pas dessiner*. C'était l'opinion courante. Très clairsemés étaient ceux qui savaient voir, et saisir, la beauté d'un dessin de Cézanne, qui étaient capables de comprendre ce qui signifiaient les traits de crayon sur ces feuilles que le commun des connaisseurs nommait "des ébauches informes."

Les proches même de l'artiste considéraient les dessins avec une pointe d'indulgence. Le collectionneur Victor Chocquet ne possédait, à côté de trente-six toiles, aucun dessin de Cézanne, dont il était l'ami et l'impavide défenseur. Camille Pissarro, Edgar Degas, Claude Monet, Auguste Renoir, Georges Rivière, Maurice Denis, pour ne citer que les plus grands, savaient pourtant les apprécier, les aimer, les admirer. D'autres préféraient s'en tenir aux études d'académie, aux petits portraits crayonnés, aux projets de composition ou encore aux dessins aquarellés, car Cézanne était réputé bon coloriste. Les projets de composition allaient avec les peintures, déjà plus côtées, en dépit du *dessin défaillant* qu'on leur reprochait. On était habitué, depuis deux siècles au moins, à louer ou à critiquer dans chaque tableau *la partie, si importante, du dessin*. Or, par distinct Cézanne cherchait la beauté dans ses sensations visuelles, contrôlées par l'intellect, en face de la nature. Il ne cherchait pas le Beau idéal défini intellectuellement par le dessin parfait; il abandonnait donc cette tradition de la Renaissance qui prônait les lois de la perspective scientifique et le soin du fini apporté aux contours linéaires. Pour autant qu'il songeait à être classique, il pensait l'être par la nature.

D'autres artistes abandonnaient la tradition en même temps que lui, mais plus prudemment, si bien que par la suite c'est à lui qu'on attribuait le mérite d'avoir ouvert la voie à l'art moderne. L'ouvrage publié en 1938 par Fritz Novotny, *Cézanne und das Ende der wissenschaftlichen Perspektive* (Cézanne et la Fin de la Perspective Scientifique) porte un titre résumant la situation d'une manière pour ainsi dire géniale. Le dessin de Cézanne n'était pas toujours *correct* selon la perspective classique, et il n'était pas linéaire. Foncièrement coloriste, Cézanne contrastait avec vigueur et harmonie les parties noires, grises et blanches de son dessin; en d'autres termes: il se servait moins des contours que des valeurs.[8] Cela ne veut pas dire que dans le dessin linéaire les valeurs soient toujours négligées, elles peuvent être obtenues par des resserrements de détails, des fonds etc. . . . Cela ne veut pas dire non plus que les contours ne jouent pas leur rôle dans le dessin de Cézanne, seulement les contours ne sont pas des lignes, mais des traits diversifiés marquant des limites. A la technique inhabituelle s'ajoutait la vision originale du peintre, le caractère artistique nouveau de la beauté cézannienne. Ce caractère échappait aux contemporains. Rarement ce mot de Baudelaire est-il mieux vérifié: "Le public est, relativement au génie, une horloge qui retarde."[9]

Le public demeurait incapable de lire l'écriture graphique du peintre provençal. Et si Diderot, en son temps, aurait donné "dix Watteau pour un Téniers," nombreux étaient, vers 1900, les critiques d'art qui auraient donné dix Cézanne pour un Cabanel. Le public n'a d'ailleurs pas encore entièrement désarmé de nos jours.

Mais revenons à la fin du XIXe siècle: Cézanne s'était caché au monde dont il n'avait reçu que des affronts, il restait ignoré. On n'exposait pas ses peintures et, à plus forte raison, aucun dessin. Quelques rares personnes allaient voir ses peintures chez Tanguy, rue Clauzel; il ne fut jamais question d'un dessin chez Tanguy. Il serait inutile que je cite à mon tour les témoignages qui sont dans les biographies; je mentionnerai pourtant celui, moins connu, de Roger Fry, un homme qui de bonne heure a su *voir*. Il dit de Cézanne: "He faded out so completely from the general artistic consciousness of his day that the present writer, when he was an art student in Paris in the nineties—a very ignorant and helpless, but still an inquisitive student—never once heard the name of the recluse of Aix."[10]

Toutefois, en 1898, Ambroise Vollard fit reproduire un dessin, nôtre n⁰ 514, pour orner l'invitation-catalogue de son exposition (mai-juin 1898). C'était le projet d'une composition des *Baigneuses* dont il existe plusieurs versions exécutées à l'huile, la composition Venturi n⁰ 547 par exemple qui avait été exposée par Vollard en décembre 1896. Le dessin n⁰ 938, un *portrait du fils de l'artiste,* fut reproduit par Théodore Duret dans son *Histoire des Peintres impressionnistes,* Paris 1906. Duret fit imprimer la reproduction en ton de sanguine, peut-être pour suggérer un rapprochement avec certains dessins de Watteau. En 1907 la *Gazette des Beaux-Arts* reproduisait à son tour, mais en noir, ce portrait du fils, en rendant compte à ses lecteurs de l'ouvrage de Théodore Duret. Par la suite Ambroise Vollard introduisait plus de soixante dessins dans son volume de 1914. A Munich, Meier-Graefe reprenait bon nombre de ces reproductions,[11] et il eut le mérite, en 1918 et 1921, de faire reproduire en facsimilé dans *Cézanne und seine Ahnen,* une "Mappe der Marées-Gesellschaft," les n⁰s 109, 491, 493, 510, 611, 880, 897, 962, 999.

Petit à petit quelques collectionneurs commençaient à s'intéresser aux dessins, alors que les peintures à l'huile et certaines aquarelles étaient depuis longtemps recherchées. Il y eut des dessins exposés à Berlin, quelques-uns vendus aux enchères à Paris, mais la plupart restèrent chez le fils de l'artiste, dans les placards d'Ambroise Vollard ou encore chez des amis de Cézanne qui les gardaient, si je ne m'abuse, comme des souvenirs plutôt que des chefs-d'oeuvre. A partir de 1931 environ on pouvait voir des dessins de Cézanne exposés à la vente dans quelques galeries à Paris. La sévère crise économique avait, dès 1930, fait baisser les prix des oeuvres d'art et la pénurie de liquidités rendait très difficile la vente de *gros morceaux*. Les prix avaient baissé, les fonds de roulement étaient gelés. Les dessins de Cézanne pouvaient convenir aux marchands: c'étaient des objets nouveaux dont ils ne possédaient pas de stocks à amortir, en plus c'étaient de petites choses et l'on pouvait garantir un grand nom. Le goût du public avait évolué sous l'influence de Derain, de Matisse, de Braque, Picasso, etc. . . . tous artistes ayant beaucoup pris à l'art de Cézanne.

Les principaux détenteurs, Paul Cézanne fils et Ambroise Vollard, vendirent donc des dessins, Cézanne fils par petits paquets, ou par carnets, Vollard au compte-gouttes, en même temps que des aquarelles. Le musée de Bâle achetait un important lot en 1934 et 1935, secondé par des collectionneurs privés.[12] Simultanément des dessins qui, grâce à Meier-Graefe, aux galeries Paul Cassirer et Alfred Flechtheim étaient entrées dans les collections d'Europe centrale, refluaient vers des galeries de Paris. Néanmoins, la plupart des marchands demeuraient sceptiques quant à leur importance artistique. Tout en vendant, ils nourrissaient des arrière-pensées ironiques. Ils furent surpris de voir, en 1936, beaucoup de dessins qui étaient passés par leurs mains exposés au musée de l'Orangerie, lors de la grande exposition Cézanne organisée par les Musées Nationaux, à l'occasion du trentième anniversaire de la mort de l'artiste. Jacques-Emile Blanche, dans l'avant-propos du catalogue, *Les Techniques de Cézanne*, formulait les réserves généralement faites par le monde de l'Hôtel Drouot et par celui des expositions d'art en écrivant: "Par les dessin seul, il s'exprime imparfaitement." Cependant René Huyghe et Charles Sterling, qui avaient été chargés par Henri Verne, alors Directeur des Musées Nationaux, de réunir les pièces à exposer, surent apprécier les dessins à leur juste valeur. Le catalogue groupe les dessins sous 26 numéros, cette exposition ouvrait les yeux à beaucoup. Aussi en 1936 eut lieu une exposition Cézanne à Bâle avec 69 dessins. Enfin, dans la même année parut le catalogue raisonné de l'oeuvre de Cézanne élaboré par Lionello Venturi, reproduisant un ensemble jamais vu de peintures, d'aquarelles et de dessins. Cet ouvrage permettait de juger plus sainement du rôle de Cézanne dans le siècle, et, pour revenir à notre propos particulier, du sens et de la valeur des dessins. Les dessins étaient également bien représentés aux expositions de San Francisco 1937, et, en 1939, à Lyon au Palais Saint-Pierre, à Paris à la Rétrospective du Centenaire des Indépendants, et à Londres à la Galerie Wildenstein. Et puis vint la guerre, suivie de grands changements dans les collections. Les dessins que le marchand Ambroise Vollard (mort en 1939) avait rassemblés furent dispersés; des cinq carnets que Maurice Renou avait cédés à un collectionneur de Lyon, quatre furent vendus aux Etats-Unis, tandis que le dernier entrait au Cabinet des Dessins au musée du Louvre (la donation de Sam Salz).

4. *Buts et moyens*

Notre catalogue est plus riche en dessins que le catalogue de Venturi, mais peut-on prétendre qu'il renferme tous les dessins de Cézanne qui nous sont parvenus? Je me garderai bien de l'affirmer. Tout d'abord, jetons un regard sur l'apport initial constitué par la partie du catalogue Venturi consacrée aux dessins. Celle-ci reproduit 375 dessins qui sont dotés d'un numéro individuel. De plus, Venturi signale une certaine quantité d'autres dessins, non reproduits, et par conséquent enregistrés sans numéro. Des 375 dessins reproduits par Venturi en 1936, notre catalogue en contient 360. La différence d'une quinzaine de numéros s'explique par le fait que plusieurs numéros de Venturi ne forment qu'un seul numéro ici, Venturi ayant recopié du livre de Vollard 1914 des croquis que Vollard avait cueillis séparément sur une même feuille. D'autres dessins furent depuis classés parmi les aquarelles, ou écartés. Notre catalogue reproduit 1242 dessins, il reproduit donc environ 882 pages de plus. Cependant, comme je l'ai dit, Venturi avait aussi signalé des dessins qu'il ne reproduisait pas. J'ai fait de mon mieux pour retrouver ces *Oeuvres inédites*, la plupart sont là, mais non pas toutes. Des dessins inédits décrits par Venturi comme appartenant aux collections Paul Gachet, par exemple, et Kenneth Clark, quelques-uns ont échappé à mes investigations.

On m'a souvent posé la question: "Votre catalogue sera-t-il complet?" J'ai toujours répondu par la négative. Certes, il va de soi qu'un catalogue de l'oeuvre dessiné doit être le plus complet possible, mais cette exigence me paraît découler d'une discipline de travail, plutôt que d'une exigence morale ou d'un idéal artistique. Le vrai but que j'ai voulu atteindre est de rassembler les dessins et de les classer de manière que l'évolution de l'art et du style en ressortent sans peine. Qu'il reste ça et là quelques croquis ayant échappé à mes recherches, ou y ayant été soustraits intentionnellement, ne me chagrine pas outre mesure.

Quant à l'authenticité des oeuvres que j'ai recueillies ou que j'ai écartées, j'en ai décidé selon ma conviction intime, donc selon un critère subjectif. Dans des cas douteux, parfois très délicats à trancher, j'ai consulté d'autres amis de l'art de Cézanne. Ainsi John Rewald, Léo Marchutz et Robert W. Ratcliffe m'ont constamment fourni des avis judicieux. En fin de compte, c'est toujours mes propres sentiments qui ont influencés mes décisions. J'admets volontiers que j'ai pu me tromper et que parmi le nombre considérable de dessins non recueillis il y en ait d'authentiques. M'accusera-t-on, en revanche, d'avoir reproduit des oeuvres non authentiques? Dès que l'on aura su en avancer des preuves convaincantes, je me rendrai à l'évidence. Plusieurs croquis attribués à la jeunesse de l'artiste m'ont paru si ambigus qu'ils m'ont laissé dans le doute. Ne sachant pas s'il fallait les attribuer à Cézanne ou à l'un de ses camarades, je les ai finalement écartés. Ce n'est qu'à partir de 1866 environ que Cézanne acquerait un crayon vraiment personnel, et encore ne se discerne-t-il clairement que dans les dessins spontanés, non académiques et non appliqués. Les biographes ne manquent jamais de citer le second prix obtenu par Cézanne en 1859 à l'Ecole Spéciale de Dessin. L'oeuvre qui merita le prix nous est inconnue, ce qui est dommage car elle eclaircirait les tenèbres qui voilent les premiers efforts de l'artiste. Nous reproduisons ici le certificat, à titre de document biographique (Fig. 1).

5. *L'ordre choisi*

En gros l'ordre choisi pour classer les dessins est la suite chronologique. Les mêmes sujets demandaient cependant à être groupés ensemble; il est intéressant d'en voir un nombre à la suite, cela fait apparaître comment le style a évolué pendant une période donnée. Le émiettement empêche de comparer. Pour limiter les séries dans le temps il a toutefois fallu placer des césures, mais celles-ci ne sont pas uniformes et les périodes, qui ont de cinq à dix ans, se chevauchent. Dans ce domaine il n'y a pas de cadres qui tiennent et chaque façon que l'on imagine a ses inconvénients aussi bien que ses avantages. Je me suis fié à mon goût et à ma sensibilité pour grouper au mieux des dessins apparentés par le sujet, et des croquis disparates qu'il fallait bien mettre quelque part. Dans certains cas j'ai renoncé au principe de réunir les mêmes sujets, préférant classer les pages selon la similitude du graphisme plutôt que selon le sujet représenté.

Il y a, d'autre part, des croquis plus ou moins poussés notant l'essentiel d'une *vision* de l'artiste, un portrait, un paysage, une draperie; ces pages peuvent se ressembler tout en ayant été dessinées à des époques différentes. Il est malaisé de les dater. En revanche ces pages montrent comment certains graphismes spontanés ont servi Cézanne dès environ 1866, mais surtout à partir de 1879, jusqu'à la fin. Des historiens d'art désirant ramener tout à des procédés rationnels me reprocheront ici comme ailleurs, et en général dans le classement des dessins, de préférer des valeurs senties à une logique systématique. Effectivement, ce qui m'intéresse au premier chef, c'est l'art, et délibérément je préfère l'ambiance d'un atelier d'artiste à celle d'une officine d'analyses artistiques, chronologiques, morphologiques et topographiques, dotée d'une annexe de pathologie sexuelle. Je ne méprise pas les systèmes, mais en s'occupant d'art il ne faut pas vouloir éliminer absolument ce qui est irrationnel. Le fond le plus précieux de l'art de Cézanne, est, et demeure, irrationnel. Il échappe peut-être trop à ceux pour qui l'art de Cézanne est essentiellement un problème de structure et qui croient qu'ils ont tout fait quand ils en ont analysé la logique et la technique, principalement lorsque la structure est d'apparence cubiste.

6. *Le caractère du dessin de Cézanne*

Nous avons fait ressortir que le dessin de Cézanne possédait un caractère particulier, voyons maintenant ce caractère de plus près. Et d'abord passons rapidement en revue ce qui a été publié de plus marquant à ce sujet. Les articles d'André Salmon, de Waldemar George, de Maurice Denis[13] parlent du dessin de Cézanne avec une sympathie qui, à l'époque où ils paraissaient, était exceptionnelle. Ils ne contiennent cependant pas de vues vraiment profondes et je ne les mentionne que pour mémoire. Lionello Venturi, tout en appréciant les dessins, se penchait de préférence sur les peintures et les nombreux problèmes qu'elles soulèvent. Le caractère des dessins fut étudié par Fritz Novotny dans son livre de 1938 *Cézanne und das Ende der wissenschaftlichen Perspektive* et dans son article de 1950 *Cézanne als Zeichner,*[14] qui approfondit ce que l'auteur avait dit succinctement en 1938. Mais avant d'aborder la thèse de Novotny je suis, contre mon gré, obligé de rappeler ici quelques lignes de l'ouvrage *Dessins de Paul Cézanne* qui, en 1938, présentait au public quarante-huit dessins reproduits avec soin. Las d'entendre critiquer les déformations et les insuffisances que l'on reprochait au Maître, je disais dans la préface: "Au terme de *déformation* s'attache un sens péjoratif qui l'oppose à l'idée d'un dessin correct, non déformé, seul capable d'être vraiment beau et satisfaisant. L'erreur consiste à croire que ce dessin existe à titre absolu, qu'il sera toujours et nécessairement plus vrai que n'importe quel autre, tandis qu'en vérité nous sommes en présence du dessin traditionnel du XIXe siècle auquel nos yeux sont habitués, et du dessin un peu différent de Cézanne qui paraîtra tout aussi vrai et satisfaisant, sinon plus, à tous les yeux qui auront appris à le voir tel qu'il est. Les adversaires de Cézanne n'ont pu regarder son dessin sans le comparer mentalement au dessin académique qui leur était familier. Le dessin de Cézanne leur apparaissait alors forcément incorrect, donc moins beau, moins vrai. La hantise du style académique les a empêchés de regarder les oeuvres de Cézanne comme il faut les regarder pour y découvrir la nature, et ils n'y découvrirent que de la gaucherie." La discussion fut située sur un plan différent par l'étude de Novotny en 1950. De ces pages écrites avec un exemplaire souci de logique et de probité nous ne pourrons, faute de place, donner qu'un aperçu très fragmentaire. Novotny commence en citant le mot de Cézanne: *"La ligne et le modelé n'existent point."* L'auteur pense que par là Cézanne déclarait renoncer à se servir de ce moyen élémentaire qu'est la ligne pour représenter les choses et leurs formes. Et l'auteur résume le sujet qu'il entend traiter en demandant: "Que voit-on lorsqu'un peintre qui déclare cela, et qui peint comme Cézanne, se met à dessiner?" Il constate ensuite que la deuxième partie de la phrase: *"le dessin est un rapport de contraste, ou simplement le rapport de deux tons, le blanc et le noir,"* consacre le fait que dans la nature la ligne se produit là où deux surfaces colorées se rencontrent.

Que la peinture puisse se passer des lignes, dit Novotny, est une observation ancienne, Cézanne toutefois l'a appliquée dans un sens nouveau: il a *dévalué* la ligne ou, si l'on préfère une expression plus neutre, il a transmué la valeur de la ligne. Dans son dessin la ligne est affaiblie, réduite. "Il en résulte quelque chose de raide, manquant de souplesse, cette étrange froideur dans la conduite des lignes qui frappe chacun lorsqu'il s'approche de l'art de Cézanne . . . Les dessins et aquarelles de Cézanne sont, en principe, de même nature que les peintures à l'huile. La forme caractéristique de son dessin surtout est aussi proche de la forme picturale que cela paraît imaginable par les moyens techniques dont dispose le graphisme . . . Il obtient ce résultat en privant les lignes de cette force d'expression qui définit les figures et les choses et les situe dans l'espace. On peut dire que le résultat des divers procédés qu'il emploie est plutôt négatif . . . Dans les dessins également la ligne demeure essentiellement une limite entre couleurs. Cela, bien sûr, constitue une particularité passablement paradoxe: les couleurs étant absentes, les lignes ne marquent guère que leur lieu de rencontre . . . Le caractère de son dessin est singulièrement ambigu: la ligne est employée de fait, mais du point de vue artistique, elle est niée." J'ai transcrit quelques passages communiquant une idée approximative de cet article. Que celui-ci appelle des observations de ma part semble évident. Mais auparavant je crois utile de citer deux phrases écrites par John Rewald dans l'introduction du catalogue de cinq carnets de croquis publiés en 1951, et de mentionner ensuite l'ouvrage *Cézanne und die alten Meister* de Gertrude Berthold, 1957, parce que l'auteur y discute les diverses opinions en présence. Cela nous fournira l'occasion d'élargir le débat. John Rewald parle assez longuement du dessin dans les peintures et du dessin au crayon de l'artiste. En ce qui touche la ligne et la perspective, son point de vue est voisin de celui de Novotny, mais avec beaucoup plus de souplesse. Il faut nous borner à relever les passages suivants, laissant de côté une foule d'observations pertinentes qui entrent moins directement dans notre propos: "Jamais Cézanne n'a parlé du dessin sans évoquer également la couleur. Le dessin, selon lui, était une logique, quoique'une logique bâtarde, entre l'arithmétique, la géométrie, et la couleur. Comme pour lui la ligne en elle-même et le modelé n'existaient pas, le dessin était ensentiellement un *rapport de contraste.* Cependant toutes ces définitions, c'est le peintre Cézanne qui les a données, car il semble bien que l'artiste ne se soit pas considéré comme un dessinateur. Il avait le plaisir de la ligne, comme il aimait à le dire, mais cela ne l'empêchait pas de reprocher aux grands dessinateurs du passé—Raphaël, Holbein, Clouet ou Ingres—de n'avoir 'que la ligne' . . . Cézanne a beaucoup dessiné, quoique toujours strictement pour lui-même, si l'on peut s'exprimer ainsi . . ."

Passons maintenant au livre de Gertrude Berthold. Dans l'introduction elle reproduit le passage de mon livre *Dessins de Paul Cézanne* (1938), déjà cité, car pour elle celui-ci constitue le meilleur point de départ. Elle écrit ensuite: "Lorsqu'on veut étudier les dessins de Cézanne, il faut partir de l'idée qu'il n'y a pas une seule et unique façon de dessiner, mais plusieurs, et que la méthode de Cézanne n'est qu'une méthode parmi beaucoup d'autres, qu'elle est neuve et n'appartient qu'à lui seul." Après avoir en premier examiné l'introduction de John Rewald de 1951, l'auteur conclut: "Rewald n'arrive pas à définir le mérite essentiel et particulier des dessins de Cézanne, notamment parce qu'il prend son départ en décrivant la *ligne* dans les peintures de Cézanne. Il est vrai qu'il attribue à celle-ci une "signification nouvelle," mais en partant de là il ne peut considérer la ligne dans les dessins que comme un moyen d'expression inférieur par rapport à la peinture." En théorie cette critique n'est pas injustifiée, elle enfonce cependant des portes ouvertes, car effectivement John Rewald a toujours hautement apprécié les dessins de Cézanne et dans ses écrits il ne les traite pas en productions inférieures. Gertrude Berthold passe à l'étude de Novotny et souligne l'importance que celui-ci attribue à la phrase de Cézanne "La ligne et le modelé n'existent pas." Berthold met le poids sur la deuxième partie de la phrase cézannienne: "le dessin est un rapport de contraste, ou simplement le rapport de deux tons, le blanc et le noir." "Cézanne," dit Berthold, "établissait donc nettement une distinction entre la *ligne* et le *dessin,* en même temps il disait ce qu'est le dessin: des rapports entre deux tons, le blanc et le noir. Là où en dessinant l'on respecte ces rapports, la ligne, c'est-à-dire celle d'un contour continu et cohérent, ne se forme point. Dans ce cas le rapport est pour ainsi dire, transversal aux lignes du contour, entre le trait noir et le papier blanc avoisinant. C'est pourquoi Cézanne dessine par traits courts, toujours interrompus, souvent doublés et triplés."

Le ton de ces critiques adressées à Novotny est inutilement agressif, mais on sent que l'auteur s'applique davantage à défendre Cézanne qu'à faire valoir sa propre personne. En dernier ressort Berthold reproche à Novotny de considérer la ligne comme un phénomène naturel, non pas comme une chose historique, une chose liée à l'esprit, et de rattacher la ligne apparaissant dans l'art à cette ligne existant dans la nature. Novotny, dit-elle, pense que le contour d'une feuille, d'une tige, d'un tronc d'arbre, transmet d'une manière mi-objective, mi-subjective, quelque chose de la vie végétale et de sa croissance. L'artiste se trouverait donc immédiatement en face des contours, son travail consisterait, non pas à créer les lignes de ceux-ci, mais à les réduire de quelque façon, et à en sacrifier une partie. Contre cette opinion Berthold avance que dans la nature il n'y a que des corps, les artistes ont le choix de les représenter par des lignes ou autrement. Dans un dessin, des lignes qui représentent un objet sont à priori des moyens artistiques, elles doivent être distinguées de tout ce qui existe naturellement et réellement, même lorsque les bords d'un objet plat que l'on regarde créent une apparence linéaire. Et d'accuser Novotny de s'en tenir obstinément à la conception académique de la ligne qui continue la tradition de la renaissance.

Cela dit, Gertrude Berthold procède aussitôt à l'étude des dessins faits d'après les oeuvres d'art les plus variées, elle en recherche les techniques et les classe chronologiquement en neuf groupes. De cette partie nous parlerons dans un prochain paragraphe, pour l'instant finissins-en avec la discussion sur la ligne. Sans aborder la vieille controverse philosophique des antinomies liées à la perception par nos sens (les relations sujet-objet), il me semble difficile de nier que nous percevons fréquemment des apparences linéaires autour de nous. En revanche je suis bien d'accord que les lignes dessinées sont symboliques et conventionnelles. Dans la nature je vois des contours suggérant des lignes en regardant une porte entr'ouverte, des maisons, la mer, des fils que l'araignée tend d'un rosier à l'autre dans mon jardin. Alors, pourquoi Cézanne a-t-il si catégoriquement nié l'existence même de la ligne? Simplement parce qu'il se défendait contre les attaques des partisans du dessin linéaire. Pour ainsi dire toutes les sentences du Maître sur l'art sont des raisonnements défensifs. Il n'était pas un peintre cérébral, il dessinait et peignait sans un plan théorique. C'est après-coup, lorsqu'on critiquait son dessin au nom des principes académiques, qu'il cherchait à la justifier par une théorie.[15] De vouloir mettre les sentences de Cézanne en système ne donnera jamais rien qui vaille. R. W. Ratcliffe a montré qu'à ses jeunes amis il répétait parfois des conseils tirés des *Propos d'atelier* de Thomas Couture. Sans remonter aux Rubénistes et aux Poussinistes, à Louis David et à Ingres, voyons quelles idées Cézanne combattait par ses sentences et citons un passage du volume *Ecole espagnole* (1869) de Charles Blanc. C'est le volume contenant les gravures copiées par Cézanne, voir les nᵒˢ 244, 726, 731, 821. Voici: "En effet, à mesure que la peinture s'élève, la couleur lui est moins nécessaire, et quand le corps humain y joue le principal rôle, elle est entraînée à devenir sculpturale, parce que le dessin est le moyen d'expression par excellence . . . Par le seul dessin on peut fort bien exprimer ce qui se passe dans l'âme; mais les corps inertes ne sauraient être bien imités que par la couleur." Il paraît hors de doute que par *dessin* il faut entendre dessin par contours linéaires et que la sculpture même valait ce que valaient les profils des surfaces lisses. Eugène Delacroix déjà s'était élevé contre ceux qui n'aimaient voir le beau que dans les lignes.[16] En disant que la ligne n'existait pas, Cézanne voulait préciser que la ligne dans le dessin était un moyen conventionnel dont il n'était pas obligé de se servir. Il affirmait être libre de choisir les moyens de son dessin de coloriste et excluait cet abaissement de la couleur préconisé par les tenants de la tradition académique. Cela n'empêchait pas Cézanne de dire à d'autres occasions: "Je ne suis pas plus bouché qu'un autre, j'ai le plaisir de la ligne quand je veux." La phrase montre bien qu'il se défendait du reproche d'être ignorant ou incapable.

Novotny sait fort bien que Cézanne n'était pas ignorant, il s'étonne seulement de ce que Cézanne ait pu renoncer au dessin linéaire et arriver tout de même à une si haute valeur artistique. Deux phrases que j'extrais de son ouvrage de 1938 (p. 74) le prouvent: "Manifestement le caractère en apparence imprécis et réticent des lignes de Cézanne (le manque de dessin que lui reprochaient ses contemporains) n'affaiblit pas la cohérence du tableau, mais au contraire lui prête une solidité particulière et bien définie. Comme je viens de le faire entendre, cette solidité résulte d'un jeu entre la surface et l'espace, jeu qui ne supporterait pas que les lignes fussent plus explicites, il tend plutôt à bannir la ligne." Si Berthold accuse Novotny d'être toujours prisonnier de la tradition académique, c'est à tort, car les pages de Novotny sur le dessin de Van Gogh, sur Kokoschka, et j'en passe, nous apprennent combien Novotny est ouvert à l'art moderne, surtout si celui-ci emploie le dessin linéaire. Ainsi y a-t-il, dans le domaine musical, des oreilles plus réceptives aux mélodies qu'à la richesse d'un accord, plus sensibles au chant d'une flûte qu'à une harpe éolienne. Il est dans la nature de l'homme d'être réceptif au dessin par contours, les dessins préhistoriques et archaïques le prouvent. La ligne définit les corps et les limites d'un espace, le contour fixe l'expression et peut donner le volume. D'autres lignes suggèrent la profondeur par des fuites, ou en s'amenuisant, ou en s'échelonnant. Des teintes ajoutées à un dessin par contours n'en font jamais un dessin de coloriste et dans l'histoire de la peinture celui-ci apparaît assez tard. En Europe l'usage des craies et des pastels introduit après l'an 1500 environ a favorisé le dessin de coloriste, après Durer par exemple, et après le prestige des lignes pures en Italie. Le dessin par contraste de ton, pour être plus rare, n'est pas un genre inférieur, loin de là. Une observation faite par Kenneth Clark fait songer qu'il est le signe d'une certaine maîtrise. Parlant de Léonard de Vinci et de Michel-Ange, il dit: "Both have learnt in old age to avoid outlines and to present their subject through interior modelling, suggested by mysterious blots and blurs. This is what Cézanne meant when he praised a picture by saying that it was *dessiné dans la forme*."[17] Notons que pour ainsi dire tout le monde paraît prédisposé au dessin linéaire, la plupart des enfants dessinent par contours. Les incorrections que l'on voit dans ces oeuvres enfantines prouvent que les déformations sont facilement acceptées lorsqu'elles sont définies par un contour ferme. Le dessin linéaire s'emploie de préférence dans les oeuvres portant à un haut degré l'empreinte de chaque époque, il se prête à la virtuosité, à la caricature, au dessin technique destiné à être compris par tous. Au contraire, le dessin de coloriste est le signe d'une disposition individuelle et les déformations y sont jugées sévèrement.

7. *Observations et descriptions*

Novotny ne considère pas l'ensemble des dessins que nous connaissons, il ne parle en somme que d'un nombre restreint d'oeuvres caractéristiques de la pleine maturité de l'artiste, voir par ex. les nᵒs 932, 1026, 1027, 1028, 1037, 1058, 1090, 1154, 1165, 1171, 1177, 1188, pour n'en nommer que quelques-uns. Or, il y a des dessins bien différents. On ne saurait dire que les traits de crayon ne sont jamais des lignes, et d'ailleurs cette recherche serait peu raisonnable. Le fait est qu'il paraît impossible de définir par une seule formule le caractère général des dessins de Cézanne du commencement à la fin. Tout au plus peut-on observer que toujours la lumière fait l'unité et, d'autre part, que certains graphismes persistent à travers les mutations du style, des hachures notamment, des manières de marquer un angle, de doubler un contour, souvent aussi des spirales. Et pourtant on reconnaît la main de Cézanne progressivement, avec une lente assurance, du moins à partir de 1866, sans cela on ne pourrait pas séparer le bon grain de l'ivraie. On ne pourrait pas faire de catalogue. Roger Fry a été frappé par ce je ne sais quoi de particulier à Cézanne: ". . . in the last resort we cannot in the least explain why the smallest product of his hand arouses the impression of being a revelation."[18] Comme Novotny, beaucoup d'autres n'ont décrit qu'une partie de tous les dessins en voulant parler du caractère général. Moi-même je me trouvais dans cette illusion lorsque j'écrivais en 1957: "Sur le papier des dessins le jeu de noirs ou des blancs s'organise pour faire naître la forme avec une clarté solide et légère . . . Souvent le dessin fait ressortir des arêtes vives là où les ombres et les lumières se joignent, donnant une impression de mosaïque infiniment souple, de compartimentage fluide, suggéré par des angles et des courbes. . . . Abandonnant le jeu calme des plans rythmés selon le goût classique, de nombreux croquis tourbillonnent avec un élan baroque, il y a des saillies festonnées, le crayon décrit les volumes par des flocons d'ombres et par des duvets de demi-teintes, les traits serpentent et s'envolent en spirales."[19]

C'est Gertrude Berthold qui a fait le tour d'horizon le plus complet en rassemblant les copies et en les groupant. Je ne tenterai pas ici de résumer des analyses ni d'être plus complet encore, car il me semble que des descriptions verbales de graphismes restent trop au-dessous de la perception visuelle. Maurice Denis disait: "Mais être précis au sujet de Cézanne, quelle difficulté!"[20] De Berthold je citerai cependant les observations sur certaines courbes et leur emploi dans les dessins d'après les marbres antiques. Il s'agit du style de la maturité: "L'équivalence des diverses catégories de formes est due à l'emploi de certaines courbes particulièrement configurées. . . . La solidité du maintien et de la charpente du corps est obtenue par des arcs identiquement incurvés qui se rapportent à la verticale et à l'horizontale." Pour caractériser le style de la vieillesse: "Alors que dans le groupe précédent le moyen des courbes, constamment et presque uniquement employées, dominait le style de tous les dessins, dorénavant ce moyen ne sera plus prépondérant. Cézanne s'en servira plus librement, là où il en aura besoin. C'est le principe d'une construction solide offrant à la fois de la plasticité et une forme ornementale unifiée qui l'avait fait naître. Ce principe domine maintenant tous les moyens techniques: alors, lorsqu'apparaît une courbe, elle exprime ce principe et par là son effet se renforce par rapport à la période précédente. Ainsi par exemple dans les copies d'après Rubens (nᵒs 1128, 1140, 1209 de ce catalogue) et de même lorsque les grandes perruques font partie du modèle (nᵒs 1207, 1212)."

Autres observations que je citerai un peu au hasard: Kurt Badt souligne que Cézanne composait toujours en observant les ombres et en marquant leur place. Citons: "La technique de ses dessins prouve qu'il procédait conformément à ce qu'il avait dit. Il dessine des ombres, dessine ce qui est noir, il pose des traits dans la mesure seulement où leur noirceur correspond à du sombre dans la réalité. . . . Ainsi distinguait-il avec soin les ombres à bord marqué de celles qui se perdent doucement."[21] Théodore Reff, parlant du motif des dessins, dit: "The motif, then, is an integration of separately perceived parts into a system of construction, as he himself explained to Gasquet by locking together the fingers of both hands (Gasquet p. 130–31). . . . He thus perceives primarily in terms of relations, not objects; hence his relative indifference to their unique qualities of substance, surface and content."[22] Alfred Neumeyer: "Even in his youthful, passionate jottings one perceives a relationship to a larger entity. In the later drawings the emphasis on the compositional context yields to an inherent adjustment to underlying form structures, such as the famous cone, sphere and cylinder or to the directional orientation."[23]

Kenneth Clark: *"He saw in depth and pattern at once. . . .* Drawings always increase our intimacy with an artist, and sometimes intimacy leads to disillusion; but with Cézanne the more we grow familiar with the large, noble, characteristic movements of his hand, the more we become confident in his greatness."[24]

8. *Chronologie*[25]

Un mot sur les périodes que l'on peut distinguer dans l'oeuvre dessiné du Maître. Lorsqu'on fixe les limites des périodes chez Cézanne, il ne s'agit que de transitions, non, si j'ose dire, de feux rouges strictement observés. D'autre part je ne suis pas tout à fait sûr que les dates indiquées soient du commencement à la fin les vraies dates, ce point-là est difficile à contrôler. En revanche la manière dont se suivent les pages datées ne me paraît pas trop douteuse. En d'autres mots: je tiens plus à la suite dans laquelle les dessins sont rangés qu'à l'exactitude de chaque date attribuée. Très peu de dates me paraissent définitivement clouées à leur place, ce sont celles qui jouissent d'une évidence externe, indépendante du style. Dans son ouvrage sur les copies, Berthold distingue neuf groupes qui se suivent dans le temps. Sa méthode consiste à chercher à la fois des changements de style et des repères chronologiques fournis par les modèles: des dates d'acquisition ou d'exposition de sculptures par exemple. Ses observations ne contredisent pas les miennes, mais elles couvrent un champ spécial et demeurent souvent liées aux repères. Dans l'aperçu chronologique qui suit, je donnerai au fur et à mesure entre parenthèses les indications de Berthold.

La date donnée à notre premier dessin est 1858 environ. (Nous reproduisons dans la Figure 1 le certificat de second prix donné à Cézanne en 1859—prix de peinture, mais nous pouvoir penser qu'à l'Ecole Spéciale de Dessin, le mot s'employait également pour le dessin aquarellé.) Le premier seuil marqué par une évolution se situe vers 1862, année du premier retour de Cézanne à Paris. (Premier groupe de Berthold: 1858–60). Le second seuil se place environ 1866, l'artiste avait alors 27 ans, le dessin acquiert un caractère plus personnel. C'est le temps de la franche camaraderie, de l'étude solitaire, des violences érotiques et du paysage dramatisé. (Berthold note un progrès vers 1866–67, en gros le deuxième groupe comprend les dessins de la décennie 1860–70). A partir de 1872 l'influence de Pissarro et la naissance du fils de Cézanne affermissent le caractère artistique, on commence à voir des dessins que tout le monde se plaît à attribuer à Cézanne. (Berthold désigne comme noyau du troisième groupe les copies faites à partir de 1872). Les années 1878–87 apportent d'abord ce qu'on nomme communément le *style constructif* du peintre, avec une clarté et une technique lentement dégagées. Le style se dépouille des influences impressionnistes. Tout en restant proche de la nature, il tend vers une vision plus classique. Il me paraît vraisemblable que les gravures de reproduction du *Magasin Pittoresque*, du *Musée des Familles,* des ouvrages de Charles Blanc, les gravures de Marc-Antoine Raimondi, aient influencé le goût du jeune Aixois et qu'on retrouve ce goût, transformé et adapté, dans les dessins exécutés autour de 1880. (Berthold situe son quatrième groupe après 1876–77 et jusque vers 1882; son cinquième entre 1880 et 1883). En 1882 déjà, mais surtout à partir de 1883, viennent quelques recherches d'une forme plus libre, avec des essais de techniques nouvelles et des retours vers une solidité qui se veut sobre, cela particulièrement autour de 1885. (Berthold désigne un sixième groupe 1883–86). Les études pour le *Mardi Gras* (1888 environ) témoignent d'une tendance à fond classique, sans renoncer entièrement à certains tours rappelant Rubens et Pierre Puget; ce dernier est présent dans les *Scènes de Carnaval*. Quelques paysages montrent des arbres aux rythmes semblables. (Le septième groupe de Berthold débute 1886, il est caractérisé par l'emploi des traits en arcs. Il se prolonge au-delà de 1890 et se transforme partiellement en première phase du huitième groupe). Autour de 1890 les dessins acquièrent comme une clarté nouvelle, c'est la maîtrise dans l'aisance du trait, que celui-ci soit réfléchi ou rapide. Peu après 1895 enfin apparaît le style de la vieillesse: impatient et précis, très libre en apparence, mais saisissant le sujet en surface et en profondeur. Il est vrai que parfois on ne le déchiffre pas aisément, les précisions sont cursives. (Berthold trouve les repères pour son huitième groupe en 1894 et 1895. A partir de 1895 on peut suivre les copies des bustes aux grandes perruques. Le neuvième groupe de Berthold se situe vers 1899, date du portrait de Vollard, notre n° 1194. L'exposition des bustes de la Comédie Française au musée du Louvre en 1900 ne fournit cependant pas les points d'appui que Berthold prétend y trouver.) Il ne reste malheureusement pas beaucoup de dessins exécutés vers 1900, ou après 1900. Il y a quelques mises en place destinées à servir de support à des aquarelles, il y a quelques pages dans les carnets, et quoi encore? Après la mort de Cézanne ses héritiers et leurs contemporains devaient juger ces esquisses confuses, illisibles et mauvaises. Ils croyaient certainement servir la renommée de l'artiste en ne conservant pas ces preuves de son affaiblissement. Quant à moi, ce sont ces pages qui m'émeuvent le plus. Pour terminer cet aperçu, rappelons les quatre périodes distinguées par Venturi dans l'évolution de Cézanne:

1. Période académique et romantique   1858–1871

2. Période impressionniste   1872–1877

3. Période constructive	1878–1887
4. Période synthétique	1888–1906

Les dates de Venturi ont souvent besoin d'être revues, mais il est toujours commode de se servir de sa définition des périodes qui a été acceptée et utilisée par presque tout le monde, avec plus ou moins de réserves.

9. *Les différents types de figures*

Dans bon nombre de dessins de baigneurs et de baigneuses les mêmes poses sont répétées, si bien qu'on peut parler d'attitudes typiques, ou de *types* tout court, appartenant à Cézanne. Quelques-unes de ces attitudes sont dérivées de statues, de peintures ou de dessins copiés par l'artiste, par exemple du marbre de *l'Orateur romain* au musée de Louvre vu de face ou de dos. Voir nᵒˢ 1050 et 421, 423, 424, 430. Autre exemple: le dessin de Signorelli *Homme debout vu de dos*, fig. 121. Voir nᵒˢ 996–998. Nommons aussi les formes qu'il a copiées sans l'intention de s'en servir dans ses compositions, par ex. les figures de *Bellone*, de *La Santé*, des *Naïades* de Rubens; *Hercule au repos*, *Milon de Crotone*, les *Atlantes* de Puget; enfin quelques bustes. On s'est demandé pour quelle raison le peintre allait dessiner au musée du Louvre et ailleurs: c'était sa manière de se familiariser avec les formes d'art du passé.[28] En transcrivant d'après sa propre vision ce que d'autres avaient créé, il développait son style. Pensons à un compositeur de musique: son originalité ne l'empêchera point de jouer les oeuvres du répertoire, de les rejouer, de les interpréter; Cézanne a parfois dessiné variations. Bernard Dorival écrivait: ". . . habitué, au Louvre, des salles de sculpture où le *Mars Borghèse* l'arrête, comme les *Esclaves* de Michel-Ange et le *Milon de Crotone* de Puget, Cézanne se sent porté vers les maîtres pour qui l'art fut construction: il se devine de leur race, et fortifie, à leur contact, les penchants essentiels de sa nature."[29]

Mais revenons aux *types* que l'artiste employait dans ses tableaux. Quelques-uns ont leur origine dans des poses de modèles vivants, que ceux-ci soient nus ou dans leurs vêtements. Cézanne ayant dessiné d'après le modèle de l'acadèmie Suisse de 1861 jusque vers 1870 et également à l'Ecole de Dessin d'Aix-en-Provence, de temps en temps aussi après 1870. Rien ne l'empêchait d'autre part de prendre des modèles à Paris pendant qu'il y séjournait, et cela jusqu'à la fin de sa vie. Dans les carnets de croquis des adresses de modèles masculins et féminins sont notées. A Paris, dès avant 1870, il y avait d'abord Hortense Fiquet qui commença par être son modèle. D'une manière générale, à Paris, il pouvait toujours saisir l'occasion d'aller dessiner dans une académie. La légende veut qu'il ait tellement redouté les modèles feminins qu'il n'en prit guère. Je n'y crois qu'à moitié. La crainte existait, mais tout relativement. Sans aucun doute Cézanne lui-même accréditait la légende en cachant anxieusement ce qu'il faisait dans ce domaine, c'était une façon de se défendre. Timide, il se tenait sur la défensive envers les hommes. Ses parents ne lui avaient pas appris à se conduire en société. En compensation il agissait offensivement en matière de peinture et en face de la nature. Sans doute il se méfiait des femmes lorsqu'il craignait d'être troublé par elles dans son travail. Après avoir traversé des expériences sur lesquelles plane un heureux mystère, il était résolu à sacrifier les pratiques de l'amour à sa vocation de peintre. "Chez Cézanne l'artiste l'a emporté sur la mâle."[30] C'est la clef de ses prétendues folies et de ses authentiques phobies. Georg Schmidt a formulé l'observation d'une manière plus générale: "L'objectivité et la sérénité de son art de la maturité sont le fruit d'une victoire magnifique sur la tentation de fonder son art sur l'aveu de ses difficultés personnelles."[31] L'ambiance provinciale bornée, existant à Aix et ailleurs, l'incompréhension totale, agressive, envers l'artiste, il faut les avoir vues à l'oeuvre pour imaginer comment Cézanne vivait dans sa ville natale bien-aimée. D'engager des femmes pour les faire poser était socialement impossible. Dans cet ordre d'idées, deux raisons personnelles à l'artiste méritent d'être mentionnées. Le peintre, premièrement, se sentait surveillé par sa soeur Marie, dévouée aux Jésuites, une vieille fille réprouvant les nudités.[32] Seconde raison: un scandale avait éclaté dans la ville, des messieurs respectables ayant photographié des femmes nues avaient été condamnés par les tribunaux. Cézanne faisait donc bien de se cacher, car aux yeux des commères, quelle différence pouvait-il y avoir entre un homme qui photographie et un homme qui dessine?

Mais retournons à nos moutons. Parmi les types de baigneuses on peut relever la *Baigneuse s'éloignant vers le fond* (nᵒˢ 510, 511, 963, 964 etc.); la *Baigneuse s'essuyant* (nᵒˢ 514, 518, 521 etc.). Parmi les baigneurs il y a le *Baigneur assis* (nᵒˢ 422, 431, 432, 433 etc.) figurant à gauche sur les tableaux; le *Baigneur descendant dans l'eau* (nᵒˢ 526, 528, 962 etc.), rappelant la pose du *Christ* d'Alonzo Cano (voir fig. 74); le *Baigneur aux mains posées sur les hanches* (nᵒˢ 946, 947); le *Baigneur aux bras écartés*. Ce dernier est, parmi les types, le seul qui pose un problème spécifiquement cézannien. Il faut donc en parler. (Voir nᵒˢ 630, 631.)

10. *Sur le baigneur aux bras écartés*

Dans l'oeuvre du peintre le *Baigneur aux bras écartés* n'apparaît qu'entre les années 1875 et 1885. Toujours la figure est isolée, et généralement ce baigneur est lié au paysage de l'Estaque. Notre catalogue reproduit douze dessins et Venturi reproduit trois peintures montrant cette pose: nᵒˢ 259, 262, 271. Le *Baigneur aux bras écartés* a une sorte de pendant dans le *Baigneur aux mains posées sur les hanches,* figure caractéristique aussi, mais elle apparaît dans des groupes avec d'autres baigneurs, ce qui la rend moins singulière. Théodore Reff s'est efforcé à éclaircir le problème par les moyens de la psychanalyse.[33] Très brièvement résumé, l'article de Reff expose que dans ces baigneurs Cézanne illustre en quelque sorte le processus lent et douloureux par lequel il aurait lutté contre la masturbation et les complexes de culpabilité. Les bras levés seraient un symbole du sexe masculin.[34] N'entrons pas dans les détails de l'argument, parfois subtile, et gardons-nous de juger si du point de vue de la science psychologique les conclusions sont contestables ou non. L'article de Th. Reff sur ce baigneur, ainsi que d'autres, appelle cependant une remarque d'ordre général sur la méthode employée. Pour analyser l'art de Cézanne et ses problèmes psychologiques, l'auteur emprunte en divers endroits de ses articles au freudisme une attitude strictement positiviste se voulant objective. Sa psychanalyse, pour traiter de la vie, de la vie artistique comme de la vie tout court, se met sur un terrain scientifique, objectif, libre de préjugés, où il n'y a plus ni morale, ni discrétion, ni convenances, ni valeurs proprement artistiques. L'attitude habituelle du critique d'art, de l'historien ou du connaisseur est abandonnée en faveur d'une attitude se situant au-delà du bien et du mal, du beau et du dégoût. D'autres auteurs, notamment Wayne V. Andersen, Sara Lichtenstein, ainsi que Meyer Schapiro, ont également suivi cette voie en écrivant sur Cézanne. Kurt Badt a plus particulièrement étudié le sens caché du dessin nᵒ 37; il emploie cependant des méthodes différentes. Notons que les auteurs que j'ai nommés en premier lieu s'efforcent sincèrement de pénétrer les causes profondes ayant poussé l'artiste à exécuter certains dessins plus ou moins érotiques ou violents, mais notons également que ces auteurs ne sont pas des psychiatres professionnels. Ceux-ci paraissent en général plus prudents. Iis restent dans les généralités, à moins qu'ils ne décrivent des cas cliniques. Sur Cézanne il n'y a d'ailleurs encore pas d'opinion couramment acceptée par les professionnels. Parlons encore de nos articles cités: ils mettent l'accent sur les aspects érotiques, angoissés, meurtriers, d'un nombre de dessins ou de peintures et fouillent la vie de l'artiste, surtout son temps de jeunesse, le moins intéressant du point de vue artistique. Ils sont à la quête de désirs refoulés, de particularités pouvant être considérées comme des symboles de déviations ou de détresses sexuelles. Ils interprètent ensuite ces symboles, et parce que les méthodes scientifiques mènent rarement au-delà de conclusions générales, ils interprètent subjectivement; dans leur légitime désir de dire des choses nouvelles sur Cézanne, ils puisent hardiment dans le redoutable arsenal des associations freudiennes.[35] Les conclusions des enquêtes de ce genre ne sont intéressantes qui si elles se placent dans une vue d'ensemble de l'homme et de son évolution artistique. Sans discuter la matière des articles, je dirai que ceux-ci sont en désaccord avec ma vue d'ensemble dans la mesure où ils ignorent que *chez Cézanne l'artiste l'a emporté sur le mâle.* Les auteurs ne partagent pas mon point de vue, car pour eux les crises demeurent au premier plan.

11. *Critique de la méthode en général*

Ce ne sont pas tellement les auteurs et leurs articles qui causent en moi une profonde inquiétude: c'est leur méthode, c'est leur attitude qui se veut objective, médicale, positiviste en face de l'art. Dessiner ou peindre est traité comme un phénomène strictement fonctionnel, le plus souvent cette activité est considérée comme un effet de troubles sexuels qui seraient à guérir. L'homme est une mécanique physico-psychique fonctionnant plus ou moins bien. L'être idéal fonctionnerait sans troubles sexuels, sans complexes de culpabilité etc. . . . . Si l'on allait au bout de l'idée, on devrait logiquement admirer la perfection chez les cellules vivantes les plus simples qui se multiplient en se partageant en deux. Il n'y a chez elles pas encore de forme particulière, ni sexes différents, ni devant ni derrière posant des problèmes. Et partant il n'y a point d'art. Mais ne nous arrêtons pas à cela, ce qui nous intéresse est de constater que l'attitude scientifique rationaliste, après avoir longtemps toléré l'art en le déclarant irrationnel, quasi nul pour le savant, ne pouvant s'intégrer dans aucune conception rationnelle de la nature, veut aujourd'hui le dévaluer sérieusement, c'est-à-dire le détruire sous le prétexte de le démythifier. Ce positivisme s'en prend non seulement à l'art, mais à tous les domaines de l'âme et de l'esprit. Pour l'homme moderne, dit-on, plus rien ne doit échapper à l'emprise des systèmes scientifiques. Tout ce qui ne se justifie pas par les méthodes objectives propres aux sciences exactes, est attaqué: la religion, l'art, l'amour, les vertus, les usages, les cérémonies traditionnelles et l'attachement à la patrie. Ainsi tout y passe, sauf peut-être l'égalitarisme et le progrès supposé inclus dans la nouveauté. Du temps de la Renaissance les défenseurs de la religion cherchaient à étouffer l'esprit scientifique et l'épanouissement de ses applications. Qu'on songe au procès de Galilée. Aujourd'hui la science fait son procès à la religion et, de la façon que nous venons de voir, aussi à l'art. Entendons-nous bien: il ne s'agit pas ici de condammer les méthodes employées par les savants, en l'espèce les psychiatres qui mettent à l'épreuve les théories freudiennes et leurs développements. Il s'agit de savoir si toutes les autres méthodes doivent nécessairement leur céder le pas, ou non, s'il n'y a pas pluralisme de méthodes selon les différentes valeurs et matières. L'*unité de la science* constitue un article de foi pour beaucoup de savants. Mais l'unité de la science et le système absolu m'apparaissent comme des hypothèses de travail[36] démenties par les faits. Les sciences évoluent sans cesse, vont-elles vers l'unité? Il y a certes des principes scientifiques valables partout, et d'abord celui de la prohibité intellectuelle et celui du scepticisme en face des contradictions. Les systèmes ne contenant pas de contradictions internes valent cependant surtout pour la démonstration, ils ne sauraient renfermer toute la vérité, car ce sont les *prémisses à la base* qui varient selon les matières et les valeurs spirituelles. Quand le language positiviste parle de l'art et de la religion comme de *superstructures non intégrées*, il oublie que ces superstructures rejoignent des *infrastructures*. On cherche une nouvelle éthique de la connaissance pour remplacer les valeurs humaines malmenées par la science, je souhaite qu'elle réponde aux besoins de l'homme tout court. Cependant, si elle se veut scientifique, elle changera continuellement. Je crois plutôt que l'*Informatique* lorsqu'elle aura réussi à intégrer non seulement les quantités, mais aussi les qualités, confirmera l'existence des valeurs artistiques et spirituelles, et qu'elle montrera les contradictions que fait surgir leur élimination. Après avoir interrogé l'Univers tout entier, elle conduira peut-être les savants les plus éclairés à concevoir une spiritualité issue d'un fonds caché et permanent et par la suite de reconnaître un art dont la source n'est pas si étroitement liée à la sexualité, un art aussi qui peut exister sans être mécanisé. Nous n'en sommes pas encore là. En fait, dès qu'on adopte le point de vue freudien strictement positiviste, la critique d'art et l'appréciation des oeuvres d'art deviennent inutiles. Il y a incomptabilité. Le critique d'art se fait psychiatre et par là scie la branche sur laquelle il est assis. La peinture devient signe de dérangement et qu'elle soit belle ou mauvaise ne compte plus pour rien.

Notons bien qu'il n'est pas question d'exclure la psychanalyse de la critique d'art. Dans les traitements qu'on fait subir aux malades mentaux la peinture et le dessin peuvent intervenier pour déceler ce qui ne va pas. Souvent les gens s'expriment mieux par l'image que par la parole, ils se découvrent eux-mêmes en traçant des images spontanément. Les dessins du malade permettent de comprendre où se situe un traumatisme; au diagnostic facilité par le dessin succède le traitement médical spécifique devant amener la guérison. Les recherches de l'artiste se guérissant par lui-même (je ne parle pas d'un vrai malade) se font généralement aux périodes de déséquilibre, aux crises faisant douter l'artiste de sa valeur, lui faisant perdre son courage. Alors les recherches parfois étranges lui servent à trouver son chemin, à se débarrasser de ce qui, en lui, fait obstacle. Elles sont le moyen de se libérer des préjugés de son époque, à trouver tout seul dans son atelier ce qu'il a au plus profond de lui-même, et d'en prendre conscience. Ainsi dessin et peinture peuvent être réparation. Mais la valeur artistique se mesure au génie de l'artiste exprimé dans les oeuvres. Citons ici deux phrases de Cézanne: "Je me remonte moi-même," et: "L'artiste éprouve de la joie à pouvoir communiquer aux autres âmes son enthousiasme devant le chef-d'oeuvre de la nature dont il croit posséder le mystère."[37] La différence entre l'attitude rationaliste qui nous semble incompatible avec la critique d'art et la seconde attitude, se caractérise par le fait que la seconde situe les origines de l'art en-dehors de la sexualité, tout en tenant compte de cette dernière. Ce ne sont pas seulement les traumatismes sexuels, les culpabilités envers son père, les amours refoulées qui ont fait peindre et fait dessiner Cézanne; il n'y a pas de circuit fermé entre la sexualité et l'art. Par exemple, en lisant l'article de Meyer Schapiro, "The Apples of Cézanne,"[38] on n'échappe pas au sentiment que l'artiste devait peindre des pommes parce que l'amour refoulé l'y contraignait de son poignet de fer. L'art est une réalité irrationnelle dont les origines demeurent mystérieuses. L'art ne doit pas être confondu avec la religion, mais la poésie du grand art est le plus souvent aux côtés de la religion. Poussé par un instinct dominateur, l'artiste crée et exprime. La psychanalyse peut utilement éclairer la nature des problèmes qui tourmentent l'artiste et qu'il cherche à maîtriser avec son singulier parti-pris. Il y a beaucoup de peintres qui évoluent exclusivement avec les problèmes de leur temps, ils les illustrent. Les plus grands créateurs, après avoir traversé une période critique décisive pour "toucher le fond," trouvent leur vocation, leur originalité dépassant le niveau ordinaire de l'époque. Chacun doit chercher la vérité qui dort au fond du puits. L'artiste conscient de cette *catabase* entend comme une voix, celle de sa *vocation*. Cézanne a bien traversé une crise de ce genre et ensuite plusieurs autres sur lesquelles nous ne savons presque rien, mais desquelles son art est sorti plus élevé spirituellement. La plupart des articles cités semblent assumer que Cézanne n'est jamais sorti des angoisses et des crises dont témoignent certains dessins de sa jeunesse, les peintures comme la *Tentation de saint Antoine* etc. On nous montre volontiers un Cézanne plus ou moins fou, tourmenté par sa chair, esclave de sa misogynie, toujours saisi de frayeur à la pensée d'une femme se dénudant. On nous décrit un provincial malpropre, rampant sous le poids de ses désirs refoulés. Avec cela, le génie comme par miracle, un don-éclair lui permettant de jeter sur la toile des chefs-d'oeuvre qui aujourd'hui obtiennent des prix fabuleux. Cette image ne me paraît pas être la bonne, en dépit des gestes extravagants envers certaines personnes qui heurtaient la sensibilité de l'homme vivant reclus dans son ambiance subjective. Pour moi, les conflits intérieurs et les crises de l'artiste s'inscrivent dans un processus menant à la libération de son art. Les crises et les angoisses peuvent être fécondes si elles sont surmontées, si elles ne finissent pas comme dans *L'Oeuvre* de Zola: "Claude s'était pendu à la grande échelle, en face de son oeuvre manquée."[39] Cézanne, grâce à son courage obstiné, grâce à son *tempérament, id est, la force initiale*,[40] a surmonté les crises, il n'a pas cédé à la chair parce que la chair aurait empêché l'épanouissement de l'esprit dans sa peinture. C'est ce qu'il entendait en écrivant à Vollard: "L'Art serait-il, en effet, un sacerdoce qui demande des purs qui lui appartiennent tout entiers?"[41] Cela ne semble plus guère compris aujourd'hui. On croit que l'irresponsabilité végétative de la chair ouvre le chemin. Mais chez Cézanne elle aurait refoulé ce que son art avait de plus insaisissable et en même temps de plus universel. L'universel dépasse l'individu et ses problèmes. Les toiles de Cézanne, et de plus en plus aussi ses dessins, possèdent une valeur universelle ou, ce qui revient au même, une force normative apparemment durable. Cet art agit sur les formes de notre temps et sur le goût, mais malheureusement ce que Cézanne a communiqué de plus inimitable est vu, est senti par un nombre trop restreint. Laissant derrière elles les scènes érotiques et les toiles tourmentées, combien de peintures, graves peut-être, mais rayonnantes, communiquent le bonheur d'une vision qui participe à l'harmonie divine entrevue par l'artiste. C'est là une chose d'expérience personnelle, cela ne se prouve pas; il faut qu'on le voie, il faut qu'on le sente.

12. *Les carnets de croquis et leurs dates d'exécution*

Les dates assignées aux dessins et aux peintures de Cézanne ont toujours donné lieu à des contestations. Il parait donc nécessaire de parler des *méthodes* employées pour repérer ces dates, et de ce qu'on peut leur reprocher, particulièrement en ce qui concerne nos dessins. Il y a d'abord quelques dessins de jeunesse datés par l'artiste, ce sont des croquis illustrant des lettres, nos 17, 27, 37, 38, 150, 151, 152. Il y a ensuite quelques académies, nos 75, 76, 77, 78. Fig. 2 reproduit la signature et la date apposées au dos du no 78; je les tiens pour authentiques, mais il faut dire que l'on peut voir le même genre de signature et de millésime au dos de plusieurs académies exclues du catalogue, dessinées d'après les mêmes modèles à l'Ecole d'Aix, et dans lesquelles on ne trouve guère la main de Cézanne. Il est vrai qu'à cette époque les études académiques de Cézanne et celles de ses camarades se ressemblaient. Mais Cézanne était doué d'un sens des volumes et d'un véritable instinct de la stabilité, alors qu'aucun de ses condisciples ne possédait ces dons au même degré, en dessinant une jambe par example, et la façon dont les cuisses rejoignent le carrefour humain des fesses. On objecte que certaines signatures paraissent valables—je ne dis pas le contraire, mais que penser d'une académie d'homme, dessin plutôt faible, qui porte au recto la signature de *Coste*, et au verso celle de Cézanne? (*Numa Coste*, voir, *Corr.* lettre XV). D'autres études au crayon peuvent être datées parce qu'elles se rapportent à une oeuvre datée par l'artiste (nos 199, 200, et nos 248, 249, 250); ou datée par d'autres circonstances, le témoignage de Paul Cézanne fils (nos 938–941) ou d'Ambroise Vollard (nos 1193, 1194). Il y a également les séjours de l'artiste qui fournissent des indices lorsque l'on reconnaît les lieux représentés (no 1173). Il y a de même des sujets connus pour avoir été traités pendant quelques années seulement; les oeuvres montrant ces sujets sont facilement groupées dans le temps. Cette dernière observation a plus d'importance pour les peintures que pour les dessins. Souvent des repères et des limites sont fournis par des événements tels que la mort du père de l'artiste (1886), ou de petits faits comme l'exposition à telle date d'une sculpture au musée du Louvre, ou d'un moulage au musée de Sculpture Comparée du Trocadéro. Quelquefois le verso d'un dessin peut offrir ce qu'on appelle un *terminus post quem*: voir les nos 361, 460, 461. Nous venons de parler des groupes formés par certains sujets; on est tenté, dans le domaine des dessins, de rechercher des groupes semblables à l'intérieur de chacun des carnets de croquis. Cela donne sans doute des résultats intéressants chez beaucoup d'artistes, chez Cézanne cependant cette méthode ne mène pas loin et il est préférable de se fier au style de chaque dessin plutôt qu'à son appartenance à tel ou tel carnet. Mais les auteurs s'impatientent devant les difficultés et les incertitudes que comporte l'analyse stylistique qui juge "par petits bouts."[42]

Il faut remarquer que jamais aucun des spécialistes ne s'était attaqué à l'ensemble des dessins connus, leurs travaux ne concernent que des choix restreints, soit selon des sujets, soit selon le cadre d'un carnet de croquis. Lorsque je me suis trouvé devant la masse de l'ensemble des dessins il m'a fallu faire un premier tri, et ce tri je l'ai fait selon le style. L'arrangement ainsi obtenu suivait au mieux l'évolution chronologique. L'idée de grouper les pièces représentant le même sujet fit ensuite modifier cet arrangement, sans toutefois trop fausser la succession dans le temps. Je partage entièrement la conviction qu'il est préférable de dater les dessins selon des critères externes, indépendants du style, autant que cela est possible. Je ne puis, en revanche, partager la grande méfiance à l'égard des jugements selon le style s'exprimant dans des termes comme "stylistical guesswork." Et ayant étudié le carnet de l'Institut d'Art de Chicago, W. V. Andersen écrit: "Realizing both the hazard and the futility of attempting to establish the sequence of the sketches in this book on a stylistic study, I have reduced the book to a topographical analysis."[43] Comme en littérature, musique ou architecture, on arrive à discerner assez nettement le style dans les dessins de Cézanne, après s'y être appliqué pendant longtemps.[44] La méfiance envers le style s'accompagne souvent d'une confiance par trop assurée dans les résultats que l'on est en mesure d'obtenir par les recherches non artistiques ressemblant à de vraies enquêtes policières: emploi du temps, témoins, identifications, lettres et notes, horaires de chemins de fer, expertises médicales, domiciles, tout doit être scruté. Mais les renseignements sûrs dont nous disposons sont rares ou déjà explorés dans la plupart des cas. Alors les chercheurs sont obligés, s'ils veulent aboutir à des conclusions, d'intercaler des suppositions vraisemblables dans la chaîne de leurs argumentations. Il me semble que lorsque l'on dénie la valeur de l'analyse selon le style, il faudrait, dans les enquêtes historiques, établir les faits d'une manière supportant à tous les échelons l'examen d'une critique historique sérieuse. Or cela n'est pas toujours le cas. Je n'aurai pas la malice d'énumérer ici certains passages relevés dans des articles prétendant dater des dessins scientifiquement et qui font appel au bon sens du lecteur pour qu'il admette des suppositions qui jettent des passerelles. Je me bornerai à revenir sur la supposition déjà mentionnée que les carnets de croquis pourraient servir de cadre permettant de dater plus sûrement les pages qu'ils renferment. Pour examiner cette idée avec la prudence qui s'impose, il sera bon de commencer par la description des carnets que nous connaissons.

Notons tout d'abord que le mot *carnet* désigne au sens propre un petit livre de compte plus haut qu'il n'est large. Lorsque les feuillets sont reliés par leur côté le plus étroit il faudrait employer le mot *album*. L'usage de dire "un carnet de Cézanne" s'est cependant établi. Commençons par les carnets de croquis de la jeunesse de l'artiste.

1. Album de jeunesse au Bezalel National Museum à Jérusalem. Il fut vendu par Jean-Pierre Cézanne, petit-fils du peintre aux grands collectionneurs Mr. & Mrs. Henry Pearlman, New York, et ceux-ci en firent don au Bezalel National Museum (1962). Sur les pages de 17,4 × 24,1 cm, toutes détachées, on trouve aussi quelques croquis de Marie Cézanne, soeur aînée de Paul. Dates: 1857–60. (Mentionnons pour mémoire un autre carnet de jeunesse dont on parle à Aix-en-Provence. J'en ai vu quelques pages, le reste n'était pas visible. Ce carnet me paraît dénué d'intérêt.)

2. Carnet de jeunesse au Cabinet des Dessins, Musée du Louvre, Paris, RF 29949. Acquis par les Musées Nationaux de Pierre Berès en 1953, ce carnet fut d'abord déposé à l'atelier des Lauves, Aix-en-Provence, et transféré au Cabinet des Dessins. Mesures des pages: 15 × 23 cm.

3. Carnet dit 10,3 × 17 cm. Carnet démembré depuis longtemps et dont peu de pages sont connues. Le catalogue de Bâle en nomme dix feuillets avec dix-neuf dessins. Il ne s'en est pas trouvé d'autres.

4. Carnet dit 18 × 24 cm, les feuillets en sont tous dispersés. Mesures: entre 17,7 × 23 et 18 × 24 cm. Le catalogue contient 68 numéros dont on peut supposer qu'ils ont appartenus à ce carnet. Le catalogue de Bâle en nommait 54. Par la suite il s'est révélé que plusieurs de ces pages provenaient d'une autre source, cela se voit par exemple aux mesures, ou parce que le papier est vergé.

Suivent maintenant les sept carnets signalés par Venturi:

5. Carnet dit Chappuis I (désigné ici: *sketchbook CP I*), Venturi nᵒs 1267–1282, voir Fig. 3. Il fut acheté en 1934, peu de temps après la mort de Paul Guillaume. Comme les six autres du catalogue Venturi, Maurice Renou et Paul Guillaume le tenaient de Paul Cézanne fils. Mesures des feuillets: 19,4 × 12, parfois 19,4 × 11,8 cm. Carnet relativement petit, commode à porter dans la poche, le dos de sa reliure était fatigué au point de ne plus retenir les feuillets. Il est démembré maintenant, je m'expliquerai sur ce point au paragraphe suivant.

6. Carnet dit Chappuis II (désigné ici: *sketchbook CP II*) Venturi nᵒs 1283–1300. Il fut acheté en même temps que le carnet CP I. Mesures des feuillets: entre 21,5 × 12,6 et 21,7 × 12,5 cm. Incomplet dès l'achat, démembré.

7. Carnet dit *Album, Paul Mellon Collection*. Venturi nᵒs 1301–1315. Acheté en 1933 à Paul Guillaume (même provenance que les précédents). Il fut acquis par Mr. & Mrs. Paul Mellon en 1967. Mesures des feuillets: 15,2 × 23,7 cm. En 1966 il avait été reproduit en facsimilé par Daniel Jacomet, Paris.

8. Carnet dit Chappuis IV (désigné ici: *sketchbook CP IV*). Venturi nᵒs 1316–1322. Voir Fig. 3. Il fut acheté en 1933 chez Paul Guillaume (même provenance que les précédents). Mesures des feuillets: entre 27,3 × 21 et 25,5 × 21,1 cm. Très incomplet dès l'achat, le dos de la reliure défait; il avait dû contenir beaucoup d'aquarelles.

Suivent trois carnets dits du Musée de Bâle.

9. Carnet I (désigné ici: *sketchbook BS I*), au Cabinet des Estampes (Kupferstichkabinett der oeffentlichen Kunstsammlung Basel). Venturi nᵒs 1323–1357. Mesures des feuillets: entre 13 × 21,8 et 13,1 × 21,4 cm; les feuillets sont souvent rognés. Acheté après la mort de Paul Guillaume par le marchand Werner Feuz (même provenance que les précédents). Tous les feuillets sont détachés. Ceux qui furent acquis par le musée de Bâle sont reproduits dans le *Beschreibender Katalog der Zeichnungen von Paul Cézanne* (Catalogue des Dessins de Bâle).

10. Carnet II (désigné ici: *sketchbook BS II*) au même lieu. Venturi nᵒˢ 1358–1397. Mesures des feuillets: entre 12,5 × 21,5 et 12,2 × 20,9 cm. Acheté, démembré et vendu par le marchand Werner Feuz de la même façon que le précédent. Les feuillets acquis par le musée de Bâle sont reproduits dans le Catalogue des Dessins de Bâle.

11. Carnet III (désigné ici: *sketchbook BS III*) au même lieu. Venturi nᵒˢ 1398–1436. Mesures des feuillets: entre 20,7 × 12,5 et 19,3 × 12,4 cm. Acheté, démembré et vendu de la même façon que les précédents. Les feuillets acquis par le musée de Bâle sont reproduits dans le Catalogue des Dessins de Bâle.

Suivent cinq carnets catalogués par John Rewald en 1951, dont aucun n'est signalé par Venturi. Provenance du lot des cinq: Cézanne fils, Paris; Maurice Renou, Paris; Poyet, Lyon; Maurice Renou, Paris; Sam Salz, New York. De ce dernier ils passèrent aux divers propriétaires actuels.

12. Premier Carnet Mrs. Enid A. Haupt, New York. Désigné ici: *first sketchbook Mrs. Enid A. Haupt*. Rewald Carnets: C I. Mesures des feuillets: 11,6 × 18,2 cm. Les feuillets sont tous détachés et encadrés, avec ceux du deuxième carnet de Mrs. Haupt il forment ainsi, sur les murs, un ensemble remarquable. John Rewald en a reproduit quelques-uns avec d'autres choisis dans les cinq carnets catalogués en 1951.

13. Carnet appartenant à The Art Institute of Chicago, désigné ici: *A.I.C. sketchbook*; Rewald Carnets: C II. Mesures des feuillets: 12,4 × 21,7 cm. Carnet non démembré; reproduit en facsimilé avec un catalogue de Carl O. Schniewind (New York: Curt Valentin, 1951).

14. Carnet du Cabinet des Dessins au musée du Louvre (Don de Sam Salz). Désigné ici: *sketchbook ML* (RF 29933); Rewald Carnets: C III. Mesures des feuillets: 13,7 × 21,6 cm. Carnet non démembré.

15. Second Carnet appartenant à Mrs. Enid A. Haupt, New York. Désigné ici: *second sketchbook Mrs. Enid A. Haupt*; Rewald Carnets: C IV. Mesures des feuillets: 12,7 × 21,6 cm. Carnet démembré.

16. Carnet appartenant à Mr. & Mrs. Leigh B. Block, Chicago. Désigné ici: *sketchbook Leigh Block*; Rewald Carnets: C V. Mesures des feuillets: 12,6 × 21,7 cm. L'ancienne reliure de ce carnet a été remplacée par une nouvelle, les feuillets furent placés dans un autre ordre et paginés en chiffres arabes. Nous ne tenons compte que de l'ancienne pagination notée par John Rewald.

17. Carnet dit *violet moiré*, appartenant à Mlle Edmée Maus, Genève. Carnet au sens propre, au format plus haut que large, mais très petit, désigné ici: *violet moiré sketchbook*. Mesures des feuillets: entre 11,7 × 6,7 et 10,2 × 6,8 cm. Provenance: Jean-Pierre Cézanne, petit-fils de l'artiste. A l'origine il était inséré dans la pochette d'un porte-monnaie en cuir, toujours en possession de la famille. Il fut exposé chez Bernheim-Jeune en 1956, dans une vitrine au milieu d'une merveilleuse exposition d'aquarelles. Daniel Jacomet le reproduisit en facsimilé peu après, en édition restreinte hors commerce. Ces reproductions sont reliées d'un tissu rose moiré.

18. Enfin il y a quelques rares feuillets qui semblent provenir de deux carnets de jeunesse qui se sont pas connus autrement. Mesures: 12,5 × 20,8 cm ou 12 × 20,5 cm ou 11,5 × 20,3 cm. Il est possible qu'il s'agisse d'un seul et même carnet.

Cherchant à déceler, dans la masse des dessins de Cézanne, certains groupes pouvant aider à circonscrire des dates d'exécution, Th. Reff et W. V. Andersen ont tenté de délimiter les périodes pendant lesquelles le peintre s'est servi de l'un ou de l'autre des carnets. Ainsi Th. Reff écrit de l'Album, Paul Mellon Collection: "... it seems more reasonable to suppose a usage within one decade than over a span of twenty-five years."[45] Il pense que la plupart des dessins de l'Album furent exécutés autour de 1895. W. V. Andersen, de son côté, a étudié le carnet 18 × 24, le carnet de l'Institut d'Art de Chicago et le carnet violet moiré. Il estime que le carnet 18 × 24 a été utilisé pendant dix années, de 1866 à 1876, alors que dans le catalogue de Bâle j'avais présumé des dates allant de 1858 à 1880.[46] Mais notons que 1858 concerne exclusivement un texte rimé non daté, rangé par John Rewald (*Corr.*) comme nᵒ VII bis à la fin de l'année 1858 (notre nᵒ 179). La limite de 1880 est celle d'une page datée 1870–80, et d'une autre datée 1873–80 (nos nᵒˢ 119, 174). Les dates des dessins commencent par 1864. Dans le présent catalogue les dates d'exécution du carnet 18 × 24 s'étendent de 1864, à 1875, avec une exception cependant: le nᵒ 476 est daté 1876–78. C'est une exception basée sur l'appréciation du style. Je refuse de remener la date du 476 à l'année 1875, simplement pour mettre de l'ordre. Je revendique pour l'artiste la liberté de saisir, au besoin, un carnet dont il ne s'est pas servi depuis des années pour y crayonner un croquis pris sur le vif, comme l'est celui de ce chien. Il faut voir là une question de méthode, ou de principe qui dépasse l'intérêt du croquis en cause. Il s'agit de la liberté de l'artiste, il s'agit de savoir s'il lui est permis de faire les choses chez lui, en un désordre libéral, ou s'il devrait se plier à la discipline universitaire avec ses périodes annuelles de travail. Selon celles-ci Cézanne aurait dû se servir d'un carnet jusqu'à remplir toutes ses pages, prendre ensuite un autre et s'y tenir. Mais d'après ce que nous savons Cézanne se servait de plusieurs carnets à la fois, sans en remplir les pages avec ordre. N'oublions pas qu'il avait généralement au moins deux lieux de travail, l'un à Aix, l'autre à Paris, à l'Estaque, à Fontainebleau ou ailleurs. Lorsqu'il se déplaçait il pouvait fort bien laisser un carnet ou deux au Jas de Bouffan, un autre au Château Noir, il pouvait en acheter un nouveau à Paris etc. Le carnet CP IV fut acheté à Barbizon, chez Bodmer (voir note 57). A Aix ou à Paris il y avait les appartements habités par Hortense avec le jeune Paul. Beaucoup de croquis ont pu être fait le soir, en famille. N'avait-il pas le droit de laisser l'un des carnets dans un tiroir chez sa femme? Bref, il ne paraît pas raisonnable de vouloir resserrer le plus possible dans le temps les dates pendant lesquelles Cézanne pouvait employer un carnet. Il ne faudrait jamais dater une page de carnet selon les exigences d'une période qu'on vient de fixer par avance, en disant que cette page fait partie du groupe et que le groupe s'inscrit dans tel espace de temps. On doit compter avec des dates d'exécution isolées au début aussi bien qu'à la fin. D'autre part W. V. Andersen, ayant étudié le carnet de l'Institut d'Art de Chicago, pense qu'il fut utilisé entre 1876–1885 (voir encore note 43); Rewald avait indiqué 1875–85; notre catalogue: 1870–85; le carnet au Cabinet des Dessins serait, selon W. V. Andersen, à dater des années 1888–90[47]; Rewald avait indiqué 1880–81, et partiellement aussi 1888–95; notre catalogue: 1888–99.

13. *Est-il impératif de conserver des carnets intacts?*

Je dirai franchement que pour ma part je ne regrette pas de ne plus voir tous les carnets de croquis conservés dans leur intégrité. Il me paraît suffisant de savoir à quel carnet une page a pu appartenir; certes, toucher un carnet de Cézanne conservé intact est émouvant, le feuilleter satisfait notre curiosité, cela nous met en contact avec l'homme et avec sa main. Mais, à y réfléchir, ce qu'on désire, ce qui importe davantage, est de voir et d'apprécier les dessins contenus dans le petit album relié de toile grise, maculé de couleur et de poussière noire. C'est voir la splendeur de quelques pages, les notes plus légères et accortes sur d'autres, c'est saisir la forme d'une série de corps humains, ou d'objets, c'est entrer dans les séductions d'un paysage. Un carnet est comparable au manuscrit d'un compositeur de musique; le manuscrit est intéressant, mais d'entendre la musique est plus intéressant encore. Une expérience longue de trente-cinq ans m'a appris qu'un dessin de Cézanne ne prend toute son importance qu'à partir de l'instant où il se présente isolé, dans un montage pas trop serré qui lui convient. Je dirai même qu'on ne pourra pas juger sa portée entièrement tant qu'on ne l'aura pas vu ainsi mis en valeur. C'est parfois le chemin des découvertes. Il y a encore d'autres inconvénients à laisser les dessins dans les carnets. Pour la bonne conservation des reliures et des feuillets il ne faut pas montrer les dessins trop souvent au cours des années, et jamais à plus de deux ou trois personnes simultanément. Le carnet montré doit être manipulé sans cesse et tourné dans plusieurs sens parce que les croquis apparaissent renversés. Des collections publiques s'accommoderont mal de cela. A l'intérieur d'un carnet on ne peut jamais rapprocher deux études afin de les comparer, et lorsqu'on veut revoir un seul croquis il faut prendre tout l'album et le feuilleter. D'autre part, à regarder un carnet de Cézanne on se fatigue vite (contrairement à ce que l'on pense), peut-être parce que de saisir la signification de tant de croquis entassée sans prétention dans des carnets d'apparence modeste, demande beaucoup de concentration. Il y a aussi l'attrait de la nouveauté qui fait que toujours on attend la page suivante, oubliant ce qu'on vient de voir. Cela est comme de manger des cérises les cueillant sur l'arbre: on cherche toujours la prochaine.

14. *La présentation du catalogue*

Pour la commodité du lecteur les reproductions des dessins sont présentées dans un volume séparé, ainsi les dessins pourront être comparés avec les reproductions des modèles ayant inspiré l'artiste, ces reproductions sont insérées dans le texte.

On pourra regretter que le volume des reproductions comporte des pages à l'italienne (en largeur) et qu'il faille tourner le volume sur le plat de la table en passant d'une page en hauteur à une page en largeur. Voici quelques raisons qui me paraissent justifier cette présentation. Il fallait avant tout veiller à bien reproduire les dessins, ce souci primait celui de faire un volume qu'on feuilletterait sans le déplacer. Il fallait également veiller à maintenir le coût du livre dans les limites raisonnables, car ce catalogue n'est pas un ouvrage de luxe, mais un instrument de travail. Il fallait, enfin, que le volume des reproductions reste maniable. Or présenter toutes les pages en hauteur eût exigé un nombre de pages considérablement plus élevé. D'autre part beaucoup de dessins auraient dû être reproduits en format encore plus réduit, à cause de leur largeur. L'expérience montre que ces dessins se placent mieux dans une page à l'italienne. De toute manière il n'est pas possible, dans un ouvrage comme celui-ci, de reproduire les dessins en conservant les proportions des feuilles originales. Le but d'un catalogue est de mettre à la disposition du public des images permettant d'identifier les dessins sans erreur, ce soin va de pair avec celui de l'ordre chronologique. Alors, afin de pouvoir présenter les oeuvres convenablement, il a souvent fallu supprimer une partie de la page blanche. C'était le cas notamment pour une série de petits croquis se trouvant sur une grande feuille. Il y a aussi les croquis d'une tête placés dans le haut d'une page, là il est nécessaire de laisser suffisamment d'espace pour ne pas déformer le rythme de l'ensemble. Cela nous conduit à observer une différence entre la façon de reproduire plusieurs peintures à celle de reproduire plusieurs dessins sur une même page. Les peintures sont transposées en noir et blanc et les couleurs, réduites à des gris foncés, remplissent ordinairement le rectangle. La transposition des dessins est moins poussée, les traits demeurent gris, les blancs demeurent clairs. Cela crée un rythme différent, il s'agit moins d'assembler des rectangles sombres sur le rectangle d'une page, que de faire cohabiter des dessins d'apparence diverse dans le rectangle de la page. Les blancs jouent un rôle, ils donnent de l'air et portent les traits de crayon. Il faut en tenir compte. C'est pourquoi il est plus facile de placer des clichés de peintures que des clichés de dessins dans les pages à la française. Cela dit, même devant les meilleures reproductions il ne faut pas perdre de vue que les originaux valent mieux encore. Le moyen de gagner une vue d'ensemble serait une exposition pour laquelle on choisirait quelques centaines parmi les plus beaux dessins du Maître. Projet chimérique sans doute, mais fondé pour moi sur un attrait merveilleux.

15. *Remerciements*

Que ceux qui m'ont aidé à dresser ce catalogue : collectionneurs, marchands, savants et amis, soient ici sincèrement remerciés. Ma reconnaissance va d'abord à John Rewald, à Barbara et Léo Marchutz, à Robert Ratcliffe, Fritz Novotny, Gertrude Berthold. M'ont efficacement aidé à rassembler des dessins peu connus : Théodore Reff, Wayne V. Andersen, Chuji Ikegami, de même que Helmut Ripperger à New York et Paule Cailac à Paris. Parmi les musées je nommerai en premier le Cabinet des Dessins au musée du Louvre, ensuite le Kupferstichkabinett Basel et The Art Institute of Chicago ; parmi les collectionneurs Lord Clark, Londres ; Mr. et Mrs. Paul Mellon, Upperville, Virginia ; Mr. et Mrs. Leigh Block, Chicago ; Mrs. Enid A. Haupt, New York. J'exprime ma gratitude à tous ceux qui m'ont fait parvenir les photographies de leurs dessins. Le lecteur trouvera leurs noms dans les notices accompagnant les reproductions, quelques uns ont cependant préféré la simple mention "collection particulière". Je tiens à remercier le Dr. Silberstein, haut placé dans l'administration des collections d'art en U.R.S.S., qui eut l'amabilité de s'assurer si les musées ou les collections particulières de ce pays détenaient des dessins à coté du grand nombre des peintures de Cézanne : il n'y en avait aucun. Concluons en soulignant le mérite de ceux qui ont traduit les textes du français en anglais. L'Introduction le fut par Paul Constable en collaboration avec M. et Mme Jacques Féjoz, Chambéry. Les textes du catalogue furent traduits et revus par Barbara Marchutz, secondée par son mari Léo. Ils accomplirent ce travail avec un vrai amour de l'art du Maître, à Aix, route de Cézanne, en un lieu où le regard se tourne vers la crête de la Sainte-Victoire.

ANNEXE A L'INTRODUCTION
Mes Confidences : document biographique inédit

Mes Confidences, album de huit pages, mesurant 104 × 135 mm. Il fut donné par Joachim Gasquet à M. et Mme Ladislas Rohozinski, à Aix-en-Provence, en 1911 ou 1912, à l'intention de leur fille Lili dont Gasquet était le parrain. L'album provenait vraisemblablement de Henri Gasquet, père de Joachim, boulanger réputé à Aix et ancien condisciple de Paul Cézanne. Leur longue amitié est illustrée par ces lignes que le peintre écrivait à Henri Gasquet le 23 décembre 1898 :

. . . cette rue Suffren qui fut notre berceau. Il est impossible que l'émotion ne nous vienne en pensant à tout ce beau temps écoulé, à cette atmosphère qu'on a respirée sans s'en douter . . .

(J. Rewald, *Cézanne, Geffroy et Gasquet*, p. 37)

Ladislas Rohozinski, musicien, avait vingt ans lorsqu'il rencontra Joachim Gasquet, poète, dans le salon de Juliette Adam, à Paris en 1908. Ils se lièrent d'une amitié durable, Rohozinski vint habiter Aix-en-Provence. Il avait, dans le même salon, fait la connaissance de Mlle Nouryé de Châteauneuf, qu'il devait épouser. C'était la fille de M. de Châteauneuf, ministre du sultan ottoman Abdulhamid II, résidant à Istanbul. Mlle Nouryé de Châteauneuf connaissait bien l'écrivain Pierre Loti, souvent reçu chez ses parents, et qui lui vantait la vie des milieux littéraires de Paris. S'étant rendue dans cette ville, la jeune demoiselle de Châteauneuf fut introduite au salon littéraire de Juliette Adam où sa beauté et un grand charme naïf la firent remarquer par les hommes de lettres et les artistes célèbres. C'est donc à elle et à son mari que Jo Gasquet transmit le petit album. A son tour elle en fit don à sa fille et à son gendre, M. et Mme Cecil Michaelis, après l'avoir conservé secret pendant quarante ans. En octobre 1971, enfin, il me fut communiqué avec la mission de le photographier et de le publier. A cette date l'impression du présent catalogue avait déjà commencé, mais à cause de son intérêt le document demandait à être publié d'une manière accessible, et comme il confirmait quelques-unes des vues exposées dans l'Introduction, il me parut approprié de l'y ajouter.

Mes Confidences date probablement des années 1866–69. Pour nous cet album constitue un authentique test caractériel.

Sur la couverture Cézanne indique le lieu où il écrivait ses réponses : au second du 30 de la rue St-Louis. Ce fut à Aix, évidemment, non à Paris, et je ne saurais dire de qui c'était le domicile. Notons seulement que la rue de Suffren, mentionnée dans la lettre citée plus haut, était adjacente. Examinons les questions et les réponses des deux pages qui suivent :

1. *Q :* Quelle est la couleur que vous préférez ?
   R : L'harmonie générale.
La réponse prouve que l'artiste avait déjà discuté la question avec ses amis et que, dès cette époque, l'harmonie de l'ensemble lui paraissait primordiale.

2. *Q :* Quelle est votre odeur favorite ?
   R : L'odeur des champs.
C'est une réponse de peintre paysagiste attaché à la terre et au grand matin.

3. *Q :* Quelle fleur trouvez-vous la plus belle ?
   R : Scabieuse.
Pour comprendre il faut regarder la scabieuse sur place, dans les prés.

4. *Q :* Quel animal vous est le plus sympathique ?
   R : (sans réponse)
Selon Louis Aurenche "il parlait amicalement aux animaux."

(J. Rewald, *Cézanne, Geffroy et Gasquet*, p. 62).

5. *Q :* Quelle couleur d'yeux et de cheveux préférez-vous ?
   R : (sans réponse)

6. *Q :* Quelle est, selon vous, la plus estimable vertu ?
   R : L'amitié.
Pour être vertueuse, l'amitié doit être désintéressée.

7. *Q :* Quel vice détestez-vous le plus ?
   R : (sans réponse)

8. *Q :* Quelle est votre occupation préférée ?
   R : Peindre.

9. *Q :* Quel délassement vous est le plus agréable ?
   R : La natation.
Il y a les *Baigneurs*. Un nageur se peint difficilement. L'eau est un élément de la nature, comme l'odeur des champs.

10. *Q:* Quel est selon vous, l'idéal du bonheur terrestre?
    R: Avoir une belle formule.

Il faut rapprocher cette réponse de celle du n° 8: peindre. Avoir un style personnel, beau et valable en général. En langage de Cézanne: réaliser. Voir *Correspondance,* lettre CLXXXIII (1905): "Le Louvre est le livre où nous apprenons à lire. Nous ne devons cependant pas nous contenter de retenir les belles formules de nos illustres devanciers."

11. *Q:* Quel sort vous paraît le plus à plaindre?
    R: Etre dénué.

S'il avait dû gagner sa vie, Cézanne n'aurait pas pu faire ce qu'il a fait. Ses amis disaient: sans argent, Cézanne serait mort. Il le savait.

12. *Q:* Peut-on vous demander l'âge que vous avez?
    R: (sans réponse—à notre regret)

13. *Q:* Quel prénom auriez-vous pris si vous l'aviez choisi?
    R: Le mien.

Rappelons que la mère de l'artiste croyait le prénom Paul de bon augure pour un peintre.

14. *Q:* Quel a été le plus beau moment de votre vie?
    R: (sans réponse)

15. *Q:* Quel en a été le plus pénible?
    R: (sans réponse)

16. *Q:* Quelle est votre principale espérance?
    R: La certitude.

Magnifique réponse, et réponse rappelant Blaise Pascal. Complément intérieur de la *belle formule,* la *certitude* devait jaillir de l'intuition contrôlée par la raison et par le métier.

17. *Q:* Croyez-vous à l'amitié?
    R: Oui.

18. *Q:* Quel est pour vous le plus agréable moment de la journée?
    R: Le matin.

Pour l'artiste impatient la peinture commençait avec le jour. Il se levait, dit-on, la nuit, pour voir si le ciel promettait une bonne lumière.

19. *Q:* Quel personnage historique vous est le plus sympathique?
    R: Napoléon.

Grande figure méditerranéenne.

20. *Q:* Quel personnage de roman ou de théâtre?
    R: Frenhoffer *(sic).*

Nouvelle confirmation de l'attachement au type d'artiste-peintre défini par Balzac dans *Le Chef-d'oeuvre inconnu.* Notons à ce propos que les enseignements de Rembrandt, tels que les rapporte Samuel van Hoogstraaten, contenaient beaucoup de ce que Balzac fait dire à Frenhofer.

21. *Q:* Quel pays habiteriez-vous de préférence?
    R: La Provence et Paris.

Il aurait pu dire: La Provence et l'Ile-de-France, mais Paris était le foyer artistique.

22. *Q:* Quel écrivain préférez-vous?
    R: Racine.

Génie français, doté d'une sensibilité passionnée qui suit la nature sans méconnaître la raison. Comme Cézanne.

23. *Q:* Quel peintre?
    R: Rubens.

24. *Q:* Quel musicien?
    R: Weber.

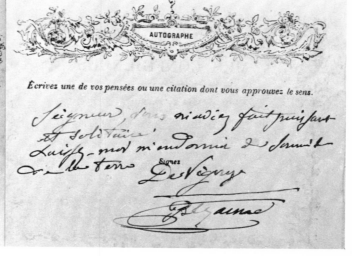

QUESTIONS

1. Quelle est la couleur que vous préférez ?
2. Quelle est votre odeur favorite ?
3. Quelle fleur trouvez-vous la plus belle ?
4. Quel animal vous est le plus sympathique ?
5. Quelle couleur d'yeux et de cheveux préférez-vous ?
6. Quelle est, selon vous, la plus estimable vertu ?
7. Quel vice détestez-vous le plus ?
8. Quelle est votre occupation préférée ?
9. Quel délassement vous est le plus agréable ?
10. Quel est, selon vous, l'idéal du bonheur terrestre ?

RÉPONSES

1. L'harmonie générale
2. L'odeur des Champs
3. Hibiscus.
4.
5.
6. L'amitié
7.
8. Peindre
9. La natation
10. Avoir une belle formule –

QUESTIONS

11. Quel sort vous paraît le plus à plaindre ?
12. Peut-on vous demander l'âge que vous avez ?
13. Quel prénom auriez-vous pris, si vous l'aviez choisi ?
14. Quel a été le plus beau moment de votre vie ?
15. Quel en a été le plus pénible ?
16. Quelle est votre principale espérance ?
17. Croyez-vous à l'amitié ?
18. Quel est, pour vous, le plus agréable moment de la journée ?
19. Quel personnage historique vous est le plus sympathique ?
20. Quel personnage de roman ou de théâtre ?

RÉPONSES

11. Être démuni
12.
13. Le mien
14.
15.
16. La certitude
17. oui
18. Le matin
19. Napoléon
20. Germ Hoffer

QUESTIONS

21. Quel pays habiteriez-vous de préférence ?
22. Quel écrivain préférez-vous ?
23. Quel peintre ?
24. Quel musicien ?
25. Quelle devise prendriez-vous si vous deviez en avoir une ?
26. Quel est, selon vous, le chef-d'œuvre de la nature ?
27. De quel site avez-vous gardé le plus agréable souvenir ?
28. Quel est votre mets de prédilection ?
29. Préférez-vous un coucher dur ou tendre ?
30. Quel peuple étranger vous est le plus sympathique ?

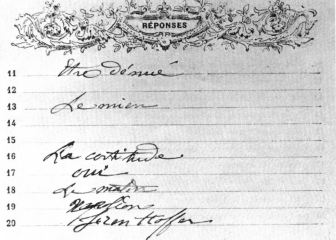

RÉPONSES

21. La Provence et Paris.
22. Racine
23. Rubens
24. Weber
25.
26. La diversité infinie –
27. Les collines de St Marc
28. Les poissons de Terre à l'huile
29. Entre les deux.
30. Aucun.

Citons Gerstle Mack: Madame Marie Gasquet, widow of Joachim Gasquet, has told me that Cézanne sometimes asked her to play the piano for him—preferably selections from *Oberon* or *Der Freischütz . . ."* (*Paul Cézanne*, 1935, p. 23). Il semble qu'à Paris Cézanne allait quelquefois à l'Opéra. Louis Aurenche raconte qu'il chantait des refrains avec lui (J. Rewald, *Cézanne, Geffroy et Gasquet*, p. 63).

25. *Q:* Quelle devise prendriez-vous si vous deviez en avoir une?
    R: (sans réponse)

26. *Q:* Quel est, selon vous, le chef-d'oeuvre de la nature?
    R: Sa diversité infinie.

A rapprocher de la réponse à la première question: l'harmonie générale. C'est dans son cadre que devait se situer la "diversité infinie." Cézanne se défendait d'être submergé par la richesse de ce qu'il observait, alors que son art se fondait sur cette richesse.

27. *Q:* De quel site avez-vous gardé le plus agréable souvenir?
    R: Les collines de St. Marc.

St-Marc-Jaumegarde se trouve à quelques kilomètres au N-E-E de la ville d'Aix-en-Provence.

28. *Q:* Quel est votre mets de prédilection?
    R: Les pommes de terre à l'huile.

Des pommes de terre bouillies, épluchées, coupées en rondelles, arrosées d'huile d'olive. La Provence produit une savoureuse huile d'olive.

29. *Q:* Préférez-vous un coucher dur ou tendre?
    R: Entre les deux.

30. *Q:* Quel peuple étranger vous est le plus sympathique?
    R: Aucun.

Autographe. Ecrivez une de vos pensées ou une citation dont vous approuvez le sens.

R: Seigneur, vous m'aviez fait puissant et solitaire
Laissez-moi m'endormir du sommeil de la terre.
—De Vigny

La citation est tirée du poème "Moïse" d'Alfred de Vigny (1797–1863). Alors que la deuxième ligne y apparaît quatre fois, la première s'y trouve quatre fois sous des formes un peu différentes.

Citation et signature furent reproduites par Joachim Gasquet à la page 208, ce détail n'est donc pas inédit. Gasquet s'est servi de "Mes Confidences" comme source, mettant plusieurs réponses dans la bouche de Cézanne, mais leur sens est noyé dans la conversation poétique.

Dans leur ensemble les réponses de Cézanne prouvent que dès l'âge de 27 à 30 ans il voyait clairement la voie qu'il devait suivre. Les problèmes personnels, les difficultés de réalisation, les critiques seront surmontés. D'autre part il ne faut pas confondre ces réponses qui concernent l'homme avec ce que le peintre a pu affirmer sur la peinture.

Beaucoup resterait à dire, mon intention cependant n'est pas d'épuiser le sujet, il me suffit d'avoir rendu accessible ce document extraordinaire.

NOTES A L'INTRODUCTION ET AU CATALOGUE RAISONNÉ

1. Les eaux-fortes et les lithographies n'ont pas été recueillies parce que ces oeuvres ne procèdent pas directement de la main de l'artiste. Elles sortent d'une presse, leur tirage multiplié donne lieu à divers *états,* chose pleine d'intérêt certes, mais différente du dessin.

2. Lettre manuscrite, datée Siena, 19 luglio 1958.

3. L'ouvrage de Wayne V. Andersen, *Cézanne's Portrait Drawings,* Cambridge, Massachusetts, M.I.T. Press, 1970, a paru au moment où la rédaction et la traduction de notre texte étaient terminées. A mon grand regret je n'ai pas pu incorporer dans le catalogue les données et les enseignements de ce livre important.

4. *Pictor semper virens:* Peintre toujours verdoyant. Voir près de la signature du brouillon de lettre *Corr.* LVII, notre nº 378, et *Corr.* lettre XXVI.

5. Voir par ex. Vollard 1914, p. 93; Borély, *L'Art vivant,* du Ier Juillet 1926; Gasquet, p. 103, 117; Rivière, 1923, p. 183.

6. Gasquet, p. 55; Rivière, 1923, p. 183.

7. Rewald, *Carnets,* p. 11.

8. Larguier, *Le Dimanche avec Paul Cézanne,* Paris, 1925, p. 136, XXX: "Contrastes et rapports de tons, voilà tout le secret du dessin du modelé." — Rewald, *History of Impressionism,* 1961, p. 62 et note 32: *"According to Monet, Cézanne was in the habit of putting a black hat and a white handkerchief next to the model in order to fix the two poles between which to establish his values."*

9. Charles Baudelaire, *L'Oeuvre et la vie d'Eugène Delacroix,* p. 13, dans *L'Art Romantique,* Paris, Garnier, 1931.

10. Roger Fry, *Cézanne,* Londres, 1927, p. 38.

11. Meier-Graefe, *Cézanne und sein Kreis,* Munich, 1922.

12. La description donnée aux pages 12 et 13 de l'introduction du Catalogue de Bâle est conforme à la vérité, mais elle est incomplète parce qu'elle passe sous silence le fait que les feuilles volantes passèrent directement de Cézanne fils au marchand Werner Feuz, alors que les trois carnets furent vendus à ce marchand par l'intermédiaire de Madame Paul Guillaume.

13. Waldemar George, *Le Dessin français de David á Cézanne,* Paris 1929 — André Salmon, *Dessin inédits de Cézanne,* dans *Cahiers d'Art* I, 1926 — Maurice Denis, *L'Amour de l'Art,* 1924, 2.

14. Fritz Novotny, *Cézanne als Zeichner,* dans *Wiener Jahrbuch für Kunstgeschichte,* XIV (XVII), 1950. Reproduit, dans *Ueber das Elementare in der Kunstgeschichte und andere Aufsätze von Fritz Novotny,* Vienne, Rosenbaum, 1968.

15. "Redoutant des critiques trop justifiées, j'avais résolu de travailler dans le silence, jusqu'au jour où je me serai senti capable de défendre théoriquement le résultat de mes essais." Lettre du 25 novembre 1889 à Octave Maus. *Corr.* CXV — "Moi, je ne sais jamais où je vais, où je voudrais aller avec ce sacré métier. Toutes les théories vous foutent dedans." J. Gasquet (1926), p. 188.

16. Eugène Delacroix, lettre à Peisse, du 15 juillet 1849. Et Raymond Escholier rapporte le passage suivant: "Pourtant, si vous êtes coloriste vous viendrez à bout avec le simple trait à faire comprendre que j'ai un relief, une épaisseur, un corps. Comment en viendrez-vous à bout? En n'arrêtant pas également partout ce contour, en le faisant très délié, *presque interrompu* en certains endroits, en l'accusant en d'autres endroits au moyen d'un second trait et, s'il le faut, d'un troisième ou encore au moyen d'un trait élargi, engraissé, qui se gardera bien d'être un fil de fer, car partout où j'ai vu un relief (...) il n'y a pas d'opacité au contour qui l'indique; ni la lumière qui frappe le contour, ni l'ombre qui glisse dessus, n'ont de point d'arrêt saisissable." (*Eugène Delacroix,* vol. I, p. 146.)

17. Kenneth Clark, *Leonardo da Vinci,* Penguin Books, 1958, p. 142.

18. Roger Fry, *Cézanne,* Londres, 1927, p. 88.

19. *Dessins* 1957, pp. 66, 67.

20. Maurice Denis, *Cézanne,* dans *L'Occident,* sept. 1907. Réimprimé dans *Théories,* Paris, Hermann, 1964, p. 156.

21. Kurt Badt, *Die Kunst Cézannes,* Munich, 1956, p. 169.

22. Theodore Reff, *Studies in the Drawings of Cézanne,* A Thesis presented by Theodore Franklin Reff to the Department of Fine Arts, Harvard University, Cambridge, Massachusetts, mai 1958, p. 177.

23. Neumeyer, 1958, p. 17.

24. Kenneth Clark, dans l'Introduction au catalogue *Paul Cézanne, an Exhibition of Watercolours,* The Arts Council of Great Britain, 1946.

25. Marques diverses accompagnent les dessins: Sur un certain nombre de dessins on trouve des notes au crayon, au crayon bleu ou à l'encre. Ces marques, il faut souligner, sont rarement visibles sur nos reproductions parce qu'il a fallu réduire les parties blanches autour des dessins. Il y a d'abord les inscriptions de la main de Cézanne, elles sont relevées dans le commentaire du dessin et il n'en sera pas question ici. Nous ne parlerons que des signes attribués à des mains étrangères. Notons d'abord les mots *tel* ou *tel ensemble,* les croix, les mots *réduire,* etc., et les chiffres. Certains dessins portent dans un coin des notes comme 5D, 2E, etc.; ce sont sans doute des prix chiffrés par des vendeurs selon des codes individuels. Dans *Dessins de Cézanne* 1957 et dans le Catalogue des Dessins de Cézanne au musée de Bâle j'ai émis l'hypothèse que peut-être les *tel* accompagnés de croix avaient été apposés par Cézanne lui-même comme signes indiquant que les croquis pouvaient servir tels qu'ils étaient aux peintures projetées. D'abord Th. Reff (voir note 26), ensuite Douglas Cooper (voir note 27), ont contesté le bien-fondé de ces suppositions. Ces marques, selon eux, furent faites par Ambroise Vollard, ou d'autres, qui désiraient faire reproduire les croquis ainsi signalés. Je leur donne raison et j'ajoute que ce sont des signes couramment employés à l'usage des clicheurs, particulièrement à ceux employant le procédé *offset.* Les croix disent combien de clichés il faudra faire; le mot *tel* près d'un dessin (quelquefois au dos)

veut dire que le clicheur se servira du dessin original, et non de sa photographie, pour faire la photographie spéciale qui deviendra cliché. Partant de là, les inscriptions comme *réduire* s'expliquent facilement. Les chiffres tels que 30 × 23 indiquent généralement les dimensions des plaques photographiques ou films employés. Il y a enfin les indications ajoutées sans gêne pas des encadreurs.

26. Th. Reff, *BurlM*, août 1963, p. 376.

27. Douglas Cooper, *Master Drawings*, vol. I, hiver 1963, p. 56.

28. Voir Gasquet 1926, p. 171.

29. Bernard Dorival, *Cézanne*, Paris, 1948, p. 69.

30. François Lehel, *Notre art dément*, Jonquières et Cie., Paris, 1926, p. 83: "C'est l'artiste qui l'a emporté sur le mâle." La seule phrase à retenir de cet ouvrage.

31. Georg Schmidt, *Aquarelle von Paul Cézanne*, Basel, 1952; en français 1953; p. 9.

32. *Quelques souvenirs sur Paul Cézanne*, par une des nièces, dans *GBA* 1960, p. 298: "Louis-Auguste avait coutume de dire: Paul se laissera manger par la peinture, et Marie par les Jésuites."

33. Th. Reff, *Cézanne's Bather with outstretched arms*, dans *GBA*, mars 1962, p. 173.

34. Th. Reff se réfère au livre de Paul Schilder, *The Image and Appearance of the Human Body*, New York, International University Press, 1950. Parlant de l'hystérie, l'auteur dit: "*The protruding parts of the body may become symbols of the male sex organ*" (pp. 171/72). En dehors de cette observation je n'ai rien trouvé dans ce livre médical qui puisse être appliqué directement au cas qui nous occupe.

35. Citons trois exemples, relevés dans des articles sur Cézanne, où des détails sont interprétés d'une manière éloignée de l'art.
1: Le morceau *Songe d'Annibal, Hannibalis somnium*, rimé par Cézanne à 19 ans, *Corr.* Lettre VI, décrit une beuverie, un "festin dans lequel on avait fait trop fréquent usage du rhum et du cognac . . . Sur la nappe le vin s'épandit à grands flots . . ." Th. Reff assimile les liquides renversés à du sperme répandu et évoque une fois de plus les sentiments de culpabilité liés à la masturbation. (Th. Reff, *Cézanne's Dream of Hannibal*, dans *AB* 1963, p. 149).
2: Sara Lichtenstein dit au sujet du dessin nº 37: "*Beheading may be coupled with emasculation in Cézanne's early* Ugolino *drawing.*" (*Master Drawings*, vol. 5, nº 2, 1967, p. 187, note 17). Il s'agit sans doute de l'emasculation du père de l'artiste dont, selon Kurt Badt, on est déjà en train de manger le crâne.
3: Meyer Schapiro parle dans son article, *The Apples of Cézanne* (Art News Annual, XXXIV, 1968, p. 51, note 30), de la peinture Venturi nº 1520a: "*In a drawing which may be a sketch for Venturi nº 115, are two nude women on one bank and a clothed fisherman on the opposite bank with a rod extending across the river to the women.*" A mon avis dans cette petite toile (non pas dessin), si l'homme regarde peut-être les baigneuses, il manifeste la volonté de s'occuper de la pêche plutôt que d'assaillir les femmes. Au lieu de suggérer qu'il éclate de désirs refoulés, on peut dire qu'il maîtrise sa chair en faveur de ce qui l'intéresse au premier chef (chez Cézanne: la peinture). Sa canne à pêche passe d'ailleurs délibérément a côté des baigneuses. Si l'on s'engage à regarder la canne à pêche comme le symbole du sexe érigé, on devrait logiquement interpréter notre dessin nº 260 (Venturi nº 1213) dans ce sens. L'on s'est abstenu de le faire, craignait-on l'effet comique? Enfin, considérant uniquement la situation méthodologique de ces interprétations, j'y découvre beaucoup d'analogies avec les méthodes astrologiques. L'astrologie, elle aussi, aspire à un déterminisme rigoureusement scientifique. Et lorsqu'on établit un horoscope, il s'agit d'interpréter individuellement des données qui passent pour être vraies en général.

36. Les hypothèses scientifiques rejoignent parfois les mythes.

37. J. Rewald, *Thèse,* p. 125: "Je n'ai pas besoin d'excitant, je me remonte moi-même."—Larguier, *Le Dimanche avec Paul Cézanne,* Paris, 1925, p. 132, X.

38. Meyer Schapiro, *The Apples of Cézanne*, dans *Art News Annual*, XXXIV, 1968, p. 35 ss.

39. Emile Zola, *L'Oeuvre*, Oeuvres complètes, Paris 1928, p. 385.

40. Larguier, *op. cit.*, pp. 88, 94; et *Corr.* lettre CLX: "Avant tout, il n'y a que le tempérament, id est, la force initiale, qui puisse porter quelqu'un au but qu'il doit atteindre."

41. Lettre à Vollard du 9 juin 1903. *Corr.* CLIX.

42. Th. Reff, *Album de Paul Cézanne*, dans *BurlM* CIX, nov. 1967, p. 653.

43. W. V. Andersen, *Cézanne's Sketchbook in The Art Institute of Chicago*, dans *BurlM*, mai 1962.

44. J'ai prêté le flanc aux critiques en inscrivant, dans *Dessins* 1957 des dates comme 1870–90. Vingt ans, c'est trop, évidemment, lorsqu'on prend cela à la lettre. Mais en fait cela ne voulait pas dire autre chose que "la date exacte m'intéresse peu, je regarde le dessin. Cherchez la date si le dessin ne vous dit rien tel que vous le voyez." Que les historiens de l'art me pardonnent, pour moi l'art primait toujours l'histoire de l'art et la présence d'un dessin valait plus que ce que l'on pouvait écrire pour fixer son exécution à telle date. Je changeais d'attitude par la force des choses en commençant à recenser les dessins du musée de Bâle, vers 1959. Il fallait établir la suite des dessins dans l'évolution du peintre, donc songer aux dates, et pour le présent catalogue la nécessité de dater se montra plus pressante encore. Les sarcasmes et les censures que mon attitude passée a suscités— et suscitera—je les accepte sans sourciller. Car mon insouciance de jadis, c'était le bon temps!

45. Th. Reff, *Album de Paul Cézanne, loc. cit.*, p. 652.

46. W. V. Andersen, *Cézanne's Portrait Drawings of the 1860's*, dans *Master Drawings* vol. 5, nº 3, 1967, p. 279, note 9.

47. W. V. Andersen, *Cézanne's Carnet violet moiré*, dans *BurlM*, juin 1965, note 19.

48. Dans le catalogue de Bâle, no 67, j'avais accepté *ideme*, que je prenais pour une fantaisie de la prononciation méridionale. Mais la fantaisie est dans l'écriture. Voir mon commentaire dans le texte du nº 461.

49. R. W. Ratcliffe et un autre connaisseur, qui préfère rester anonyme, sont de l'opinion que ce dessin n'est pas de Cézanne.

50. Ambroise Vollard, *En écoutant Cézanne, Degas, Renoir*, Paris, 1938, p. 215.

51. La Bodinière était le nom d'une galerie louée par le marchand d'art Le Barc de Bouteville pour une exposition à laquelle Cézanne dut participer.

52. Je dois ces renseignements à Hans Schedelmann de Salzburg, connaisseur érudit en armures, qui ajoute qu'il est impossible de décider si cette armure était antique ou si elle était une des nombreuses copies faites au XIXe siècle.

53. Notes de la vente à l'Hotel Drouot, commissaire-priseur Maître Chevalier, le 9 mars et les jours suivants, 1903.

54. Dans de catalogue de Bâle (nº 104) ce dessin (notre nº 553) est daté 1880–82. Cette date a suscité des controverses, ainsi

que celles des nᵒs 552 (Cat. Bâle nᵒ 105, daté 1885–1900) et 554 (Cat. Bâle nᵒ 106, daté 1882–92). Th. Reff (*BurlM*, août 1963, p. 376) pense que la date 1880–82 est erronée, et alors que Neumeyer (1958) avait proposé 1894–1900, Reff propose 1895–1900. Douglas Cooper (dans *Master Drawings*, vol. I, nᵒ 4, 1963, p. 56) indique 1896–1900 pour les trois dessins 552, 553, 554. Il faut donc que j'explique pourquoi, ici, j'ai retenu la date 1881–84, également pour les trois. Lorsqu'on compare notre 553, *Nature morte au bougeoir,* avec une page exécutée entre 1895 et 1900, par exemple notre nᵒ 1135 (Cat. Bâle nᵒ 174), on voit d'abord que certains détails techniques se ressemblent: les arcs de cercle, les contours verticaux, même quelques hachures marquant les ombres. Il y a des lignes horizontales chercheuses très proches les unes des autres, en bas au milieu, sur les deux dessins. Toutefois, lorsque d'une manière approfondie on examine l'ensemble, on est frappé par une véritable différence de rythme et de sentiment. Cela n'est pas tellement difficile à voir. La *Nature morte au bougeoir* représente une vision plus naturaliste, les objets y conservent leurs formes et leurs poids individuels, les rondeurs et les volumes verticaux paraissent pesants, les hachures vont dans des sens divers: il n'y a pas d'envolée. Certes, il y a le pied du bougeoir, dont la montée est rendue par des traits serpentins, multipliés. Mais comparez le dossier de chaise du nᵒ 1135, mieux, les fleurs décoratives du panneau. Comparez également les nᵒs 1106, 1186, et au nᵒ 1056 surtout, les parties de l'aisselle et du ventre. Le dessin du bougeoir appartient à une période antérieure, période où l'ordonnance rythmée de la surface (les détails en un certain ordre assemblés) était encore recherchée patiemment, élaborée par une quête consciente de l'équilibre, bref, construite. Entre 1895 et 1900 le rythme décoratif de la page s'établit dans un jaillissement moins conscient. Le trait ne cherche plus guère, il s'emporte en trouvant. Le dessin palpite, et quand le motif comporte de la stabilité, celle-ci suggère néanimoins le mouvement. Les traits en arc de cercle acquièrent une inimitable nervosité et les hachures s'incorporent sans la moindre insistance. Surface et profondeur, volumes et rythmes linéaires s'allient mystérieusement. Les natures mortes nᵒs 552, 553, 554 sont certainement de très bons dessins, mais leur qualité est bien différente: elle demeure dans une sorte de fixité, rançon d'une intention monumentale. Pour soutenir la date qu'il propose, M. Reff avance deux raisons (les autres n'en donnent pas): l'arrangement des objets et le choix d'un point de vue extrêmement bas. Il écrit: "*Nᵒ 104 (du Cat. Bâle), Nature morte au bougeoir, as 1880–82, clearly belongs, like all the comparable still lifes cited by M. Chappuis (V. 1493, 1541, etc.) to the later 1890's—a date also supported by the radical overlapping and cutting of objects and by the extremely low viewpoint.*"

La manière scientifique dont ces raisons sont énoncées ne doit pas faire illusion sur leur fragilité. Car il est aisé de trouver des arrangements et des points de vue semblables à d'autres

époques que celle de 1895–1900. Voir par exemple Venturi nᵒs 357, 430, 594, 597, 598, pour les objets; Venturi nᵒs 12, 59, 69, etc. pour le choix de l'angle bas de vision. On m'objectera que mes propres raisons ne paraissent pas moins fragiles. Je suis près de l'admettre, à la condition cependant que l'on m'accorde une part de probabilité, car ici, si l'on veut raisonner scientifiquement, il convient d'appliquer le calcul de probabilité.

55. *Les Incas.* Paris et Limoges, 1850, chez Martial Ardent Frères. Il est possible que la signature a été rajoutée par le fils du peintre.

56. La date d'éxécution de ce dessin a été beaucoup discutée. Venturi le place entre 1872 et 1877, le catalogue de Bâle préfère 1886–96. Dans leur critiques du catalogue, Th. Reff (*BurlM,* août 1963, p. 376) et Douglas Cooper (*Master Drawings,* Vol. I, nᵒ 4, 1963, p. 56) sont d'accord pour une fois avec Venturi, le premier donnant la date 1872–77, le second 1873–75. Mais le coup de crayon est plus libre et en même temps plus stylisé qu'à cette période dans l'oeuvre de l'artiste. Douglas Cooper apparente ce dessin aux peintures Venturi nᵒs 231, 234, et au dessin Venturi nᵒ 1228 (notre nᵒ 319). Le Venturi nᵒ 231 et nos dessins nᵒs 251 et 252, qui sont contemporains, et aussi notre nᵒ 319, semblent avoir moins de rapport que la peinture Venturi nᵒ 234, *Déjeuner sur l'herbe.* Toutefois, il est important de souligner l'affinité entre Venturi nᵒ 234 et les aquarelles Venturi nᵒs 875, 876, et spécialement au dessin au lavis Venturi nᵒ 1225 (notre nᵒ 356); probablement aussi notre nᵒ 654(b), quoique ceci semble moins certain. Le groupe de personnages dans la partie inférieure du nᵒ 356 est une étude pour la toile. Le dessin actuel, *Les Spectateurs,* devrait ainsi être comparé à notre nᵒ 356 et aux aquarelles Venturi nᵒs 875, 876. Malgré certaines qui le précèdent, je suis convaincu que l'ensemble est dans le style plus mûr de Cézanne.

57. Le nom de Bodmer a été noté par Cézanne dans son carnet violet moiré au verso de notre nᵒ 972. Je lis *Bodmer 43 fr 70.* Il est probable que l'artiste acheta des fournitures au petit magasin de Bodmer. Dans *BurlM,* juin 1965, p. 317, Wayne Andersen donne une autre interpretation de cette annotation (qu'il reproduit, fig. 48). Voir la page 111 verso: *Bodmer/le 3h 10.* Andersen écrit (note 28): "*Bodmer could be Barthélémy-Marc Bodmer (1848–1904), a romantic landscape painter who lived in Geneva and painted in the Geneva-Annecy region. . . . The notation probably refers to a rendez-vous.*" Toutefois, puisque le timbre associe le nom de Bodmer, à Barbizon, il ne faut pas oublier Karl Bodmer, peintre, graveur et lithographe, né près de Zurich en 1809 et mort à Barbizon le 30 octobre 1893. Devenu français, il s'installe à Barbizon; là, J.-F. Millet peignit son portrait. Je ne suis pas certain, cependant, qui s'occupait du magasin, car il y avait d'autres Bodmer sur les lieux, tel Frédéric-Adolphe, dessinateur et graveur, né à Barbizon et connu pour avoir exposé au Salon de 1878.

CATALOGUE RAISONNÉ

1. STUDIES, INCLUDING A FIGURE OF MOSES, circa 1858

$9\frac{1}{16} \times 5\frac{7}{8}$ inches—23 × 15 cm. Page 52 verso of the *Carnet de jeunesse* (early sketchbook) in the Cabinet des Dessins. Pencil and pen. Verso: No. 2.

(a) Madonna and Child (pencil).—(b) Unfinished sketch of a head.—(c) Boy walking with his arm forward, curious coiffure.—(d) Right (pen and pencil): Moses, seen front view, a cross hanging from a chain round his neck, and the word *Moïse*, erased.

BIBLIOGRAPHY: Berthold, p. 159 (not reproduced).

COLLECTIONS: P. Berès, Paris. Cabinet des Dessins of the Louvre, Paris (RF 29949).

2. THE JUDGMENT OF SOLOMON, circa 1859

$9\frac{1}{16} \times 5\frac{7}{8}$ inches—23 × 15 cm. Page 52 of the *Carnet de jeunesse* (early sketchbook) in the Cabinet des Dessins of the Louvre. Pencil and pen. Verso: No. 1.

Copy of a work representing *The Judgment of Solomon* (I Kings 3:16). On the left a man is seen cutting through the body of a child whom he holds by one foot. The mother, intervening in a dramatic movement, is the best-drawn figure. Inscription added in ink.

BIBLIOGRAPHY: Berthold, cat. No. 313 (reproduced) and p. 159. *Selearte*, No. 52, July-August 1961, p. 8. A sixteenth-century Tuscan bas-relief in the Musée Jacquemart-André, Paris, is suggested as the original model. In 1969 no work corresponding to the sketch was to be found in the museum, which has however a depository outside Paris. In any case the direct model was a reproduction.

COLLECTIONS: P. Berès, Paris. Cabinet des Dessins of the Louvre, Paris (RF 29949).

3. FIGHTING WARRIOR, 1856–58

$5\frac{13}{16} \times 7\frac{1}{4}$ inches—23 × 15 cm. Pencil on ordinary brownish-colored paper; top edge restored, left and right. Verse: No. 190.

Battle scene; rather weak drawing in the style made fashionable by the followers of Louis David. A hero stands sword in hand, astride an enemy thrown to the ground. Further off, three other warriors are fighting. Cf. No. 28 and also Nos. 4 and 5.

BIBLIOGRAPHY: Venturi, Vol. I, p. 350, *Oeuvres Inédites* (not reproduced). Basel catalog, No. 1 (reproduced).

COLLECTIONS: Cézanne *fils*, Paris. W. Feuz, Bern. Kunstmuseum, Basel.

4. NUDE WARRIORS FIGHTING, 1856–57

$6\frac{7}{8} \times 9\frac{7}{16}$ inches—17,5 × 24 cm. Page from an early sketchbook. Pencil. Verso: sketch by Marie Cézanne, *Ruins of a castle*.

Battle scene of ancient times: some of the warriors are naked, others clothed and helmeted. Men climbing ramparts in the foreground, two carrying spears at right.

BIBLIOGRAPHY: Bezalel National Museum, New acquisitions, 5.6.1962, No. 42.

COLLECTIONS: Cézanne *fils*, Paris. Jean-Pierre Cézanne, Paris. Mr. and Mrs. Henry Pearlman, New York. Bezalel National Museum, Jerusalem.

5. NUDE WARRIORS FIGHTING, 1856–57

$6\frac{7}{8} \times 9\frac{1}{2}$ inches—17,5 × 24,1 cm. Page from an early sketchbook. Pencil. Verso: sketch by Marie Cézanne, *Environs of Fribourg*.

Battle of ancient warriors, in the style of David. In the foreground, a warrior is running a sword through his breast; in the background another warrior lifts an axe against his adversary. Apparition of an eagle, top left.

BIBLIOGRAPHY: Bezalel National Museum, *New acquisitions*, 5.6.1962, No. 42.

COLLECTIONS: Cézanne *fils*, Paris. Jean-Pierre Cézanne, Paris. Mr. and Mrs. Henry Pearlman, New York. Bezalel National Museum, Jerusalem.

6. FOUR FIGURES, INCLUDING TWO MISERS, SEATED, circa 1858

$9\frac{5}{8} \times 6\frac{7}{8}$ inches—24,4 × 17,5 cm. Page from an early sketchbook. Pencil. Verso: a landscape, falsely attributed to Cézanne.

(a) Top: man sitting down, as though posing as a model; unfinished study.—(b) Man sitting on a stool clutching a moneybag to his breast, while a naked man with a sword in his hand seizes him by the shoulder.—(c) Right: man seated, seen front view, also clasping a moneybag.

BIBLIOGRAPHY: Bezalel National Museum, *New acquisitions*, 5.6.1962, No. 42.

COLLECTIONS: Cézanne *fils*, Paris. Jean-Pierre Cézanne, Paris. Mr. and Mrs. Henry Pearlman, New York. Bezalel National Museum, Jerusalem.

7. ONE MAN GRASPING THE WRIST OF ANOTHER, 1856–58

$6\frac{7}{8} \times 9\frac{5}{8}$ inches—17,5 × 24,4 cm. Page from an early sketchbook. Pencil. Verso: sketch by Marie Cézanne.

Two men, seen as though on the stage. One is holding the other by the wrist and both are barefoot; the ground is sketched in summarily, even timidly.

BIBLIOGRAPHY: Bezalel National Museum, *New acquisitions*, 5.6.1962, No. 42.

COLLECTIONS: Cézanne *fils*, Paris. Jean-Pierre Cézanne, Paris. Mr. and Mrs. Henry Pearlman, New York. Bezalel National Museum, Jerusalem.

8. MEN HANDLING GUNS; A FACE, 1856–57

$6\frac{7}{8} \times 9\frac{5}{8}$ inches—17,5 × 24,1 cm. Page from an early sketchbook. Pencil. Verso: sketch by Marie Cézanne.

(a) Soldier wearing a kepi and wielding a gun which he aims down towards the right. Another soldier is seen behind him, back view, raising his gun.—(b) Juvenile face, reminiscent of the style of the Le Nain brothers.

BIBLIOGRAPHY: Bezalel National Museum, *New acquisitions*, 5.6.1962, No. 42.

COLLECTIONS: Cézanne *fils*, Paris. Jean-Pierre Cézanne, Paris. Mr. and Mrs. Henry Pearlman, New York. Bezalel National Museum, Jerusalem.

9. TWO MEN BEARING A LOAD; A MUSICIAN, 1856–57

$9\frac{5}{8} \times 6\frac{7}{8}$ inches—24,4 × 17,5 cm. Page from an early sketchbook. Pencil. Verso: drawing by Marie Cézanne.

(a) Two men carrying a kind of trough.—(b) Right: man in a kepi playing an ophicleide, a musical instrument with trumpet-shaped bell.

BIBLIOGRAPHY: Bezalel National Museum, *New acquisitions*, 5.6.1962, No. 42.

COLLECTIONS: Cézanne *fils*, Paris. Jean-Pierre Cézanne, Paris. Mr. and Mrs. Henry Pearlman, New York. Bezalel National Museum, Jerusalem.

10. MAN BOUND, circa 1858

$9\frac{1}{8} \times 5\frac{7}{8}$ inches—23,2 × 14,9 cm. Page 32 verso of the *Carnet de jeunesse* in the Cabinet des Dessins. Pencil. Verso: No. 59.

(a) Man, nude, his wrists and ankles bound. Unfinished drawing, partly traced.—(b) Head of a young man wearing a cap, seen from above.—(c) At right angles: profile of a face.

BIBLIOGRAPHY: Berthold Cat. No. 312 (reproduced).

COLLECTIONS: P. Berès, Paris. Cabinet des Dessins of the Louvre (RF 29949).

11. TWO FACES AND A LEAF, 1856–57

$9\frac{5}{8} \times 6\frac{7}{8}$ inches—24,4 × 17,5 cm. Page from an early sketchbook. Pencil. Verso: sketch by Marie Cézanne.

(a) Top: woman's face surrounded by a veil.—(b) Man's face sketched in with hatching, the left eye darkened by shadow.—(c) Below: a leaf (or perhaps a tree seen from a distance), calling to mind the screen Venturi No. 3 (date uncertain).

BIBLIOGRAPHY: Bezalel National Museum, *New acquisitions*, 5.6.1962, No. 42.

COLLECTIONS: Cézanne *fils*, Paris. Jean-Pierre Cézanne, Paris. Mr. and Mrs. Henry Pearlman, New York. Bezalel National Museum, Jerusalem.

12. BUSH AND FACES, 1856–57

$9\frac{5}{8} \times 6\frac{7}{8}$ inches—24,4 × 17,5 cm. Page from an early sketchbook. Pencil and pen; heavy grease marks. Verso: childish drawings.

(a) Top: pencil sketch of a bush.—(b) Right: head with abundant hair.—(c) Center: pen drawing of a face, evidently crossed out.—(d) At right angles: profile of a head

(pencil). The sketches (b) and (d) are studies for a copy of *The Kiss of the Muse*, Venturi No. 11, after the painting by Frillié in the Musée Granet, Aix-en-Provence.

BIBLIOGRAPHY: Bezalel National Museum, *New acquisitions*, 5.6.1962, No. 42.

COLLECTIONS: Cézanne *fils*, Paris. Jean-Pierre Cézanne, Paris. Mr. and Mrs. Henry Pearlman, New York. Bezalel National Museum, Jerusalem.

13. UNFINISHED HEAD, 1857–59

$6 \times 9\frac{3}{8}$ inches—15,2 × 23,8 cm. On the endpaper of the *Carnet de jeunesse* in the Cabinet des Dessins. Pencil on white moiré paper. Verso: blank page.

Insignificant sketch; this little face, placed within the moirés, recalls certain lunar masks.

BIBLIOGRAPHY: Berthold, p. 155 (not reproduced).

COLLECTIONS: P. Berès, Paris. Cabinet des Dessins of the Louvre, Paris (RF 29949).

14. THREE SEATED FIGURES, 1856–57

$6\frac{7}{8} \times 9\frac{5}{8}$ inches—17,5 × 24,4 cm. Page from an early sketchbook. Pencil. Verso: a drawing by Marie Cézanne.

Left: man smoking a pipe, comfortably seated, seen in profile. Cf. No. 34 (d). Center: figure seen from behind. Right: young man, seen front view. In light pencil strokes.

BIBLIOGRAPHY: Bezalel National Museum, *New acquisitions*, 5.6.1962, No. 42.

COLLECTIONS: Cézanne *fils*, Paris. Jean-Pierre Cézanne, Paris. Mr. and Mrs. Henry Pearlman, New York. Bezalel National Museum, Jerusalem.

15. MEN ROUND A TABLE, circa 1858

About $6\frac{1}{2} \times 5\frac{7}{8}$ inches—about 16,5 × 15 cm. Page 53 of the *Carnet de jeunesse* in the Cabinet des Dessins. Pencil and pen; the lower edge of the page is torn off. Verso: No. 54.

Men eating, two seen front view, two back view; one is drinking from a bottle. Cf. Nos. 24, 147 (f).—On the left, drawn at an earlier date: head with kepi.

BIBLIOGRAPHY: Berthold, p. 159 (not reproduced).

COLLECTIONS: P. Berès, Paris. Cabinet des Dessins of the Louvre, Paris (RF 29949).

16. TWO MOUNTED POLICEMEN, 1857–59

$9\frac{1}{16} \times 5\frac{7}{8}$ inches—23 × 15 cm. Page 35 verso of the *Carnet de jeunesse* in the Cabinet des Dessins. Pencil. Ink stains have seeped through the paper. Verso: handwriting and sketches by an alien hand.

Two policemen wearing cocked hats and riding side by side, seen from behind. The body of the rider on the left is seen in three-quarter view from the right, which seems strange.—Many hesitations and retouches in the drawing. Cf. No. 189.

BIBLIOGRAPHY: Berthold, p. 157 (not reproduced).

COLLECTIONS: P. Berès, Paris. Cabinet des Dessins of the Louvre, Paris (RF 29949).

17. DRAWINGS COMPOSING A REBUS, May 3, 1858
    Pen, on a letter to Emile Zola.

Small sketches illustrating a letter from Cézanne to his friend Zola: a scythe (une *faux*), a hedge (une *haie*), a May tree (un arbre de *mai*), two women (*les femmes*), meaning *il faut aimer les femmes*.

BIBLIOGRAPHY: *Correspondance* (reproduced fig. 2 but mistakenly indicated as being in the Bibliothèque Nationale, Paris).

EXHIBITION: Wildenstein, London, 1939, Autograph Letters, Nr. 1.

COLLECTIONS: Emile Zola, Paris. Mme. Zola, Paris. E. Fasquelle, Paris. M. and Mme. Leblond-Zola, Paris.

18. VARIOUS STUDIES, INCLUDING ONE OF A SOLDIER, circa 1858
    $5\frac{7}{8} \times 9\frac{1}{16}$ inches—15×23 cm. Page 12 of the *Carnet de jeunesse* in the Cabinet des Dessins. Pencil, round stain. Groups of geological terms written over the whole page by an alien hand. Verso: No. 20.

(a) Right top: a head in left three-quarter view.—(b) Higher up on the page: profile of a head.—(c) Below the stain: man holding a cane.—(d) Soldier in eighteenth-century uniform. Cf. No. 19 (b).—(e) Top: rough sketch of a figure.—(f) Top right corner: head and shoulders of a woman.—(g) Lower down, lightly drawn: two figures facing right.

BIBLIOGRAPHY: Berthold, p. 156 (not reproduced).

COLLECTIONS: P. Berès, Paris. Cabinet des Dessins of the Louvre, Paris (RF 29949).

19. STUDIES, INCLUDING A SOLDIER MAKING A BOW, circa 1858.
    $5\frac{7}{8} \times 9\frac{1}{16}$ inches—15×23 cm. Page 11 verso of the *Carnet de jeunesse* in the Cabinet des Dessins. Pencil. Groups of geological terms cover the drawings. (It is said that Fortuné Marion, a friend of Cézanne's, thus explained the geological structure of the Aix countryside to the artist). Childish drawings. Verso: No. 23.

(a) Left top: man in a top hat, running.—(b) Soldier in eighteenth-century uniform, making a bow.—(c) Top, at right angles: two caricatural Chinese heads, probably studies for the painting Venturi No. 13.—(d) Top right: head and shoulders of a bearded man.—(e) Branch with four leaves; to the left, practically obliterated, a grape.—(f) Scattered over the page: ten lightly traced heads or figures, partly defaced by scribbles.

BIBLIOGRAPHY: Berthold, p. 156 (not reproduced).

COLLECTIONS: P. Berès, Paris. Cabinet des Dessins of the Louvre, Paris (RF 29949).

20. STUDIES, INCLUDING A ROMAN AUGUR, 1858–59
    $9\frac{1}{16} \times 5\frac{7}{8}$ inches—23×15 cm. Page 12 verso of the *Carnet de jeunesse* in the Cabinet des Dessins. Pencil and pen, round stain with scrapings of paint. Verso: No. 18.

Page upright: (a) Top: group of three cupids.—(b) Couple performing a dance figure.—(c) Couple, the woman with her back turned.—(d) To the right of the stain: child squatting.—(e) Lower, on the left: flying cherub, head and shoulders of an angel, head of another angel.—(f) Little girl, standing and pointing with her index finger.—(g) Bottom: woman in a flounced dress.—(h) Group of the three Fates.—Page lengthwise: (i) Top right: two cherubs (pen).—(k) Head seen in profile (pen).—(l) Left: draped figure carrying a crook, copy of a Roman augur (ink sketch, later than the pencil drawings).

BIBLIOGRAPHY: Berthold, p. 156 (not reproduced).

COLLECTIONS: P. Berès, Paris. Cabinet des Dessins of the Louvre, Paris (RF 29949).

21. STUDIES OF DANCERS AND HORSES, 1858–59
    $9\frac{1}{16} \times 5\frac{7}{8}$ inches—23×15 cm. Page 8 verso of the *Carnet de jeunesse* in the Cabinet des Dessins. Pencil and white gouache, paper torn. Verso: No. 39.

(a) Top left: woman dancer, seated; repetition of No. 39 (a).—(b) Top right: couple dancing.—(c) Below the couple dancing, and cut in two by the tear, the man taking a long step as he carries off his partner, who is drawn more lightly.—(d) Lower down: two couples; in one the man is seen in profile (correction over white gouache), in the second a male dancer is seen from the back. Berthold's description of the second differs: "nude woman, seen back view, dancing." The hairstyle is indeed ambiguous, but clothing is indicated at the elbows and wrist.—(e) Left: study of a colonnade.—(f) Head and neck of a horse, five versions. Cf. No. 88.—(g) Half-length figure of a man in a top hat, two versions.—(h) Lower left: two lightly sketched figures, one of them nude.

BIBLIOGRAPHY: Berthold, p. 155 (not reproduced).

COLLECTIONS: P. Berès, Paris. Cabinet des Dessins of the Louvre, Paris (RF 29949).

22. MAN AND RIDER, 1858–59
    $9\frac{1}{16} \times 5\frac{7}{8}$ inches—23×15 cm. Page 2 verso of the *Carnet de jeunesse* in the Cabinet des Dessins. Pencil. Verso: No. 53.

(a) Man in a large hat, standing.—(b) At right angles: man on horseback riding into the distance.

COLLECTIONS: P. Berès, Paris. Cabinet des Dessins of the Louvre, Paris (RF 29949).

23. STUDIES, INCLUDING A MAN WITH A GUN, 1859–62
    $9\frac{1}{16} \times 5\frac{7}{8}$ inches—23×15 cm. Page 11 of the *Carnet de jeunesse* in the Cabinet des Dessins. Pencil. Ink stains, counterproof of No. 246, and foxing. Verso: No. 19.

(a) Top right: in the middle of a circular, radiant nimbus, the face of a moon or sun.—(b) To the right: smaller head, surrounded by a nebulous crown. Both seem to relate to the painting Venturi No. 13. Two heads, No. 19 (c), are studies for the same subject.—(c) Left: man squatting, seen from behind.—(d) Man with a gun, in profile. The birds on the left are not by the hand of the artist.—(e) Below: rough sketch of a foot.—(f) Head.

BIBLIOGRAPHY: Berthold, p. 155 (not reproduced).

COLLECTIONS: P. Berès, Paris. Cabinet des Dessins of the Louvre, Paris (RF 29949).

24. STUDIES, INCLUDING MAN BEATING A BASS DRUM, 1858–59

$5\frac{7}{8} \times 9\frac{1}{16}$ inches—15 × 23 cm. Page 21 of the *Carnet de jeunesse* in the Cabinet des Dessins. Pencil and pen, two stains with traces of paint. Over the whole page, geological schemas by an alien hand. Verso: No. 33.

(a) Pencil sketch heightened with ink: young man beating a bass drum and cymbal.—(b) Top center: boy kneeling in an attitude of prayer.—(c) Sketch of a figure, front view.

BIBLIOGRAPHY: Berthold, p. 156 (not reproduced).

COLLECTIONS: P. Berès, Paris. Cabinet des Dessins of the Louvre, Paris (RF 29949).

25. MAN AND WOMAN, 1858–59

$3\frac{1}{4} \times 5\frac{7}{8}$ inches—8,2 × 15 cm. Part of page 41 of the *Carnet de jeunesse* in the Cabinet des Dessins. Pencil on brown paper. Verso: No. 26. Fragment of a page.

Upper part of two figures: young man with his hand on the shoulder of a young woman.

BIBLIOGRAPHY: Berthold, p. 158 (not reproduced).

COLLECTIONS: P. Berès, Paris. Cabinet des Dessins of the Louvre, Paris (RF 29949).

26. MAN AND WOMAN, 1858–59

$3\frac{1}{4} \times 5\frac{7}{8}$ inches—8,2 × 15 cm. Part of page 41 verso of the *Carnet de jeunesse* in the Cabinet des Dessins. Pencil on brown paper; heavy stains. Verso: No. 25. Fragment of a page.

Half-length figures of a young man and young woman. They resemble the couple of No. 25, but seem less rigid.

BIBLIOGRAPHY: Berthold, p. 158 (not reproduced).

COLLECTIONS: Berès, Paris. Cabinet des Dessins of the Louvre, Paris (RF 29949).

27. SKETCHES AND CARICATURES, July 1859

Pen drawings, on a letter to Emile Zola.

Among these numerous caricatures we mention only: (a) two studies of the hindquarters of a horse; cf. No. 21 (f).—(b) Man with a clown's hairstyle approaching a nude woman.—(c) Soldier with a gun; cf. No. 8 (b).

BIBLIOGRAPHY: *Correspondance* (reproduced fig. 6). Coll. *Cézanne, Génies et Réalités*, Hachette, Paris, 1966 (reproduced p. 109).

EXHIBITIONS: Orangerie, Paris, 1936, No. 173.—Lyons, 1939, No. 84.

COLLECTIONS: Emile Zola, Paris. Mme. Zola, Paris. E. Fasquelle, Paris. M. et Mme Leblond-Zola, Paris.

28. ANCIENT WARRIOR ON A CHARIOT, 1856–58

$5\frac{7}{8} \times 7\frac{1}{16}$ inches—15 × 18 cm. Pencil on ruled paper. Folds, stains, margin missing top right. Verso: No. 242.

Nude warrior, erect on a two-wheeled chariot. The outlines are partly traced. The rumps of the horses are seen, and the warrior is looking down at an enemy, thrown to the ground, his legs thrashing the air. Top right: lightly drawn rough sketch, not traced, of a combatant in a Greek helmet. For the chariot driver, cf. No. 3 and also the later sketch No. 29.

COLLECTIONS: Mouradian & Vallotton, Paris. Present owner unknown.

29. ANCIENT RACING CHARIOT, 1858–59

$5\frac{7}{8} \times 9\frac{1}{16}$ inches—15 × 23 cm. Page 40 verso of the *Carnet de jeunesse* in the Cabinet des Dessins. Pencil, traces of ink which have seeped through from overleaf. Verso: No. 68.

(a) Drawn with very fine strokes: a racing chariot of ancient times, the driver holding the reins of two horses. For this man, cf. Nos. 3, 28.—(b) On the right are two men who seem to be standing on the back part of the chariot, but probably they were already on the page before (a) was drawn. One of the men holds a pole.

BIBLIOGRAPHY: Berthold, p. 158 (not reproduced).

COLLECTIONS: P. Berès, Paris. Cabinet des Dessins of the Louvre, Paris (RF 29949).

30. STUDIES, INCLUDING A HELMETED SOLDIER, 1858–59

$9\frac{1}{16} \times 5\frac{7}{8}$ inches—23 × 15 cm. Page 28 of the *Carnet de jeunesse* in the Cabinet des Dessins. Pencil, pen, and ink which has seeped through the paper. Verso: No. 62.

(a) Seventeenth-century soldier, standing and facing right. Vertical and diagonal hatching, the pencil strokes heightened with ink. With his right hand he raises a weapon of which the guard is visible; in the other he holds a dagger.—(b) Top: woman's head.—(c) Lower left: torso of an angel, caricature.—(d) Still lower left: cherub. —(e) Below: head and shoulders of a bearded man.— (f) Top right: two studies of a hand.—(g) Head of a woman wearing headbands.—(h) Head of a man with beard.—(i) Head and wings of an angel, study for No. 51 (a).—(k) Cherub flying horizontally towards the right (strokes added by an alien hand).—(l) Seated cherub.

BIBLIOGRAPHY: Berthold, p. 156 (not reproduced).

COLLECTIONS: P. Berès, Paris. Cabinet des Dessins of the Louvre, Paris (RF 29949).

31. ORATOR HARANGUING THE PEOPLE, 1858–61

$5\frac{7}{8} \times 147$ inches—15 × 14,7 cm. Page 31 of the *Carnet de jeunesse* in the Cabinet des Dessins. Pencil. More than a third of the page is torn off. Verso: No. 61.

Subject copied; it represents a gathering of men, women, children, and soldiers assembled before an orator who can be seen above their heads. The outlines seem to have been traced.

BIBLIOGRAPHY: Berthold, p. 157 (not reproduced).

COLLECTIONS: P. Berès, Paris. Cabinet des Dessins of the Louvre, Paris (RF 29949).

32. PORTRAIT AND CARICATURES, 1857–59

$9\frac{1}{16} \times 5\frac{7}{8}$ inches—23 × 15 cm. Page 6 of the *Carnet de jeunesse* in the Cabinet des Dessins. Pencil. Verso: No. 34.

(a) Head and shoulders of a youngish man, copied from a portrait of the mid-nineteenth century. The hand of Cézanne, his curved strokes and hatching, are evident in the necktie, lapels, curls, and mustache. Top right: caricature of a man; cf. No. 405.—Higher on the page: unfinished study.

BIBLIOGRAPHY: Berthold, cat. No. 314 (reproduced), and p. 155.

COLLECTIONS: P. Berès, Paris. Cabinet des Dessins of the Louvre, Paris (RF 29949).

33. STUDIES, INCLUDING A MAN SMOKING, 1858–59

$9\frac{1}{16} \times 5\frac{7}{8}$ inches—23 × 15 cm. Page 21 verso of the *Carnet de jeunesse* in the Cabinet des Dessins. Pencil, two stains. Over the whole page, geological schemas by an alien hand. Verso: No. 24.

(a) Top left: study of two women.—(b) Right: man kneeling to a woman and holding her hand; no doubt it is a proposal.—(c) To the left: small, expressive head.—(d) Below: young dandy, smoking; cf. Nos. 14, 34.—(e) Right: half-length study of the dandy, in right profile.

BIBLIOGRAPHY: Berthold, p. 156 (not reproduced).

COLLECTIONS: P. Berès, Paris. Cabinet des Dessins of the Louvre, Paris (RF 29949).

34. PAGE OF STUDIES, WITH A MAN SMOKING, AND HEADS, 1858–59

$9\frac{1}{16} \times 5\frac{7}{8}$ inches—23 x 15 cm. Page 6 verso of the *Carnet de jeunesse* in the Cabinet des Dessins. Pencil. Verso: No. 32.

(a) Top left: a peddler with his tray.—(b) Head in a sculptured helmet, copy from an unknown model, though it resembles the Hercules in a lion-muzzle head-dress from the Temple of Aegina, discovered in 1811 (Munich, Staatliche Antikensammlungen, No. A 86). See fig 4.—(c) Head and shoulders of a man with beard and

FIG. 4. Head of Herakles (detail), marble from the east pediment of the Temple of Aegina. Munich, Staatliche Antikensammlungen, No. A 86.   *(Photograph: F. Kaufmann)*

mustache; near to his chin, a finger.—(d) Young man, seated and ostentatiously smoking a pipe, cf. No. 14 (a).—Left hand, with cuff of sleeve.—(f) Foot.—(g) Woman's head.—(h) Sketch of a head, with hatching.

BIBLIOGRAPHY: Berthold, p. 155 (not reproduced).

COLLECTIONS: P. Berès, Paris. Cabinet des Dessins of the Louvre, Paris (RF 29949).

35. STUDIES, INCLUDING A WOMAN PLAYING A MANDOLIN, 1858–59

$5\frac{7}{8} \times 9\frac{1}{16}$ inches—15 × 23 cm. Page 27 of the *Carnet de jeunesse* in the Cabinet des Dessins. Pencil, partly obliterated round stain. On part of the page, schemas of geological stratifications by an alien hand. Verso: No. 51.

(a) Top left: half-length study of two figures.—(b) Lower left: couple seated, the woman on the man's left knee; cf. No. 235.—(c) Center: a man sitting at a round table, his arms around a woman playing the mandolin.—(d) Young man, half lying, half sitting, and raising his arm in a lyrical gesture. A kneeling woman can be seen behind his head.—(e) Above: man reading a newspaper.—(f) Waiter with tray.—(g) Bourgeois wearing glasses.

BIBLIOGRAPHY: Berthold, p. 156 (not reproduced).

COLLECTIONS: P. Berès, Paris. Cabinet des Dessins of the Louvre, Paris (RF 29949).

36. CARD PLAYERS, 1858–60

About $8\frac{5}{8} \times 10\frac{5}{8}$ inches—22 × 27 cm. Pencil on white paper. Verso: blank page.

Tracing done from an unidentified engraved reproduction.—Cézanne completed the figures in pencil. Although the light pencil strokes might appear to precede the harsher outlines, this seems incorrect to me; cf. two other tracings: Nos. 164, 457. No. 28 seems to be partially traced. This is probably the first suggestion of the *Card Players* theme.

COLLECTION: Louis Giniès, Aix-en-Provence.

37. SYMBOLIC DRAWING, inscribed *La Mort règne en ces lieux*, January 17, 1859

Pen drawing on a letter to Emile Zola.

Drawing on a letter Cézanne wrote two days before his twentieth birthday, to Emile Zola. Inscription upper left: *La Mort règne en ces lieux* (Death reigns in these parts). Kurt Badt has attempted to analyse the meaning of this scene, which he refers to as "the drawing of Ugolino." (Kurt Badt, *Die Kunst Cézannes*, Munich, 1959, p. 68). In brief: Badt thinks that this drawing expresses Cézanne's hatred of his father for preventing him from painting; the father in the drawing would symbolize the future painter, the children the future paintings, the "inhuman mortal" being the artist's father, and the latter's head on the table a symbol of the inheritance. Badt's reasoning is too subtle to be summarized here. Concerning the composition of the drawing he points out two characteristic signs: the T formed by the arms on the left, which is repeated in the painting *Mardi Gras*, Venturi No. 552, and the V formed by legs of the men seated at the table, which, with the table legs and figures, is repeated in *The Card Players*, Venturi Nos. 559, 560.

BIBLIOGRAPHY: *Correspondance* (reproduced fig. 3). Badt, op. cit. (reproduced fig. 7). Douglas Cooper, stacked Cards? *Times Literary Supplement*, May 27, 1965. Kurt Leonhard, *Paul Cézanne*, Rewohlt, Hamburg, 1966 (reproduced p. 27). A. Neumeyer, *AB*, Vol. XLIX, 1967, p. 272.

EXHIBITIONS: Orangerie, Paris, 1936, No. 173. Lyons, 1939, No. 80. Wildenstein, London, 1939, Autograph Letters, No. 3.

COLLECTIONS: Emile Zola, Paris. Mme. Zola, Paris. E. Fasquelle, Paris. M. and Mme Leblond-Zola, Paris.

38. BATHING, June 20, 1859

Pen drawing on a letter to Emile Zola.

This page recalls the schooldays of the artist, who was twenty when he drew it. The subject of the *Bathers* here finds its first really characteristic expression.

BIBLIOGRAPHY: *Correspondance* (reproduced fig. 5). German edition, Zurich, 1962 (reproduced p. 97). Rewald, *Paul Cézanne*, Spring Books, London, 1959 and 1965 (reproduced p. 6). *The World of Cézanne* (reproduced p. 23).

EXHIBITIONS: Orangerie, Paris, 1939, No. 173. Lyons, 1939, No. 82. Wildenstein, London, 1939, Autograph Letters No. 5.

COLLECTIONS: Emile Zola, Paris. Mme. Zola, Paris. E. Fasquelle, Paris. M. and Mme Leblond-Zola, Paris.

39. STUDIES, INCLUDING A BATHER, 1859–60

$5\frac{7}{8} \times 9\frac{1}{16}$ — 15 × 23 cm. Page 8 verso of the *Carnet de jeunesse* in the Cabinet des Dessins. Pencil, page torn. Verso: No. 21.

(a) Top left: seated woman holding a fan. — (b) To the right: small sketch of a woman wearing a crinoline and holding a parasol; cf. Venturi Nos. 3, 119. — (c) Below: head of a young man. — (d) Center: bather, a band on his head, walking over some large stones; to his right, a head emerging from the water; cf. Nos. 38, 187. — (e) On the right next to the first bather: head of a man. — (f) Upside down: man crouching. — (g) On the right side of the page and at right angles: man lying on his stomach. — (h) Lower edge: rough sketches of three faces. — (i) Right, above the water: two men facing each other, seen in profile, cf. No. 236.

BIBLIOGRAPHY: Berthold, p. 155 (not reproduced).

COLLECTIONS: P. Berès, Paris. Cabinet des Dessins of the Louvre, Paris (RF 29949).

40. SKETCHES: A MAN STANDING, AND HEADS, 1859–60

$9 \times 6\frac{5}{8}$ inches — 22,8 × 16,8 cm. Page XXI from an early sketchbook. Pencil. Verso: No. 115.

(a) Top left: head with a tuft of hair. — (b) Right: head of a bearded man; cf. Nos. 27, 30. — (c) Center: standing man, probably a bather. — (d) Head of a man with a goatee; cf. Nos. 19, 21, 25, 48. — (e) Below: profile of a head; cf. Nos. 12, 405. — (f) Three leaves, pointed like arrows. — (g) Undefinable object, or perhaps (seen upside down) a landscape study; cf. No. 120.

BIBLIOGRAPHY: Catalog, W. H. Schab, New York, 1964, *Graphic Arts of Five Centuries*, No. 130 (reproduced).

COLLECTIONS: W. H. Schab, New York. Private Collection, Switzerland.

41. THREE PEN SKETCHES, about 1858

$5\frac{5}{8} \times 7\frac{3}{16}$ inches — 14,3 × 18,2 cm. Pen and ink on ruled writing paper glued to cardboard. Various stains: lower right, white oil paint laid on with a palette knife; above, white paint with a fingerprint. Folds in paper, lower left. The reverse side is inaccessible.

(a) Top: reclining couple. — (b) Center: man walking toward the left carrying a stick. — (c) Below: naked man climbing a wall; traditional pose in the drawing schools.

BIBLIOGRAPHY: Venturi, Vol. I, p. 351, *Oeuvres Inédites* (not reproduced). Basel catalog, No. 2 (reproduced).

COLLECTIONS: Cézanne *fils*, Paris. W. Feuz, Bern. Kunstmuseum, Basel.

42. TWO FIGURES, circa 1858

$9\frac{1}{16} \times 5\frac{7}{8}$ inches — 23 × 15 cm. Page 30 of the *Carnet de jeunesse* in the Cabinet des Dessins. Pencil, faint stains. Verso: No. 43.

(a) Man, standing, holding a bottle of wine, his right hand on his chin. — (b) Further away, a man taking a walk, one finger close to his eye. — The drawing of (b) seems weaker than (a).

COLLECTIONS: P. Berès, Paris. Cabinet des Dessins of the Louvre, Paris (RF 29949).

43. STUDIES, INCLUDING A COUPLE OUTDOORS, circa 1858

$9\frac{1}{16} \times 5\frac{7}{8}$ inches — 23 × 15 cm. Page 30 verso of the *Carnet de jeunesse* in the Cabinet des Dessins. Pencil, small stains. Verso: No. 42.

(a) Woman sitting near a tree, a man approaching her; cf. the painting Venturi No. 116. — (b) Study of a head. — (c) Left profile of a man, wearing a cap, cf. No. 54 (e). — (d) Three unfinished sketches of a man drinking from a bottle.

COLLECTIONS: P. Berès, Paris. Cabinet des Dessins of the Louvre, Paris (RF 29949).

44. PROMENADE, circa 1859

$4\frac{1}{2} \times 7\frac{7}{8}$ inches — 11,5 × 20 cm. Page from a sketchbook. Pencil, numerous stains and color showing through from the watercolor on verso, Venturi No. 812.

Two groups of people walking toward each other in a public place. In the background, a dandy is driving a carriage. The scene is in the style of Constantin Guys.

COLLECTIONS: Cézanne *fils*, Paris. Jean-Pierre Cézanne, Paris. Sale, Sotheby's, London, April 10 and 11, 1962, No. 131 (watercolor on verso cataloged). Private collection. Sale, Sotheby's, London, July 8, 1965, No. 5.

45. FIVE MEN AROUND A FIRE, circa 1859

$9\frac{1}{8} \times 5\frac{7}{8}$ inches — 23;3 × 15 cm. Page 24 verso of the *Carnet de jeunesse* in the Cabinet des Dessins. Pencil. Verso: No. 69.

The plainly visible squaring of this drawing indicates Cézanne's intention of translating it into a painting, though no corresponding work is known. The squares are numbered from 1 to 8 at the lower edge. The saber strapped over the seated man's shoulder, the bayoneted gun of the central figure, and the conical hats are characteristic of the bandits of the Roman Campagna, a fashionable subject at that time.

COLLECTIONS: P. Berès, Paris. Cabinet des Dessins of the Louvre, Paris (RF 29949).

46. SKETCHES OF HEADS AND FIGURES, circa 1859

$8\frac{1}{4} \times 5\frac{1}{8}$ inches—21 × 13 cm. Pen. Verso: blank page.

Between 1858 and 1860 Cézanne studied law at the University of Aix. This is a page from an exercise book in which the young man noted what he remembered of a lecture on penal procedure. He was obviously bored, to the point where finally his pen wandered from the words, "How is this fine to be proportioned," to a first sketch, then on to others. Here is the text: "14. Only the galleys entailed no fine; all the others entailed one.—The fine was intended to reimburse the costs of the trial. The penalty of a fine is essentially divisible.—2ndly. Restorable; if an innocent man has been condemned, his money can be refunded.—Equable and appreciable, i.e. it can be proportioned according to the income of the delinquent. How is this fine to be proportioned . . . "—There are ten sketches: imaginary heads or portraits.

EXHIBITION: Quatre-Chemins, Paris, 1936.

COLLECTIONS: Cézanne *fils*, Paris. Present owner unknown.

46A. PEN STUDIES, circa 1859

$8\frac{1}{4} \times 5\frac{1}{8}$ inches—21 × 13 cm. Pen. Verso: a page of notes on a law lecture: *Des Huissiers* (On Bailiffs). Not reproduced.

(a) Lower left: seated man, wearing a pointed hat. Shepherd or brigand of the Roman Campagna, cf. No. 45. —Top right: (b) Standing man.—Left: (c) Rough sketch of a profile.

BIBLIOGRAPHY: *Correspondance*, fig. 11, reproduces the verso, through which the present drawings can be discerned.

COLLECTIONS: Cézanne *fils*, Paris. Galerie Zak, Paris. Present owner unknown.

47. STUDIES: FAUNS AND MAN WITH GUN, 1859–62

$7\frac{1}{16} \times 5\frac{1}{2}$ inches—18 × 14 cm. Pen and pencil on ruled paper, various stains. Verso: blank page.

Faunlike figures, studies for a composition.—(a) Left: faun sitting on a stone, his hand raised in a didactic gesture.—(b) The same figure, but sitting on the ground; cf. No. 48, left.—(c) Man standing, a gun over his shoulder, with a dog, above which can be seen a pencil outline.—(d) Top left: half-length figure of a faun, corrections to the arm.—(e) Top right: head and shoulders of a man and the barrel of a gun.—(f) Below (d): study of a bent arm.—(g) Repetition of the arm.

COLLECTIONS: Mouradian & Vallotton, Paris. Present owner unknown.

48. PASTORAL SCENE, 1859–62

$2\frac{3}{8} \times 3\frac{9}{16}$ inches—6 × 9 cm. Ink, pencil, and bister. Verso: blank page.

Left: a faun sitting with both arms in front, beating time with his right arm. In the foreground, a she-faun seated on the ground, her back turned and her elbows raised above her shoulders. It may be noted that the hoofs of this faun are hardly in proportion to her thighs. Right corner: flask and loaf of bread. Background: two crouching men playing musical instruments. The scene is framed by a sylvan vault; the bush in the background recalls *The Burning Bush* by Nicolas Froment in St. Sauveur Cathedral, Aix-en-Provence. Cf. No. 47, and also the horse's legs in No. 27.

BIBLIOGRAPHY: Venturi No. 1180. Vollard 1914 (reproduced p. 21).

COLLECTIONS: Cézanne *fils*, Paris. Mouradian & Vallotton, Paris. Present owner unknown.

49. SCENE WITH PRISONERS, 1859–62

$9\frac{1}{16} \times 5\frac{7}{8}$ inches—23 × 15 cm. Page 50 of the *Carnet de jeunesse* in the Cabinet des Dessins. Pencil and pen on brown paper, ink smudged. Verso: No. 72.

(a) Pencil sketch, scarcely visible: man standing.—(b) Pen: three nude men with their hands tied behind their backs are brought before a helmeted figure by a man seen back view. Here, as in other early works, the figures seem to obey the principle "No one notices you if you don't gesticulate." Berthold rightly observes the extent to which the drawing of the human form is still uncertain.

BIBLIOGRAPHY: Berthold, p. 159 (not reproduced); date given in the text, p. 45, as before 1866.

COLLECTIONS: P. Berès, Paris. Cabinet des Dessins of the Louvre, Paris (RF 29949).

50. CARICATURE OF *Jupiter and Thetis*, painting by Ingres, 1858–60

$9\frac{1}{16} \times 5\frac{7}{8}$ inches—23 × 15 cm. Page 49 of the *Carnet de jeunesse* in the Cabinet des Dessins. Pencil and pen on light-brown paper. Paper torn on the right. Verso: No. 114.

Caricature inspired by the painting *Jupiter and Thetis* by Dominique Ingres, in the Aix-en-Provence museum. See fig. 5. First sketched in pencil, the final drawing is done with a firm pen stroke; certain parts remain unfinished, notably Juno watching from above the clouds on the left, and the eagle on the right. Cézanne was probably drawing from memory, showing Jupiter—inaccurately—with his head tilted and his arm around Thetis; it is a caricature, rather than a copy as has been asserted. Below the sketch, an erased inscription.

BIBLIOGRAPHY: Berthold, p. 158 (reproduced Abb. 63); dated 1858–62 in the text, p. 44.

COLLECTIONS: P. Berès, Paris. Cabinet des Dessins of the Louvre, Paris (RF 29949).

51. STUDIES, INCLUDING AN ANGEL, 1858–59

$9\frac{1}{16} \times 5\frac{7}{8}$ inches—23 × 15 cm. Page 27 verso of the *Carnet de jeunesse* in the Cabinet des Dessins. Pencil and pen, ink smudged. Verso: No. 35.

(a) An angel flying down to a painter who is between his easel and a large drawing portfolio (seen lower left). The later sketch (c) partly hides the painter, but his right profile can be seen, close to the ink smudge. This carica-

FIG. 5. Jean-Auguste-Dominique Ingres (1780–1867):
Jupiter et Thetis, painting in the Musée Granet,
Aix-en-Provence.   *(Photograph: Giraudon)*

ture is explained by the inscription below: "A messenger straight from heaven awards Chaillan the crown for Painting." Chaillan was a fellow-student of Cézanne's at the Aix drawing school, between 1858 and 1862.— (b) Top left, at right angles: dancer in a tulle skirt.— (c) Upside down in the center of the page: sketch of a man with his hands bound; pen drawing, ink smeared.

BIBLIOGRAPHY: Berthold, p. 156 (reproduced Abb.62). Berthold sees seven different studies on this page, from A to G.

COLLECTIONS: P. Berès, Paris. Cabinet des Dessins of the Louvre, Paris (RF 29949).

52. TWO WOMEN STANDING, circa 1865

$9\frac{1}{16} \times 5\frac{7}{8}$ inches—23 × 15 cm. Page 47 verso of the *Carnet de jeunesse* in the Cabinet des Dessins. Pen and pencil, with traces of ink due to an accidental counterproof, on light-brown paper. Verso: No. 70.

(a) Ink drawing of two standing women, one with her arm outstretched.—(b) At right angles, in pencil: face of a man; cf. No. 68 (b).

BIBLIOGRAPHY: Berthold, p. 158 (reproduced Abb. 65). Date given in the text, p. 45, as circa 1866.

COLLECTIONS: P. Berès, Paris. Cabinet des Dessins of the Louvre, Paris (RF 29949).

53. SKETCH OF HEADS, circa 1860

$9\frac{1}{16} \times 5\frac{7}{8}$ inches—23 × 15 cm. Page 2 of the *Carnet de jeunesse* in the Cabinet des Dessins. Pencil, small stains. Verso: No. 22.

(a) Page upright: two studies of a young man wearing a cap, both perhaps portraits of Baptistin Baille.—(b) Page lengthwise: sketches of six heads, with hands or fingers, and three vases, scattered over the page.

COLLECTIONS: P. Berès, Paris. Cabinet des Dessins of the Louvre, Paris (RF 29949).

54. CARICATURE, circa 1860

$5\frac{7}{8} \times 10\frac{1}{4}$ to $10\frac{13}{16}$ inches—15 × 26 to 27,5 cm. Page 53 verso of the *Carnet de jeunesse* in the Cabinet des Dessins. Pen and pencil. Part of page torn off. Verso: No. 15.

(a) Page lengthwise: (a) upper edge, in ink, head of a man, mainly drawn with straight strokes.—(b) Right: torso of a boy, unfinished pen sketch.—Page upright, in pencil: (c) study of a young seated bather; same gesture as that of the bather, No. 433A.—(d) To the right: man standing gazing.—(e) Below: boy in a cap.—(f) At right angles: large Arab head.

BIBLIOGRAPHY: Berthold, p. 159 (not reproduced).

COLLECTIONS: P. Berès, Paris. Cabinet des Dessins of the Louvre, Paris (RF 29949).

55. SEATED WOMAN, DRAPED, 1858–61

$4\frac{5}{8} \times 3\frac{15}{16}$ inches (sight)—11 × 10 cm. Pen. Page numbered 21, in pencil. Verso: No. 226.

Berthold is of the opinion that this is a copy by Cézanne of some unknown work. I am rather inclined to think that the sketch was done from life.

BIBLIOGRAPHY: Berthold, cat. No. 316 (reproduced).

COLLECTIONS: Lucien Blanc, Aix-en-Provence. Atelier Cézanne, Aix-en-Provence.

56. WOMAN READING, AND STUDIES, 1860–65

$8\frac{1}{4} \times 6\frac{1}{2}$ inches—21 × 16,5 cm. Page from a sketchbook. Pencil and wash. Verso: No. 213.

(a) Woman seated, chin in hand, holding an open book on her knees (wash, with pencil).—(b) Left, earlier sketch: man at a window, smiling ostentatiously, and a woman passing below the window waving a torch.

COLLECTION: Cézanne *fils*, Paris. Jean-Pierre Cézanne, Paris. Sale, Galerie G. Giroux, Brussels, Feb. 6, 1954. A. Maurice, Brussels.

57. PAGE OF FIGURE STUDIES, 1860–65

$4\frac{7}{8} \times 8\frac{5}{16}$ inches—12,3 × 21,1 cm. Page 39 verso from a sketchbook. Pencil and pen. Verso: No. 189.

Page lengthwise, in pencil: academy study of a male nude, sitting on a stool. This drawing offers certain analogies to the painting Venturi No. 100, *The Negro Scipion*, and also to Venturi No. 83. Cézanne has attempted to model the figure by contours.—(b) Unfinished study of the same subject.—(c) Right: study of a man kneeling; academic pose.—(d) Lower edge, center: man lying on his side, leaning on his elbow; study repeated on the right side of the wash drawing Venturi No. 812.—Page upright: (e) Pen and pencil study of a standing woman, seen front view. Although she is draped, her lower abdomen is uncovered. To the right are a man and a woman, evidently a study for the small canvas, *The Judgment of Paris,* Venturi No. 16, painted in 1860-61. Venus, seated in profile, raises her arms to take the apple offered her by Paris, who has his arm round her shoulder. He is depicted with a goatee beard. The standing woman represents the frustrated Juno.—(f) on Juno's left, a light sketch of Minerva in right profile.—(g) Top center, partly hidden beneath (a): scarcely visible sketch of Juno walking away, her head turned to the right; this is a first rough sketch of the figure of Juno as she appears in Venturi No. 16. Further right, scarcely recognizable, the hand of Paris holding the apple.

BIBLIOGRAPHY: Th. Reff, Cézanne and Hercules, *AB* Vol. XLVIII, 1966, p. 35 et sqq., reproduced fig. 6. Meyer Schapiro, The Apples of Cézanne, *Art News Annual*, Vol. XXXIV, 1968, p. 53; the author has doubts as to the subject.

COLLECTIONS: Huguette Berès, Paris. Mrs. Charles B. Nunnally, Atlanta. On loan to High Museum of Art, Atlanta.

58. ROMAN BUST AND OTHER STUDIES, circa 1859

$9\frac{1}{16} \times 5\frac{7}{8}$ inches—23 × 15 cm. Page 4 verso of the *Carnet de jeunesse* in the Cabinet des Dessins. Pencil. Verso: childish drawings attributed to Marie Cézanne, perhaps retouched by her brother Paul (not reproduced).

(a) Study of a bust representing a Roman, his garment fastened on the shoulder by a clasp.—(b) Upside down: half-length figure of a dandy in a top hat; cf. No. 145. —(c) At right angles: a coachman on his seat.

BIBLIOGRAPHY: Berthold, cat. No. 299 (reproduced), and p. 155.

COLLECTIONS: P. Berès, Paris. Cabinet des Dessins of the Louvre, Paris (RF 29949).

59. CABARET SCENE, AND HEAD; cabaret, 1856–58; head, 1858–61

$5\frac{7}{8} \times 9\frac{1}{8}$ inches—14,9 × 23,2 cm. Page 32 of the *Carnet de jeunesse* in the Cabinet des Dessins. Pencil, smudged ink-blot. Verso: No. 10.

(a) Three soldiers in a cabaret. Two bottles on a table and a notice on the wall *Défense de se souler* (drunkenness is forbidden). Certain contours are perhaps traced.—(b) Left: head of a man, bent forward. Copy of an unidentified work; cf. Nos. 58, 392.

BIBLIOGRAPHY: Berthold, p. 157 (not reproduced); she describes (b) as the head of a woman drawn from a live model, not copied from a work of art. This may be so.

COLLECTIONS: P. Berès, Paris. Cabinet des Dessins of the Louvre, Paris (RF 29949).

60. STUDIES; HALF-LENGTH FIGURES, AND HORSE, circa 1859

$5\frac{7}{8} \times 9\frac{1}{16}$ inches—15 × 23 cm. Page 5 of the *Carnet de jeunesse* in the Cabinet des Dessins. Pencil. Verso: No. 127.

Page lengthwise: (a) head and shoulders of a woman.— (b) horse lying down with its head turned, a blanket apparently wrapped around its body. Higher, to the right,

a study of the same subject, partially covered by (c). Perhaps a copy.—Page upright: (c) portrait of a man with a mustache; cf. No. 32, which is earlier, but similar.

COLLECTIONS: P. Berès, Paris. Cabinet des Dessins of the Louvre, Paris (RF 29949).

61. PENCIL AND PEN SKETCHES, 1864–67

$5\frac{7}{8} \times 5\frac{13}{16}$ inches—15 × 14,7 cm. Page 31 verso of the *Carnet de jeunesse* in the Cabinet des Dessins. Pencil and pen. Verso: No. 31.

First the pencil sketches, which are earlier:—(a) Left: man sitting on a stool (covered by pen drawing).—Right: a man standing with his arms crossed; his head, too large, is seen in left profile.—(c) Pen: studies of four rather confusing figures which perhaps relate to the composition No. 62; two of them are on the ground, two standing, with a tree trunk on the right. They are drawn with a strange vehemence, a kind of challenge hurled at academic drawing.

BIBLIOGRAPHY: Berthold, p. 157 (not reproduced).

COLLECTIONS: P. Berès, Paris. Cabinet des Dessins of the Louvre, Paris (RF 29949).

62. STUDIES, INCLUDING A KNIFE-GRINDER; pencil 1857–58, pen 1864–66.

$9\frac{1}{16} \times 5\frac{7}{8}$ inches—23 × 15 cm. Page 28 verso of the *Carnet de jeunesse* in the Cabinet des Dessins. Pencil and pen. Verso: No. 30.

(a) Pencil: man wearing a large belted coat; his hat is covered by the pen sketch.—(b) Woman holding herself erect, like a statue of Minerva; (a) and (b) are probably copies.—(c) Pen, upside down in relation to (a) and (b): bathing scene, surrounded by a frame of strokes. Confused study for the watercolor Venturi No. 819 and the oil Venturi No. 113. Cf. also our Nos. 61 (c), 95, 261.—(d) Rough sketch overlapping into the top part of the frame. —(e) Lower right: a knife-grinder working at a big wheel.

BIBLIOGRAPHY: Berthold, p. 156 (reproduced Abb. 66); the date 1866–67 is discussed on pp. 45, 46.

COLLECTIONS: P. Berès, Paris. Cabinet des Dessins of the Louvre, Paris (RF 29949).

63. VARIOUS STUDIES; pencil, circa 1858; pen 1864–66

$5\frac{7}{8} \times 9\frac{1}{8}$ inches—15 × 23,2 cm. Page 29 verso of the *Carnet de jeunesse* in the Cabinet des Dessins. Pencil and pen. Verso: No. 64.

Page upright, pencil drawings: (a) *The Resurrection of Christ,* copy from an unknown work. It is surprising to see that the four men at the bottom of the page, guarding the sepulcher, are in European dress, and it may be that the soldier wearing a kepi, on the left, also forms part of the composition. Another kepi can be seen to the right, near an unidentifiable object covered by a pen drawing. There must be several subjects.—Page lengthwise, in ink; (b) Lower left: a man lying on his stomach, raising his arm as though calling for somebody.—(c) Above: male nude, seated like a model posing, cf. No. 101.—(d) Above: two rough sketches.—(e) Right: rough sketch, head and shoulders.—(f) Smudged sketch, same subject as No. 62 (c).

BIBLIOGRAPHY: Berthold, p. 157 (not reproduced); text, p. 45, date 1866–67.

COLLECTIONS: P. Berès, Paris. Cabinet des Dessins of the Louvre, Paris (RF 29949).

64. STUDIES, INCLUDING ORIENTALS SMOKING; head (b) 1866–67, others circa 1858.

$5\frac{7}{8} \times 9\frac{1}{8}$ inches—15 × 23,2 cm. Page 29 of the *Carnet de jeunesse* in the Cabinet des Dessins. Pencil; fly-specks and small blemishes. Verso: No. 63.

(a) Three Orientals forming a group; two are smoking pipes, the third holds a stick.—(b) Right: head of a bearded man, probably a copy. The beard and face are strongly contrasted, while the abundant hair is only lightly drawn, producing a curious effect.—(c) Top left: child feeling for its mother's breast.—(d) Head and shoulders of a man, wearing a hat and glasses.—(e) Study of a head with kepi.

BIBLIOGRAPHY: Berthold, cat. No. 315 (reproduced) and p. 156; text, p. 45, date 1866–67.

COLLECTIONS: P. Berès, Paris. Cabinet des Dessins of the Louvre, Paris (RF 29949).

65. SEATED WOMAN SEEN FRONT VIEW, 1860–63

$9\frac{3}{8} \times 5\frac{15}{16}$ inches—23,8 × 15,1 cm. Leaf paginated 54, removed from the *Carnet de jeunesse* in the Cabinet des Dessins of the Louvre. Pencil. Verso: an unidentified sketch.

(a) Seated woman, her hands joined and feet crossed; both costume and attitude have an oriental look.—(b) Right background: young man in a top hat holding a switch. The upper part of this page is smudged with rubbings, in reverse of our No. 54.

COLLECTIONS: Huguette Berès, Paris. Present owner unknown.

66. PAGE OF STUDIES, 1862–65

$8\frac{1}{4} \times 4\frac{7}{8}$ inches—21 × 12,3 cm. Page from a sketch-book. Pencil and pen on grayish-brown paper. Verso: No. 164.

(a) Beneath Gothic arches, a scene of reunion: a little girl flys into the arms of a woman; the latter is drawn twice. Cf. the painting Venturi No. 24.—(b) Lower left: woman standing, her dress reaching the ground; cf. the portrait of the artist's sister Marie, reproduced in the catalog of an exhibition at Lucien Blanc's gallery, Aix-en-Provence, 1953, No. 21.—(c) Upside down, pen drawing: head and shoulders of a man; cf. No. 654 (b). The same head is roughly sketched near the right edge of the page (ink smudged).

COLLECTIONS: Private collection, Paris. Jean Cailac, Paris. Private collection, Basel. A. Chappuis, Tresserve.

67. PAGE OF STUDIES, INCLUDING A SEATED WOMAN; pencil, 1857–58; pen, 1865–67

$5\frac{7}{8} \times 9\frac{1}{16}$ inches—15 × 23 cm. Page 10 of the *Carnet de jeunesse* in the Cabinet des Dessins. Pencil and pen. Verso: No. 246.

Page of studies comprising more than twenty pencil sketches of heads or half-length figures. The most important: (a) Top left: boy sitting on a stone, leaning on his elbow and holding his head. This pose is to be repeated frequently by the artist; cf. Venturi No. 109.—(b) Toward the top right corner: head, having some resemblance to Achille Emperaire (but Cézanne did not meet Emperaire until after 1861, in Paris).—(c) Page upright: man with a goatee.—(d) Pen drawing, over the pencil drawings: woman in a large hat sitting in an armchair; cf. No. 151.

BIBLIOGRAPHY: Berthold, p. 155 (not reproduced), text p. 45. W. V. Andersen, Cézanne's Portrait Drawings from the 1860's, *Master Drawings*, Vol. 5, No. 3, 1967 (reproduced p. 270).

COLLECTIONS: P. Berès, Paris. Cabinet des Dessins of the Louvre, Paris (RF 29949).

68. THE PRISONER, 1865–67

$9\frac{1}{16} \times 5\frac{7}{8}$ inches—23 × 15 cm. Page 40 of the *Carnet de jeunesse* in the Cabinet des Dessins. Pen and pencil on brown paper, stains. Verso: No. 29.

(a) Pen: in the center of the page a bearded man is leading another man away prisoner, holding him by the wrist. A man and woman in the background follow them; indications of buildings. Cf. Nos. 7, 49, 70, 71.—(b) Pencil: head of a man wearing a cap—sketch anterior to (a).

BIBLIOGRAPHY: Berthold, p. 158 (reproduced Abb. 70), text p. 45.

COLLECTIONS: P. Berès, Paris. Cabinet des Dessins of the Louvre, Paris (RF 29949).

69. STUDIES; pencil 1857–58, pen 1865–67

$9\frac{1}{16} \times 5\frac{7}{8}$ inches—23 × 15 cm. Page 24 of the *Carnet de jeunesse* in the Cabinet des Dessins. Pencil and pen. Verso: No. 45.

(a) Pencil: struggle between three men, two against one. The man in the middle is being seized from front and back.—(b) Pen: three studies of a man who is leading another (see No. 68 for the complete scene.) The artist evidently intended to express the man's apprehension; the drawing is admirable.—(c) At right angles: faint pencil sketch of a face in left three-quarter view.

COLLECTIONS: P. Berès, Paris. Cabinet des Dessins of the Louvre, Paris (RF 29949).

70. THE PRISONER, 1865–67

$9\frac{1}{16} \times 5\frac{7}{8}$ inches—23 × 15 cm. Page 47 of the *Carnet de jeunesse* in the Cabinet des Dessins. Pencil, pen strokes, ink stains; light-brown paper. Verso: No. 52.

(a) Page upright: prisoner being led away; same subject as No. 68.—(b) Page lengthwise: study of the same subject, but the prisoner is on the left.—(c) Between (a) and (b): light sketch of a woman, hiding her face.

BIBLIOGRAPHY: Berthold, p. 158 (not reproduced).

COLLECTIONS: P. Berès, Paris. Cabinet des Dessins of the Louvre, Paris (RF 29949).

71. TWO STUDIES, 1865–67

$5\frac{7}{8} \times 9\frac{1}{16}$ inches—15 × 23 cm. Page 44 verso of the *Carnet de jeunesse* in the Cabinet des Dessins. Pencil and pen, stains; on brown paper. Verso: a water-color.

(a) Pencil: a prisoner; same subject as No. 68.—(b) upside down: pen sketch of a figure (ink smudged).

BIBLIOGRAPHY: Berthold, p. 158 (not reproduced).

COLLECTIONS: P. Berès, Paris. Cabinet des Dessins of the Louvre, Paris (RF 29949).

72. PORTRAIT OF A FRIEND, 1862–65

$9\frac{1}{16} \times 5\frac{7}{8}$ inches—23×15 cm. Page 50 verso of the *Carnet de jeunesse* in the Cabinet des Dessins. Pencil on brown paper; stains of ink from the reverse side. Verso: No. 49.

The expression on the face seems slightly ironic, as in certain portraits by Gustave Courbet. On the left side this drawing presages the characteristic Cézanne treatment. The portrait no doubt represents one of the artist's friends, but his identity is unknown.

BIBLIOGRAPHY: Berthold, p. 159 (not reproduced).

COLLECTIONS: P. Berès, Paris. Cabinet des Dessins of the Louvre, Paris (RF 29949).

73. DRAWING FROM A PLASTER CAST OF AN ANTIQUE SACRED BUST; 1858-60

$22 \times 14\frac{3}{8}$ inches—$56 \times 36,5$ cm. Pencil on laid paper, several traces of folds, stains. Verso: No. 475 bis.

(a) Bust; the original has not been definitely identified. The drawing technique is timid, but precise: the contours first, the strokes then accentuated and shadows indicated by hatching; cf. our No. 74 and Venturi No. 6, in which the face presents certain analogies. It was perhaps for drawings of this kind, or for a painting done in a similar manner, that Cézanne won a second prize in 1859.—(b) Study of a foot on the same sheet, of which no photograph could be procured.

BIBLIOGRAPHY: Th. Reff, *AB*, June 1960 (reproduced); reference to Salomon Reinach, *Recueil de têtes antiques idéales ou idéalisées*, Paris, 1903, pls. 274 and 275.

COLLECTIONS: Mouradian & Vallotton, Paris. Present owner unknown.

74. DRAWING FROM A PLASTER CAST: FEMALE TORSO, circa 1860

Measurements not known. Pencil. Verso: blank page.

Copy of a plaster cast of an antique figure, probably belonging to the École des Beaux-Arts in Aix-en-Provence. Left: three-quarter view of a torso, academic drawing scrupulously executed; cf. No. 73. A number of individual sketches are drawn around the plaster cast, including a nude woman reclining at the foot of a tree, her legs stretched out toward the right; cf. Venturi No. 124 and our No. 199.

BIBLIOGRAPHY: Berthold, cat. No. 287. Rewald, *Cézanne et Zola*, Paris, 1939, fig. 4. Reff, *AB*, June 1960, p. 148, where he identifies the model as the plaster cast of a statue of Venus, citing Salomon Reinach, *Repertoire de la Statuaire grecque et romaine*, Paris, 1897, Vol. I, p. 336, and particularly No. 1405. He also mentions similar casts figuring in a catalog of plaster casts for sale at the Louvre, 1896.

COLLECTION: Present owner unknown.

75. MALE NUDE, 1862

$23\frac{5}{8} \times 15\frac{3}{8}$ inches—60×39 cm. Pencil. Verso: blank page with signature and date 1862.

Bearded nude model, his right hand leaning on a prop, his left hand on his right shoulder; cf. Nos. 76, 77, 78.

BIBLIOGRAPHY: J. Rewald, *Cézanne et Zola* (thesis), Paris, 1936 (reproduced fig. 8).

COLLECTION: Former joint reserve of the Musée Granet and the École des Beaux-Arts, Aix-en-Provence.

76. MALE NUDE, 1862

$24 \times 18\frac{1}{2}$ inches—61×47 cm. Pencil. Verso: signature and date 1862.

Bearded nude model, drawn at the Aix École des Beaux-Arts, which at that time was part of the Musée Granet; today they are separate. This drawing was discovered in the joint reserve in 1925. Other similar academy nudes: Nos. 73, 74, 75, 77, 78.

BIBLIOGRAPHY: Venturi, No. 1162. A. Neumeyer, *Cézanne Drawings*, New York, 1958, No. 1 (reproduced). Chiuji Ikegami, The Drawings of Paul Cézanne, *Bijutsushi*, No. 76, Tokyo, 1970, p. 129 (reproduced).

COLLECTION: Musée Granet, Aix-en-Provence.

77. MALE NUDE, 1862

$23\frac{5}{8} \times 15\frac{3}{8}$ inches—60×39 cm. Pencil. Verso: blank page with signature and date 1862.

Bearded nude model, his right hand gripping his left wrist; cf. Nos. 75, 76, 78.—(b) Study of an old man, seated. —(c) Head and forelegs of a cat.

BIBLIOGRAPHY: J. Rewald, *Cézanne et Zola* (thesis), Paris, 1936 (reproduced fig. 7).

COLLECTION: Former joint reserve of the Musée Granet and the École des Beaux-Arts, Aix-en-Provence.

78. MALE NUDE, 1862

$23\frac{3}{4} \times 15\frac{3}{8}$ inches—$60,3 \times 39$ cm. Pencil, heightened with crayon. Verso: blank page with the signature: P. Cézanne 1862.

(a) Back view of a standing man, leaning on a stick (not drawn) to hold the pose. The contour is continuous, while the limbs and planes of the body are modeled as though done from a plaster cast of the antique. Black crayon accents on the head are drawn more freely.—(b) Two caricatural sketches: heads of pigs, with some rhymes written in pencil, mostly effaced, though a few words are legible: "........ | *le choléra, ça* | .... | .... | *Dans la culotte il devait faire* | *Chacun sait ça*."—(c) Study of a woman in a bonnet, spinning.

BIBLIOGRAPHY: Venturi, No. 1627. *Dessins* 1957, No. 2 (reproduced). *The World of Cézanne* (reproduced p. 18).

EXHIBITIONS: Kunsthalle, Basel, 1936, No. 98. Wildenstein, London, 1939, No. 74.

COLLECTIONS: Henri Pontier, Aix-en-Provence. Gustave Coquiot, Paris. W. Walter, Paris. A. Chappuis, Tresserve. Private collection, Paris.

FIG. 6. Puget Room in the Louvre, after 1886. *(Photograph: Alinari-Giraudon, 1906)*

79. SEATED NUDE MODEL, SEEN BACK VIEW. Academy drawing, 1862–64

24 × 18⅛ inches—61 × 46 cm. Soft pencil on gray laid paper. Verso: blank page.

Back view of a male nude, seated. Study in modeling, the light coming from the left.

BIBLIOGRAPHY: Venturi No. 1170: "Traces of squaring in preparation for the study are visible under the drawing." This remark by Venturi seems to be incorrect: there are only the watermark lines and a fold.— *The World of Cézanne* (reproduced p. 19).

EXHIBITIONS: La Peinture française à Florence, Palazzo Pitti, Florence, 1945, No. 196.

COLLECTIONS: Egisto Fabbri, Florence. Duchessa Caffarelli, Florence.

80. MALE NUDE, 1862–64

18 × 11 inches—45,7 × 27,9 cm. Charcoal on gray paper. Verso: blank page.

Man standing, seen against a background of cross hatching, the light falling on him from the left. Probably the same model as No. 79, studied at the Académie Suisse. Right: sketch of a hand.

COLLECTIONS: Private collection, Paris. Sale, Hôtel Drouot, April 30, 1952, No. 11; buyer unknown. Sale,

Christie's, London, December 6, 1968, No. 11 (reproduced). Present owner unknown.

81. MAN LYING ON THE GROUND, 1862–65

8¹⁵⁄₁₆ × 11¾ inches—22,7 × 29,9 cm. Black crayon on laid paper, heavy stains. Watermark: MICHALLET. Top right: stamp of F. Koenigs. Verso: No. 205.

Male nude reclining at full length on his back. The head is in the foreground and the feet, stretched out into the background, stand out clearly against a screen of hatching. The fingers should be noticed. Cf. Nos. 95, 106, 113.

BIBLIOGRAPHY: Venturi No. 1167. H. R. Hoetink, *Franse Tekeningen uit de 19e Eeuw*, Rotterdam, 1969, No. 14 verso (reproduced); date 1867 69.

COLLECTIONS: F. Koenigs, Haarlem. Boymans-van Beuningen Museum, Rotterdam (Inv. F II 25).

82. ACADEMY STUDIES: TWO WOMEN, circa 1866

9⅛ × 12 inches—23 × 30,5 cm. Pencil, stains. Verso: blank page.

(a) Nude woman lying on her back, the nape of her neck against a cushion and her feet in the foreground. One notes a flaccid breast, somewhat ridiculous.—(b) Below (a) and upside down: clothed female model lying on her left side, her head resting against her hand. These studies are not too successful. Venturi suggests that they were drawn from nature and that Mme Cézanne was the model. This last supposition seems to me unwarranted.

BIBLIOGRAPHY: Venturi No. 1227. *Der Cicerone*, 1929 (reproduced p. 505). W. V. Andersen, Cézanne's Portrait Drawings from the 1860's, *Master Drawings*, Vol. 5, No. 3, 1967 (reproduced p. 274).

EXHIBITION: Von Ingres bis Picasso, J. B. Neumann, Munich, 1929, No. 10 (reproduced pl. 29 in the catalog).

COLLECTIONS: Meller, Budapest. Present owner unknown.

83. AFTER PUGET: *Perseus rescuing Andromeda*

$7\frac{7}{8} \times 4\frac{5}{16}$ inches—20 × 11 cm. Pencil. Verso: head of the young Paul, study defaced by childish scribbles (not classified).

After the marble by Pierre Puget, *Perseus rescuing Andromeda*, in the Louvre. See fig. 6. At one time there was also a plaster cast in the Trocadero. Cf. Nos. 84, 499; the latter is a study of the same subject, but done much later. Around the eye, a circle has been drawn by the artist's son.

BIBLIOGRAPHY: Venturi, Vol. I, p. 352, *Oeuvres Inédites*, (not reproduced). Berthold, cat. No. 125 (reproduced Abb. 76).

EXHIBITIONS: Pennsylvania Museum of Art, Philadelphia, 1934, No. 57. The Hague, 1956, No. 108 (reproduced; erroneously, with the description of our No. 499, Venturi No. 1445). Zurich, 1956 (same error). Munich, 1956 (same error). Belvedere, Vienna, 1961, No. 87. Aix-en-Provence, 1961, No. 42.

COLLECTIONS: Pierre Loeb, Paris. Weyhe Gallery, New York. Purrmann, Montagnola. Dr. R. Purrmann, Starnberg.

84. AFTER PUGET: ANDROMEDA, 1864–67

$7\frac{5}{16} \times 4\frac{15}{16}$ inches—18,5 × 12,5 cm. Pencil. Verso: blank page.

Study of the figure of Andromeda in Pierre Puget's marble *Perseus rescuing Andromeda*, in the Louvre. See fig. 6. Two other studies by Cézanne after this work are known, Nos. 83, 499.

COLLECTIONS: Cézanne *fils*, Paris. Galerie L. G. Baugin, Paris.

85. AFTER RAPHAEL: VENUS, 1866–69

$9\frac{7}{16} \times 6\frac{11}{16}$ inches—24 × 17 cm. Page from the sketchbook 18 × 24 cm. Pencil. Verso: blank page.

From Raphael's drawing, *Venus receiving from Psyche the flask containing water from the Styx*, in the Cabinet des Dessins of the Louvre. See fig. 7. Another copy, No. 480.

BIBLIOGRAPHY: Venturi No. 1450. Berthold, cat. No. 265 (reproduced). G. Rivière, *Le Maître Paul Cézanne*, Paris, 1923 (reproduced p. 151).

EXHIBITIONS: Aquarelles et Baignades de Cézanne, Galerie Renou & Colle, Paris, 1935. Orangerie, Paris, 1936, No. 165. Paul Cassirer, London, 1939, No. 4. Zurich, 1956, No. 169. Belvedere, Vienna, 1961, No. 92.

COLLECTIONS: Cézanne *fils*, Paris. Cassirer, Berlin. M. Feilchenfeldt, Zurich.

86. STUDY FOR *Afternoon in Naples*, 1862–65

$5\frac{1}{4} \times 4$ inches—13,3 × 10,2 cm. Pencil, top of the sheet torn. Verso: blank page.

Study for the watercolor Venturi No. 820, or just a variant. In the center: the seated woman. At the feet of the servant: a large patterned vase and a cat. The woman's body is drawn with particular care; her pose and abundant hair should be remarked.

BIBLIOGRAPHY: Venturi No. 1177. Vollard 1914 (reproduced p. 60).

EXHIBITION: Munich, 1956, No. 117.

COLLECTION: Th. Werner, Berlin.

87. AFTER MICHELANGELO: SOLDIER AT BATHING PLACE, 1864–68

$2\frac{3}{4} \times 3\frac{15}{16}$ inches—7 × 10 cm. Pen, on laid paper. Verso: blank page.

Unfinished sketch, the ink browned with age, after an engraving by Marcantonio Raimondi called *The Climbers*, representing the soldiers in Michelangelo's cartoon *The*

FIG. 7. Raphael Sanzio (1483–1520): *Venus receiving from Psyche the flask containing water from the Styx*. See Apuleius, *The Metamorphoses*, Book VI, Chapter XVI. Drawing in the Cabinet des Dessins of the Louvre (RF 3875). Our title is not precisely the same as that of the fresco in the Farnesina. The drawing shows Psyche holding a transparent vase, not an opaque box; therefore it represents Psyche bringing back the crystalline *urnula* containing water from the Styx, not the *pyxis* containing the invisible gift of Proserpina.

FIG. 8. Marcantonio Raimondi (1475–1530): *The Climbers*, engraving (1510). Three male figures from Michelangelo's cartoon, *The Battle of Cascina*; the landscape is after Lucas van Leyden. 28,5 cm. × 22,5 cm. Bartsch 487; Passavant 254.
(Photograph: Bibliothèque Nationale, Paris)

Battle of Cascina. Near the soldier's arm a kind of hook-shaped form is the beginning of a gable. See fig. 8. Cf. Nos. 358, 359.

BIBLIOGRAPHY: Berthold, cat. No. 261 (reproduced).

COLLECTIONS: Private collection, Germany. A. Chappuis, Tresserve.

87bis. MAN AND HORSE, 1863–66

$6\frac{7}{8} \times 4\frac{3}{4}$ inches—17,5 × 12 cm. Pencil, numbers in ink. Verso: blank page.

(a) A man walking, and a horse with one foreleg raised in the pose of horses often seen on monuments. Confused sketch near the man's head.—(b) In ink: a few numbers and calculations.

COLLECTIONS: Dr. H. Thommen, Basel. Sale, Sotheby's, London, Dec. 3, 1970, No. 29 (reproduced). Mrs. Ehrmann.

88. HANDWRITING, HEAD OF A WOMAN, AND HORSE'S HEAD; horse; circa 1864; handwriting, circa 1874.

$6\frac{11}{16} \times 9\frac{7}{16}$ inches—17 × 24 cm. Page from the sketch-book 18 × 24 cm. Pencil. Verso: blank page.

Page covered with the rough draft of a letter in pencil; the writing is later than the sketches (a) and (b), which are underneath. The text of this draft has been published in the *Correspondance*, letter No. XXX, and a part of it in Vollard's book, 1914, pp. 33-34.—(a) Head of a horse; the sketch is remarkable in spite of its uncertain technique.

It calls to mind the knight of a chess set.—(b) In the center of the page, covered by the writing, an unfinished sketch: Mme Cézanne. It can be compared with No. 270, dated 1872–73.

BIBLIOGRAPHY: Venturi, Vol. I, p. 352, *Oeuvres Inédites* (not reproduced). *Correspondance* (reproduced fig. 20).

COLLECTIONS: Ambroise Vollard, Paris. Pierre Loeb, Paris. Barnes Foundation, Merion, Pennsylvania.

89. MAN ON HORSEBACK, SEEN BACK VIEW, 1863–65

$3\frac{9}{16} \times 4\frac{5}{16}$ inches—9 × 11 cm. Probably half a page from the sketchbook 10,3 × 17 cm; 89A would be on the reverse side of the other half. Pencil. Verso: formerly No. 89A, according to Venturi.

Fine, vigorous, though unfinished drawing which may well have been done from a *Man on Horseback* by Leonardo da Vinci, as Venturi suggests. The model has, however, not been definitely determined; it could also be by Rubens.

BIBLIOGRAPHY: Venturi, Vol. I, p. 349, *Oeuvres Inédites*: "Etudes (10 × 17 cm.). Recto: *Portrait de femme de Velasquez.* Verso: *Cavalier de Léonard.* Papier blanc." Berthold, cat. No. 339 (not reproduced).

COLLECTIONS: Kenneth Clark, London. Galerie Motte, Geneva. Present owner unknown.

89A. AFTER VELASQUEZ: PORTRAIT OF A WOMAN, date uncertain

$3\frac{15}{16} \times 3\frac{1}{4}$ inches (?)—10 × 8 cm (?). Probably a half page from the sketchbook 10,3 × 17 cm. Pencil. Verso: formerly No. 89, according to Venturi.

This sketch is known only by Venturi's reference to it (see our No. 89, Bibliography).

BIBLIOGRAPHY: Venturi, Vol. I, p. 349, *Oeuvres Inédites* (not reproduced).

COLLECTIONS: Kenneth Clark, London. Present owner unknown.

90. TWO MEN, AND WOMAN DANCER, 1861–65

$4\frac{1}{2} \times 8$ inches—11,5 × 20,3 cm. Page 24 from a sketchbook. Pencil and pen; ink sketch from verso seen in transparency.

(a) Left, in pencil: a man bends over another man lying down in front of him. Probably a detail copied from a painting or engraving.—(b) Right, pen drawing: woman dancer standing with her arms outstretched.

COLLECTIONS: Cézanne *fils*, Paris. Jean-Pierre Cézanne, Paris. Private collection, Paris. Sale, Parke-Bernet, New York, December 13, 1967, No. 4. Samuel J. Lefrak, Forest Hills, N.Y.

91. ARTIST, HIS BACK TURNED, 1864–65

$9 \times 6\frac{15}{16}$ inches—22,9 × 17,7 cm. Page from the sketch-book 18 × 24 cm. Black crayon, corners damaged. Verso: No. 175.

Back view of a young painter in a studio, his shoulder hidden by a canvas standing at a diagonal; the perspective at the base of the canvas has been corrected. The artist is seated, one foot resting on the rung of a stool covered with papers. Probably the sketch of one of Cézanne's fellow-students at the Academy.

BIBLIOGRAPHY: Venturi, Vol. I, p. 351, *Oeuvres Inédites* (not reproduced). Basel catalog, No. 7 (reproduced). Douglas Cooper, in *Master Drawings*, Vol. 1, No. 4, 1963, p. 55; date 1864–65.

COLLECTIONS: Cézanne *fils*, Paris. W. Feuz, Bern. Kunstmuseum, Basel.

92. WOMAN SITTING ON A BENCH, 1864–65

$9 \times 6\frac{15}{16}$ inches—22,8 × 17,6 cm. Page from the sketchbook 18 × 24 cm. Colored crayons and black crayon, pen and ink on brown drawing paper glued to cardboard, traces of framing. Verso: blank page.

Young woman seen in lost profile, seated, knitting, with a ball of wool on the bench beside her. To the left and right of her head: zigzag lines, in ink.—Top right: study of a head in a cocked hat, some strokes red. There is some doubt as to the authenticity of this work. The leaf is from the sketchbook 18 × 24 cm., and a counterproof of this drawing is on the back of No. 142; if it is not by Cézanne, another artist must have borrowed the sketchbook. Although the colors are flat, the drawing cannot be definitely rejected.

BIBLIOGRAPHY: Venturi, Vol. I, p. 351, *Oeuvres Inédites* (not reproduced). Basel catalog, No. 10 (reproduced).

COLLECTIONS: Cézanne *fils*, Paris. W. Feuz, Bern. Kunstmuseum, Basel.

93. MALE NUDE, 1862–65

$19\frac{3}{4} \times 13\frac{3}{8}$ inches—50,2 × 34 cm. Charcoal. Verso: blank page.

(a) Study, probably done at the Académie Suisse in Paris. Seated model, his head held high. The stumping of the shadows is less pronounced than in No. 111.—(b) Top right: head with a prominent chin.

BIBLIOGRAPHY: Rewald, *History of Impressionism*, New York, 1946, p. 54 (reproduced); New York, 1961, p. 62 "Study of a Negro Model" (reproduced).

COLLECTION: Present owner unknown.

94. MALE NUDE, 1863–66

$11\frac{1}{4} \times 7\frac{1}{2}$ inches—28,5 × 19 cm. Charcoal, paper torn on the left through the calf of the leg. Verso: blank page.

(a) Man standing, leaning to the right, his hands clasping a model's prop. Two parallel horizontal strokes between his chin and underarm.—(b) In the background: study of drapery.

BIBLIOGRAPHY: Venturi No. 1168. André Salmon, Dessins inédits de Cézanne, *Cahiers d'Art*, Paris, 1926 (reproduced p. 263).

COLLECTIONS: Cézanne *fils*, Paris. Ch. Viau, Paris; Sale, Coll. Ch Viau, Paris, May 21, 1931, No. 35 (reproduced). Present owner unknown.

95. RECLINING MALE NUDE, BACK VIEW, 1863–65.

Measurements unknown. Charcoal on laid paper, stains. Verso: blank page.

Man lying on his left side, leaning on one elbow. Academy pose; indications of prop. Cf. No. 261.

BIBLIOGRAPHY: Venturi No. 1164. André Salmon, Dessins inédits de Cézanne, *Cahiers d'Art*, Paris, 1926 (reproduced p. 266).

COLLECTIONS: Cézanne *fils*, Paris. Present owner unknown.

96. STUDY OF NUDES DIVING, 1863–66

$7\frac{1}{16} \times 10\frac{5}{8}$ inches—18 × 27 cm. Pencil on yellowish paper: the background washed with white (this white is perhaps not by the hand of Cézanne). The reverse side is inaccessible.

Two nude men lying on the ground, their arms stretched forward like bathers diving. Top left: repetition of eyes and nose. Cf. Venturi No. 818, a small watercolor entitled La Chute d'Icare *(The Fall of Icarus)*, also our No. 258 and the watercolor Venturi No. 1615. On the yellow paper the bodies stand out against a background washed with white. This drawing is conspicuous among others of the same period for its original research into volume and for certain strokes which presage the artist's future evolution. The fact that this study remained in Cézanne's possession would seem to indicate that it had particular value for him.

BIBLIOGRAPHY: Neumeyer No. 12 (reproduced). Longstreet 1964 (reproduced).

COLLECTIONS: Kraushaar Galleries, New York. Arthur B. Davies. Los Angeles County Museum of Art (The Mr. and Mrs. William Preston Harrison Collection, No. A.809.37-173).

97. MALE NUDE, 1863–66

$19\frac{1}{4} \times 12\frac{3}{16}$ inches—49 × 31 cm. Charcoal on laid paper. Verso: No. 98.

The same model as seen in Nos. 98 and 99, drawn with a certain boldness. The head seems too big; a correction indicates better proportions. The right elbow can be seen behind the curve of the buttocks.

BIBLIOGRAPHY: Rewald, *The Ordeal of Paul Cézanne*, London, 1950 (reproduced).

COLLECTIONS: Mouradian & Vallotton, Paris. Private collection, Paris.

98. MALE NUDE, 1863–66

$19\frac{1}{4} \times 12\frac{3}{16}$ inches—49 × 31 cm. Charcoal on laid paper, traces of a fold. Verso: No. 97.

Study of a nude; man standing, probably a model at the Académie Suisse. Cf. the studies Nos. 97 and 99 and others of the same nature. Although the drawing No. 99 is more complete, it is nevertheless possible that the present one came later. The multiplicity of lines modeling the body and establishing the planes should be noted.

BIBLIOGRAPHY: Rewald, *The Ordeal of Paul Cézanne*, London, 1950 (reproduced). Idem, *History of Impressionism*, New York, 1961 (reproduced p. 62).

COLLECTIONS: Mouradian & Vallotton, Paris. Private collection, Paris.

FIG. 9. Peter Paul Rubens (1577–1640): *L'apothéose de Henri IV et la Régence de Marie de Médicis*, one of the Medici series painted between 1622 and 1625, now in the Louvre. Our illustration shows the left part of the canvas. Oil, 3,94 m. × 7,27 m. Musée National du Louvre, *Catalogue des Peintures* III, 1922, No. 2095. *(Photograph: Giraudon)*

99. MALE NUDE, 1863–66

$19\frac{1}{4} \times 12\frac{3}{16}$ inches—49 × 31 cm. Charcoal heightened with white, on laid paper. Verso: blank page.

The same model as seen in Nos. 97 and 98, his hand gripping a prop just above his thigh. The light coming from the left creates marked contrasts and the highlights are emphasized; in places there are rubbings covered by hatching.

COLLECTION: Fitzwilliam Museum, Cambridge, England (Inv. PD. 55-1961).

100. MALE NUDE, LEANING ON HIS ELBOW, 1863–66

$12\frac{3}{16} \times 15\frac{3}{4}$ inches—31 × 40 cm. Soft black pencil on thin blue paper. Verso: blank page.

The model is lifting himself slightly by the arms, with the help of supports. The play of contrasts from black to light gray on the blue paper should be mentioned.

BIBLIOGRAPHY: Venturi, Vol. I, p. 347, *Oeuvres Inédites* (not reproduced). Chuji Ikegami, The Drawings of Paul Cézanne, *Bijutsushi*, No. 76, Tokyo, 1970 (reproduced pl. IIa).

COLLECTIONS: Dr. Gachet, Auvers. Paul Gachet, Auvers. Bridgestone Gallery, Tokyo.

101. SEATED NUDE MODEL LEANING ON HIS ELBOW, circa 1863

$11\frac{13}{16} \times 17\frac{3}{4}$ inches—30 × 45 cm. Black crayon on blue paper. Verso: blank page.

Young nude model, leaning on his left elbow, his right foot tucked under his left thigh; cf. No. 100.

BIBLIOGRAPHY: Venturi No. 1165. Vollard, 1914 (reproduced p. 5).

COLLECTIONS: Dr. Gachet, Auvers. Paul Gachet, Auvers (No. 32 of the manuscript catalog). James Lord, New York. J. K. Thannhauser, New York.

102. AFTER RUBENS: DETAIL OF *The Apotheosis of King Henri IV*, 1864–65

15$\frac{15}{16}$ × 11$\frac{13}{16}$ inches—40,5 × 30 cm. Pencil; lower right: stamp of the Rignault collection (Lugt 2218), as on Nos. 155, 422. Verso: page blank, except for the date 1865 by an alien hand.

Copy of the group on the left side of Rubens' painting *The Apotheosis of King Henri IV* in the Louvre. See fig. 9. Henri IV is lifted up to heaven by an old man (allegorical figure of Time) and the eagle of Jupiter. Jupiter welcomes him, holding him by the elbow. The purpose of this copy was to create a fine drawing. It is Cézanne's only study of this part of the painting, though all through his life he studied the central figure of Bellona. At the bottom of the page are the words: "This drawing was given to me by Paul Cézanne in 1865, [signed] Jacomin."

COLLECTIONS: Jacomin, Paris. Joseph Rignault, Avignon. Budot Lamotte, Paris. Sale, Hôtel Drouot (Maître Bellier, Room 9), Paris, June 5, 1953, No. 1. Private collection, Paris. P. Nathan, Zurich.

103. MALE NUDE, BACK VIEW, 1863–65

9$\frac{1}{16}$ × 6$\frac{11}{16}$ inches—23 × 17 cm. Page from the sketchbook 18 × 24 cm. Pencil. Verso: blank page.

(a) Back of a nude male model, his hands crossed on his head. Academy pose.—(b) Left: a foot.—(c) Shoulder and right arm.

BIBLIOGRAPHY: Venturi No. 1163. Berthold (reproduced Abb. 74), text p. 46, dated 1866–67. A. Neumeyer, 1958, No. 2 (reproduced).

EXHIBITIONS: The Hague, 1956, No. 92. Zurich, 1956, No. 145. Munich, 1956, No. 111.

COLLECTIONS: Sale, Bollag, Zurich, April 3, 1925, No. 34 (reproduced pl. XV). Jon Nicholas Streep, New York. Hammer Galleries, New York.

104. MALE NUDE, circa 1865

11$\frac{3}{8}$ × 9$\frac{13}{16}$ inches—28,9 × 24,9 cm. Charcoal and gouache on thick brownish paper, brown stain. Verso: No. 227.

(a) Male model seen from the thighs up, his left arm raised and elbow bent. Vigorous strokes; white is combined with the charcoal.—(b) Top left: roughly sketched little figure of a man near a building; cf. No. 323 (a) for the figure. Probably drawn at the Académie Suisse.

BIBLIOGRAPHY: Venturi No. 1584. Basel catalog No. 18 (reproduced).

COLLECTIONS: Cézanne *fils*, Paris. W. Feuz, Bern. Kunstmuseum, Basel.

105. STUDIES OF NUDES, 1867–68

16$\frac{1}{4}$ × 11$\frac{3}{4}$ inches—41,3 × 29,9 cm. Charcoal and pencil on gray-brown laid paper. Watermark: D & C BLAUW. Verso: No. 112.

(a) Lower half of page: study more detailed than the others, a figure and its shadow. A pencil line (not by Cézanne) separates this half from the upper part of the page; for the inscriptions, see Note 25.—(b) Upper left: model tugging at a rope.—(c) Model with his back turned and arms raised.—(d) Model in profile. Two rough sketches.

BIBLIOGRAPHY: Venturi, Vol. I, as verso of No. 1589 (not reproduced). Berthold, text p. 45 (not reproduced). Basel catalog No. 19 (reproduced). Chiuji Ikegami, The Drawings of Paul Cézanne, *Bijutsushi*, No. 76, Tokyo, 1970 (detail reproduced p. 133).

COLLECTIONS: Cézanne *fils*, Paris. W. Feuz, Bern. Kunstmuseum, Basel.

106. MALE NUDE LYING ON HIS BACK, 1865–67

Measurements not known. Charcoal on laid paper. Verso: blank page.

Male nude lying on his back, his face toward the background. The diagonal strokes under the chin and the drawing of the feet should be noted. The artist has added a man fleeing, like a felon, up a staircase seen through an arch. For the staircase, cf. No. 176 (e).

BIBLIOGRAPHY: Venturi No. 1166. André Salmon, *Cahiers d'Art*, Paris, 1926 (reproduced p. 264).

COLLECTIONS: Cézanne *fils*, Paris. Present owner unknown.

107. ACADEMY STUDIES: FEET AND KNEES, 1864–69

12$\frac{3}{16}$ × 18$\frac{7}{8}$ inches—31 × 48 cm. Black crayon on ordinary paper, stains on the lower edge of the page. Verso: blank page.

(a) Top: right foot of a man lying on his back; a shadow indicates the ground.—(b) Below: study of a foot, the sole foreshortened.—(c) Near to (b): study of a leg.—(d) Above: study of a knee slightly bent; attempt at modeling.—(e) Above: same subject. Cf. Nos. 104, 106.

EXHIBITION: Kunsthalle, Basel, 1936, No. 104.

COLLECTIONS: Ambroise Vollard, Paris. W. Walter, Paris. Present owner unknown.

108. ACADEMY STUDIES: HEAD AND KNEES, 1864–69

12$\frac{1}{4}$ × 18$\frac{13}{16}$ inches—31,2 × 47,9 cm. Black crayon on laid paper, lower left corner of the paper missing. Verso: blank page.

(a) Left: head of a man lying on his back; the ear is characteristic of Cézanne.—(b) Top right: knee and calf.—(c) Below: a knee. Cf. Nos. 107, 109, 110.

EXHIBITION: Kunsthalle, Basel, 1936, No. 103. Europäische Meisterwerke aus Schweizer Sammlungen, Munich, 1969, No. 23 (reproduced Abb. 20); cited in *Critica d'Arte*, fasc. 110, repr. p. 59 (article on Munich exhibition).

COLLECTIONS: Ambroise Vollard, Paris. A. Hahnloser, Winterthur. H. Hahnloser, Bern.

109. STUDY OF A HEAD AND HANDS, 1867–69

$12\frac{3}{8} \times 19\frac{1}{4}$ inches—$31,5 \times 49$ cm. Charcoal on brown paper. Verso: blank page.

Head of a reclining man and two studies of a right hand for the painting Venturi No. 105. Drawn from the same model as No. 100, this page should be classified among the studies done at the Académie Suisse. Venturi and Neumeyer consider it to be a portrait of Emperaire, but the nose and eyes lack the nobility and sensitivity of Emperaire's, and it is the head of a vigorous man, not a cripple.

BIBLIOGRAPHY: Venturi No. 1193. Meier-Graefe, *Cézanne und sein Kreis*, Munich, 1922 (reproduced p. 90). *Der Cicerone*, 1929 (reproduced p. 675). A. Neumeyer, 1958, No. 26 (reproduced). *Art Lover Library*, Gal. Günther Franke, Munich & New York, III, 22.

EXHIBITIONS: Art Institute, Chicago, and Metropolitan Museum of Art, New York, 1952, No. 9 (reproduced).

COLLECTIONS: David Lederer, Berlin; D. Lederer sale, Berlin, October 25, 1925, No. 225 (reproduced). Paul Franke, Munich. Elvira B. Reilly, New York.

110. MALE NUDE, circa 1865

$12\frac{3}{16} \times 18\frac{11}{16}$ inches—$31 \times 47,5$ cm. Charcoal on light-brown paper. Oil stains. Verso: blank page.

(a) Detailed study of a male model sitting with his back against a wall, his feet seen in perspective. Study for the painting *The Autopsy*, Venturi No. 105, and probably drawn at the Académie Suisse.—(b) Top: contours of knees, sketched several times; cf. No. 107.—(c) Name of the model: Pierre . . . (illegible) and handwritten address.

BIBLIOGRAPHY: Rewald, *Paul Cézanne*. New York, 1948, (reproduced fig. 13). Idem, *The Ordeal of Paul Cézanne*, London, 1950, (reproduced fig. 3). Idem, *History of Impressionism*, New York, 1961 (reproduced p. 63). Idem, *Paul Cézanne*, Spring Books, London, 1959 and 1965 (reproduced fig. 3). A. Neumeyer, 1958, No. 4 (reproduced). *Dessins*, 1957, No. 3 (reproduced). Yvon Taillandier, *Paul Cézanne*, Paris, New York, Munich, 1961 and 1965 (reproduced p. 14). Longstreet, 1964 (reproduced). *The World of Cézanne* (reproduced p. 24). Chiuji Ikegami, The Drawings of Paul Cézanne, *Bijutsushi*, No. 76, Tokyo, 1970 (reproduced p. 132).

EXHIBITION: Phillips Collection, Washington D.C., Chicago, Boston, 1971, No. 65 (reproduced).

COLLECTIONS: Mrs. Benny Goodman. Maynard Walker Gallery. Art Institute of Chicago, Gift of Tiffany and Margaret Blake.

111. MALE NUDE AND CARICATURE, 1863–66

$19\frac{11}{16} \times 11\frac{13}{16}$ inches—50×30 cm. Charcoal on white paper. Verso: blank page.

(a) Standing male nude, strong shadows; probably drawn at the Académie Suisse. See No. 112 for another study of the same pose.—(b) Caricature of a man with side whiskers, wearing glasses. In derision, the artist depicts him on a pedestal.

BIBLIOGRAPHY: Rewald, *History of Impressionism*, New York, 1961 (reproduced p. 62). Basel catalog (reproduced fig. 38).

COLLECTIONS: Cézanne *fils*, Paris. Galerie Moos, Geneva. Sale, Galerie Motte, Geneva, May 11, 1957, No. 101 (reproduced), mistakenly described as Venturi No. 1584. Private collection, New York.

112. MALE NUDE, 1867–68

$16\frac{1}{4} \times 11\frac{3}{4}$ inches—$41,3 \times 29,9$ cm. Charcoal on gray-brown laid paper with the watermark D & C BLAUW. At the top edge three white reference marks. Verso: No. 105.

Male nude, drawn from the thighs up. The head, relatively large, is turned away. Lower edge, upside down: rough sketch of the neck and chest. Cf. No. 111.

BIBLIOGRAPHY: Venturi No. 1589, dated 1885–92. Basel catalog, No. 110 (reproduced), dated 1884–90. Douglas Cooper, in *Master Drawings*, Vol 1, No. 4, 1963, p. 56, dated 1867–68.

COLLECTIONS: Cézanne *fils*, Paris. W. Feuz, Bern. Kunstmuseum, Basel.

113. MAN LYING DOWN, 1865–70

$7\frac{5}{16} \times 8\frac{7}{8}$ inches—$18,5 \times 22,5$ cm. Soft pencil *(gros crayon)* on gray paper. Verso: blank page.

Man asleep on his back, one arm under his neck and the other across his eyes, a hat on his stomach. Venturi calls this drawing *Workman Asleep*, and it calls to mind the subject of *The Harvesters*, Venturi Nos. 874, 1517.

BIBLIOGRAPHY: Venturi No. 1169. Vollard, 1914 (reproduced p. 185). Meier-Graefe, *Cézanne und sein Kreis*, Munich, 1922 (reproduced p. 46). Ikouma Arishima, Cézanne, *Ars*, 1926 (reproduced p. 43).

COLLECTIONS: H. Müller, Basel. Emile Dreyfus, Basel. Haeberli, Basel. Dr. E. Dreyfus Foundation, Kunstmuseum, Basel.

114. VAULT IN A LANDSCAPE, 1859–60

$9\frac{1}{16} \times 5\frac{7}{8}$ inches—23×15 cm. Page 49 verso of the *Carnet de jeunesse* in the Cabinet des Dessins. Pencil on pale brown paper; ink which has seeped through from overleaf disfigures the sketch. Verso: No. 50.

In the foreground of this sketch (which is earlier than the one overleaf) there is a hewn-stone vault with the date 1620 on the keystone, written in a way which integrates poorly with the drawing; a few trees in the background, seen through the arch. An early example of compositions in the form of a vault, ogive, or pyramid, much favored by Cézanne.

BIBLIOGRAPHY: Berthold, p. 158 (not reproduced).

COLLECTIONS: P. Berès, Paris. Cabinet des Dessins of the Louvre, Paris (RF 29949).

115. STUDY OF A LANDSCAPE, WITH A SMOKESTACK AND SMALL TOWER, 1859–60

$6\frac{5}{8} \times 9$ inches—$16,8 \times 22,8$ cm. Page XXI from an early sketchbook. Soft pencil. Verso: No. 40.

Study showing in the distance a small pointed tower and a smokestack beyond steep-banked promontories rising out of a stretch of water, with a wooded hill far away on the right. The three successive tongues of land should be noticed.

BIBLIOGRAPHY: Catalog W. H. Schab, New York, 1964, *Graphic Arts of Five Centuries*, verso of No. 130.

COLLECTIONS: W. H. Schab, New York. Private collection, Switzerland.

116. NUDE FIGURES IN A LANDSCAPE, 1864–67

Measurements unknown. Pencil.

Landscape with trees and a path in the center leading back toward a river, its banks running horizontally, with a low hill behind. The path leads to a kind of pond and an open area seen in diamond-shaped perspective. The two couples in the foreground recall the subject of *An Afternoon in Naples*. For the man on the left, cf. the pen sketch No. 979, and for the woman on the left, the woman-faun of No. 48. The woman on the right imitates the pose of the *Crouching Venus*.

BIBLIOGRAPHY: Venturi No. 1266. Vollard, 1914 (reproduced p. 167).

COLLECTIONS: Ambroise Vollard, Paris. Present owner unknown.

117. PAGE OF STUDIES, INCLUDING A BRIDGE, AND A DETAIL AFTER DELACROIX, 1864–67

$7\frac{1}{16} \times 9\frac{7}{16}$ inches—18 × 24 cm. Page from the sketchbook 18 × 24 cm. Black crayon, heavy stains from the reverse side, No. 131.

River scene with a bridge, and a boat with a smokestack in the foreground; in the distance a tower on a hill. There is a curious similarity between this sketch and Daubigny's painting *The Ferry* (reproduced in *History of Impressionism* by John Rewald, New York, 1961, p. 103).—(b) At right angles: man in a cap, sitting down.—(c) Upside down: studies from *The Abduction of Rebecca* by Eugène Delacroix (1846). See fig. 10. Cézanne probably drew these from a photograph, or one of the reproductions cited by Robaut 974 and *Le Memorial* 355, making a study of the head and arm of the horseman carrying off Rebecca, as well as of her hand. The subject is taken from Walter Scott's novel *Ivanhoe*.—(d) Same subject, more complete, with Rebecca's left arm. Beside it: her right forearm and left thumb.

BIBLIOGRAPHY: *Cézanne dessinateur* ((c) and (d) reproduced fig. 21).

COLLECTIONS: Mouradian & Vallotton, Paris. Present owner unknown.

118. TREE AND HOUSE, 1867–70

$5\frac{7}{8} \times 7\frac{1}{16}$ inches—14,9 × 18 cm. Soft pencil on white writing paper with blue lines glued to thick cardboard. Paper torn top left, and small hole at top right; fold in the center, gray stains. Reverse side inaccessible.

Tree in the form of a curve, its foliage stretching out to the right; the trunk is duplicated. In the background, a house with three front windows. A curious tension pervades this very simple sketch.

BIBLIOGRAPHY: Venturi, Vol. I, p. 351, *Oeuvres Inédites*: "Tronc de chêne. Maison au loin" (not reproduced). Basel catalog No. 47 (reproduced).

COLLECTIONS: Cézanne *fils*, Paris. W. Feuz, Bern. Kunstmuseum, Basel.

FIG. 10. Eugène Delacroix (1799–1863): *Rebecca enlevée par les ordres du templier Boisguilbert*, episode during the sack of the Château de Front de Boeuf. "She is already in the hands of two African slaves ordered to conduct her away from the scene of battle." (From Walter Scott, *Ivanhoe*.) Detail of the canvas, 100 cm. × 82 cm., exhibited in the Salon of 1846. The Metropolitan Museum of Art, New York. No. 355 of the *Mémorial de l'exposition Delacroix* by M. Sérullaz, Paris, 1963; No. 498 describes a version of the same subject in the Louvre, painted in 1858.   (*Photograph: Archives photographiques, Paris*)

119. STUDY OF A LANDSCAPE, COVERED BY A CHILD'S DRAWINGS, 1867–70

$9\frac{1}{8} \times 6\frac{7}{8}$ inches—23,1 × 17,5 cm. Page from the sketchbook 18 × 24 cm. Pencil, lower left an embossed stamp: RERES. Verso: No. 323.

Covered by childish scribbles spread over the whole page: a landscape study by Cézanne. On the lower right a winding road is indicated; the hatching on both sides, the tree, and further off, a mountain are not by the child. Probably a landscape at L'Estaque. (We reproduce only the part sketched by Cézanne).

BIBLIOGRAPHY: Venturi, Vol. I, as verso of No. 1189 (not reproduced). Basel catalog No. 84 (full-page reproduction).

COLLECTIONS: Cézanne *fils*, Paris. W. Feuz, Bern. Kunstmuseum, Basel.

120. THE RAILWAY CUTTING, circa 1870

$5\frac{1}{2} \times 9\frac{1}{16}$ inches—14 × 23 cm. Pencil and pen. Verso: blank page.

Landscape, preliminary study for the small canvas Venturi No. 42 and *La Tranchée* (the railway cutting) in the Munich Museum, Venturi No. 50; the latter, however, is painted from a different spot. The landscape, not far from the Jas de Bouffan, remained unchanged until until about 1960; see the photograph in *Le Point*, August

1936, p. 5. In the center are seen the hut and two railway signals (one of them, a red disc, looks like a tree on the drawing). The accents in ink are audacious. In this rather harsh sketch there is a kind of grandeur which surpasses contemporary conceptions.

BIBLIOGRAPHY: Venturi No. 1205. Vollard, 1914, p. 168 (reproduced pl. 55). F. Novotny, *Cézanne und das Ende der wissenschaftlichen Perspektive*, Vienna, 1938, p. 200, No. 63 (not reproduced). B. Dorival, *Cézanne*, Paris, 1948 (reproduced p. 94).

COLLECTIONS: Cézanne *fils*, Paris. Ambroise Vollard, Paris. Present owner unknown.

121. LANDSCAPE AT L'ESTAQUE, 1870–72

$9\frac{7}{16} \times 12\frac{5}{8}$ inches—24 × 32 cm. Pencil. Verso: No. 238.

Like a number of other sketches of the same period, this landscape at L'Estaque is drawn on the back of a decorative etching; it is a study for the canvas Venturi No. 407. It should be noted that Cézanne has sacrificed a small part of the house in the center for the sake of the composition, a procedure he adopted often later, mainly in his paintings.

BIBLIOGRAPHY: Neumeyer, 1958, No. 64 (reproduced).

COLLECTIONS: Private collection, Berlin. Ottinger, New York. Sale, Christie's, London, December 16, 1938, No. 56. Hugo Perls. James Lord, New York. J. K. Thannhauser, New York. The Art Institute, Chicago.

122. L'ESTAQUE, 1870–73

15 × 15 inches—38 × 38 cm. Pencil on laid paper, various stains, smudges, flyspecks; vertical folds on the left and to the right, lower edge torn. Verso: an engraving.

Each trunk of a group of trees in the foreground is seen separately, the foliage in a single mass. The planes and angles of two buildings in the middleground can be distinguished but the ensemble seems muddled. A wide screen of trees spreads out in front of the sea, of which a restricted view is visible extending down to the top of the house. Originally this drawing was on the right side of a large page, the left side comprising numerous stains and large areas of hatching.

BIBLIOGRAPHY: Venturi No. 1570. André Salmon, *Cahiers d'Art*, Paris, 1926, p. 263 (reproduced). Idem, *Der Querschnitt*, Berlin, 1927.

EXHIBITION: Fujiyama Collection, Tôyoko Gallery, Tokyo, 1962 (reproduced).

COLLECTIONS: Cézanne *fils*, Paris. Mouradian & Vallotton, Paris. Private collection, U.S.A. Aiichiro Fujiyama, Tokyo.

123. LANDSCAPE WITH POPLAR TREE, 1873–76

$11\frac{7}{16} \times 6\frac{1}{2}$ inches—26,5 × 16,5 cm. Pencil. Verso: blank page.

A poplar tree standing proudly erect and beyond it a stretch of plain on several levels. A characteristic little tree and its shadow, marking the distance, should be noted.

EXHIBITIONS: Quatre-Chemins, Paris, 1936.

COLLECTIONS: W. Walter, Paris. Present owner unknown.

124. BELLEVUE, NEAR AIX, 1870–73

$8\frac{11}{16} \times 6\frac{5}{16}$ inches—22 × 16 cm. Probably a page from the sketchbook 18 × 24 cm. Black crayon on brown paper, touches of white effaced and almost invisible. Reverse side inaccessible.

The top part of the house *Bellevue* in profile against the sky. Half hidden by trees, the wall of the house seems almost white in spite of the brown paper. Cf. two sketches of the same subject, Nos. 900, 901, both drawn later. At first sight this drawing appears to be a study for the painting Venturi No. 412, but it may well be that this motif attracted Cézanne's interest as early as 1870, and that other studies prior to Venturi No. 412 have been lost.

BIBLIOGRAPHY: Venturi No. 1508. A. Salmon, *Cahiers d'Art*, Paris, 1926, p. 263 (reproduced). Idem, *Der Querschnitt*, Berlin, 1927. F. Novotny, *Cézanne und das Ende der wissenschaftlichen Perspektive*, Vienna, 1938, p. 202, No. 74 (not reproduced).

COLLECTIONS: Cézanne *fils*, Paris. Galerie Baugin, Paris. Chr. Bernoulli, Basel. Private collection, Basel.

124A. L'ESTAQUE, 1872–73

Measurements unknown. Black crayon.

Speaking of the years 1872 and 1873, Paul Gachet said: "Van Ryssel had just made an engraving of the fine black crayon drawing of *L'Estaque* which Cézanne had brought him." Today Cézanne's drawing is not known, but we reproduce here the etching done by Van Ryssel (Dr. Gachet) after Cézanne. The etching is dated 1873. See fig. 11. Robert Ratcliffe observes that the etching does not reverse the drawing, judging by the light which must be that of early morning; cf. Venturi No. 411.

BIBLIOGRAPHY: Paul Gachet, *Cézanne à Auvers, Cézanne Graveur*, Les Beaux-Arts, Paris, 1952, brochure with no pagination.

COLLECTIONS: Dr. Gachet, Auvers. Present owner unknown.

FIG. 11. *Vue de L'Estaque,* etching by P. Van Ryssel (Dr. Gachet) after a black crayon drawing by Paul Cézanne. Signed lower right and dated 1873. In the upper left corner is a duck, Dr. Gachet's signature-emblem.

(Photograph: Bibliothèque Nationale, Paris)

125. PAGE OF STUDIES, 1865–69

$5\frac{1}{16} \times$ about $13\frac{3}{4}$ inches—$12,8 \times$ about 35 cm. Pencil. Verso: roughly sketched landscape with trees (not classified).

Vollard had the whole page photographed when it was still intact. A copy of the photograph was discovered by John Rewald in 1966 and we would like to thank him for communicating this document. We will discuss here only the sketch on the lower right of the page, the other two sketches, Nos. 125A and 125B, now being separate. This sketch shows two men apparently about to throw themselves on a woman. To the right, separated by a stroke, a woman's head. This study and the one above were perhaps used for a painting, now lost.

COLLECTIONS: Ambroise Vollard, Paris; later the sheet was cut into three, see Nos. 125A, 125B; the latter two are in known collections, whereas the sketch on the lower right seems to have been lost.

125A. A WOMAN CAUGHT UNAWARES, 1865–69

$4\frac{1}{2} \times 6\frac{11}{16}$ inches—$11,5 \times 17$ cm. Pencil, blots of ink. Part of the original sheet of No. 125. Verso: tree tops, cut off by the lower edge.

On the left, two men; on the right, a woman. The woman, taken unawares, wants to flee; a bedpost and drapery are indicated in the center. On both sides of this scene, but cut off by the left and right edges of the paper, are fragments of heads; they are seen more completely on No. 125. Cf. also No. 126.

COLLECTIONS: Ambroise Vollard, Paris. Private collection, Paris. Sale, Hôtel Drouot (Maître Oury), Paris, March 16, 1959, No. 75 (reproduced). F. M. Gross, London.

125B. PAGE OF STUDIES, INCLUDING A SKULL, circa 1868

$5\frac{1}{16} \times 9\frac{1}{8}$ inches—$12,8 \times 23,2$ cm. Pencil, rust spots and brown stains. Cut out of sheet of No. 125. Verso: blank page.

(a) Skull on a table; detailed drawing with volumes and hollows stressed. The style is similar to that of the portrait of Emperaire, No. 230. For the subject, cf. Venturi Nos. 61, 68.—(b) Left: head and shoulders of a woman.—(c) Above: study of a face.—(d) Left hand with bent wrist.

BIBLIOGRAPHY: Rewald, *Letters*, London, 1941, No. 8 (reproduced). Idem, *Paul Cézanne*, New York, 1948, p. 74 (reproduced). Idem, *Paul Cézanne*, Spring Books, London, 1959 and 1965, p. 40 (reproduced).

EXHIBITIONS: Boymans Museum, Rotterdam, 1933, No. 12. Paul Cassirir, London, 1939, No. 3. Nice, Aix-en-Provence, Grenoble, 1953, catalog No. 25 (reproduced).

COLLECTIONS: Ambroise Vollard, Paris. Cassirer, Berlin. E. M. Remarque, Ascona. W. Feilchenfeldt, Zurich. J. Rewald, New York. E. W. Thaw, New York. Private collection, New York.

126. PAGE OF STUDIES, WITH FIGURES IN PROFILE, 1866–71

$7\frac{1}{16} \times 10\frac{13}{16}$ inches—$18 \times 27,5$ cm. Pencil and pen. Reverse side inaccessible.

Sketches relating to a scene of violence between several men and a woman. From left to right: (a) Man making the gesture of seizing a body. Berthold (cat. No. 317) thinks that Cézanne copied this figure from somewhere. The sketch does in fact present certain analogies to a drawing by Delacroix.—(b) Above: head of a man, bent forward; cf. Nos. 125A, 289.—(c) Man in front of a reclining woman.—(d) Head seen in right profile.—(e) Indefinable object; contrast obtained by diagonal hatching.—(f) Below, from left to the far right: series of eight heads (pencil).—(g) Center: man leaning over a woman, his hand between her thighs.—(h) Top right: light pencil sketches; a man similar to (a) can be discerned.—(i) Below: man seizing a woman; cf. No. 162.

BIBLIOGRAPHY: Berthold, cat. No. 317 (reproduced).

EXHIBITIONS: Galerie A. Flechtheim, Berlin, 1929, No. 32. Munich, 1956, No. 151.

COLLECTIONS: Th. Werner, Berlin.

127. STUDIES, INCLUDING A MAN ON HORSEBACK— studies 1857–59; man and rider 1865–67

$5\frac{7}{8} \times 9\frac{1}{16}$ inches—15×23 cm. Page 5 verso of the *Carnet de jeunesse* in the Cabinet des Dessins. Pencil. Verso: No. 60.

(a) Right: almost effaced studies: young man smoking a pipe, man wearing a cap, a chair and unrecognizable objects.—(b) Left: man stretching out his arm against a man on horseback coming from the right, as though to stop him.

COLLECTIONS: P. Berès, Paris. Cabinet des Dessins of the Louvre, Paris (RF 29949).

128. PAINTER HOLDING A PALETTE, 1868–71

$4\frac{1}{16} \times 6\frac{11}{16}$ inches—$10,3 \times 17$ cm. Page from the sketchbook $10,3 \times 17$ cm. Pencil and pen, faint stains. Verso: No. 187.

(a) Painter holding a palette, his clothing floating behind him; a painting standing on an easel to his right. Left: a young man and behind him the rough sketch of a third person. Kurt Badt has remarked that this drawing probably illustrated an episode from *The Unknown Masterpiece* by Balzac, and the Basel Museum catalog, confirming this interpretation, named the drawing: *Frenhofer displays his masterpiece* (No. 78). In his review of the Basel catalog, Th.Reff observes that there is disparity between the drawing and the scene which describes Frenhofer showing his masterpiece, and that it more likely represents a painter imagined by Cézanne with a female model. According to Reff, the drawing might conceivably illustrate an earlier episode of the story: Frenhofer touching up the painting *Mary the Egyptian* of Pourbus. This is quite possible. From Emile Bernard we know of Cézanne's particular interest in Balzac's character Frenhofer (Emile Bernard, *Souvenirs sur Paul Cézanne*, Paris, 1921, p. 44).—(b) Lines written in ink: "*C'est dans (l'esperance. En attendant) l'espoir que vous (veuillez) voudrez bien (faire accéder à ma demande qu'il a l'honneur) lui en accorder la permission qu'il a l'honneur d'être très humble serviteur.*"

BIBLIOGRAPHY: Venturi No. 1575, *Peintre au travail*. Basel catalog No. 78, *Frenhofer montrant son chef-d'oeuvre*. Kurt

Badt, *Die Kunst Cézannes*, Prestel, Munich, 1956, note 39 on p. 61. Th.Reff, *BurlM*, August 1963, p. 375. Idem, Cézanne and Hercules, *AB*, Vol. XLVIII, 1966, p. 41, note 77. Kurt Leonhard, *Paul Cézanne*, Rowohlt, Hamburg, 1966, p. 99, *Frenhofer zeigt sein Werk* (reproduced).

COLLECTIONS: Cézanne *fils*, Paris. W. Feuz, Bern. Kunstmuseum, Basel.

129. THE PAINTER, 1868–71

$6\frac{3}{4} \times 4\frac{1}{16}$ inches—17,1 × 10,3 cm. Page from the sketchbook 10,3 × 17 cm. Pencil, small yellow stains. Verso: No. 316.

A painter holding a palette, his back turned, is sketching-in the figure of a female nude with a brush; his smock reaches to his feet. The Basel catalog states: "This drawing probably represents the painter Frenhofer, hero of *The Unknown Masterpiece* by Balzac." Th.Reff rejects this suggestion and stresses that the style of the drawing is close to that of Daumier. Marked with a cross. The word *seul*. See Note 25.

BIBLIOGRAPHY: Venturi, Vol. I, p. 350, *Oeuvres Inédites* (not reproduced). Basel catalog, No. 77 (reproduced). Th.Reff, *BurlM*, August 1963, p. 375. Idem, Cézanne and Hercules, *AB*, Vol. XLVIII, 1966, p. 41, note 77. Longstreet, 1964 (reproduced).

COLLECTIONS: Cézanne *fils*, Paris. W. Feuz, Bern. Kunstmuseum, Basel.

130. PAGE OF STUDIES: BIBLICAL SCENES, 1864–67

$4\frac{3}{4} \times 8\frac{1}{16}$ inches—12 × 20,5 cm. Page 22 from a sketchbook. Pencil and pen. Verso: No. 144.

(a) Page upright: scene illustrating the story of *The Woman taken in Adultery* (John 8), pen drawing. Christ is seated on the left and there are two other seated figures, both head in hand, an attitude often portrayed by the artist.—(b) Page lengthwise, drawn with a soft pencil: the father welcoming his son, from the parable of *The Prodigal Son* (Luke 15). Of the son, the back only is roughly indicated. The sketches on this page are copies.

COLLECTIONS: Cézanne *fils*, Paris. Maurice Renou, Paris. M. X, auctioneer, Paris. Present owner unknown.

131. STUDY OF A GARMENT, 1864–68

$9\frac{7}{16} \times 7\frac{1}{16}$ inches—24 × 18 cm. Page from the sketchbook 18 × 24 cm. Black crayon, heavy ink or varnish stains and other blemishes. Verso: No. 117.

Study of a garment hanging from a nail: probably work trousers. Vigorous hatching. Lower right: a kind of protrusion seen in perspective. Cf. Nos. 549, 1076.

COLLECTIONS: Mouradian & Vallotton, Paris. Present owner unknown.

132. "GRATIFY MY DESIRE," illustration for *Tartuffe*, 1866–70

$5\frac{1}{4} \times 8\frac{5}{16}$ inches—13,3 × 21,1 cm. Page from a sketchbook. Pencil. Verso: scribble by an alien hand (according to a note by the Van der Heydt Museum).

(a) Illustration for Molière's comedy *Tartuffe; or The Impostor*, Act IV, Scene 5. Ambroise Vollard, when he

reproduced this drawing in 1914, gave it the title "Cover this breast . . . ," supposing that it illustrated the second scene of Act III, where Tartuffe says to Dorine: "Cover this breast I may not see." But the presence of the husband under the table indicates a quite different passage from the comedy: toward the end of the fifth scene of Act IV, Tartuffe, entreating Elmire while her husband, Orgon, is hiding under the table, says: "Gratify my desire." This is no doubt the proper title. Vollard was fond of quoting but did not worry about being exact. Venturi adopts Vollard's title, but notes it inaccurately—*cachez* (hide) for *couvrez* (cover)—and specifies, mistakenly, "scene inspired by the last act of Tartuffe."—(b) At right angles: second sketch of the husband peeping out. Cf. No. 133.

BIBLIOGRAPHY: Venturi No. 1191. Vollard, 1914 (reproduced p. 11). Th.Reff, Cézanne, Flaubert, St. Anthony, and the Queen of Sheba, *AB,* June 1962, p. 121 and note 80; he thinks that it represents the scene with Dorine, but rectifies Venturi's slip (reproduced fig. 8).

EXHIBITION: Kunsthalle, Basel, 1936, No. 110.

COLLECTIONS: Ed. van der Heydt, Zantvoort. Van der Heydt Museum, Wuppertal (Inv. KK 1959/104).

133. STUDY OF A FIGURE, KNEELING, 1866–70

$5\frac{5}{16} \times 8\frac{1}{4}$ inches—13,5 × 21 cm. Pencil and pen, child's scribbles. Verso: authentification by Jean-Pierre Cézanne.

(a) Pencil: kneeling figure, a study for the illustration of *Tartuffe; or The Impostor*, "Gratify my desire," No. 132. Orgon, a man of ripe old age, emerges from his hiding place; here he is sketched as if nude, though in places clothing is indicated. His head seems to be dragging off a corner of the tablecloth under which he had been keeping quiet. A preference to interpret the figure as a female nude is defensible.—(b) Pen: profile of a head.

COLLECTIONS: Sale (Catalog No. 128), Kornfeld & Klipstein, Bern, June 13, 1968, No. 140: *Kniender weiblicher Akt* (not reproduced). Private collection, Basel.

134. BEGGAR AND COW, 1869–71

Measurements unknown. Fragment of a page of studies. Pencil and pen on laid paper, part of the page cut off. Verso: blank page.

(a) Top right: sketch of a man leaning on his cane and holding out his hat for alms.—(b) Same figure but without the legs.—(c) Sketch of a head.—These three sketches in pencil.—(d) Right: a cow, seen in lost right profile (pen and pencil). We know these sketches only by the photograph discovered by John Rewald in 1966.

COLLECTIONS: Ambroise Vollard, Paris. Present owner unknown.

135. STUDIES FOR *The Orgy*, 1864–68

$4\frac{5}{8} \times 9\frac{3}{16}$ inches—11,7 × 23,3 cm. Page from the sketchbook 18 × 24 cm. Pencil. Verso: No. 173.

(a) Top left: man seizing a woman by the waist to lift her.—(b) Lower left: head and shoulders of a man seen from behind carrying a vase on his shoulder; study for the pitcher-carrier in the foreground of *The Orgy*, Venturi No.

92.—(c) Center left: man leaning over and seizing a woman, study for the couple in the lower right corner of the painting. Cf. Nos. 136 (e), 138 (a).—(d) Top center: man seated, almost lying down, seen in right profile with a woman bending over him. Sketch of the group lower left. —(e) Right of (d): repetition of the woman. Below, a pitcher and its circular mouth. The horizontal line of the table should be noticed.—(f) Above: study of the woman who leans on the table at the foot of the last column. For the crosses and words, see Note 25.

BIBLIOGRAPHY: Venturi No. 1184. Basel catalog No. 15 (reproduced). Vollard, 1914 ((a) reproduced p. 35 and also on the spine of the cloth cover).

COLLECTIONS: Cézanne *fils*, Paris. W. Feuz, Bern. Kunstmuseum, Basel.

136. STUDIES FOR *The Orgy*, 1864–68

$6\frac{15}{16} \times 9\frac{7}{16}$ inches—17,7 × 24 cm. Page from the sketchbook 18 × 24 cm. Pencil, restored tear, touches of white and accidental traces of yellow and red, light stains. Verso: No. 171.

(a) Top left: young man crouching, nude; leaning forward, he grasps and overturns a receptacle from which fruit rolls out. Above his shoulder: the word *Blanc*.—(b) Right: confused sketch showing a man's legs and a woman's skirt, study for the couple on the lower left of *The Orgy*, Venturi No. 92. The sketches (a) and (b) form one composition; in the painting the young man has been transformed into the female figure whose leg stretches out towards the couple (b). The word *Blanc* indicates the whiteness of the tablecloth; it was an audacious presage of Impressionism to paint the figures against a light ground.—(c) Sketch of a man, leaning forward.—(d) Lower left: still life with a basket of fruit (white gouache), a dog, two large vases, and other objects.—(e) Confused sketch, probably a couple, and the horizontal edge of a table near their feet.—(f) Study of a woman. For the crosses and words, see Note 25.

BIBLIOGRAPHY: Venturi, Vol. I, p. 351, *Oeuvres Inédites* (not reproduced). Basel catalog No. 16 (reproduced).

COLLECTIONS: Cézanne *fils*, Paris. W. Feuz, Bern. Kunstmuseum, Basel.

137. STUDY FOR *The Orgy*, 1864–68

$9\frac{3}{8} \times 4\frac{5}{8}$ inches—23,8 × 11,7 cm. Page from the sketchbook 18 × 24 cm. Pencil, brown stain and other green and pink stains. Verso: No. 138.

Study for the painting Venturi No. 92, known as *The Orgy*. Top left: columns in perspective with two figures on the cornice; two figures below in front of the columns. Opposite: a protruding balcony, foreshortened, supported by a column. Center: study of an awning waving in the wind. Lower foreground: bunch of flowers and drapery, and first rough sketch for the corner of the table. Lower center: head, raised arm, vase, horizontal lines of the tables. Cf. the other studies: Nos. 135, 136, 138, 139, 156.

BIBLIOGRAPHY: Venturi, Vol. I, p. 351, *Oeuvres Inédites* (not reproduced). Basel catalog, No. 14 (reproduced).

COLLECTIONS: Cézanne *fils*, Paris. W. Feuz, Bern. Kunstmuseum, Basel.

138. STUDY FOR *The Orgy*, AND PAINTER OUTDOORS, 1864–68

$9\frac{3}{8} \times 6\frac{15}{16}$ inches—23,8 × 17,7 cm. Page from the sketchbook 18 × 24 cm. Pencil, various brown stains. Verso: No. 137.

(a) Young man throwing himself on a woman; study for the couple on the lower right of *The Orgy*, Venturi No. 92; cf. No. 135 (c).—(b) Below to the right: a detail of the folds of a dress, repeated.—(c) Upside down: caricature of a woman painter sitting in front of a landscape; to the left of her elbow the paper has been scraped.—(d) In the corner: sketch and lines of hatching.

BIBLIOGRAPHY: Venturi, Vol. I, p. 351, *Oeuvres Inédites* (not reproduced). Basel catalog, No. 17 (reproduced).

COLLECTIONS: Cézanne *fils*, Paris. W. Feuz, Bern. Kunstmuseum, Basel.

139. PORTRAIT, AND STUDY FOR *The Orgy*, 1864–68

$6\frac{15}{16} \times 9\frac{1}{4}$ inches—17,6 × 23,5 cm. Pencil, small stains, and ink traces from the reverse side: No. 178.

(a) Head of a man, treated as though figuring on a medal; perhaps a portrait of the painter Frédéric Bazille.—(b) Framed by strokes, a study of four figures for the painting Venturi No. 92 known as *The Orgy*. Cf. the lute-player, and a man looking down at the top right of the canvas. The trumpeter figures only in the drawing, whereas the man at left, on a light-colored slope, is shown both in the drawing and top left of the painting.—(c) Left, at right angles: unfinished sketches of oriental vases.—(d) Small, hasty sketch of an oriental headdress, with the annotation: "yellow background, tiger skin, inside lacquer with black stripe." A cross and the words *tel seul* (Note 25).

BIBLIOGRAPHY: Venturi, Vol. I, p. 350, *Oeuvres Inédites* (not reproduced). Basel catalog, No. 12 (reproduced).

COLLECTIONS: Cézanne *fils*, Paris. W. Feuz, Bern. Kunstmuseum, Basel.

140. STUDIES FROM ASSYRIAN PAINTINGS, 1864–68

$8\frac{5}{8} \times 6\frac{11}{16}$ inches—22 × 17 cm. Black crayon. Verso: blank page.

Various skeches, with annotations. A profile on the right and a seated figure at the upper edge perhaps form part of other subjects. The handwritten notes refer to colors and objects, for example: *Boucle d'oreille, homme, Bracelet d'or, Costume jaune, denticules bleus, Coloration des murs émaillés jaune teinte de Sienne brûlée, femme*. Cf. No. 139 (d).

EXHIBITIONS: Galerie Alfred Flechtheim, Berlin, 1927, catalog No. 54. Quatre-Chemins, Paris, 1936.

COLLECTIONS: Private collection, Berlin. W. Walter, Paris. Present owner unknown.

141. AFTER EUGÈNE DELACROIX: SARDANAPALUS, 1866–67

$7 \times 9\frac{7}{16}$ inches—17,8 × 24 cm. Page from the sketchbook 18 × 24 cm. Pencil and black crayon, several stains. Verso: No. 183.

(a) Sardanapalus is reclining on a couch with his head against his hand; drawn from the painting *The Death of Sardanapalus* (1827) by Delacroix in the Louvre (Robaut 198), or from a reproduction.—(b) Lower center: head of the Nubian guard who kills the horse.—(c) Lower left:

head of a bearded Oriental; copy from an undetermined model.—(d) On the knees of Sardanapalus, the pointed end of an upright lance; the point itself is sketched a second time.—(e) Right: two studies of a foot. Left: numbers.

BIBLIOGRAPHY: Berthold, cat. No. 242 (reproduced Abb. 81). Reff, Cézanne and Hercules, *AB*, Vol. XLVIII, 1966, p. 40, note 74.

EXHIBITION: *Quatre-Chemins*, Paris, 1936.

COLLECTION: Th. Werner, Berlin.

142. WILD ANIMAL AND CROCODILE, 1866–69

$4\frac{15}{16} \times 7$ inches—12,5 × 17,9 cm. Half page from the sketchbook 18 × 24 cm. Pencil on brown paper. Verso: a counterproof of No. 92.

Fight between a wild beast and a crocodile at the water's edge, in front of a vast hilly landscape. After an undetermined work. The treatment of the landscape calls to mind a Barye watercolor rather than a work by Delacroix.

BIBLIOGRAPHY: Venturi, Vol. I, p. 352, *Oeuvres Inédites*, "*D'après Delacroix*" (not reproduced). Berthold, cat. No. 291 (reproduced)—measurements: height and length transposed. Basel catalog, No. 30 (reproduced). Sara Lichtenstein, Cézanne and Delacroix, *AB*, March 1964, p. 55, No. 7. The author thinks that the subject may have been copied from Delacroix, Robaut Nos. 1281, 1449, 1841.

COLLECTIONS: Cézanne *fils*, Paris. W. Feuz, Bern. Kunstmuseum, Basel.

143. PORTRAIT OF A PAINTER, 1871–74

Measurements unknown. Pencil on ordinary paper. Verso: blank page.

This young artist, his eyes fixed on his subject and with a pencil in his mouth, is sketched from life; cf. No. 225.

BIBLIOGRAPHY: Venturi No. 1197.

COLLECTIONS: Camille Pissarro. Ludovico Rodo Pissarro, Paris.

144. HALF-LENGTH STUDY OF A WOMAN AND ANOTHER SKETCH; pen, 1857–60; pencil, 1864–67

$4\frac{3}{4} \times 8\frac{1}{16}$ inches—12 × 20,5 cm. Leaf from a sketchbook, page 22 verso. Pencil and pen. Verso: No. 130.

(a) Page upright: half-length study of a woman, standing (pen drawing, the ink of her hair is smudged); cf. No. 13.—(b) Page lengthwise: head and shoulders of a woman asleep. She wears a bonnet tied round her head, with a ribbon-end on the right. Vigorous hatching, strong blacks. This drawing calls to mind certain portraits by Gustave Courbet, for example the women in *The Burial at Ornans*. On the other hand it is fairly close to the painting Venturi No. 22, which is dated 1864.

COLLECTIONS: Cézanne *fils*, Paris. M. Renou, Paris. M. X, auctioneer, Paris. Present owner unknown.

145. STUDIES FOR THE ILLUSTRATION OF *Une Charogne*; couple (a), circa 1858; studies, 1866–69

$5\frac{7}{8} \times 9\frac{1}{16}$ inches—15 × 23 cm. Page 36 verso of *Carnet de jeunesse* in the Cabinet des Dessins. Pencil and pen. Verso: No. 148.

(a) Page upright: couple in fancy dress, dancing.—(b) Page lengthwise, lower right: in a scene framed with strokes a man and a woman (the upper part of her body sketched a second time) are halted in front of an animal lying dead on the ground. The man points out the carcass with the tip of his cane. This is an interpretation of Charles Baudelaire's poem *Une Charogne* (a carrion), No. XXX of *Les Fleurs du Mal*.—(c) Top, framed by strokes: similar study with a woman standing.—(d) Top right: study of the man's hand (pencil and pen).—(e) To the left: three studies of the hand holding the cane (pen).—(f) Left: the standing woman, sketched like a nude model; she is holding her hand to her nostrils, in a gesture of disgust. Cf. Nos. 146, 147.

BIBLIOGRAPHY: Berthold, p. 157 (not reproduced). *Cézanne dessinateur* (reproduced p. 305). W. V. Andersen, Cézanne's Portrait Drawings from the 1860's, *Master Drawings*, Vol. 5, No. 3, 1967 (reproduced pl. 15a).

COLLECTIONS: P. Berès, Paris. Cabinet des Dessins of the Louvre, Paris (RF 29949).

146. STUDIES FOR THE ILLUSTRATION OF *Une Charogne*, (a)—(d) 1856–59; (e)—(h) 1866–69

$5\frac{7}{8} \times 9\frac{1}{16}$ inches—15 × 23 cm. Page 37 of the *Carnet de jeunesse* in the Cabinet des Dessins. Pencil, spatterings of ink. Verso: No. 147.

(a) Pencil, faintly drawn: studies of a rider and horses; cf. Nos. 21 (f), 89.—(b) Upside down: woman with her back turned.—(c) At right angles: hexagonal, openwork piece of furniture or a smoking brazier. Above: a rounded object.—(d) Lower left: the couple illustrating Baudelaire's poem *Une Charogne* [see No. 145 (b)], sketched as if from nude models, though the man has a hat and cane and the woman a parasol held down, open.—(e) Top left: study of the woman.—(f) Center: unfinished study of the woman.—(g) Lower right: the two figures together, the woman wearing a dress.

BIBLIOGRAPHY: Berthold, p. 157 (left side reproduced Abb. 69), text p. 46. *Cézanne dessinateur* (reproduced p. 306).

COLLECTIONS: P. Berès, Paris. Cabinet des Dessins of the Louvre, Paris (RF 29949).

147. STUDIES, INCLUDING NUDES, A SOLDIER, AND A JOCKEY; 1856–59, except the nudes, which date from 1866–69

$5\frac{7}{8} \times 9\frac{1}{16}$ inches—15 × 23 cm. Page 37 verso of the *Carnet de jeunesse* in the Cabinet des Dessins. Pencil and pen. Verso: No. 146.

Page lengthwise, left: (a) Head of an impertinent individual.—(b) Standing female nude, study for the illustration of Baudelaire's poem *Une Charogne*; see Nos. 145, 146.—(c) The same figure, but larger.—(d) Study of a plant (pencil heightened with ink).—(e) Standing woman. Page upright: (f) wounded soldier pressing a cloth to his stomach.—(g) Sketched on his thigh: a little winged cherub.—(h) Bottom of page: two men in turbans, crouching.—(i) Right: jockey galloping (pencil and pen).—(k) Top left: head of a woman.

BIBLIOGRAPHY: Berthold, p. 158 (not reproduced). *Cézanne dessinateur* (part reproduced p. 306 and on the cover). W. V. Andersen, Cézanne's Portrait Drawings from the 1860's, *Master Drawings*, Vol. 5, No. 3, 1967 (reproduced pl. 156).

COLLECTIONS: P. Berès, Paris. Cabinet des Dessins of the Louvre, Paris (RF 29949).

148. SEATED MAN WITH HIS BACK TURNED, 1864–67

$9\frac{1}{16} \times 5\frac{7}{8}$ inches—23 × 15 cm. Page 36 of the *Carnet de jeunesse* in the Cabinet des dessins. Pencil. Verso: No. 145.

Apart from some scribbles and an essay in perspective, this page shows a man sitting down, wearing a hat shaped like a candle-snuffer. It is possible that Cézanne copied the figure from Goya.

BIBLIOGRAPHY: Berthold, p. 157 (not reproduced).

COLLECTIONS: P. Berès, Paris. Cabinet des Dessins of the Louvre, Paris (RF 29949).

149. GAME OF BILLIARDS, 1865–70

$4\frac{3}{4} \times 8\frac{1}{4}$ inches—12 × 21 cm. Page from a sketchbook, probably sketchbook II of the Basel Museum. Pencil. Reverse side inaccessible.

A billiard table seen in perspective from above, with four young men around it, playing or discussing the stroke. The cue rack can be seen and, against the wall, a scoreboard. In the right background, a figure sitting smoking a pipe, and in the foreground, a dog. Though this sketch may seem clumsy, it pictures the little scene with remarkable intensity. It used to hang, framed, in the house of Cézanne's son, Paul (1937).

BIBLIOGRAPHY: Venturi No. 1188. Vollard, 1914 (reproduced p. 7). K. Pfister, *Cézanne*, Potsdam, 1927 (reproduced p. 19). Th. Rousseau Jr., *Paul Cézanne*, Flammarion, Paris, 1953 (reproduced pl. 5); and English edition, Collins (& Abrams, Amsterdam), 1954, (reproduced pl. 5).

COLLECTIONS: Cézanne *fils*, Paris. Sale X, Paris, June 18-19, 1942. Present owner unknown.

150. DELPHIN WORKING WITH A SPADE, June 30, 1866

Measurements not known. Pen sketch on a letter to Emile Zola.

Sketch to give Zola an idea of a painting, which is now lost. Rod. Walter identified the figure as Delphin, son of the blacksmith of Gloton (Yvelines), stoking the fire of the forge (see *GBA* for February, 1962, Cézanne at Bennecourt in 1866).

BIBLIOGRAPHY: *Correspondance* (reproduced fig. 9); German edition, Leipzig, 1939 (reproduced fig. 9); Zurich, 1962, (reproduced p. 97). Rod. Walter, loc. cit. (reproduced p. 112).

EXHIBITIONS: Orangerie, Paris, 1936, No. 173. Lyons, 1939, No. 81. Wildenstein, London, 1939, Autograph Letters No. 4.

COLLECTIONS: Emile Zola, Paris. Mme Zola, Paris. E. Fasquelle, Paris. M. and Mme Leblond-Zola, Paris.

151. GIRL AND DOLL, fall 1866

Measurements not known. Pen sketch on a letter to Emile Zola.

A sketch framed by strokes in a letter written to Zola, to give him an idea of a small painting. It represents Cézanne's sister: *Rose reading to her Doll*. The painting is probably lost. Cf. No. 67.

BIBLIOGRAPHY: *Correspondance* (reproduced fig. 10), letter XXI to Zola. Rewald, *Renaissance*, March-April 1937 (reproduced). Berthold (reproduced Abb. 64). W. V. Andersen, Cézanne's Portrait Drawings from the 1860's, *Master Drawings*, Vol. 5, 1967 (reproduced p. 267).

EXHIBITION: Wildenstein, London, 1939, Autograph Letters No. 6.

COLLECTIONS: Emile Zola, Paris. Mme Zola, Paris. E. Fasquelle, Paris. M. and Mme Leblond-Zola, Paris.

152. MARION AND VALABRÈGUE, fall 1866

Measurements not known. Pen sketch on a letter to Emile Zola.

Another sketch, on the same page as No. 151, to give Zola an idea of a future painting: *Marion and Valabrègue on their way to the motif*. Of this painting only a sketch in oils is known to us, Venturi No. 96. Cf. No. 153.

BIBLIOGRAPHY: *Correspondance* (reproduced fig. 5), letter XXI to Zola. Rewald, *The Ordeal of Paul Cézanne*, London, 1950 (reproduced fig. 3). Idem, *Paul Cézanne*, Spring Books, London, 1959 and 1965 (reproduced p. 19). W. V. Andersen, Cézanne's Portrait Drawings from the 1860's, *Master Drawings*, Vol. 5, 1967, No. 3 (reproduced p. 267).

EXHIBITION: Wildenstein, London, 1939, Autograph Letters No. 6.

COLLECTIONS: Emile Zola, Paris. Mme Zola, Paris. E. Fasquelle, Paris. M. and Mme Leblond-Zola, Paris.

153. MARION AND VALABRÈGUE, 1866

$11 \times 7\frac{9}{16}$ inches—28 × 19,2 cm. Pencil, stains, upper corners of page damaged. Verso: blank page.

Study for a painting: *Marion and Valabrègue on their way to the motif*, of which only a sketch in oils is known, Venturi No. 96.—(a) The two friends seen together, probably Marion on the left and Valabrègue on the right (the sketch isolated from the rest by a stroke which is not by Cézanne's hand). Marion's feet are drawn as though seen from above and those of Valabrègue in foreshortening. The reason for this is more apparent in Venturi No. 96, where Marion is farther forward than his friend. For his foreground figures, Cézanne sometimes adopted the posture of saints on stained-glass windows and tympani in Romanesque art, where the treatment of the feet tends to bring the figure forward (foreshortening produces the opposite effect); cf. for example Venturi Nos. 552, 553, 561. At a period closer to Cézanne than the Romanesque, this same treatment is evident in Courbet's *La Rencontre*, or *Bonjour Monsieur Courbet*, 1854, and Manet's *Lola de Valence*, 1862. Contrast the feet of the *Bathers* seen back view, Venturi Nos. 580, 581, 582. See Note 25.—(b) Right: unfinished study of Valabrègue.—(c) Below: same study, less worked on.—(d) At right angles: another study, with repetition of the top hat, cf. No. 152.

BIBLIOGRAPHY: *Correspondance*. Letter XXI does not mention this drawing but refers to the subject. Berthold, text p. 45. Basel catalog, No. 5 (reproduced). W. V. Andersen, Cézanne's Portrait Drawings from the 1860's, *Master Drawings*, Vol. 5, 1967, No. 3, p. 265 (reproduced pl. 14).

COLLECTIONS: Cézanne *fils*, Paris. W. Feuz, Bern. Kunstmuseum, Basel.

154. Two heads and two other studies, circa 1866

$9\frac{5}{16} \times 6\frac{15}{16}$ inches—23,7 × 17,7 cm. Page from the sketchbook 18 × 24 cm. Black crayon and India ink, the corners of the page damaged; tears in the margins, small hole, stains with vestiges of blue-green. Verso: No. 174.

Studies for the portrait of Valabrègue, Venturi No. 126. —(a) and (b): The same head, twice; (a) is heightened with India ink (see the collar of the coat). For the crosses and words, see Note 25.—(c) Below (b) and at right angles: man in a hat, standing with his back turned.—(d) Right, and upside down: same subject, with strong shadows.

BIBLIOGRAPHY: Basel catalog, No. 8 (reproduced). *Correspondance* (reproduced fig. 8). M. Scolari and A. Barr, Cézanne in the Letters of Marion to Morstatt, 1865–68, *Magazine of Art*, Feb., April, May, 1938, and Cézanne d'après les lettres de Marion à Morstatt, *GBA*, 1938, p. 47. Rewald, *The Ordeal of Paul Cézanne*, London, 1950 (reproduced). *Basler Nachrichten*, October 20, 1956 (reproduced). Rewald, *Paul Cézanne*, Spring Books, London, 1959 and 1965, (a) reproduced p. 55. W. V. Andersen, Cézanne's Portrait Drawings from the 1860's, *Master Drawings,* Vol. 5, 1967, No. 3, p. 265 (reproduced pl. 16).

COLLECTIONS: Cézanne *fils*, Paris. W. Feuz, Bern. Kunstmuseum, Basel.

155. Portrait of Eugène Delacroix, 1864–66

$5\frac{1}{2} \times 5\frac{1}{8}$ inches—14 × 13 cm. Part of a page from the sketchbook 18 × 24 cm. Pencil and soft crayon *(crayon gras)*. Stamp of the Rignault Collection (Lugt 2218), as on Nos. 102, 422. Verso: No. 192.

Portrait bust of Eugène Delacroix, probably drawn from a photograph by Durrieu (1857; another photograph 1858). The shadows are emphasized. The signature at lower left, *P. Cézanne,* does not seem to be authentic, although the drawing certainly is. Cf. No. 156 (a); No. 619 shows the same subject but in another style.

BIBLIOGRAPHY: Sara Lichtenstein, An Unpublished Portrait of Delacroix, and some Figure Sketches by Cézanne, *Master Drawings,* Vol. 4, No. 1, 1966 (reproduced pl. 33). Drawing dated early 1870's.

COLLECTIONS: J. Rignault, Avignon. Musée Calvet, Avignon.

156. Portrait of Delacroix and various studies, 1864–68

$9\frac{3}{8} \times 6\frac{15}{16}$ inches—23,9 × 17,7 cm. Page from the sketchbook 18 × 24 cm. Pencil, pen, and wash, paper slightly torn on the right, upper corners damaged, brown stains. Verso: No. 169.

(a) Portrait of the painter Eugène Delacroix (pencil, ink, and wash). Probably done from a photograph taken by Durrieu in 1858 or, even more likely, from a reproduction of this photograph. Another one taken by Durrieu in 1857 also exists (both reproduced by S. Lichtenstein; see Bibliography). Cf. No. 155.—(b) On the right and at right angles: landscape (pen and pencil) and three men, two lying asleep on the ground and the third, in a Barbizon hat, seated. This sketch is related to the subject of *The Harvesters;* see Venturi Nos. 249, 874, 1517.—(c) Lower right, upside down: reclining woman (pencil); see Ven-

turi Nos. 379, 380, 897.—(d) In a rectangle framed by strokes, later in date than (a) and (e): vigorous study for the painting Venturi No. 92. The diagonal perspective of the table can be seen to the right, and on the left, the foreground group.—(e) Intermingled with this study, but definitely earlier, a man's head seen full face.—(f) Next to Delacroix: rough draft of a figure, probably the one carrying a pitcher in the background of the canvas. For the crosses and words, see Note 25.

BIBLIOGRAPHY: Venturi, Vol. I, p. 351, *Oeuvres Inédites* (not reproduced). Berthold, cat. No. 239 (reproduced). Basel catalog No. 13 (reproduced). Sara Lichtenstein, An Unpublished Portrait of Delacroix, and some Figure Sketches by Cézanne, *Master Drawings,* Vol. 4, No. 1, 1966, p. 39 (reproduced).

COLLECTIONS: Cézanne *fils*, Paris. W. Feuz, Bern. Kunstmuseum, Basel.

157. Portrait of a man, 1868–70

$5\frac{7}{16} \times 5\frac{3}{16}$ to $5\frac{3}{8}$ inches—13,8 × 13,2 to 13,7 cm. Pencil on beige paper. Verso: blank page.

In 1964, Wayne V. Andersen suggested that this drawing, for many years thought to be a self-portrait by Cézanne, was more probably a portrait of the artist's friend Boyer, of whom there are three oil portraits, Venturi Nos. 130, 131, 132. Among other observations, Andersen points out that Boyer's hair curled inward on the sides of his head whereas Cézanne's turned outward. The drawing is small, but its effect impressive.

BIBLIOGRAPHY: Venturi No. 1236. Vollard, 1914 (reproduced p. 26). *Dessins,* 1957 (reproduced as frontispiece). W. V. Andersen, A Cézanne Self-Portrait Reidentified, *BurlM,* Vol. CVI, 1964, p. 284 (reproduced). Dated 1869–70.

EXHIBITION: Orangerie, Paris, 1936, supplement No. 181.

COLLECTIONS: Cézanne *fils*, Paris. Paul Guillaume, Paris. Kenneth Clark, London.

158. Writer sitting at his table, 1867–69

$5\frac{1}{8} \times 2\frac{5}{8}$ inches—12,9 × 6,7 cm. Pencil on ordinary paper. Verso: blank page.

The writer is seated behind a little table, writing with one hand, the other held up to his chin. Though there may be a tendency to assume that this man is Emile Zola, I can see nothing to justify the supposition. However, the sketch can be compared with Nos. 220, 221, 222, which are related to the paintings Venturi Nos. 117, 118. The man's crossed feet, the large inkpot beside the paper, and the shelves of a bookcase in the background are worth noting.

EXHIBITION: Kunstnerforbundet, Oslo, 1954.

COLLECTIONS: Arnstein Arneberg, Oslo. Huguette Berès, Paris. Present owner unknown.

159. Young woman, seated, 1865–68

$8\frac{1}{4} \times 5\frac{1}{8}$ inches—21 × 13 cm. Black crayon. Verso: five sketches in pencil and violet crayon, by Camille Pissarro, signed C.P.

Young woman, sitting down holding a round hat and some flowers. In the right background a few bare trees are seen, possibly an academy curtain. On the lower left are the words: *Croquis par Cézanne.*

BIBLIOGRAPHY: Venturi No. 1223: "Il faut dire que le style du dessin a très peu de Cézanne."

COLLECTIONS: Camille Pissarro; C. Pissarro sale, Paris, December 3, 1928, No. 63 (reproduced in the catalog). Santamarina, Paris.

160. MAN, SEEN BACK VIEW: caricature of the artist's father, 1865–68

$9 \times 6\frac{15}{16}$ inches—22,8 × 17,7 cm. Page from the sketchbook 18 × 24 cm. Black crayon, India ink, small stains. Verso: No. 195.

Man of a certain age, standing on a garden path with his back turned; further off to the right a tree can be seen in front of an undefined background. The man's legs are parted and like stilts. A cap covers his head, above a thick-set neck. From the attitude of the arms held away from the body the man appears to be reading a newspaper. The artist has caricatured his father, borrowing the style of Honoré Daumier. In the right margin, calligraphic exercises in ink call to mind certain signatures of the artist.

BIBLIOGRAPHY: Venturi, Vol. I, p. 351, *Oeuvres Inédites* (not reproduced). Basel catalog, No. 9 (reproduced).

COLLECTIONS: Cézanne *fils*, Paris. W. Feuz, Bern. Kunstmuseum, Basel.

161. FIGURE WITH UMBRELLA, seen back view, 1866–69

$5\frac{5}{8} \times 6\frac{11}{16}$ inches—14,3 × 16,9 cm. Page from the sketchbook 18 × 24 cm., cut down. Black crayon on brown drawing paper, heightened with accents of white crayon; brown stain. Verso: No. 179.

Back view of a figure, the head and shoulder hidden by an umbrella. Fine early sketch; the line of the waist should be noticed.

BIBLIOGRAPHY: Venturi, Vol. I, p. 350, *Oeuvres Inédites* (not reproduced). Basel catalog, No. 11 (reproduced).

COLLECTIONS: Cézanne *fils*, Paris. W. Feuz, Bern. Kunstmuseum, Basel.

162. PAGE OF STUDIES, INCLUDING SEVERAL SCENES OF VIOLENCE, 1864–67

$9 \times 13\frac{3}{4}$ inches—22,8 × 35 cm. Pencil on thick paper, soiled in places, corners damaged and paper torn, holes restored, vertical fold on the left, stains. Verso: No. 699.

Left, from bottom to top: (a) Murder scene; the murderer's arm is sketched twice. Above: (b) Man stretched out as though dead, around him a few indications of landscape. Above: (c) Murder scene with three figures. Higher left, drawn with a different pencil: (d) Sketch of a torso, the elbow lifted and bent. Lower edge, toward the center: (e) Two men carrying an inanimate woman. Above: (f) repetition of the man raising his arm to strike. Above: (g) Two undecipherable sketches. Center: (h) Man standing with his arms folded; sketch reinforced with black crayon. Bottom of the page again: the number 27, and (i) Reclining man leaning on his elbow. Above: (k) in a rectangle formed by strokes, a man holding up a woman, and on the

right a fallen chair. Bottom right: (l) Two men carrying an inanimate woman with a man in a top hat watching them; cf. No. 163. Above right: (m) Man kneeling on one knee; cf. No. 57 (c). Above: (n) Murder scene in a setting rendered by perspective; cf. No. 254; Venturi Nos. 108, 121, 123; *Correspondance*, pl. 14.

BIBLIOGRAPHY: Venturi, Vol. I, p. 352, *Oeuvres Inédites* (not reproduced). Basel catalog, No. 4 (reproduced). Longstreet, 1964 (reproduced).

COLLECTIONS: Cézanne *fils*, Paris. W. Feuz, Bern. Kunstmuseum, Basel.

163. THE MURDER, 1868–71

$5\frac{1}{8} \times 6\frac{1}{8}$ inches—13 × 15,5 cm. Pencil. Verso: blank page.

The two corpses in the foreground are lying on a board floor drawn in diminishing perspective. In the right middleground there is a laid table; on the left a police inspector is seen arriving, accompanied by a figure holding a lantern. The dramatic feeling is intensified by the picture on the wall, drawn in impossible perspective, and the two overturned chairs. Cf. No. 162. Pencil lines have been scribbled by a child across the page.

BIBLIOGRAPHY: Venturi, Vol. I, p. 349, *Oeuvres Inédites* (not reproduced). Basel catalog, mentioned under No. 4.

COLLECTION: Kenneth Clark, London.

164. THE MUSICIANS, 1867–69

$4\frac{7}{8} \times 8\frac{1}{4}$ inches—12,3 × 21 cm. Page from a sketchbook. Pencil on gray-brown paper. Verso: No. 66.

Study showing eight musicians, led by a conductor. Considering the costumes, it is probable that Cézanne drew the figures from an engraving; certain strokes are probably traced, though independent research is evident in the conductor's arm. Cf. No. 218.

COLLECTIONS: Private collection, Paris. Jean Cailac, Paris. Private collection, Basel. A. Chappuis, Tresserve.

165. FROM AN UNDETERMINED WORK: MITRED BISHOP, 1866–67

$9\frac{7}{16} \times 6\frac{15}{16}$ inches—24 × 17,7 cm. Page from the sketchbook 18 × 24 cm. Soft pencil, numbers in ink. Verso: No. 241.

A bishop (or mitred abbot), standing, holding a stick in his right hand and an open book in his left. Drawn from an undetermined work. The shadow should be observed. Calculations, in ink, are spread all over the page around the sketch.

BIBLIOGRAPHY: Venturi, Vol. I, No. 1581 (not reproduced). Berthold, cat. No. 284 (reproduced). Basel catalog, No. 26 (reproduced).

COLLECTIONS: Cézanne *fils*, Paris. W. Feuz, Bern. Kunstmuseum, Basel.

166. JOB AND HIS FRIENDS, 1864–67

$10\frac{7}{16} \times 8\frac{3}{8}$ inches—26,5 × 21,2 cm. Pencil, brush drawing with brown wash. Verso: blank page.

The signature at the upper right is probably not authentic.

Job, sitting on the ground, is confronted by three friends. For Job's pose, cf. No. 171; for the heads and figures of the friends, cf. Nos. 144, 155, 157, 164, 165, 168.

COLLECTIONS: G. Wildenstein, Paris. Private collection, Paris. Galerie Muensterberg, Basel. Weiss-Hesse, Olten. Private collection, Switzerland.

167. AFTER E. DELACROIX: *The Entombment*, 1866–67

$7\frac{1}{16} \times 9\frac{7}{16}$ inches—18 × 24 cm. Page from the sketchbook 18 × 24 cm. Soft pencil. Verso: No. 180.

After Eugène Delacroix: *Mise au Tombeau* in the Church of St. Denis-du-Saint-Sacrement, mural measuring 3,50 m. × 4,75 m. painted in 1843 (Robaut 768). See fig. 12. Engraved by Hédouin for *L'Artiste*. R. W. Ratcliffe notes that Cézanne had in mind the arm and head of this Christ when he painted *The Abduction*, Venturi No. 101, canvas dated 1867.

COLLECTIONS: Cézanne *fils*, Paris. Paul Guillaume, Paris. Kenneth Clark, London. Michael Sadler, Oxford. F. A. Drey, London.

168. AFTER PAUL VERONESE: *The Marriage at Cana*, 1866–69

$6\frac{15}{16} \times 9$ inches—17,7 × 22,8 cm. Page from the sketchbook 18 × 24 cm. Black crayon, paper torn, top left corner damaged, brown stains. Verso: No. 248.

Group of guests at table. Left: servant bending over to decant the wine; the pencil outline of his leg has been graven into the paper. Detail from the right part of *The Marriage at Cana* by Veronese, in the Louvre. See fig. 13.

BIBLIOGRAPHY: Venturi No. 1578. Berthold, cat. No. 269 (reproduced). Basel catalog No. 28 (reproduced).

COLLECTIONS: Cézanne *fils*, Paris. W. Feuz, Bern. Kunstmuseum, Basel.

169. AFTER PAUL VERONESE: *The Marriage at Cana*, 1866–69

$6\frac{15}{16} \times 9\frac{3}{8}$ inches—17,7 × 23,9 cm. Page from the sketchbook 18 × 24 cm. Black crayon. Verso: No. 156.

(a) Head and shoulders of a bearded man in left profile, from *The Marriage at Cana* by Veronese, in the Louvre. See fig. 14: the figure above the balustrade, holding a stick.— (b) Head of a young woman, tilted forward; see also fig. 14: the fourth person seated at table on the left side.—(c) Left hand, open and raised, and right thumb. Detail taken from *The Adoration of the Shepherds* by J. de Ribera, in the Louvre; see fig. 15.

BIBLIOGRAPHY: Venturi, Vol. I, p. 351, *Oeuvres Inédites* (not reproduced). Berthold, cat. No. 309 (reproduced). Basel catalog, No. 29 (reproduced).

COLLECTIONS: Cézanne *fils*, Paris. W. Feuz, Bern. Kunstmuseum, Basel.

170. AFTER PAUL VERONESE: ESTHER AND ONE OF LOT'S DAUGHTERS, 1866–69

$9\frac{7}{16} \times 6\frac{7}{8}$ inches—24 × 17,4 cm. Page from the sketchbook 18 × 24 cm. Pencil, right corners damaged, small stains. Verso: No. 184.

FIG. 12. *Mise au tombeau*, encaustic mural by Eugène Delacroix (1799–1863), 3,55 m. × 4,75 m. (1843). Detail from the painting in the church of St. Denis-du-Saint-Sacrement, Paris. Robaut 768. An engraving was made by Hédouin for *L'Artiste*.   (*Photograph: Archives photographiques, Paris*)

Woman standing with her left hand hanging limply from her forearm. From the figure of Esther in the painting *Esther and Ahasuerus* by Veronese, in the Louvre. See fig. 16. —(b) Right: her hand, repeated twice.—(c) At right angles, at Esther's feet: seated man, back view; see fig. 16: the figure on the right.—(d) Across the bottom of the page: a woman standing, drawn from one of Lot's daughters in *The Burning of Sodom* by Veronese, in the Louvre; see fig. 17: the first figure on the left. As well as capturing the attitudes, Cézanne has succeeded in rendering the broad surfaces of light cast on the figures in Veronese's painting.

BIBLIOGRAPHY: Venturi, Vol. I, as verso of No. 1580 (not reproduced). Berthold, cat. No. 268 (reproduced). Basel catalog, No. 27 (reproduced).

COLLECTIONS: Cézanne *fils*, Paris. W. Feuz, Bern. Kunstmuseum, Basel.

171. AFTER FRA BARTOLOMMEO: STUDY OF CHRIST, 1866–69

$6\frac{15}{16} \times 9\frac{7}{16}$ inches—17,7 × 24 cm. Page from the sketchbook 18 × 24 cm. Pencil, corners damaged, restored tear, faint brown stains. Verso: No. 136.

(a) From a drawing by Fra Bartolommeo della Porta for *The Entombment of Christ*, in the Louvre. See fig. 18.—(b) Rapid sketch of a couple, standing; above, rough draft of a scene, too obscure to define.

BIBLIOGRAPHY: Venturi, Vol. I, p. 351, *Oeuvres Inédites* (not reproduced). Berthold, cat. No. 252 (reproduced Abb. 80). Basel catalog, No. 21 (reproduced). Longstreet, 1964 (reproduced).

COLLECTIONS: Cézanne *fils*, Paris. W. Feuz, Bern. Kunstmuseum, Basel.

172. AFTER MICHELANGELO: *The Resurrection*, circa 1867

9 1/16 × 6 11/16 inches—23 × 17 cm. Page from the sketchbook 18 × 24 cm. Pencil, smudges. Verso: No. 476.

(a) Top right: the figure of Christ from Michelangelo's drawing *The Resurrection*, in the Louvre. See fig. 19. Cf. No. 994.—(b) Top left: same figure but without the shroud and with no indication of the sarcophagus.—(c) Bottom right: the guard standing.—(d) The seated guard sketched in faintly on the left of Michelangelo's drawing. Cézanne has rendered the outlines and movement of the bodies but has not modeled the volumes.

BIBLIOGRAPHY: Venturi, Vol. I, p. 349, *Oeuvres Inédites* (not reproduced). Berthold, cat No. 254 (not reproduced).

COLLECTIONS: Kenneth Clark, London. Sale, Galerie Motte, Geneva, November 10, 1967, No. 15 (not reproduced). Private collection.

173. AFTER MURILLO: THE SAN DIEGO OF *The Angel's Kitchen*, 1866–69

9 3/16 × 6 15/16 inches—23,3 × 17,7 cm. Page from the sketchbook 18 × 24 cm. Black crayon. Verso: No. 135.

(a) San Diego, from Murillo's painting *The Angels' Kitchen* (1646), in the Louvre; see fig. 20. The praying saint is miraculously carried aloft.—(b) Lower right, upside down: dog jumping.

BIBLIOGRAPHY: Basel catalog, No. 23 (reproduced).

COLLECTIONS: Cézanne *fils*, Paris. W. Feuz, Bern. Kunstmuseum, Basel.

174. MAN KNEELING, HIS ARMS RAISED, 1866–67

4 5/8 × 9 5/16 inches—11,7 × 23,7 cm. Page from the sketchbook 18 × 24 cm. Soft pencil, corners damaged, tears in the margins, small hole, heavy stains. Verso: No. 154.

(a) Man with his right knee on the ground in an attitude of prayer, his arms raised.—(b) and (c) studies repeating the head.—(d) Right: the subject of (a) repeated. These four sketches represent a figure from the painting Venturi No. 245, *The Apotheosis of Delacroix*.—(e), (f), and (g): three heads, from top to bottom on the left side of the page.

BIBLIOGRAPHY: Venturi, Vol. I, p. 351, *Oeuvres Inédites* (not reproduced). Basel catalog, No. 39 (reproduced).

COLLECTIONS: Cézanne *fils*, Paris. W. Feuz, Bern. Kunstmuseum, Basel.

175. TWO MEN; WOMAN BESIDE A COFFIN; 1866–67

6 15/16 × 9 inches—17,7 × 22,9 cm. Page from the sketchbook 18 × 24 cm. Soft pencil, corners damaged. Verso: No. 91.

FIGS. 13 and 14. Paolo Caliari, known as Paul Veronese (1528–88): *The Marriage at Cana* (details), in the Louvre. Oil on canvas, 6,60 m. × 9,90 m. Canvas painted for the refectory of San Giorgio in Venice. Maurice Denis testifies to Cézanne's particular interest in this painting and records his remark made in 1906: "I have planned out a sketch of *The Marriage at Cana* for the contrasts. I find the same contrasts in Delacroix's *Bouquet*." In his bedroom he had hung a *Bouquet de fleurs* by Delacroix (Catalogue of the Cézanne Retrospective Exhibition, Paris, 1939. Preface by Maurice Denis, p. 5). Musée National du Louvre, *Catalogue des Peintures* II, 1926, No. 1192. *(Photograph: Giraudon)*

FIG. 15. Jusepe de Ribera (1591–1652): *Adoration of the Shepherds*, in the Louvre. Oil on canvas, 2,38 m. × 1,79 m., signed lower right and dated 1650 (detail). Seymour de Ricci, *Description raisonnée des peintures du Louvre*, Paris, 1913, No. 1721.
(Photograph: Giraudon)

In the center of the page, two men who perhaps form part of the same composition.—(a) Back view of a man in a Barbizon hat, walking away holding a long stick; cf. the man with a knapsack on his back in the center of Venturi Nos. 245, 891.—(b) Lower right: man with a stick walking toward the right; a Barbizon hat is sketched near his neck.—(c) Study, at right angles, repeating the mourning woman of Nos. 176, 177.—Upper left (d) and lower left (e): two sketches of the woman beside a coffin. Most of the figures are heightened with black crayon.

BIBLIOGRAPHY: Venturi Vol. I, p. 351, *Oeuvres Inédites* (not reproduced). Basel catalog, No. 38 (reproduced).

COLLECTIONS: Cézanne *fils*, Paris. W. Feuz, Bern. Kunstmuseum, Basel.

176. FIGURES NEAR A COFFIN, 1866–68

$9\frac{7}{16} \times 6\frac{15}{16}$ inches—24 × 17,7 cm. Page from the sketchbook 18 × 24 cm. Pencil, corners damaged, restored tear at the lower edge, accidental dabs of watercolor and a fingerprint. Verso: No. 247.

(a) Top: grave in a cemetery: the grave-digger with his spade is standing on the left. In the coffin, the body of a girl. To the left, a kind of shaded vault.—(b) Below: the scene of the three figures around the coffin, the man standing covered up by (a).—(c) Lower left: woman kneeling beside a coffin.—(d) Near the right edge: study of the same figure, and study of an arm.—(e) In the center,

FIG. 16. Paolo Caliari, known as Paul Veronese (1528–88): *Esther and Ahasuerus*, in the Louvre. Oil on canvas, 2 m. × 3,10 m. Musée National du Louvre, *Catalogue des Peintures* II, 1926, No. 1189.
(Photograph: Giraudon)

FIG. 17. Paolo Caliari, known as Paul Veronese (1528–88):
The Burning of Sodom, in the Louvre. Oil on canvas, 93 cm. ×
120 cm. (detail). Musée National du Louvre, *Catalogue des
Peintures* II, 1926, No. 1187.   *(Photograph: Giraudon)*

FIG. 18. Fra Bartolommeo della Porta (1472–1517): study
after the dead Christ of *The Entombment*, canvas in the Pitti
Palace, Florence (also attributed to Baccio della Porta).
The drawing is in the Louvre. *Notice des Dessins . . . au Musée
National du Louvre*, by M. Reiset, Paris, 1866: "No. 53,
Andrea del Sarto and Fra Bartolommeo, four drawings
combined on one sheet by Mariette . . . 4. Black chalk study
of the body of the dead Christ, seated on a stone." On the
canvas, one of the arms is painted in a different position; the
dissimilarity is described by Adolfo Venturi as follows:
". . . con il braccio sollevato dall'invisibile mano materna,
artificiosamente, mentre nella pittura s'abbassa, stroncato da
morte." (A. Venturi, *Storia dell'Arte Italiana*, Vol. IX, p. 327,
drawing reproduced fig. 235). See also: Knapp, *Fra
Bartolomeo della Porta und die Schule von San Marco*, Halle 1903,
fig. 86.

at right angles: in a rectangle formed by strokes, sketch
of a young woman flinging herself onto a corpse. In the
background, a stairway. Cf. Nos. 175, 177.

BIBLIOGRAPHY: Venturi, Vol. I, p. 351, *Oeuvres Inédites*
(not reproduced). Basel catalog, No. 37 (reproduced).

COLLECTIONS: Cézanne *fils*, Paris. W. Feuz, Bern. Kunstmuseum, Basel.

177. WOMAN BESIDE A COFFIN, circa 1866

$9\frac{5}{16} \times 6\frac{15}{16}$ inches—23,6 × 17,7 cm. Page from the
sketchbook 18 × 24 cm. Pencil, top left corner
damaged, small tear lower left, brown stains. Verso:
No. 258.

(a) Top: kneeling woman, leaning over a coffin; a chair
and a lamp in the background.—Center (b) and lower
right (c): two sketches repeating the kneeling woman.—
(d) Left: head of a woman. All these studies are heightened with black crayon. Cf. Nos. 175, 176, 178. R. W.
Ratcliffe relates this drawing to the painting Venturi
No. 86, *The Magdalene*, in the Musée du Jeu de Paume,
Paris. He points out not only that the pose is similar, but
also that the floor tiles are indicated in the canvas.

BIBLIOGRAPHY: Venturi No. 1576. Basel catalog, No. 36
(reproduced).

COLLECTIONS: Cézanne *fils*, Paris. W. Feuz, Bern. Kunstmuseum, Basel.

178. SKETCH OF THE ARTIST'S FATHER, HEAD OF A
WOMAN, AND CALCULATIONS, circa 1866

$6\frac{15}{16} \times 9\frac{1}{4}$ inches—17,6 × 23,5 cm. Page from the
sketchbook 18 × 24 cm. Pen and pencil. Verso: No.
139.

(a) Pen: sketch of Cézanne's father wearing a cap and
holding a newspaper; cf. Nos. 409, 413, 662bis.—(b)
Pencil: head of a woman, bent forward as though she is
dozing. Beside the head (c): the fingers of an almost closed

FIG. 19. Michelangelo Buonarotti (1475–1564): *The
Resurrection*, drawing in sanguine, 15,5 cm. × 17 cm., in the
Cabinet des Dessins of the Louvre (Inv. 691bis).

(Photograph: Giraudon)

FIG. 20. Bartolomé Esteban Murillo (1618–82): *The Angels' Kitchen* (Miracle of Saint Diego) (detail). St. Diego (Franciscan, sixteenth century) miraculously lifted into the air while praying; at the same moment his prayer is heard and angels appear to prepare a meal in the monastery kitchen, void of provisions. Oil on canvas, 1,80 m. × 4,50 m. In the Louvre. Seymour de Ricci, *Description raisonnée des peintures du Louvre*, Paris, 1913, No. 1716. *(Photograph: Giraudon)*

hand. For (b) and (c), cf. No. 177. Over the rest of the page there are calculations and an effaced text: "*La mort c'est l'oubli/Le sommeil, la joie du malheureux/La mort est belle comme [une]/l'espérance—qui a pu dire qu'elle avait les dents crochues?—son sourire est doux comme le miel, ses yeux donnent le repos.*" (Death is forgetfulness/Sleep, the joy of the unfortunate/ Death is as beautiful as [a]/hope—who can have said she had crooked teeth?—her smile is as sweet as honey, her eyes bring rest.) These lines sound like a translated quotation: they denote supreme resignation. Nos. 176 and 177 express grief in face of death.

BIBLIOGRAPHY: Venturi, Vol. I, p. 350, *Oeuvres Inédites* (not reproduced). Basel catalog, No. 35 (reproduced). Douglas Cooper, in *Master Drawings*, Vol. 1, No. 4, 1963, p. 55. W. V. Andersen, Cézanne's Portrait Drawings from the 1860's, *Master Drawings*, Vol. 5, 1967, p. 265 ((a) reproduced, fig. 6).

COLLECTIONS: Cézanne *fils*, Paris. W. Feuz, Bern. Kunstmuseum, Basel.

179. CLOSED HAND, VERSES WRITTEN IN PENCIL, 1868–71

6$\frac{11}{16}$ × 5$\frac{5}{8}$ inches—16,9 × 14,3 cm. Page from the sketchbook 18 × 24 cm. Pencil on brown paper, brown stain. Verso: No. 161.

(a) Study of a left hand, the fingers almost doubled into the palm. The heaviest strokes are graven into the paper. —(b) Verses written in pencil (first line hidden by the mount):

> *Ma gracieuse Marie*
> *Je vous aime et vous prie*
> *De garder les mots d'écrit*

Que vous envoient vos amis.
Sur vos belles lèvres roses
Ce bonbon glissera bien
Il passe sur bien des choses
Sans en gâter le carmin.
Ce joli bonbon rose
Si gentiment tourné
Dans une bouche rose
Serait heureux d'entrer.

Right edge: fragment of another stanza.

BIBLIOGRAPHY: Venturi, Vol. I, p. 351, *Oeuvres Inédites* (not reproduced). Basel catalog, No. 3 (reproduced). *Correspondance* (verses reproduced Letter No. VII bis).

COLLECTIONS: Cézanne *fils*, Paris. W. Feuz, Bern. Kunstmuseum, Basel.

180. STUDIES, 1869–72

7$\frac{1}{16}$ × 9$\frac{7}{16}$ inches—18 × 24 cm. Page from the sketchbook 18 × 24 cm. Soft pencil. Verso: No. 167.

(a) Copy of the figure of Venus, detail from Eugène Delacroix's *Ceiling of Apollo*, in the Louvre. See fig. 21, and cf. No. 181.—(b) Dog running, perhaps a copy.—(c) Preliminary study for *Afternoon in Naples*. The elements of the subject are similar to those in other versions but arranged in a different way. The reclining woman appears to be holding a cigar, or perhaps a hookah with its jar on the floor at the foot of the bed. At that period the art students and young soldiers expressed their audacity by shouting "*A nous les femme qui fument!*"

COLLECTIONS: Cézanne *fils*, Paris. Paul Guillaume, Paris. Kenneth Clark, London. Michael Sadler, Oxford. F. A. Drey, London.

FIG. 21. Eugène Delacroix (1799–1863): *Le Plafond d'Apollon* in the Louvre, inaugurated in 1851. Wood engraving printed in *L'Illustration*, December 1851 *(Apollon vainqueur du serpent Python*, Robaut 1118). *(Photograph: Bibliothèque Nationale, Paris)*

181. WOMAN BATHING, AND COPIES AFTER DELACROIX, 1869–72

8¼ × 10¼ inches—21 × 26 cm. Pencil. Verso: blank page.

(a) Framed by strokes: two women bathers in a river landscape. The left side of the frame cuts off the continuation of the far bank, which was drawn earlier and originally formed part of the subject.—(b) Below: four details copied from a reproduction of the *Ceiling of Apollo* by Eugène Delacroix in the Louvre. See fig. 21. These are: the allegoric figure of a *River,* cf. Nos. 195 (d), 494; a seated *Venus,* cf. No. 180; a floating *Corpse;* a *Wild Animal,* cf. No. 194bis.

EXHIBITIONS: Quatre-Chemins, Paris, 1936. Kunstkopien, Kunsthalle, Basel, 1937, No. 195.

COLLECTIONS: Camille Pissarro; C. Pissarro sale (attributed to Eugène Delacroix), Paris, Dec. 3, 1928. Pierre Dubaut, Paris.

182. AFTER LUCA SIGNORELLI: THE DEMON AND THE DAMNED, drawing known as *The Living carrying the Dead,* 1867–70

9 7/16 × 7 1/16 inches—24 × 18 cm. Page from the sketchbook 18 × 24 cm. Pencil and red crayon, vertical tear restored. Verso: No. 257.

The most complete of Cézanne's copies from Signorelli's drawing in the Louvre. See fig. 22. The treatment with pencil and crayon was rarely practiced by the artist.

BIBLIOGRAPHY: Venturi, Vol. I, p. 349, *Oeuvres Inédites* (not reproduced). Berthold, cat. No. 251 (reproduced). *The World of Cézanne* (reproduced p. 147).

EXHIBITION: Kunsthalle, Basel, 1936, No. 158.

COLLECTION: Kenneth Clark, London.

183. AFTER LUCA SIGNORELLI: MALE NUDE, 1866–69

11 × 7 inches—24 × 17,8 cm. Page from the sketchbook 18 × 24 cm. Pencil. Verso: No. 141.

From a drawing by Signorelli in the Cabinet des Dessins of the Louvre. See fig. 23. Cézanne owned a photograph of this work. Cf. Nos. 184, 674.

BIBLIOGRAPHY: Berthold, cat. No. 248 (reproduced).

EXHIBITION: Munich, 1956, No. 127.

COLLECTION: Th. Werner, Berlin.

184. AFTER LUCA SIGNORELLI: MALE NUDE, 1866–69

4 5/8 × 9 7/16 inches—11,7 × 24 cm. Page from the sketchbook 18 × 24 cm. Pencil, right corners damaged, small brown stain. Verso: No. 170.

Male nude, standing, from a drawing by Signorelli in the Cabinet des Dessins of the Louvre. See fig. 23. Cézanne owned a photograph of this work. Two other copies: Nos. 183, 674. For the cross, see Note 25.

BIBLIOGRAPHY: Venturi No. 1580. Berthold, cat. No. 247 (reproduced Abb. 77). Basel catalog, No. 22 (reproduced). Longstreet, 1964 (reproduced).

COLLECTIONS: Cézanne *fils,* Paris. W. Feuz, Bern. Kunstmuseum, Basel.

185. STUDIES, INCLUDING *L'Ecorché,* AND A MAN'S FACE IN PROFILE, 1866–70

7 5/16 × 4 5/16 inches—18,6 × 11 cm. Page from a sketchbook. Pencil, small ink blots. Verso: No. 243.

(a) Page upright: profile of a face, probably copied from a portrait of Frédéric Chopin.—(b) Study from *L'Ecorché,* see fig. 36. Judging by the style, it is one of the earliest of the studies from this famous plaster cast.

COLLECTIONS: Cézanne *fils,* Paris. Private collection, New York.

186. STUDIES AFTER DELACROIX, 1867–70

6 15/16 × 9 3/8 inches—17,6 × 23,8 cm. Page from the sketchbook 18 × 24 cm. Soft pencil, paper torn at the top, upper left corner restored. Verso: blank page.

(a) Top left: head of a woman, from Eugène Delacroix's *Women of Algiers,* in the Louvre. See fig. 24. Cézanne adopted this profile for the central woman bather in the painting Venturi No. 383.—(b) Top right: head, after the fallen soldier in Delacroix's canvas *Liberty guiding the People,* in the Louvre. See fig. 25.—(c) Lower left: head and shoulders of a man wearing a white collar, from an

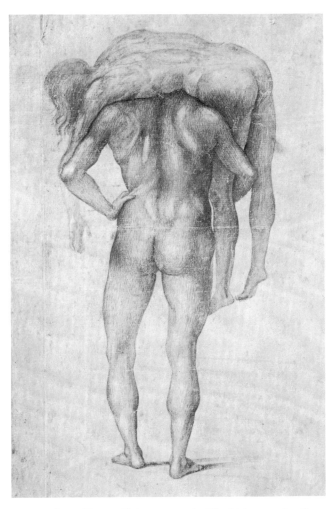

FIG. 22. Luca Signorelli (1440–1525): *The Living carrying the Dead* (or *The Demon*), drawing in the Cabinet des Dessins of the Louvre (Inv. No. 1801). Cézanne owned a photograph which is now in the Aix studio. *(Photograph: Roger Viollet)*

FIG. 23. Luca Signorelli (1440–1525): *Study of two standing men*, drawing in the Cabinet des Dessins of the Louvre (Inv. No. 1799). *(Photograph: Giraudon)*

unknown work.—(d) Struggle between a man on the ground and a wild animal, from an undetermined work, probably by Delacroix. Above to the left, crossed out: rough sketch of the same subject.—(e) Right edge, upside down, the handwritten words: "*Matr . . . est p . . . nostr/ regnum Jes . . . Christ . . ./Virgo prudentia/Maria bellissima/ virgo prudentia : ora pro nobis/sancta dei genitrix/ora pro nobis.*" The words *sancta dei genitrix* form part of the Litany of the Virgin; the rest of the text relates to no well-known liturgy. The word *bellissima* is Italian. See Note 25.

BIBLIOGRAPHY: Venturi No. 1585. Berthold, cat. No. 243 (reproduced) identifies the model of (a). Basel catalog, No. 31 (reproduced) identifies the model of (b) and the subsequent use of (a). Sara Lichtenstein, Cézanne and Delacroix, *AB*, March 1964, p. 55, Nos. 8-10, proposes Robaut No. 1095 for (d).

COLLECTIONS: Cézanne *fils*, Paris. W. Feuz, Bern. Kunst-museum, Basel.

187. FIGURES AT THE WATER'S EDGE, 1868–71

$4\frac{1}{16} \times 6\frac{11}{16}$ inches—10,3 × 17 cm. Page from the sketchbook 10,3 × 17 cm. Pencil, small stains. Verso: No. 128.

(a) Man lying on his stomach, looking forward.—(b) Stretch of water with a man swimming, and to his right the head of another bather, floating.—(c) Right, added later: bearded man sitting on the ground.

BIBLIOGRAPHY: Venturi, Vol. I, as verso of No. 1575 (not reproduced). Basel catalog, No. 75 (reproduced).

COLLECTIONS: Cézanne *fils*, Paris. W. Feuz, Bern. Kunst-museum, Basel.

188. LANDSCAPE, INCLUDING A MAN FISHING AND TWO LOVERS, 1868–70

$4\frac{1}{16} \times 6\frac{3}{4}$ inches—10,3 × 17,1 cm. Page from the sketchbook 10,3 × 17 cm. Pencil, restored tear top right, folds, ink stains, white gouache. Verso: No. 211.

Preliminary study for the painting Venturi No. 115.

BIBLIOGRAPHY: Venturi, Vol. I, as verso of No. 1574 (not reproduced). Basel catalog, No. 41 (reproduced).

COLLECTIONS: Cézanne *fils*, Paris. W. Feuz, Bern. Kunst-museum, Basel.

189. STUDIES OF SEVERAL FIGURES, 1865–70

$4\frac{7}{8} \times 8\frac{5}{16}$ inches—12,3 × 21,1 cm. From a sketch-book, paginated 39. Pencil, pen, and wash. Verso: No. 57.

(a) Pen sketch of a woman. The position of her arms indicates that she is in an armchair; the nostalgic expression on her face harmonizes with the romanticism expressed by the whole figure. Cf. the subject of *The Conversation*, Venturi No. 231, and our Nos. 251, 252.—(b) Right: pen sketch of two men wearing policemen's helmets; this rapid sketch recalls the subject of *The Carnival*, see No. 937. A roughly sketched head seems to indicate that the man on the right is clasping a woman to his chest.—(c) Lower left, in pencil: upper part of a figure emerging from the water, one arm stretched out to the left; cf. No. 258.—(d) Page upright, brush drawing over the other sketches: a woman, seen from the back as she walks away; drawn in flowing, pictorial strokes. Cf. No. 190.

COLLECTIONS: Cézanne *fils*, Paris. Huguette Berès, Paris. Mrs. Charles B. Nunnally, Atlanta, Georgia; on loan to the Atlanta Art Association.

190. COMPOSITION WITH FIVE FIGURES, 1868–71

$5\frac{13}{16} \times 7\frac{1}{4}$ inches—14,8 × 18,4 cm. Soft pencil on thin brownish paper, top part of the page restored, fold lower left, tears and stains. Verso: No. 3.

Preliminary study for a composition. Left, a group of three figures walking away together. Right, two lovers sitting on the ground. For one of the women walking, see No. 189 (d). Unusual page, the drawings very beautiful in the *fêtes galantes* tradition. See Note 25.

BIBLIOGRAPHY: Venturi, Vol. I, p. 350, *Oeuvres Inédites* (not reproduced). Basel catalog, No. 46 (reproduced). Dessins, 1957, No. 1 (reproduced).

COLLECTIONS: Cézanne *fils*, Paris. W. Feuz, Bern. Kunst-museum, Basel.

FIG. 24. Eugène Delacroix (1799–1863): *Femmes d'Alger dans leur appartement*, in the Louvre (detail on the left side). Oil on canvas, 1,80 m. × 2,29 m.; painted in 1834. Musée National du Louvre, *Catalogue des Peintures* I, 1924, No. 210. Robaut No. 482.   *(Photograph: Archives photographiques, Paris)*

FIG. 25. Eugène Delacroix (1799–1863): *La Liberté guidant le peuple*, in the Louvre (detail). Oil on canvas, 2,60 m. × 3,25 m. Painted in 1830, signed and dated. Robaut No. 326. Musée National du Louvre, *Catalogue des Peintures* I, 1924, No. 209.   *(Photograph: Giraudon)*

190A. TWO SKETCHES: (a) 1863–66; (b) 1868–71. (Not reproduced.)

$4\frac{3}{4} \times 7\frac{1}{2}$ inches—12,1 × 19 cm. Pencil, traces of framing. Verso: watercolor Venturi No. 880.

(a) Sketch covered by (b): man riding a horse, back view. His gestures show that he is speaking to someone on his left.—(b) Two lovers sitting on the ground under the foliage of a tree. Cf. No. 190, the two lovers on the right.

COLLECTIONS: Cézanne *fils*, Paris. Norton Simon, Inc. Los Angeles, County Museum of Art.

191. STUDIES OF A FEMALE FIGURE, 1867–70

$9\frac{3}{8} \times 6\frac{15}{16}$ inches—23,9 × 17,7 cm. Page from the sketchbook 18 × 24 cm. Soft pencil, corners damaged on the right. Verso: No. 240.

Sketches rendering movement, from an unidentified model. The same theme repeated five times: a woman under the stress of violent emotion, her hair streaming out to the right, clasping her head in her hands. Cézanne seems to have drawn directly from a painting, his main concern being to note the movement of arm, head, and waist of the woman, whom we see kneeling in No. 192. Cf. the studies Nos. 192, 193, 194.

BIBLIOGRAPHY: Venturi, Vol. I, as verso of No. 1577 (not reproduced). Basel catalog, No. 33 (reproduced).

COLLECTIONS: Cézanne *fils*, Paris. W. Feuz, Bern. Kunstmuseum, Basel.

192. STUDIES OF FIGURES IN MOVEMENT, 1866–69

$5\frac{1}{8} \times 5\frac{1}{2}$ inches—13 × 14 cm. Fragment of a page from the sketchbook 18 × 24 cm. Black crayon, corners cut. Verso: No. 155.

(a) Top left: figure doubled up: a confused sketch.—(b) Top right: woman carrying a basket or dish, cf. No. 193. —(c) Lower left: woman in profile, her knees bent, clutching her head, cf. Nos. 191, 193, 194.—(d) Right: fragment of another figure and the notation *No. 4 bis*, this latter by an alien hand.

BIBLIOGRAPHY: Sara Lichtenstein, An unpublished Portrait of Delacroix, and some Figure Sketches by Cézanne, *Master Drawings*, Vol. 4, p. 39 (reproduced pl. 34). Publishing this drawing for the first time, the author suggests that (a) is done from the drawing *The Education of Achilles* by Delacroix in the Louvre, (b) from *Ovid in Scythia* by the same artist, and (c) from *The Massacre of the Innocents*, painting by N. Poussin in the Musée Condé, Chantilly. Date proposed 1872–73.

COLLECTIONS: Joseph Rignault, Avignon. Musée Calvet, Avignon (Inv. No. 22.304).

193. PAGE OF STUDIES, 1867–70

$6\frac{3}{4} \times 9\frac{1}{16}$ inches—17,2 × 23 cm. Page from the sketchbook 18 × 24 cm. Pencil, corners of paper missing upper left and lower right. Verso: No. 194.

Page of studies comprising seven sketches: the figure of a woman clasping her head, seen four times; also a small dragon or reptile, a woman standing, seen in left lost profile, and lastly the rough sketch of a figure lying face down. The models for these copies have not been identified. Cf. Nos. 191, 192, 194.

COLLECTIONS: Paul Eluard, Paris. F. Baron, Paris. Marie Pierre de Cicco, New York. Present owner unknown.

194. PAGE OF STUDIES, 1867–70

$6\frac{3}{4} \times 9\frac{1}{16}$ inches—17,2 × 23 cm. Page from the sketch-book 18 × 24 cm. Pencil, corners of paper missing upper right and lower left. Verso: No. 193.

A dozen sketches done in a museum, designed to seize the movement of different figures. To date the sources remain untraced. The drawings are studies of figures, nude or draped, perhaps by Rubens or a Venetian painter. Half-way up on the left is the woman with her elbow raised who figures also in Nos. 191 and 193.

COLLECTIONS: Paul Eluard, Paris. F. Baron, Paris. Marie Pierre de Cicco, New York. Present owner unknown.

194bis. AFTER DELACROIX: WILD ANIMAL, AND FIGURE IN MOVEMENT, 1865–68

$7\frac{1}{16} \times 9\frac{7}{16}$ inches—18 × 24 cm. Page from the sketch-book 18 × 24 cm. Black crayon. Verso: No. 224 bis.

Three rapid studies: (a) Wild animal, its hindquarters seen from below; detail from the Apollo ceiling, see fig. 21. Cf. No. 181. This sketch was done in the Louvre from the original painting, whereas No. 181 seems to have been copied from an engraved reproduction.—(b) Figure in movement; the model for this sketch has not yet been identified. R. W. Ratcliffe thinks it is a study for *The Orgy*, Venturi No. 92. Cf. our No. 135 (d).—(c) Sketch of a head.

BIBLIOGRAPHY: Venturi, Vol. I, p. 349, *Oeuvres Inédites*: "Tigre de Delacroix; ange en prière" (not reproduced).

EXHIBITIONS: International Choice, Towner Art Gallery, Eastbourne, 1960, No. 97. Henry Roland Collection, City Art Gallery, Manchester, 1962, No. 24. H. R. Collection, City Art Gallery, Leeds, 1962, No. 24. Modern Drawings from the H.R. Collection, Fitzwilliam Museum, Cambridge, 1968, No. 2.

COLLECTIONS: Ambroise Vollard, Paris. Kenneth Clark, London. Sir Leigh Ashton, London. Dr. Henry Roland, Woking, Surrey.

195. STUDIES AFTER DELACROIX'S *Ceiling of Apollo*, 1867–70

$9 \times 6\frac{15}{16}$ inches—22,8 × 17,7 cm. Page from the sketchbook 18 × 24 cm. Soft pencil, tear at the upper edge, corners damaged. Light stains over the whole page. Verso: No. 160.

Sketches of three figures from Delacroix's Apollo Ceiling in the Louvre.—(a) Top center: The god Apollo drawing his bow and aiming at the serpent Python below him. See fig. 26.—(b) Left and at right angles: same subject.—(c) Right, beneath (a): same subject.—(d) Lower left, upside down: a figure seen back view, representing a *River*; see fig. 27 and cf. Nos. 181, 494.—(e) Right edge: *Minerva*, who is seen in the painting armed with a lance and shield; see fig. 28.

BIBLIOGRAPHY: Venturi, Vol. I, p. 351, *Oeuvres Inédites* (not reproduced). Berthold, cat. Nos. 240, 241 (reproduced); the models of (a), (b), (c), and (d) are determined. Basel catalog, No. 32 (reproduced) identifies the model of (e). Sara Lichtenstein, Cézanne and Delacroix, *AB*, March 1964, p. 55, Nos. 11, 12.

COLLECTIONS: Cézanne *fils*, Paris. W. Feuz, Bern. Kunst-museum, Basel.

FIG. 26. Eugène Delacroix (1799–1863): *Apollon sur son char*, detail of the Apollo ceiling in the Louvre. Musée National du Louvre, *Catalogue des Peintures* I, Plafonds et Peintures décoratives, p. 294. (*Photograph: R. W. Ratcliffe*)

196. THE DEATH OF CLEOPATRA, 1868–70

$3\frac{3}{4} \times 6\frac{5}{16}$ inches—9,5 × 16 cm. Fragment cut out of a page of studies. Pencil. Verso: unknown.

Sketch considered to be a preliminary study, but which is more probably drawn from a painting or tapestry. Lower left, written in pencil: *Mort de Cléopatre*. Classical architecture: fluted pilaster and arch of a vault. The model is as yet untraced.

COLLECTION: Pierre Dubaut, Paris.

197. THE RAPE, SKETCH, 1868–70

$4 \times 6\frac{11}{16}$ inches—10,2 × 17 cm. Page from the sketch-book 10,3 × 17 cm. Pencil, touches of white, fold upper right. Verso: No. 268.

A man about to violate a prostrate figure. The victim's hair is standing on end. A curtain in the background. On the right edge, cut-off fragment of a sketch which originally continued on the adjoining page. See Note 25.

BIBLIOGRAPHY: Venturi, Vol. I, p. 350, *Oeuvres Inédites* (not reproduced). Basel catalog, No. 44 (reproduced).

COLLECTIONS: Cézanne *fils*, Paris. W. Feuz, Bern. Kunst-museum, Basel.

FIG. 27. Eugène Delacroix (1799–1863): *Allegorical Figure of a River*, detail of the Apollo ceiling in the Louvre. Musée National du Louvre, *Catalogue des Peintures* I, Plafonds et Peintures décoratives, p. 294.   (*Photograph: R. W. Ratcliffe*)

FIG. 28. Eugène Delacroix (1799–1863): *Minerve et Mercure*, detail of the Apollo ceiling in the Louvre. Musée National du Louvre, *Catalogue des Peintures* I, Plafonds et Peintures décoratives, p. 294.   (*Photograph: R. W. Ratcliffe*)

198. THE REPUBLIC: ALLEGORY, circa 1871

$4\frac{1}{16} \times 6\frac{3}{4}$ inches—10,3 × 17,1 cm. Page from the sketchbook 10,3 × 17 cm. Pencil. Verso: No. 444.

This sketch is related to the enigmatic subject of a water-colored drawing (verso of No. 209). The woman is standing under a kind of arch, brandishing a sword with her right hand, her left holding a large French flag. See fig. 29. In the background: a mountain, and a sun disk with face and rays as in a child's drawing.

BIBLIOGRAPHY: Venturi, Vol. I, p. 350, *Oeuvres Inédites*, "Esquisse pour la 'Tentation de Saint-Antoine'" (not reproduced). Basel catalog, No. 42, "Tentation de saint Antoine" (reproduced). Th.Reff, *BurlM*, August 1963, p. 375: "The woman with raised arms is evidently invoking the rising sun, not offering herself, nor is it easy to discover a hermit in the tangle of lines before her." Douglas Cooper, in *Master Drawings*, Vol. 1, No. 4, 1963, p. 55.

COLLECTIONS: Cézanne *fils*, Paris. W. Feuz, Bern. Kunstmuseum, Basel.

199. FEMALE NUDES, DECORATED VASE, 1866–67

$9\frac{3}{16} \times 6\frac{15}{16}$ inches—23,4 × 17,7 cm. Page from the sketchbook 18 × 24 cm. Pencil on thick paper, upper corners of the paper damaged, several stains. Verso: No. 236.

(a) Four studies of a reclining female model leaning on her elbow. For the crosses and handwritten remarks, see Note 25. These studies served for one of the women in the left background of the canvas Venturi No. 101, *The Abduction*, dated 1867. There is also a watercolor of the same subject, Venturi No. 821, which is related to our drawing No. 200. L. Gowing, Th.Reff, and W. V. Andersen maintain that this woman's pose is inspired directly by Nicolas Poussin's painting *Echo and Narcissus*, in the Louvre. This is possible, although the nymph's knees are leaning to the left; also Cézanne could draw from female models at the Académie Suisse, and no one

FIG. 29. Paul Cézanne: *Allégorie de la République après 1870*. 11,9 cm. × 12,3 cm. Pencil and watercolor. Verso: No. 209. This subject, a woman carrying a sword and flag and surrounded by vanquished men, was often found in French reviews and newspapers after the events of 1870–71. The woman personifies the Commune when her flag is red; here the flag is the Tricolor and presumably represents the Republic. Collection of H. Vollmoeller, Zurich.

can know how often he employed models in his own studio. The four studies show different and quite usual poses.— (b) Below: study of a decorated vase shaped like a soup tureen with stylized figures for handles; cf. the vase in Venturi No. 106, *A Modern Olympia*.

BIBLIOGRAPHY: Venturi, Vol. I, p. 351, *Oeuvres Inédites* (not reproduced). Berthold, text pp. 45, 46 (reproduced Abb. 68). Basel catalog, No. 6 (reproduced). Th.Reff, Copyists in the Louvre, *AB*, XLVI, 1964, p. 555. W. V. Andersen, Cézanne's Portrait Drawings from the 1860's, *Master Drawings*, Vol. 5, No. 3 (reproduced p. 268).

COLLECTIONS: Cézanne *fils*, Paris. W. Feuz, Bern. Kunstmuseum, Basel.

200. STANDING MALE NUDE SEEN BACK VIEW, AND TWO STUDIES FOR *The Abduction*; NUDE, circa 1861, studies 1866–67

Pencil. Verso: blank page.

(a) Standing male nude seen back view, resembling No. 103; the legs are not modeled.—(b) Study for the painting Venturi No. 101, *The Abduction*, or more probably for the small watercolor of the same subject, Venturi No. 821. This project for a composition is framed with strokes. The couple is portrayed, and in the background are some women with arms raised. In the foreground, a confused sketch of a figure in lost profile.—(c) Right: repetition of this figure.—(d) The couple from *The Abduction* but with the ravisher's legs in a different position and his hair not disarranged by the wind.

BIBLIOGRAPHY: Venturi, Vol. I, p. 347 (not reproduced). Chûji Ikegami, The Drawings of Cézanne, *Bijutsushi*, No. 76, Tokyo, 1970 (reproduced pl. IIb).

EXHIBITIONS: Watercolors and Drawings, Museum of Modern Art, Tokyo, August 1954. Masterpieces of Occidental Painting, Municipal Museum, Kyoto, 1957, No. 88. Isetam, Tokyo, 1963, No. 9 (reproduced).

COLLECTIONS: Dr. Gachet, Auvers. Paul Gachet, Auvers. Private collection, Tokyo.

201. STUDIES, 1867–69

$6\frac{11}{16} \times 9\frac{7}{8}$ inches—17 × 25,1 cm. (in the center). Black crayon on blue paper, margins irregularly torn, an obliterated stain. Verso: blank page.

(a), (b), (c): Three studies of a right arm with clenched hand.—(d) Study of a shoulder.—(e) More complete figure, seen in right three-quarter view, resembling studies Nos. 202, 203.

BIBLIOGRAPHY: Venturi No. 1174.

COLLECTIONS: Camille Pissarro. Ludovico Rodo Pissarro, Paris. Sale X, Paris, February 22, 1942. James Lord, New York.

202. NUDE: WOMAN PULLING ON HER STOCKING, 1867–69

$6\frac{5}{16} \times 9\frac{1}{16}$ inches—16 × 23 cm. Page from the sketchbook 18 × 24 cm. Black crayon on blue paper, round stain. Verso: No. 204.

Seated female model seen in profile. Study for the painting Venturi No. 93. Cf. Nos. 201, 203.

BIBLIOGRAPHY: Venturi No. 1173.

EXHIBITION: Galerie Zak, Paris, 1934.

COLLECTIONS: Camille Pissarro. Anonymous sale, Paris, June 1, 1933, No. 8. Ludovico Rodo Pissarro, Paris. Galerie Zak, Paris. Present owner unknown.

203. NUDE: WOMAN PULLING ON HER STOCKING, 1867–69

$6\frac{5}{16} \times 9\frac{1}{16}$ inches—16 × 23 cm. Page from the sketchbook 18 × 24 cm. Black crayon on blue paper, round stain. Verso: blank page.

Seated female model seen in profile; two studies of the same pose, for the painting Venturi No. 93. Cf. Nos. 202, 204.

BIBLIOGRAPHY: Venturi No. 1172. J. Rewald, Sources d'inspiration de Cézanne, *AA*, May 1936, p. 189 (reproduced fig. 99).

EXHIBITION: Galerie Zak, Paris, 1934.

COLLECTIONS: Camille Pissarro. Ludovico Rodo Pissarro, Paris. Dr. and Mrs. Peter Neubauer, New York.

204. NUDE: WOMAN DOING HER HAIR, 1867–69

$6\frac{5}{16} \times 9\frac{1}{16}$ inches—16 × 23 cm. Page from the sketchbook 18 × 24 cm. Black crayon on blue paper, round stain. Verso: No. 202.

Two fine studies of the same model in the same pose, for the painting Venturi No. 93, which was also in Camille Pissarro's collection. Cf. Nos. 202, 203.

BIBLIOGRAPHY: Venturi No. 1171. J. Rewald, Sources d'inspiration de Cézanne, *AA,* May 1936, p. 189 (the right part reproduced fig. 99).

COLLECTIONS: Camille Pissarro. Ludovico Rodo Pissarro, Paris. Mr. and Mrs. Philip Weisberg, New York.

205. ACADEMY DRAWING: MALE NUDE IN THE POSE OF AN OARSMAN, 1867–69

$8\frac{15}{16} \times 11\frac{3}{4}$ inches—22,7 × 29,9 cm. Pencil on laid paper, watermark MICHALLET. Verso: No. 81.

Three studies of a male model posing as an oarsman; the central figure is the most complete. Movement is expressed in these studies, which is rare in the academy nudes.

BIBLIOGRAPHY: Venturi No. 1175. Huyghe–Jacottet, *Le Dessin français au XIXe siècle,* Lausanne, 1948, No. 104, (reproduced). Neumeyer, 1958, No. 3 (reproduced). Longstreet, 1964 (reproduced). H. R. Hoetink, *Franse Tekeningen uit de 19e Eeuw,* Rotterdam, 1968, No. 14 recto (reproduced); date 1867–69. Chûji Ikegami, The Drawings of Cézanne, *Bijutsushi* No. 76, Tokyo, 1970 (reproduced p. 132).

EXHIBITIONS: Amsterdam, 1946, No. 4. The Hague, 1956, No. 93 (reproduced). Zurich, 1956, No. 146 (reproduced). Munich, 1956, No. 112 (reproduced).

COLLECTIONS: F. Koenigs, Haarlem. Boymans-van Beuningen Museum, Rotterdam (Inv. F II 25).

206. FLYING FIGURE AND ARCHITECTURAL STUDIES, 1866–69

$9\frac{15}{16} \times 6\frac{3}{4}$ inches—23,6 × 17,2 cm. Page from the sketchbook 18 × 24 cm. Pencil, stains. Stamp of the Koenigs collection. Verso: No. 233.

(a) Figure flying through the air like an angel. According to H. R. Hoetink, Curator of the Boymans-van Beuningen Museum, this study is from Paul Veronese's oval painting *Jupiter striking down Crime* in the Louvre.—(b) Three architectural studies: capital of a small column supporting a lintel; copied from an unidentified source.

BIBLIOGRAPHY: Venturi, No. 1185. Berthold, cat. No. 306 (reproduced). *Selearte*, anno X, No. 52, 1961, "the original model is the angel upper right in *The Circumcision* by Malosso (G. B. Trotti), formerly in the Louvre." First at St. Philippe-du-Roule, since 1969 this painting is at St. Nicolas-des-Champs. The angel is portrayed as a gentle adolescent; the garments on his back correspond to the sketch, but the arms and one of the legs do not correspond. H. R. Hoetink, *Franse Tekeningen uit de 19e Eeuw*, Rotterdam, 1968, No. 21 verso; date 1866–70 (reproduced).

COLLECTIONS: F. Koenigs, Haarlem. Boymans-van Beuningen Museum, Rotterdam (Inv. F II 120).

207. STUDIES, INCLUDING THE *Milo of Crotona*, (a) 1866–69, (b) 1870–73

$9\frac{3}{8} \times 12\frac{3}{16}$ inches—23,8 × 31 cm. Pencil on laid paper. Stamp of the Koenigs collection. Verso: No. 354.

Two subjects, on a page of which the lower edge has been cut off.—(a) Upper part of Pierre Puget's marble statue *Milo of Crotona*, in the Louvre. See fig. 30.—(b) Framed by strokes: a country scene with three men lighting a wood fire and a fourth, his back turned, gathering wood. A dog, two leafy trees.

BIBLIOGRAPHY: Venturi No. 1448. Berthold, cat. No. 99 (reproduced Abb. 75). H. R. Hoetink, *Franse Tekeningen uit de 19e Eeuw*, Rotterdam, 1968, No. 19 verso (reproduced); date: (a) slightly earlier than (b), which is 1876–77.

COLLECTIONS: Cassirer, Berlin. F. Koenigs, Haarlem. Boymans-van Beuningen Museum, Rotterdam, Inv. F II 118.

208. MALE NUDE, 1864–67

$7\frac{7}{8} \times 10\frac{1}{8}$ inches—20 × 25,7 cm. Charcoal on laid paper. Stain covering the lower left corner, blots (cleaned). Verso: blank page.

(a) Left: man lying on his right side, seen as though on an inclined plane. The study seeks to define contours by the use of multiple strokes.—(b) Right: bent leg seen from in front, with a highlight above the knee; genitals.

BIBLIOGRAPHY: Berthold (reproduced Abb. 73). Rewald, *History of Impressionism*, New York, 1961 (reproduced p. 63).

EXHIBITION: Kunsthalle, Basel, 1936, No. 102.

COLLECTIONS: W. Walter, Paris. C. Pickhardt, Sherborn, Mass. C. E. Pickhardt, Cambridge, Mass.

209. MAN ON HORSEBACK AND WOMAN AT A WINDOW, circa 1868

$4\frac{11}{16} \times 4\frac{7}{8}$ inches—11,9 × 12,3 cm. Fragment of a page from a sketchbook. Pen. Verso: watercolor drawing, see fig. 29.

FIG. 30. Pierre Puget (1620–94): *Milo of Crotona*. Formerly in the park of the Château de Versailles (1682), now in the Louvre. 270 cm. × 140 cm. Musée National du Louvre, *Catalogue des Sculptures* II, 1922, No. 1466. Puget created three figures, heroic in conception, representing Strength: Strength in action—Hercules slaying the Hydra (Musée de Rouen); Strength reposing—Hercules resting; Strength overcome by suffering and death—Milo of Crotona.

(Photograph: R. W. Ratcliffe)

The lower edge of the page has been cut off. A rider is seen guiding his horse toward the right background, while a woman makes a gesture to him from a window surrounded by the foliage of a climbing plant. Romantic scene, probably copied from an illustration. The arcs formed by the horse's mane and the top of the doorway should be noticed.

COLLECTIONS: Juliette Cramer, Paris. H. Wollmoeller, Zurich.

210. AFTER GÉRICAULT: *Turkish horse in a stable*, 1867–71

$9\frac{1}{16} \times 7\frac{1}{16}$ inches—23 × 18 cm. Page from the sketchbook 18 × 24 cm. Pencil. Verso: blank page.

This drawing, which Venturi had seen in reproduction and which he excluded from his 1936 catalog, is drawn from the canvas *Turkish Horse in a Stable* by Géricault, in the Louvre; source identified by R. W. Ratcliffe in 1963. See fig. 31. For the treatment, cf. Nos. 171, 184. The horse has an oriental saddle, but neither girth nor bridle.

BIBLIOGRAPHY: Eugenio d'Ors, *Cézanne*, Paris, 1930 (reproduced pl. X). *Cézanne dessinateur* (reproduced fig. 19).

EXHIBITION: Kunsthalle, Basel, 1921, No. 48.
COLLECTIONS: Bernheim-Jeune, Paris. Vallotton, Lausanne. Tanner, Zurich. Albin Tanner, Meggen, Lucerne.

FIG. 31. Théodore Géricault (1791–1824): *Cheval turc dans une écurie*, 35 cm. × 25 cm. Oil on paper backed by canvas, in the Louvre. Catalog, 1959, No. 931. Acquired in 1849.
(Photograph: Archives photographiques, Paris)

FIG. 32. Engraving from Charles Blanc, *Ecole hollandaise*, Paris, 1861, reproducing a picture by Paulus Potter (1625–54) *Horses at the trough*, or *Cart horses at a cottage door in the neighborhood of Delft*, in the Louvre. *Catalogue sommaire des peintures exposées au Musée du Louvre*, by Louis Demonts and Lucien Huteau, Paris, 1923, No. 2526—XII.
(Photograph: Chappuis)

FIG. 33. Giambattista Moroni (1525–78), or Bartolommeo Passarotti (1529–92): *Ritratti d'Incogniti*, painting in the Pinacoteca Capitolina, Rome. See Settimo Bocconi, *Musei Capitolini, Pinacoteca e Tabularium*, Rome, 1925, p. 257, No. 70.
(Photograph: Alinari-Giraudon)

211. AFTER P. POTTER: *Horse at the trough*, 1870–73

$4\frac{1}{16} \times 6\frac{3}{4}$ inches—10,3 × 17 cm. Page from the sketchbook 10,3 × 17 cm. Pencil, restored tear above the horse's croup, lengthwise fold near the hoofs. Several repairs, ink stains. Verso: No. 188.

Drawing after an engraving of Paulus Potter's painting in the Louvre reproduced in Blanc's *Ecole hollandaise* (see fig. 32). In delicate strokes with the contours reinforced; details such as the hairs of the fetlocks are represented. On the right, a handwritten notation: *N 3 Fossés St.-Jacques*, and *24f*, crossed out.

BIBLIOGRAPHY: Venturi No. 1574. Basel catalog, No. 63 (reproduced). Longstreet, 1964 (reproduced).

COLLECTIONS: Cézanne *fils*, Paris. W. Feuz, Bern. Kunstmuseum, Basel.

212. STUDIES AFTER PASSAROTTI, DOMENICHINO, AND AN UNKNOWN MASTER, 1867–70

$6\frac{15}{16} \times 9\frac{1}{16}$ inches—17,7 × 23 cm. Page from the sketchbook 18 × 24 cm. Pencil, tear upper left, brown stain and paper scraped at the lower edge, blotches of color. Verso: No. 232.

(a) Left: two men of the sixteenth century, one of them holding a kind of clarinet. From a reproduction of the painting *Portrait of Two Unknown Men* by G. Moroni or B. Passarotti, in the Pinacoteca Capitolina, Rome; see fig. 33.—(b) Center: a right hand.—(c) Above: head and shoulders of a woman with arms raised, from the painting *Diana and her Companions* by Domenichino; see fig. 34.—(d) Right: head of a woman, in left profile, from an undetermined model.—(e) On this women's forehead: seated female nude; see fig. 34, the woman on the right. Above: sketch of a finger. See Note 25.

BIBLIOGRAPHY: Venturi No. 1579. Berthold, cat. Nos. 272, 286 (reproduced Abb. 33). Basel catalog, No. 24 (reproduced). Th.Reff, *AB*, June 1960, p. 148. Longstreet, 1964 (reproduced).

COLLECTIONS: Cézanne *fils*, Paris. W. Feuz, Bern. Kunstmuseum, Basel.

213. HEAD AND SHOULDERS OF A GIRL, 1867–70

$8\frac{1}{4} \times 6\frac{1}{2}$ inches—21 × 16 cm. Page from a sketchbook. Pencil. Verso: No. 56.

Girl seen in right lost profile; the tassel of her bonnet hangs down between her shoulders. Perhaps a copy.

COLLECTION: Cézanne *fils*, Paris. Jean-Pierre Cézanne, Paris. Sale, Galerie G. Giroux, Brussels, Feb. 6, 1954. A. Maurice, Brussels.

FIG. 34. Domenico Zampieri, known as Domenichino (1581–1641): *La Caccia di Diana,* 1617 (detail). Borghese Gallery, Rome. *(Photograph: Anderson-Giraudon)*

214. AFTER SEBASTIANO DEL PIOMBO: *Christ in Limbo,* 1869–70

$9\frac{1}{4} \times 4\frac{15}{16}$ inches—23,5 × 11 cm. Pencil on laid paper. Verso: No. 775.

The drawing represents the figure of Christ, from *Christ in Limbo* by Sebastiano del Piombo. Cézanne copied an engraving of this picture in Charles Blanc's book *Ecole Espagnole* (1869), where it is attributed to the painter Navarette; see fig. 35. Cf. the painting of the same subject, Venturi No. 84.

BIBLIOGRAPHY: Venturi, Vol. I, p. 352, *Oeuvres Inédites* (not reproduced). Berthold, cat. No. 285 (not reproduced). Th.Reff, *AB,* June 1960 (reproduced fig. 2).

COLLECTIONS: Pierre Loeb, Paris. Mr. and Mrs. J. Rewald, New York. E. Thaw, New York. M. Feilchenfeldt, Zurich.

215. WOMAN, STANDING, 1867–70

$9\frac{1}{16} \times 5\frac{15}{16}$ inches—23 × 15 cm. Page from a sketchbook. Black crayon.

Unfinished sketch of a woman, study similar to Nos. 216 and 218. Beneath it can be seen the counterproof of a sketch resembling No. 216, not otherwise known.

COLLECTION: Present owner unknown.

216. WOMAN, STANDING, 1866–69

$8\frac{1}{2} \times 5\frac{1}{2}$ inches—21,5 × 14 cm. Page from a sketchbook. Black crayon and pen on light-brown paper. Verso, blank page.

(a) Woman standing with her right hand held to her chin; cf. No. 217.—(b) Underneath this drawing and upside down: pen and pencil sketch representing an ancient warrior in a helmet, seen in right profile. This sketch is earlier than the former.

COLLECTIONS: Private collection, Paris. Sale, Sotheby's, London, Nov. 25, 1964, No. 118 (reproduced). Rayner. Present owner unknown.

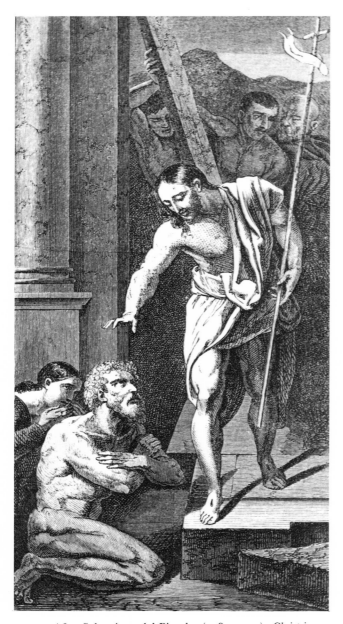

FIG. 35. After Sebastiano del Piombo (1485–1547): *Christ in Limbo,* engraving printed in Charles Blanc, *Ecole espagnole* (1869), where the work is attributed to the painter Navarrete.
(Photograph: Chappuis)

217. HEAD AND SHOULDERS OF A WOMAN, 1866–69

$8\frac{1}{16} \times 4\frac{15}{16}$ inches—20,5 × 12,5 cm. Black crayon. Verso: blank page.

Vigorous drawing of the head and shoulders of a woman, probably done from an academy model. For the treatment, cf. Nos. 112 and 216.

COLLECTIONS: Private collection, Paris. Sale, Sotheby's, London, Nov. 25, 1964, No. 119 (reproduced). Roberts, London.

218. WOMAN STANDING, KNOWN AS *La Musicienne*, 1866–69

$8\frac{1}{16} \times 4\frac{15}{16}$ inches—20,5 × 12,5 cm. Black crayon and pencil, small stains. Verso: pencil and watercolor studies.

(a) Woman standing up holding a conductor's baton.—(b) Lengthwise: light sketches covered by (a), and undecipherable except for the head of a bearded man, perhaps a pastiche of the *Jupiter* of Ingres; see No. 50.

COLLECTIONS: Huguette Berès, Paris. Present owner unknown.

219. STUDIES OF VARIOUS FIGURES, 1870–72

$4\frac{7}{8} \times 8\frac{9}{16}$ inches—12,4 × 21,7 cm. Page XLII verso of the sketchbook A.I.C. Pencil and pen. Verso: some numbers written by the artist's son and a cat's ears drawn by Cézanne; small rough sketch, not classified. Reproduced by Schniewind.

(a) Left, pen drawing: head and shoulders of a bearded man wearing a low-crowned hat; his eyes are most expressive. In front of the hat is an ellipse, in pencil, which brings to mind certain signatures of the artist.—(b) Center, in pencil: man sitting down, seen in right lost profile with his hand raised. Schniewind thought that this man was Alexis (see the canvas *Reading at Zola's,* Venturi No. 118, and also Nos. 221, 222), but this identification is debatable and there is little concordance between dates.—(c) Top, pen: head of a man wearing a cap.—(d) Right: head of a bearded man.—(e) Rough pen sketch of the same profile.

BIBLIOGRAPHY: Rewald, *Carnets:* C II, p. XLII verso (reproduced p. 16). Schniewind, text p. 32 (reproduced). Perruchot, *La Vie de Cézanne,* Paris, 1958 (partially reproduced on the inside of the cover). Andersen, *Sk.* (not reproduced).

COLLECTIONS: Cézanne *fils,* Paris. M. Renou, Paris. Poyet, Lyons. M. Renou, Paris. Sam Salz, New York. Art Institute, Chicago.

220. READING AT ZOLA'S, 1867–69

$5\frac{5}{16} \times 4\frac{1}{8}$ inches—13,5 × 10,5 cm. Pencil on beige paper. Verso: blank page.

Zola and another man are seen sitting in what seems to be a rather small room. Study for the paintings Venturi Nos. 117 and 118, but without any direct relation to either. Cf. Nos. 219 (b), 221, 222.

BIBLIOGRAPHY: Venturi No. 1199. Vollard 1914 (reproduced p. 61). W. V. Andersen, Cézanne's Portrait Drawings from the 1860's, *Master Drawings,* Vol. 5, No. 3, 1967 (reproduced pl. 20).

COLLECTION: Kenneth Clark, London.

221. READING AT ZOLA'S, 1867–69

$5\frac{1}{8} \times 6\frac{1}{8}$ inches—$13 \times 15,5$ cm. Pencil on paper browned with age. Verso: blank page.

Zola and another man are seen sitting in a room. Study for the painting Venturi No. 118. Cf. Nos. 219 (b), 220, 222.

BIBLIOGRAPHY: Venturi No. 1198. W. V. Andersen, Cézanne's Portrait Drawings from the 1860's, *Master Drawings*, Vol. 5, No. 3, 1967 (reproduced pl. 23).

COLLECTIONS: Durand-Ruel, Paris. Sale, Bollag, Zurich, April 3, 1925, No. 38 (reproduced). Present owner unknown.

222. READING SESSION, STUDIES, 1866–67

$5\frac{5}{8} \times 7\frac{3}{4}$ inches—$14,3 \times 19,6$ cm. Pencil on laid paper browned with age, small stains. Verso: No. 773.

Study for the painting *Reading at Zola's*, Venturi No. 118. —(a) Left: two men at a table; the one seated, seen in right lost profile, is holding a pen, the other is sketched both seated and standing, one figure over the other.— (b) Right: man sitting on a chair holding a paper, his legs crossed and his hair falling down over the nape of his neck. (c) Above: rough sketch repeating his head and arm.— A few years later Cézanne did a painting showing Zola and Alexis sitting in front of a house (Venturi No. 117) in poses resembling those in our drawing, but this does not prove that the bearded figure of the drawing is a portrait of Zola; writers of similar aspect appear in other works. Cf. Nos. 158, 220, 221. See Note 25.

BIBLIOGRAPHY: Venturi, Vol. I, p. 351, *Oeuvres Inédites* (not reproduced). Basel catalog, No. 54 (reproduced). J. Rewald, *Cézanne*, Paris, 1939 (reproduced fig. 22). Th.Reff, *BurlM*, August 1963, p. 375. Douglas Cooper, in *Master Drawings*, Vol. 1, No. 4, 1963, p. 56. H. Mitterand & J. Vidal, *Album Zola*, N.R.F., 1963 (reproduced). W. V. Andersen, Cézanne's Portrait Drawings from the 1860's, *Master Drawings*, Vol. 5, No. 3, 1967 (reproduced pl. 22).

COLLECTIONS: Cézanne *fils*, Paris. W. Feuz, Bern. Kunstmuseum, Basel.

223. READING IN THE GARDEN, circa 1868

$4\frac{15}{16} \times 8\frac{15}{16}$ inches—$12,5 \times 22,6$ cm. Pencil on pale gray paper, light stains. Verso: fragmentary sketch of a house, not listed.

Five men around a table outdoors, two of them standing, the figure in the center looking through some papers. This drawing corresponds to a project of Cézanne's alluded to by Marion in his latter to Morstatt of May 24, 1868: "Cézanne intends to do a canvas for which he will use the portraits. One of us, in the middle of a landscape, will be talking while the others listen. I have your photograph and you will figure in it." (See Scolari and Barr, in the Bibliography). Cf. Venturi No. 1190.

BIBLIOGRAPHY: Venturi, Vol. I, p. 351, *Oeuvres Inédites* (not reproduced). Basel catalog, No. 53 (reproduced). M. Scolari and A. Barr, Cézanne d'après les lettres de Marion à Morstatt 1865–68, *GBA*, Jan. 1938; also, Cézanne in the Letters of Marion to Morstatt 1865–68, *Magazine of Art*, Feb., April, May, 1938. Douglas Cooper, in *Master Drawings*, Vol. 1, No. 4, 1963, p. 56.

COLLECTIONS: Cézanne *fils*, Paris. W. Feuz, Bern. Kunstmuseum, Basel.

224. AROUND A TABLE IN THE GARDEN, circa 1868

$8\frac{1}{4} \times 11$ inches—21×28 cm. Pastel, white gouache, and pencil. Reverse side inaccessible.

Preliminary study for a painting; for the subject, see No. 223. In the present version Cézanne seems to be striving for the effect of volumes and values.

BIBLIOGRAPHY: Venturi No. 1190 (date 1870-77).

COLLECTIONS: Cézanne *fils*, Paris. Present owner unknown.

224 bis. AROUND A TABLE IN THE GARDEN, circa 1868

$7\frac{1}{16} \times 9\frac{7}{16}$ inches—18×24 cm. Black crayon. Verso: No. 194 bis.

Six men around a table under the trees. On the left two are seated and one is standing; on the right the first is seated, a second standing, and a third, in a Barbizon hat, crouching. This last man is sketched in two different attitudes: one shows him leaning toward a cat, the other standing erect. In the left background: two silhouettes of a child, or a child and a dog. Cf. Nos. 223, 224, and the commentary of No. 223. Lower right: the word *tel*, see Note 25.

BIBLIOGRAPHY: Venturi, Vol. I, p. 349, *Oeuvres Inédites*, "Déjeuner. A table, sous les arbres" (not reproduced).

COLLECTIONS: Ambroise Vollard, Paris. Kenneth Clark, London. Sir Leigh Ashton, London. Dr. Henry Roland, Woking, Surrey.

225. MAN SITTING DOWN, 1871–74

$8\frac{1}{2} \times 5$ inches—$21,6 \times 12,7$ cm. Page VIII verso from the second sketchbook Mrs. Enid A. Haupt. Pencil. Verso: No. 587.

Man in a round hat, his arms stretched forward as though sketching or playing cards. I am tempted to relate this sketch to No. 143, portraying a young artist.

BIBLIOGRAPHY: Rewald, *Carnets:* CIV, page VIII verso, "Study for a cardplayer or smoker?" (not reproduced).

COLLECTIONS: Cézanne *fils*, Paris. M. Renou, Paris. Poyet, Lyons. M. Renou, Paris. Sam Salz, New York. Mrs. Enid A. Haupt, New York.

226. PAGE OF STUDIES, INCLUDING ONE OF ACHILLE EMPERAIRE, pen: 1858–61; pencil: 1867–70

$3\frac{15}{16} \times 4\frac{5}{16}$ inches—10×11 cm. (sight). Pencil and pen. Verso: No. 55.

(a) Top: pencil sketch of Achille Emperaire; cf. Nos. 227, 228, 229, 242.—(b) Upside down: lower half (top cut off) of a figure in a dress, carrying a lantern; pen drawing.

BIBLIOGRAPHY: W. V. Andersen, Cézanne's Portrait Drawings from the 1860's, *Master Drawings*, Vol. 5, No. 3, 1967 (reproduced on the left, p. 273).

COLLECTIONS: Lucien Blanc, Aix-en-Provence. Atelier Cézanne, Aix-en-Provence.

227. STUDIES OF HEADS, ONE OF ACHILLE EMPERAIRE, 1867–70

$11\frac{3}{8} \times 9\frac{13}{16}$ inches—$28,9 \times 24,9$ cm. Pencil and pen on strong brownish paper, stains. Verso: No. 104.

(a) Pencil: head of Achille Emperaire, in left profile.—

(b) India ink: three studies of a man's head, one of them smudged. Cf. Nos. 226, 242. For the word *tel* and a cross (at lower right, not visible in photograph), see Note 25.

BIBLIOGRAPHY: Venturi, Vol. I, as verso of No. 1584 (not reproduced). Basel catalog, No. 51 (reproduced). W. V. Andersen, Cézanne's Portrait Drawings from the 1860's, *Master Drawings*, Vol. 5, No. 3 (reproduced fig. 7). Error: figs. 7 and 8 are transposed.

COLLECTIONS: Cézanne *fils*, Paris. W. Feuz, Bern. Kunstmuseum Basel.

228. PORTRAIT OF ACHILLE EMPERAIRE, 1867–70

$12 \times 9\frac{1}{2}$ inches—30,6 × 24,1 cm. Charcoal on gray laid paper. Watermark: M in a shield and, separate, the number 579. Stains and traces of paint, several holes, tear above the head. Verso: blank page.

Portrait of the painter Achille Emperaire, somewhat similar to the canvas Venturi No. 88. The composition has a certain affinity to Italian primitive paintings.

BIBLIOGRAPHY: Venturi, Vol. I, p. 352, *Oeuvres Inédites* (not reproduced). Basel catalog, No. 49 (reproduced). W. V. Andersen, Cézanne's Portrait Drawings from the 1860's, *Master Drawings*, Vol. 5, No. 3 (reproduced fig. 18).

COLLECTIONS: Cézanne *fils*, Paris. W. Feuz, Bern. Kunstmuseum, Basel.

229. HEAD OF ACHILLE EMPERAIRE, 1867–70

$17 \times 12\frac{9}{16}$ inches—43,2 × 31,9 cm. Charcoal on paper browned with age, the lines of the laid paper are apparent. Watermark: D & C BLAUW. Top: corners restored, small strip added. Verso: blank page.

Portrait of the painter Achille Emperaire (who was born and died in Aix-en-Provence, 1829–98) showing the head, slightly turned toward the right, and a collar. Study for the painting Venturi No. 88. Cf. Nos. 228, 230. Remarkable early work, done with the intention of producing a fine drawing. Emperaire was born ten years before Cézanne and was a cripple; the two fellow-citizens, who had grown up in Aix without knowing each other, met in Paris.

BIBLIOGRAPHY: Venturi No. 1194. Basel catalog, No. 50 (reproduced both in the volume of plates and on its dustcover). Vollard, 1914 (reproduced p. 161). Raymond Cogniat, *Le Siècle des Impressionnistes*, Flammarion, Paris, 1959 (reproduced p. 84). Longstreet, 1964 (reproduced). W. V. Andersen, Cézanne's Portrait Drawings from the 1860's, *Master Drawings*, Vol. 5, No. 3, p. 265 (reproduced pl. 20). Chiuji Ikegami, The Drawings of Cézanne, *Bijutsushi* No. 76, Tokyo, 1970 (reproduced pl. I).

EXHIBITIONS: Orangerie, Paris, 1936, No. 149. De Watteau à Cézanne, Geneva, 1951, No. 90.

COLLECTIONS: Cézanne *fils*, Paris. L. Lichtenhan, Basel. Kunstmuseum, Basel.

230. PORTRAIT OF ACHILLE EMPERAIRE, 1867–70

$19\frac{1}{4} \times 12\frac{3}{16}$ inches—49 × 31 cm. Charcoal, pencil, and white color on laid paper, stains. Verso: blank page.

The painter Achille Emperaire, Cézanne's friend, seen in left three-quarter profile, his head bent over his shoulder.

Study for the painting Venturi No. 85. Cf. Nos. 226, 228, 229, 242.

BIBLIOGRAPHY: Venturi No. 1195. Vollard, 1914 (reproduced p. 17). F. Novotny, *Cézanne*, Phaidon, Vienna, Paris, and London, 1937 (reproduced pl. 116). W. V. Andersen, Cézanne's Portrait Drawings from the 1860's, *Master Drawings*, Vol. 5, No. 3 (reproduced fig. 19). *GBA*, Feb. 1968, *La Chronique des Arts*, No. 1189, No. 66 (reproduced p. 19).

EXHIBITIONS: Orangerie, Paris, 1936, No. 141. Kunsthalle, Basel, 1936, No. 99 (reproduced). San Francisco, 1937, No. 54 (reproduced). Wildenstein, London, 1939, No. 75. Vingt ans d'acquisitions au Musée du Louvre, Paris, 1967–68, No. 450.

COLLECTIONS: Cézanne *fils*, Paris. Renou & Colle, Paris. A. Chappuis, Tresserve. Cabinet des Dessins of the Louvre, Paris (RF 31 778).

231. HEAD OF A MAN, 1867–70

$11\frac{13}{16} \times 9\frac{1}{4}$ inches—30 × 23,5 cm. Charcoal on laid paper. Watermark: crown surrounded by crescents. Verso: blank page.

Head of a man with a mass of hair, contrasts of light on his face; he is wearing a smock, indicated by a few strokes. The whole is somewhat academic, but the characteristic Cézanne treatment is apparent in the blocking-in, the grisaille, the contours of the cheek on the left, and the fading off toward the ear on the right.

COLLECTIONS: A. L. sale, Berlin, Oct. 29, 1925, No. 224 (reproduced). Henry Oppenheimer, London; Oppenheimer sale, Christie's, London, July 1936, "Paul Cézanne, study of a man's head, charcoal $11\frac{3}{4} \times 9\frac{1}{4}$ inches (not reproduced). Private collection, England. Arthur Tooth & Sons, London.

232. PORTRAIT OF FORTUNÉ MARION, AND *L'Écorché*, 1869–73

$9\frac{1}{16} \times 6\frac{15}{16}$ inches—23 × 17,7 cm. Page from the sketchbook 18 × 24 cm. Pencil and pen, tear lower right. Verso: No. 212.

(a) Head and shoulders, with the lapel of the coat, of a young bearded man, probably Fortuné Marion.—(b) Right: trousered legs, crossed.—(c) Upper left, upside down, in ink: abdomen and thighs drawn from *L'Écorché*, see fig. 36.—(d) Bottom left, pen drawing: head and chest of *L'Écorché*.

BIBLIOGRAPHY: Venturi, as verso of No. 1579 (not reproduced). Berthold, cat. No. 81 (reproduced). Basel catalog, No. 52 (reproduced). W. V. Andersen, Cézanne's Portrait Drawings from the 1860's, *Master Drawings*, Vol. 5, No. 3, p. 265 (reproduced pl. 17b).

COLLECTIONS: Cézanne *fils*, Paris. W. Feuz, Bern. Kunstmuseum, Basel.

233. PORTRAIT OF THE PAINTER GUILLAUMIN, 1869–72

$9\frac{5}{16} \times 6\frac{3}{4}$ inches—23,6 × 17,2 cm. Page from the sketchbook 18 × 24 cm. Soft pencil, numerous stains. Verso: No. 206.

Portrait of a young bearded man: the painter Armand Guillaumin (1841–1927), a friend of Cézanne's. W. V.

FIG. 36. *L'Ecorché:* figure (formerly attributed to Michelangelo) showing the muscles of the human body. Our photograph is taken from a modern plaster cast, made for drawing schools from a wax model at that time in the Kaiser Friedrich Museum in Berlin, similar to the one owned by Cézanne (now mutilated). Height: about 21cm. The exact origin of this sculptured figure remains obscure.

(Photograph: Giraudon)

Andersen compares this drawing with the self-portrait by Guillaumin in the Vincent W. van Gogh collection, Laren. The resemblance to the portrait in the Gachet Donation (see fig. 37) seems to me even more striking, although the figure is facing the other way. Cf. the etching Venturi No. 1159, *Guillaumin au pendu.*

BIBLIOGRAPHY: Venturi No. 1196. W. V. Andersen, *Cézanne's Portrait Drawings from the 1860's, Master Drawings,* Vol. 5, No. 3 (reproduced fig. 17a; dated circa 1867). H. R. Hoetink, *Franse Tekeningen uit de 19e Eeuw,* Rotterdam, 1968, No. 21 (reproduced; dated 1866); the author does not identify Guillaumin.

EXHIBITIONS: Kunsthalle, Basel, 1936, No. 111. Amsterdam, 1946, No. 7.

COLLECTIONS: F. Koenigs, Haarlem. Boymans-van Beuningen Museum, Rotterdam (Inv. F II 120).

234. HEAD OF A WOMAN, 1869–73

$17\frac{3}{4} \times 11\frac{7}{16}$ inches—45×29 cm. Fragment of a large sheet. Pastel and sanguine, folds and stains. Reverse side inaccessible.

Head seen in right profile; vigorous drawing. The stroke resembles that of No. 232.

BIBLIOGRAPHY: Venturi No. 1209, dated 1865–70.

COLLECTION: Dr. Corsy, Jas de Bouffan, Aix-en-Provence.

235. THE EMBRACE, 1869–72

$5\frac{13}{16} \times 7\frac{7}{16}$ inches—$14,8 \times 18,8$ cm. Pencil. Verso: No. 235bis.

(a) Left: drawing reproduced by Vollard, 1914. *The Embrace,* title chosen by Vollard, was nearer to the truth than Venturi's title, *Sketch for Tartuffe,* since the drawing does not correspond to any scene in Molière's comedy. In spite of the erotic pose, the style of the study is prudent, accentuating the force of the woman's body as opposed to that of the man. Cf. the watercolored drawing Venturi No. 1206.—(b) Right and upside down: four men around a table. Though they have been taken for card players, to me it seems rather to be a scene of animated discussion, even accusation. Across the leg of the man sitting on the right there is a cropping line in the form of a triangle, by an alien hand. See Note 25.

BIBLIOGRAPHY: Venturi No. 1186 ((a) only reproduced, after Vollard). Vollard 1914 ((a) only reproduced, p. 155). Meier-Graefe, *Cézanne und sein Kreis,* Munich, 1922 ((a) only reproduced, p. 34, after Vollard). Ikouma

FIG. 37. Self-portrait (detail) of Armand Guillaumin (1841–1927), in the Louvre, gift of Paul Gachet and Marguerite Gachet (RF 1949–18).

(Photograph: Musée National du Louvre, Service d'Etudes du Département des Peintures)

Arishima, Cézanne, *Ars*, 1926 (14th year Tai-Sho) ((a) reproduced, after Vollard).

COLLECTIONS: Cézanne *fils*, Paris. Unknown collection. Ivan Albright, Chicago.

235 bis. GROUP IN THE COUNTRY, 1869–72

$7\frac{1}{4} \times 7\frac{7}{16}$ inches—18,4 × 18,8 cm. Pencil. Verso: No. 235.

Preliminary study for a composition, part of which has been cut off on the left, where there was a reclining figure; only the feet remain visible. Considering the distance, the couple in the center seems rather large, but is well resolved in spite of the lack of detail; the pair perhaps represent a painter showing a canvas to his Muse. A man is seen stoking a fire on the right, and the air on this side is full of smoke. A mountain in the background. Cf. No. 207 (b).

COLLECTIONS: Cézanne *fils*, Paris. Unknown collection. Ivan Albright, Chicago.

236. DISCUSSION BETWEEN TWO MEN, RECLINING NUDE WOMAN, 1868–72

$4\frac{5}{8} \times 9\frac{13}{16}$ inches—11,7 × 23,4 cm. Page from the sketchbook 18 × 24 cm. Pencil and pen, lower corners damaged, large brown and green stains. Verso: No. 199.

(a) Nude woman stretched out on her back and two men behind her in animated discussion. A Mephistophelian figure is indicated in the right background. Heavy black accents. For the woman, cf. Nos. 254 (mirror image) and 239.—(b) Lower right, pen: half-length studies of the two men; cf. a sketch of the same kind, No. 39. Above: the nude woman, repeated in pencil.—(d) Above, pencil and pen: the same figure.—(e) Notations: *"Gazette des Beaux-Arts rue Vivienne près du boulevard librairie internationale/chez Colin Blanc de Cremnitz."*

BIBLIOGRAPHY: Venturi, Vol. I, p. 351, *Oeuvres Inédites* (not reproduced). Basel catalog, No. 40 (reproduced). W. V. Andersen, Cézanne's Carnet violet moiré, *BurlM*, June 1965, p. 313, remarks that the pose of the woman was directly inspired by that of *The Woman with a Parrot* by Gustave Courbet, of which Cézanne owned a photograph.

COLLECTIONS: Cézanne *fils*, Paris. W. Feuz, Bern. Kunstmuseum, Basel.

237. STUDIES OR COPIES, 1869–73

$5\frac{1}{2} \times 9\frac{1}{16}$ inches—14 × 23 cm. Fragment of a page of studies. Black crayon, stains, folds, part of paper missing at the lower edge. Verso: several undecipherable signs.

(a) Left: seated figure turning toward a crouching woman; a standing figure, in movement, seems also to make up part of this group.—(b) Right: nude woman, her hair blown by the wind, seizing a horse. Various pencil strokes and numbers across the page.

EXHIBITION: Quatre Chemins, Paris, 1936.

COLLECTIONS: Cézanne *fils*, Paris. W. Walter, Paris. Present owner unknown.

238. STUDIES AROUND A DECORATIVE ETCHING, 1868–71 (son's head, circa 1878).

$12\frac{5}{8} \times 9\frac{7}{16}$ inches—32 × 24 cm. Pencil. The etching represents a decorative vase, accompanied by the inscription: *Marchant Editeur. Alliance des Arts, r. de Rivoli* 140. *Imp Delâtre.* Numerous stains; traces of glue in the margins. Verso: No. 121.

Center: etching of a decorative vase, by an alien hand.—(a) Lower left: a man standing, holding a fishing rod, his elbow resting on a block of stone, a basket at his feet.—(b) Above: man in a similar pose but without the fishing rod, his elbow on a table; a woman on the left. Cf. Nos. 148, 239 (a).—(c) Lower left: back view of a man holding a fishing rod (sketched in three positions).—(d) Above: head of a woman, detail copied from the decorative vase. It may be remarked that this copy belies the allegation that Cézanne considered the pages of engravings which he used for drawing as just worthless waste paper.—(e) Above, in the margin: sketch of his son's head.

BIBLIOGRAPHY: Neumeyer, 1958, No. 13 (reproduced).

COLLECTIONS: Hugo Perls, Berlin. James Lord, New York. J. K. Thannhauser, New York. Art Institute, Chicago.

239. PAGE OF STUDIES, 1868–71

$12\frac{5}{8} \times 7\frac{7}{8}$ inches—32 × 20 cm. Pencil on gray laid paper, stains, traces of folds. Verso: No. 378.

(a) Lower left: sketch of a man fishing.—(b) Center, at right angles: sketch of a scene, its significance obscure. A reclining figure can be seen in the foreground; further back the edge of a table with a man sitting at the left side and a woman behind it to whom another woman, gesticulating with her arm, is talking. Cf. No. 236.—(c) Right: figure cut off by the edge of the paper.

BIBLIOGRAPHY: Venturi No. 1232.

COLLECTIONS: Cézanne *fils*, Paris. Paul Guillaume, Paris. A. Chappuis, Tresserve. Private collection, Paris.

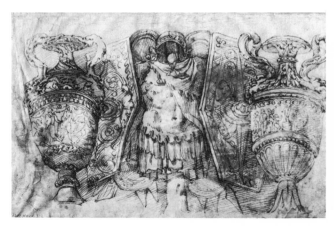

FIG. 38. Polidoro Caldara, known as Polidoro da Caravaggio (1495–1545): *Trophy between two vases,* ink drawing in the Cabinet des Dessins of the Louvre. See Henry Chennevières: *Les Dessins du Louvre* II, Paris, 1882, la planche Caravage 2, and, in the text enumerating the drawings, the note: "Trophée entre deux vases, plume d'une énergie savante, Coll. Baldinucci." This kind of drawing was generally used for theater scenery of fête settings, sometimes for ceiling designs.   *(Photograph: R. W. Ratcliffe)*

240. MOTHER AND CHILD, ORNAMENTAL VASE, FIGURE OF A WOMAN, 1866–71

$6\frac{15}{16} \times 9\frac{3}{8}$ inches—17,7 × 23,9 cm. Page from the sketchbook 18 × 24 cm. Pencil, upper corners damaged, small stains and flyspecks over the whole page, splotches of paint lower right. Verso: No. 191.

(a) Mother carrying a child who looks toward the viewer; the drawing of the head is retouched. From an undetermined model.—(b) Decorative vase, after a drawing by Polidoro da Caravaggio in the Cabinet des Dessins of the Louvre; see fig. 38.—(c) Seated woman, swinging round from the hips; from an undetermined model.

BIBLIOGRAPHY: Venturi No. 1577. Berthold, cat. No. 288 (reproduced). Basel catalog, No. 25 (reproduced). Th. Reff, *AB*, June 1960, p. 184.

COLLECTIONS: Cézanne *fils*, Paris. W. Feuz, Bern. Kunstmuseum, Basel.

241. AFTER GIULIO ROMANO AND AN UNKNOWN WORK, 1869–72

$9\frac{7}{16} \times 6\frac{15}{16}$ inches—24 × 17,7 cm. Page from the sketchbook 18 × 24 cm. Pencil, corners damaged. Verso: No. 165.

(a) Left: soldier in pseudo-classical uniform, running toward the rear, his finger pointed to the sky. From a cartoon for a tapestry in the series *Fructus belli* depicting the burning of a town, by Giulio Romano, in the Louvre; see fig. 39.—(b) Center of the page: right leg, from the same cartoon; see the man carrying a cripple.—(c) Above right: man bending over, his right leg doubled up and his left studied in three different positions. Perhaps from an unidentified work, though research would indicate it is more probably a study.

BIBLIOGRAPHY: Venturi No. 1581. Berthold, cat. No. 310 (reproduced). Basel catalog, No. 34 (reproduced). Longstreet, 1964 (reproduced).

COLLECTIONS: Cézanne *fils*, Paris. W. Feuz, Bern. Kunstmuseum, Basel.

242. STUDIES, INCLUDING EMPERAIRE, A BATHER, AND A BOAT, 1867–72

$7\frac{1}{16} \times 5\frac{15}{16}$ inches—18 × 15 cm. Pencil on ruled paper, ink stains, folds, paper soiled. Verso: No. 28.

(a) Top left: standing bather; corrections to the hand on the hip.—(b) Top center: caricatural sketch of Achille Emperaire; cf. Nos. 226, 227, 228. This sketch is earlier than (a).—(c) Drawn later than (b): a boat with two oars across it, its prow rising to the right.—(d) Lower left: rapid silhouette of a woman.—(e) Lower right: the same subject.—(f) between (d) and (e), upside down: head of a man which recalls the faces found in the early sketchbooks; it was done a little later than the drawing on the reverse side, No. 28.

COLLECTIONS: Mouradian & Vallotton, Paris. Unknown collection. Norman Schlenoff, New York.

243. PAGE OF STUDIES, WITH HEADS, 1867–72

$7\frac{5}{16} \times 4\frac{5}{16}$ inches—18,6 × 11 cm. Pencil, numerous brown stains. Verso: No. 185.

(a) Left: head of a young person with abundant hair.—(b) Upper right: similar head, in left profile, the eyes fixed on the sky.—(c) Lower right: woman seen back view,

FIG. 39. Giulio Pippi, known as Giulio Romano (1492–1546): *Capture and Burning of a Town*, cartoon (detail) for a tapestry in the series *Fructus Belli*, in the Louvre. Distemper on paper backed by canvas, 3,50 m. × 5,74 m. In 1786 the English miniaturist Cosway presented Giulio Romano's four large cartoons for the tapestries *Fructus Belli* and *Histoire de Scipion* to King Louis XVI. From 1953 on, the present cartoon has been hung in the Salon Carré of the Louvre, after being for long years at Fontainebleau. One wonders where Cézanne may have seen it. *Catalogue des Peintures Hautecoeur*, 1926, Ecole italienne, p. 97, No. 1422 (a).

(Photograph: R. W. Ratcliffe)

looking upwards. Cf. the painting Venturi No. 87 in which there are certain similarities.

COLLECTIONS: Cézanne *fils*, Paris. Private collection, New York.

244. SKETCH OF A LANDSCAPE; HEADS, AFTER PAREJA. Heads 1869–72, landscape 1883–86

$12\frac{3}{16} \times 9\frac{1}{16}$ inches—31 × 23 cm. Pencil on laid paper, smudges. Verso: No. 834.

(a) Three heads, from Juan de Pareja's painting *The Calling of St. Matthew*, reproduced in Charles Blanc's book *Ecole Espagnole* (1869). Cf. No. 726. The head seen in profile is that of Christ.—(b) Page lengthwise: unfinished landscape. It may perhaps be compared with the watercolor Venturi No. 938.

COLLECTION: Private collection, New York.

245. MALE NUDE (fragment), 1867–70

$6\frac{1}{2} \times 6\frac{3}{4}$ inches—16,6 × 17,1 cm. Black crayon. Verso: No. 820.

The page, cut to the size of the drawing on the reverse side, shows only part of a nude figure: chin and mustache, half of the chest, and one arm with the hand closed around a stick held near to the waist.

BIBLIOGRAPHY: Basel catalog, No. 20 (reproduced).

COLLECTIONS: Cézanne *fils*, Paris. W. Feuz, Bern. Kunstmuseum, Basel.

246. MAN, NEAR A WOMAN LYING ASLEEP OUTDOORS, 1868–71

$5\frac{7}{8} \times 9\frac{1}{16}$ inches—15 × 23 cm. Page 10 verso of the *Carnet de jeunesse* in the Cabinet des Dessins. Drawn in ink with a reed pen. Verso: No. 67.

A child's pencil drawing, not reproduced, may be disregarded. Framed by strokes: a reclining woman, in a landscape difficult to analyse: far off to the right the sea can be seen. A man wearing a striking hat approaches from the left. Cf. Nos. 236, 254, 281. The treatment and effect call to mind Japanese artists, and perhaps Van Gogh.

BIBLIOGRAPHY: Berthold, p. 155 (not reproduced). Aix-Nice-Grenoble catalog, 1953, No. 49, where Jean Leymarie entitles this drawing "Venus and Adonis, study for the painting Venturi No. 124."

COLLECTIONS: P. Berès, Paris. Cabinet des Dessins of the Louvre, Paris (RF 29949).

247. TOWEL OVER THE BACK OF A CHAIR, 1870–72

$6\frac{15}{16} \times 9\frac{7}{16}$ inches—17,7 × 24 cm. Page from the sketchbook 18 × 24 cm. Pen and wash in India ink, ocher color added to the wash, pencil, restored tear on the right, paper soiled. Verso: No. 176.

The back of a chair with a piece of towelling thrown over it; study of a drapery with marked black accents.

BIBLIOGRAPHY: Venturi, Vol. I, p. 351, *Oeuvres Inédites* (not reproduced). Basel catalog, No. 48 (reproduced). Douglas Cooper, in *Master Drawings,* Vol. 1, No. 4, 1963, p. 56, compares this study with the still lifes Venturi Nos. 69, 70, 71 and dates it 1870–72.

COLLECTIONS: Cézanne *fils,* Paris. W. Feuz, Bern. Kunstmuseum, Basel.

247A. SKETCH, circa 1870–72

Page XXIII verso from the sketchbook Leigh Block. Pencil on yellowed paper. Verso: blank page.

Undecipherable sketch; the faint stroke renders reproduction impracticable.

BIBLIOGRAPHY: Rewald, *Carnets:* C V, p. XXIII verso (not reproduced).

248. STUDIES FOR THE PAINTING *Pastorale,* circa 1870

$6\frac{15}{16} \times 9$ inches—17,7 × 22,8 cm. Page from the sketchbook 18 × 24 cm. Soft pencil, tear lower left, light stains, smudges. Verso: No. 168.

(a) Still life comprising bottle, glass, bread, and apple, on a napkin.—(b) Sketch of a hoisted sail. Studies for the painting *Pastorale,* Venturi No. 104. Cf. Nos. 249, 250.

BIBLIOGRAPHY: Venturi, Vol. I, as verso of No. 1578 (not reproduced). Basel catalog, No. 55 (reproduced).

COLLECTIONS: Cézanne *fils,* Paris. W. Feuz, Bern. Kunstmuseum, Basel.

249. STUDIES FOR THE PAINTING *Pastorale,* circa 1870

$8\frac{7}{8} \times 11\frac{7}{8}$ inches—22,5 × 30,2 cm. Pencil, left corners restored, holes upper left and toward the center, numerous stains. Verso: decorative lithograph (see Basel catalog, fig. 93).

Six sketches scattered over the page, five of them for the painting *Pastorale,* Venturi No. 104. Cf. No. 250. From left to right: (a) Below: back of a reclining woman, the head not drawn; over her feet a man crouching and lighting his pipe. In the painting the man is seated in the stern of a

sailboat.—(b) Above: second sketch of the same woman. —(c) Above and upside down: man in a hat, squatting.— (d) Top center: nude woman, crouching.—(e) Lower right, upside down: man lying on the ground leaning on his elbow.—(f) Upper right: still life with fruit and bottle, its shadow cast on the wall behind; cf. the still life Venturi No. 71 in which this shadow also figures. Its contour seems to have inspired that of the trees seen on the canvas, but not in our No. 250. See Note 25.

BIBLIOGRAPHY: Venturi No. 1582. Basel catalog, No. 56 (reproduced).

COLLECTIONS: Cézanne *fils,* Paris. W. Feuz, Bern. Kunstmuseum, Basel.

250. STUDY FOR *Pastorale,* circa 1870

$4 \times 5\frac{1}{4}$ inches—10,2 × 13,4 cm. Pencil. Verso: blank page.

The drawing shows three women and three men. The man leaning on his elbow is generally identified as the artist himself. The bottle and glass in silhouette should be noted. Page full of contrasts, uniting human figures and background in a dream atmosphere. Study for the painting Venturi No. 104. Cf. Nos. 248, 249.

BIBLIOGRAPHY: Venturi No. 1208. Vollard, 1914 (reproduced p. 41).

EXHIBITIONS: Orangerie, Paris, 1936, No. 142. Aquarelles et baignades de Cézanne, Galerie Renou & Colle, Paris, 1935. Collection of Mr. and Mrs. Henry Pearlman, Knoedler & Co., New York, 1959, No. 21 (reproduced). Idem, Detroit Institute of Arts, 1967, No. 6.

COLLECTIONS: Cézanne *fils,* Paris. Curt Valentin, New York. Mr. and Mrs. Henry Pearlman, New York.

251. WOMAN SITTING DOWN WITH A DOG AT HER FEET, 1871–73

$5\frac{7}{16} \times 3\frac{11}{16}$ (top), $3\frac{1}{2}$ (bottom) inches—13,8 × 9,3 (8.8) cm. Pencil on gray-brown laid paper, stains, scrapings of oil paint. Verso: blank page.

Young woman sitting in an armchair, a dog lying on the ground to the left. Study for the painting Venturi No. 231, *The Conversation.* Cf. our No. 252, a more complete study of the same subject; the present sketch, however, seems more freely drawn.

BIBLIOGRAPHY: Venturi, Vol. I, p. 350, *Oeuvres Inédites* (not reproduced). Basel catalog, No. 135 (reproduced; dated 1885–90). Douglas Cooper, in *Master Drawings,* Vol. 1, No. 4, 1963, p. 56, dated circa 1873.

COLLECTIONS: Cézanne *fils,* Paris. W. Feuz, Bern. Kunstmuseum, Basel.

252. STUDY FOR *The Conversation,* 1871–73

$4\frac{1}{2} \times 5\frac{1}{2}$ inches—11,5 × 14 cm. Pencil. Verso: blank page.

Study for the painting Venturi No. 231. The tree, man, woman, and dog, from left to right, should be remarked. Right: hat and parasol on a bench; cf. No. 251. The naïve worldliness of the gentleman typifies a provincial *salon* and betrays a certain immaturity.

BIBLIOGRAPHY: Venturi No. 1212. Vollard, 1914 (reproduced p. 19). G. Rivière, *Le Maître Paul Cézanne,* Paris,

1923 (reproduced p. 45). Basel catalog, mention under No. 135.

EXHIBITIONS: Nice-Aix-Grenoble, 1953, No. 27 (reproduced in the catalog facing p. 21).

COLLECTIONS: Cézanne *fils*, Paris. Mr. and Mrs. John Rewald, New York. Atelier Cézanne, Aix-en-Provence.

253. MEN ON HORSEBACK, 1870–73

About $6\frac{1}{2} \times 3\frac{15}{16}$ inches—16,5 × 10 cm. Pencil. Verso: unknown.

In the foreground, a man on horseback and the croup of his mount; he is carrying a long gun slung over his shoulder and is preceded by a file of riders, armed men on foot, and baggage. On the right, a tree with a man hiding in its branches. Cf. the watercolor Venturi No. 896 and the oils Venturi Nos. 244, 246.

BIBLIOGRAPHY: Venturi No. 1210. Vollard, 1914 (reproduced p. 113). G. Rivière, *Le Maître Paul Cézanne*, Paris, 1923 (reproduced p. 109, and described in error as watercolor).

COLLECTIONS: Cézanne *fils*, Paris. Present owner unknown.

254. SCENE OF VIOLENCE, 1869–72

$5\frac{9}{16} \times 7\frac{3}{16}$ inches—14,1 × 18,2 cm. Reed pen, ink which has faded to brown, wash. Stain lower right. Verso: traces of several sketches of heads, effaced after being crossed out. The entire sheet is reinforced on the back with transparent Japan paper.

Astride the knees of a woman lying on the ground, a man leans over to seize his victim. The woman's head is thrown back, her long hair in disorder, her left arm stretched out on the ground. Near the right edge: rough sketch of a third figure. Cf. No. 162, Venturi Nos. 121, 123, and *Correspondance*, fig. 14.

BIBLIOGRAPHY: Venturi, Vol. I, p. 350, *Oeuvres Inédites* (not reproduced). Basel catalog, No. 45 (reproduced). Douglas Cooper, in *Master Drawings*, Vol. 1, No. 4, 1963, p. 56. W. V. Andersen, Watercolor in Cézanne's Artistic Process, *Art International*, VII, May 1963, p. 23 (reproduced p. 24).

COLLECTIONS: Cézanne *fils*, Paris. W. Feuz, Bern. Kunstmuseum, Basel.

255. OUTING IN A BOAT, 1871–74

$4\frac{1}{16} \times 6\frac{5}{8}$ inches—10,3 × 16,8 cm. Pencil on paper which has turned gray, upper corners damaged, small stain on the left. Verso: No. 328.

Four people drifting in a small boat in front of a background of trees. A man is lying in the prow smoking a pipe, and behind him a standing man handling a boathook, though his feet can scarcely be in the boat. Below the trees, a line running horizontally at the level of the figures' shoulders indicates the shore. The style of this drawing seems to be influenced by Honoré Daumier.

BIBLIOGRAPHY: Basel catalog, No. 58 (reproduced).

COLLECTIONS: Cézanne *fils*, Paris. W. Feuz, Bern. Kunstmuseum, Basel.

256. GROUP SITTING UNDER A TREE, 1871–74

$4\frac{1}{16} \times 6\frac{5}{8}$ inches—10,3 × 16,8 cm. Page from the sketchbook 10,3 × 17 cm. Pencil on paper which has turned gray, small tear lower left. Verso: No. 291.

A group of people sitting in a circle under a tree. The silhouettes stand out against a light background. Left: a man holding a pencil or knife seems to be speaking to the others; there is a man leaning on his elbow, seen full face, and another in an artist's smock, his back turned (some see in this figure a woman in an apron). To the right there is a seated figure leaning toward the center, perhaps a dog, as W. V. Andersen says, and lastly a bearded man in a Barbizon hat.

BIBLIOGRAPHY: Venturi No. 1204. Basel catalog, No. 59 (reproduced). Vollard, 1914 (reproduced p. 15). G. Rivière, *Le Maître Paul Cézanne*, Paris, 1923, (reproduced p. 93 under the title "The Brigands." Douglas Cooper, in *Master Drawings*, Vol. 1, No. 4, 1963, p. 55, "Three men and a woman."

EXHIBITIONS: Meisterzeichnungen französischer Künstler, Kunsthalle, Basel, 1935, No. 196. The Hague, 1956, No. 99. Zurich, 1956, No. 154.

COLLECTIONS: Cézanne *fils*, Paris. W. Feuz, Bern. Kunstmuseum, Basel.

257. STUDY FOR *The Eternal Feminine*, 1870–75

$7\frac{1}{16} \times 9\frac{7}{16}$ inches—18 × 24 cm. Page from the sketchbook 18 × 24 cm. Pencil, restored tear. Verso: No. 182.

First rough sketch for the compositions known as *L'Eternel Féminin—Triomphe de la Femme*. The figure arrangement is repeated almost exactly in the more elaborated study No. 258; originally the two drawings were next to each other in the same sketchbook. For the subject, cf. Venturi Nos. 247, 895, 904.

COLLECTION: Kenneth Clark, London.

258. STUDY FOR *The Eternal Feminine*, 1870–75

$6\frac{15}{16} \times 9\frac{5}{16}$ inches—17,7 × 23,6 cm. Page from the sketchbook 18 × 24 cm. Pencil and black crayon, lower left corner damaged, small tear lower left, brown stains. Verso: No. 177.

(a) Framed by a rectangle: study for the painting *L'Eternel Féminin*; see Venturi Nos. 247, 895, 904. Cf. our Nos. 257, 464. Allegorical subject with a touch of irony. A number of men crowd round a nude woman seated majestically on a divan. The placing of the female figure to the left calls to mind Eugène Delacroix's painting *The Death of Sardanapalus*. Cf. No. 141 (also from the sketchbook 18 × 24 cm.). The whole drawing is heightened with black crayon.—(b) Lower left: a man throwing himself forward, his arms spread-eagled; cf. Nos. 96, 189.—(c) Figure with knees drawn up, pose repeated in the sketch directly above, inside the rectangle (a).—(d) Right: figure seen from above, the leg stretched out; modifications to the arm extended in the opposite direction.—(e) Upper right: head and shoulder of a man, who in later versions of the same subject becomes a painter in front of his easel. Handwritten indications:—14—(Vollard's reproduction is 14 cm. wide), the words "*le dessin seul*," and an arrow. See Note 25.

BIBLIOGRAPHY: Venturi No. 1207 ((a) reproduced). Basel catalog, No. 79 (reproduced). Vollard, 1914, p. 159 ((a) reproduced). Meier-Graefe, *Cézanne und sein Kreis*, Munich, 1918 etc., p. 41 ((a) reproduced). Frantisek Rachlik, *Cézanne*, Prague, 1948 (reproduced pl. 7). Yvon Taillandier, *Paul Cézanne*, Paris, New York, Munich, 1961 and 1965 (reproduced p. 55).

COLLECTIONS: Cézanne *fils*, Paris. W. Feuz, Bern. Kunstmuseum, Basel.

259. MAN FISHING, 1872–75

$2\frac{3}{4} \times 5\frac{1}{8}$ inches — 7 × 13 cm. Very black pencil. Verso: blank page.

Left: a couple walking toward the background; in the foreground, a woman sitting down holding a closed parasol and a man with a fishing rod lying on his stomach, seen front view in foreshortening. In the background between the two: head and shoulders of a man in a hat, standing rigid. Right, in a thicket: yet another figure, which seems to have been left unfinished. Preliminary study for a canvas stressing the artist's intention to achieve a strictly rhythmical composition.

BIBLIOGRAPHY: Venturi No. 1211. Vollard, 1914 (reproduced p. 73).

COLLECTIONS: Cézanne *fils*, Paris. Present owner unknown.

260. AT THE WATER'S EDGE, 1872–75

$3\frac{7}{16} \times 4\frac{3}{4}$ inches — 9 × 12 cm. Pencil slightly heightened with watercolor. Verso: blank page.

Landscape with trees and a stream to the right in which three people are fishing with rods. The figure in the center is a seated woman, the two others men, one standing, the other seated. A sack lying on the ground is no doubt to hold the fish. The composition with its studied diagonals is interesting, but the subject ridiculous.

BIBLIOGRAPHY: Venturi No. 1213. Vollard, 1914 (reproduced p. 131).

COLLECTIONS: Ambroise Vollard, Paris. Present owner unknown.

261. RECLINING NUDE, BACK VIEW, 1871–74

$4\frac{5}{8} \times 7\frac{5}{8}$ inches — 11,8 × 19,4 cm. Page VIII from the sketchbook CP I. Pencil. Verso: No. 475.

Nude seen from the back, the legs stretched out to the right. Pose studied more than once by Cézanne; cf. for example Venturi Nos. 113, 819, 823, and our No. 405 (f); also our No. 262.

BIBLIOGRAPHY: Venturi, Vol. I, under No. 1270 (not reproduced).

COLLECTIONS: Cézanne *fils*, Paris. Paul Guillaume, Paris. A. Chappuis, Tresserve. Private collection, Paris.

262. RECLINING WOMAN, BACK VIEW, 1871–74

$4\frac{9}{16} \times 7\frac{3}{16}$ inches — 11,6 × 18,2 cm. Page 7 from the first sketchbook Mrs. Enid A. Haupt. Pencil. Verso: No. 765.

Female nude in the pose of a model, a band round her head; her hair hides her neck and underarm. Cf. the watercolors Venturi Nos. 819, 823, and the oil No. 113; also our drawings Nos. 62, 95, 261.

BIBLIOGRAPHY: Rewald, *Carnets*, C I, p. 7 (reproduced p. 82). Berthold, cat. No. 302 "Copy from an undetermined model" (reproduced).

COLLECTIONS: Cézanne *fils*, Paris. M. Renou, Paris. Poyet, Lyons. M. Renou, Paris. Sam Salz, New York. Mrs. Enid A. Haupt, New York.

263. PAGE OF STUDIES, 1871–76

About $8\frac{1}{4} \times 4\frac{7}{8}$ inches — 21 × 12,3 cm. Page from a sketchbook. Pen and pencil. Verso: blank page.

(a) Pen drawing of three Orientals; the first is standing and wears a shawl, the others are seated. — (b) Above left: figure of a dancer, her arms raised; cf. the dancer in Nos. 271, 317. — (c) Above the standing man: rough pen sketch of the head and arm of (b). — (d) Top: woman, study for *The Temptation of St. Anthony*; see No. 448 (b).

BIBLIOGRAPHY: *Cézanne dessinateur* ((d) reproduced fig. 38). Th.Reff, Cézanne and Hercules, *AB*, Vol. XLVIII, 1966, p. 41.

COLLECTIONS: Private collection, Paris. J. Cailac, Paris. Acosta Gallery, Beverley Hills, California.

264. SEATED ORIENTAL AND LANDSCAPE WITH FIGURES, 1871–74

$8\frac{7}{8} \times 7\frac{13}{16}$ inches — 22,5 × 19,8 cm., decreasing left and right. Pencil on laid paper with the watermark: HALLINES surmounted by a fleur-de-lys; horizontal fold, brown stains at the edges. Verso: No. 735.

(a) Three figures in the left foreground, trees on the right and a mountain in the background; the sea can be seen between the figures and trees. — (b) Above a dividing line: man in oriental costume sitting cross-legged on the ground. — (c) Right, unfinished portrait-sketch of the artist. See Note 25.

BIBLIOGRAPHY: Venturi, Vol. I, p. 352, *Oeuvres Inédites* (not reproduced). Basel catalog, No. 80 (reproduced).

COLLECTIONS: Cézanne *fils*, Paris. W. Feuz, Bern. Kunstmuseum, Basel.

265. INDOOR SCENE WITH TWO MEN, 1871–74

$6 \times 4\frac{7}{8}$ inches — 15,2 × 12,3 cm. — the four corners cut off. Pencil, trace of folds. Verso: blank page.

The upright figure stands out against a large patch of shadow indicated by hatching. Perhaps a copy. Cf. Nos. 132, 242, 267. At the top of the page is the following inscription copied from an auction catalog: "*No. 261. Dessin de Cézanne.*" John Rewald has advised me: "The photograph of this drawing comes from the family of the Parisian expert Marignane; it was found in a frame together with a letter from Cézanne and a number of photographs of the artist and members of his family."

COLLECTIONS: Marignane, Paris. Present owner unknown.

266. MAN SITTING ON A CHAIR, 1871–74

$7\frac{1}{4} \times 9\frac{7}{16}$ inches — 18 × 24 cm. Pencil on laid paper. Verso: blank page.

This is no doubt an academy pose, the arm over the back of the chair being held in place by a bar which the artist indicates above and below the clenched hand. The immobility of the model results in one of those almost obsessive figures occasionally found in Cézanne's work.

BIBLIOGRAPHY: Venturi No. 1202. Vollard, 1914 (reproduced as a tailpiece, p. 173). Meier-Graefe, *Cézanne und sein Kreis*, Munich, 1922 (reproduced p. 52). Ikouma Arishima, *Cézanne*, Ars 1926 (reproduced p. 118). Longstreet, 1964 (reproduced).

EXHIBITIONS: De David à Cézanne, La Vieille Fontaine, Lausanne, 1953, No. 106. Zurich, 1956, No. 153. Munich, 1956, No. 119.

COLLECTIONS: Cézanne *fils*, Paris. W. Feuz, Bern. Carl Roesch, Diessenhofen.

267. STUDIES, INCLUDING FIGURES AND A COLONNADE, 1871–74
$4\frac{15}{16} \times 8\frac{9}{16}$ inches—12,5 × 21,7 cm. Page III from the sketchbook CP II. Pencil, a few stains. Verso: No. 807.

(a) Upper left: top part of a portico in receding perspective, with a right-angle break and trees rising above the entablature; the poplar sketched on the right probably forms part of this unfinished composition.—(b) Lower left: men grouped around a large table.—(c) A woman in a voluminous dress sitting on a chair with her back turned, a man standing beside her; cf. No. 319 and Venturi Nos. 116, 231.

BIBLIOGRAPHY: Venturi, Vol. I, under No. 1282 (not reproduced).

COLLECTIONS: Cézanne *fils*, Paris. Paul Guillaume, Paris. A. Chappuis, Tresserve.

268. BEARDED MAN, HIS ARMS CROSSED, 1869–74
$6\frac{11}{16} \times 4$ inches—17 × 10,2 cm. Page from the sketchbook 10,3 × 17 cm. Pencil, fold upper right. Verso: No. 197.

(a) His arms crossed over his chest, the man holds in one hand a longish object, not clearly characterized. The object seems to have been drawn last, over the garment that appears underneath. The Basel catalog speaks of "a birch rod with its twigs pointed to the ground." Max Dellis (see Bibl.), rejecting this interpretation, proposes the title: *Frenhofer, armed with his lansquenet sword, watching over his unknown masterpiece*. We read (p. 191): "The rod is nothing other than the weapon of the lansquenet, a two-edged sword of a short, broad, and flat shape." Max Dellis compares our drawing with Nos. 128, 129, as being a third illustration of Balzac's novel. To interpret the drawing thus seems tempting indeed: all three pages are from the same sketchbook and the man's garment nearly reaches the ground, as it does in No. 129. But one can also argue against this interpretation, pointing out that the character of Frenhofer does not match the wantonness of the man, with his beard, or with the ill-defined thing he carries. Nowhere in his novel does Balzac show Frenhofer actually on guard in front of his studio. Moreover, the style of drawing No. 268 seems to me somewhat later than that of Nos. 128, 129. The volumes of the body are rendered more perceptibly, the lights suggest those of a copy after an engraving, and the man's whole attitude is more

obtrusive in comparison with the two former sketches of Frenhofer. Whatever may be the truth, the argument remains a minor one.—(b) Face of a man looking directly at the viewer; this forms part of a very faint sketch, crossed out.—Marked: V (see Note 25).

BIBLIOGRAPHY: Venturi, Vol. I, p. 350, *Oeuvres Inédites* (not reproduced). Basel catalog, No. 76 (reproduced). Max Dellis, Notes relatives à quelques dessins de Paul Cézanne, *GBA*, March 1971, p. 189, reproduced p. 191.

COLLECTIONS: Cézanne *fils*, Paris. W. Feuz, Bern. Kunstmuseum, Basel.

269. FIGURES AND A HEAVILY LADEN HORSE, 1871–74
$3\frac{7}{8} \times 5\frac{1}{4}$ inches—9,9 × 15,3 cm. Pencil, light stains. Verso: No. 293.

Horse carrying a voluminous load, led by a man with a sack over his shoulder; their shadows are cast in the foreground. Left: figure in a hat. From a distance this drawing creates a powerful effect. See Note 25.

BIBLIOGRAPHY: Venturi, Vol. I, p. 350, *Oeuvres Inédites* (not reproduced). Basel catalog, No. 74 (reproduced).

COLLECTIONS: Cézanne *fils*, Paris. W. Feuz, Bern. Kunstmuseum, Basel.

270. FRAGMENT FROM A PAGE OF STUDIES, ONE OF MME CÉZANNE, 1871–74
$4\frac{15}{16} \times 7\frac{7}{16}$ inches—12,5 × 18,8 cm. Pencil, various stains, traces of a fold; strip of paper added on the left. Verso: No. 274.

(a) Portrait of Mme Cézanne; the page has been cut off in line with her chin. Cf. No. 271 and Venturi No. 226.—(b) With a harder pencil: several small strokes on a level with her forehead; their significance is not clear. Notations by a photographer in the upper corners.

COLLECTION: Walter Kern, Winterthur.

271. PAGE OF STUDIES, 1871–74
$8\frac{3}{4} \times 11\frac{1}{4}$ inches—22,2 × 28,5 cm. Pencil on laid paper. Verso: blank page.

(a) Upper left: Mme Cézanne, her head slightly bent.—(b) Head in a bonnet, the background indicated by hatching.—(c) Lower left: head and shoulders of a figure; the facial expression recalls Goya's work. Venturi thinks that these three sketches represent Mme Cézanne, but it seems to me that (b) and (c) are drawn from other models.—(d) Lower center: crouching nude woman, study for *A Modern Olympia*, Venturi No. 106. Cf. our No. 274.—(e) Upper right: same subject.—(f) Below (e) and partly intermingled with (g): the leg of (e) repeated on a larger scale.—(g) Figure of a woman, front view; study of movement for No. 317.

BIBLIOGRAPHY: Venturi No. 1221. Genthon, Istvan, *Cézanne*, Budapest, 1964 (reproduced p. 9). Longstreet, 1964 (reproduced).

EXHIBITION: Majovsky collection, Budapest, 1935, No. 67.

COLLECTIONS: Meller, Budapest. Paul de Majovsky, Budapest. Museum of Fine Arts, Budapest.

272. AFTER BACCHIACCA: *Portrait of a Young Man*, 1871–74

$11\frac{13}{16} \times 7\frac{7}{8}$ inches—30 × 20 cm. Pencil on ordinary paper glued to cardboard. Verso: blank page.

(a) *Portrait of a Young Man*, from a canvas in the Louvre formerly attributed to Raphael, now to Bacchiacca. Cf. No. 608. Although he knew the original, Cézanne no doubt did this sketch from a reproduction (for example, one printed in *Le Magasin Pittoresque*, 1845, p. 9). See fig. 40. In our drawing the adolescent has a serious expression, whereas the painting shows him smiling. No. 608 shows a face still further removed from that of the painting. The painting has often been reproduced, but Cézanne's direct source remains obscure. Features in common between this young man and *The Student*, Venturi No. 679, may be noticed.—(b) Unfinished architectural detail; flattened arch, with decorative elements. Copy, of which the original has not been identified.

BIBLIOGRAPHY: Venturi No. 1624. Berthold, cat. No. 266 (reproduced). *Dessins*, 1938, No. 18 (reproduced).

EXHIBITIONS: Kunsthalle, Basel, 1936, No. 127 (reproduced). Lyons, 1939, No. 62. Wildenstein, London, 1939, No. 81.

COLLECTIONS: Pierre Loeb, Paris. A. Chappuis, Tresserve. Private collection, Paris. James Lord, New York. M. Feilchenfeldt, Zurich.

273. PEASANT GIRL WEARING A FICHU, circa 1873

$8\frac{5}{8} \times 6\frac{11}{16}$ inches—22 × 17 cm. Pencil on laid paper with the watermark MICHALLET. Verso: blank page.

Head of a young girl wearing a fichu. While closely allied by simplicity of form to Manet's *Olympia*, the figure here expresses genuine naïveté. In his *Cézanne à Auvers, Cézanne graveur*, Paul Gachet wrote: "The best-known of Cézanne's prints is the *Head of a Girl*, from the model who posed for the admirable pencil drawing." The etching mentioned by Gachet is dated 1873, near the signature (see Venturi No. 1160).

BIBLIOGRAPHY: Venturi, Vol. I, p. 347 (not reproduced). J. Rewald, *Cézanne et Zola*, Paris, 1936, mentioned p. 81. Paul Gachet, *Cézanne à Auvers, Cézanne graveur*, Les Beaux-Arts, Paris, 1952 (mentioned).

EXHIBITION: Orangerie, Paris, 1936, No. 145.

COLLECTIONS: Dr. Gachet, Auvers. Paul Gachet, Auvers. A. Daber, Paris. Henry McIlhenny, Philadelphia.

274. FRAGMENT FROM A PAGE OF STUDIES, 1871–74

$4\frac{15}{16} \times 7\frac{7}{16}$ inches—12,5 × 18,8 cm. Pencil, various stains, traces of a fold. Verso: No. 270.

(a) Right, halfway up the page: crouching woman, study for *A Modern Olympia*, Venturi No. 106. R. W. Ratcliffe has observed that lower down can be seen the knee of the visitor who figured in the drawing before the page was cut, as in the painting. Cf. No. 271 (d) and (f).—(b) Above: the same figure, less finished.—(c) Center: sketch of the same figure, without the head.—(d) Above the hands of (c): half-length study for the servant appearing in the background of the oil.—(e) Above, close to the rectangular frame: study of the servant, standing, and against her shoulder the little sketch (g).—(f) Left, framed by strokes, at right angles and partly cut off: compositional

FIG. 40. *Young Man*, engraving after an oil portrait in the Louvre, formerly attributed to Raphael, now to Bacchiacca. The engraving was printed in *Le Magasin Pittoresque*, 1845, p. 9.
(Photograph: Chappuis)

study for the painting Venturi No. 108 known as *The Thieves and the Donkey*. See No. 761.—(g) Sketch of the donkey, for study (f). For the word *tel*, see Note 25.

EXHIBITION: Kunsthalle, Basel, 1936, No. 154.

COLLECTION: Walter Kern, Winterthur.

275. STUDY FOR *Afternoon in Naples*, 1870-74

Measurements not known. Pencil; part of the page missing on the right. Verso: blank page.

Study for the painting Venturi No. 112. This version shows the woman lying against the man's back, one of her hands appearing on the left. Neither cat nor pipe is included, but all the other minor elements of the subject appear, including the owl. Cf. No. 276, and also No. 278.

BIBLIOGRAPHY: Venturi No. 1178. Vollard, 1914 (reproduced p. 121); this reproduction, copied by Venturi, is touched up and leaves out the upper margin.

COLLECTIONS: Ambroise Vollard, Paris. Kenneth Clark, London.

276. STUDIES FOR *Afternoon in Naples*, 1870-74

$7\frac{1}{2} \times 8\frac{7}{8}$ inches—19 × 25 cm. Pencil on laid paper, light stains, frame marks. Verso: the watercolor Venturi No. 897.

(a) Upper right: sketch, cut off by the edge, of a woman leaning on her elbow across a man's back. Cf. Venturi No. 112 and our No. 275.—(b) Upper left: rough study of a figure, back view.—(c) Below: unfinished sketch of a different version: the woman lying on her back, the man on his stomach. The woman carrying the tray is seen in lost profile. Cf. Nos. 275, 278.

COLLECTIONS: Octave Mirbeau, Paris. Josse Hessel, Paris. G. F. Reber, Lausanne. Auguste Pellerin, Paris. René Lecomte, Paris. M. Feilchenfeldt, Zurich.

277. STUDY FOR *Afternoon in Naples*, 1870–74

$8\frac{5}{8} \times 13\frac{1}{8}$ inches—22 × 33,3 cm. Pencil. Verso: blank page.

The couple, in complete abandon.

BIBLIOGRAPHY: Venturi No. 1179. Vollard, 1914 (reproduced p. 53).

EXHIBITION: Isetam, Tokyo, 1963, No. 18 (reproduced).

COLLECTIONS: Cézanne *fils*, Paris. Private collection, Tokyo.

278. STUDY FOR *Afternoon in Naples*, 1870–74

$5\frac{1}{2} \times 7\frac{7}{8}$ inches—14 × 20 cm. Pencil on pale gray laid paper, scarcely visible touches of white watercolor. Verso: blank page.

This drawing shows how Cézanne attempted to create rhythm when filling in a surface. It is a fine work, though clarity and unity are not yet mastered.

BIBLIOGRAPHY: *Dessins*, 1938, No. 3 (reproduced).

EXHIBITION: Kunsthalle, Basel, 1936, No. 108.

COLLECTIONS: Ambroise Vollard, Paris. A. Chappuis, Tresserve. L. Lichtenhan, Basel. Wertheimer, Paris. Atelier Cézanne, Aix-en-Provence.

279. STUDY FOR *Afternoon in Naples*, 1871–75

$3\frac{1}{4} \times 4\frac{3}{4}$ inches—8 × 12 cm. Pencil. Verso: blank page.

The three figures of the scene are so grouped that the woman with the tray appears behind the couple. It seems to me that this drawing, as well as our No. 283, served for the painting Venturi No. 223. On the left and to the right: sketches of the woman with the tray.

BIBLIOGRAPHY: Venturi No. 1181. Longstreet, 1964 (reproduced).

EXHIBITIONS: Zurich, 1956, No. 152. Munich, 1956, No. 118.

COLLECTIONS: Cézanne *fils*, Paris. W. Feuz, Bern. Carl Roesch, Diessenhofen.

280. STUDY FOR *Afternoon in Naples*, 1871–75

$4\frac{7}{8} \times 8\frac{9}{16}$ inches—12,4 × 21,7 cm. Page VI of the sketchbook A.I.C. Pencil, stains. Verso: No. 818.

(a) Left: unfinished sketch of foliage.—(b) Head of a cat, also unfinished.—(c) Right: study for *Afternoon in Naples*. We see the servant and at her feet a large receptacle emitting spirit fumes. The man is lying flat on his stomach smoking a pipe, the woman seated. An owl flies over the scene. Cf. particularly No. 278.

BIBLIOGRAPHY: Rewald, *Carnets*: C II, p. VI (not reproduced). Schniewind, text p. 26 (reproduced). Andersen, *Sk.*, (reproduced fig. 24b).

COLLECTIONS: Cézanne *fils*, Paris. M. Renou, Paris. Poyet, Lyons. M. Renou, Paris. Sam Salz, New York. Art Institute, Chicago.

281. WOMAN READING OUTDOORS, 1875–76

$3\frac{15}{16} \times 5\frac{1}{2}$ inches—10 × 14 cm. Pencil on laid paper. Verso: blank page.

Preliminary study for a composition; the strokes forming its frame have been widened to alter the proportions. In a wooded landscape a young woman is lying on the ground reading a book; her thigh and arms form right angles to the rising diagonal of her body, of which the round feminine volumes create a rhythmical line. The position of the arm has not been definitely decided, and above the figure a few simple curves rise toward the top, where the sketch of a little cupid can be seen; cf. the cupid in Venturi No. 1187, and another in Venturi No. 124. This sketch has, however, been considered as a preliminary study for a Magdalene reading a sacred text. Gisela Hopp (see Exhibitions) thinks it is inspired by an engraving in Charles Blanc's *Ecole lombarde* (1875) representing a Mary Magdalene attributed at that time to Correggio. The engraving shows a young girl reclining, leaning on her elbow with her head turned to the left, reading a book. Our sketch follows the upper part of the body closely, but the buttocks and legs are entirely different. The possibility that Cézanne may have retained this model in mind for a subject such as Venturi No. 124 is strengthened by Charles Blanc's own commentary: "Il y a, dans ce beau corps amoureusement couché sur le gazon, plus d'élégance que de tristesse, plus de volupté que de repentir."

EXHIBITION: Kunsthalle, Basel, 1936, No. 116. Europäische Meisterwerke aus Schweizer Sammlungen, Munich, 1969, catalogue by Gisela Hopp, No. 26 (reproduced Abb. 21).

COLLECTIONS: A. Hahnloser, Winterthur. H. R. Hahnloser, Bern.

282. SEATED FEMALE NUDE, BACK VIEW, 1872–75

$3\frac{15}{16} \times 3\frac{15}{16}$ inches— 10 × 10 cm. Pencil. Verso: blank page.

Study from a live model, or from a figure in an album of nudes. The arm, accentuated at the elbow, is stretched out horizontally, the line of the thigh corresponding. It is thought that this study was used for the canvas *Afternoon in Naples*.

COLLECTIONS: Cézanne fils, Paris. Jean-Pierre Cézanne, Paris. James Lord, New York.

283. FEMALE NUDE FOR *Afternoon in Naples*, 1872–75

$3\frac{1}{2} \times 5\frac{5}{8}$ inches—8,9 × 14,2 cm. Pencil on gray paper, with part of watermark: INES (first letters cut off by edge). Verso: a few strokes with no apparent signification.

Study for the subject *Afternoon in Naples*. Back view of a seated nude woman, her body swinging round to the right and her hair falling down her back. Cf. No. 279, and Venturi No. 223.

BIBLIOGRAPHY: Venturi No. 1183. Basel catalog, No. 73 (reproduced). Vollard, 1914 (reproduced p. 70). Longstreet, 1964 (reproduced).

COLLECTIONS: Cézanne *fils*, Paris. W. Feuz, Bern. Kunstmuseum, Basel.

284. STUDY FOR *Afternoon in Naples*, 1872–75

$3\frac{7}{8} \times 8\frac{1}{8}$ inches—9,8 × 20,6 cm. Pencil on gray-brown paper, three almost vertical folds, erasure, and several stains. Verso: upper part of a print reproducing *The Departure of the Conscripts*, canvas by M.-A. Verdier, published in *L'Artiste*, 1852; see fig. 94 of the Basel catalog.

Study for *Afternoon in Naples*. The woman's legs on the left are drawn in two versions: doubled up and in the air. This drawing was formerly on the same page as No. 285 and above it.

BIBLIOGRAPHY: Venturi, Vol. I, p. 351, *Oeuvres Inédites* (not reproduced). Basel catalog, No. 70 (reproduced).

COLLECTIONS: Cézanne *fils*, Paris. W. Feuz, Bern. Kunstmuseum, Basel.

285. THE COUPLE, STUDY FOR *Afternoon in Naples*, 1872–75

$5\frac{9}{16} \times 11\frac{3}{4}$ inches—14,1 × 29,8 cm. Pencil on gray-brown paper, three vertical folds, stains. Verso: lower part of engraving reproducing *The Departure of the Conscripts*, canvas by M.-A. Verdier, printed in *L'Artiste*, 1852; see fig. 94 of the Basel catalog. The whole sheet is glued to cardboard.

(a) Left: the couple, nude on a divan; study for *Afternoon in Naples*.—(b) To the right of the couple and partially covering the figures: repetition of the subject, but more similar to No. 284; drawn in contours. Lower left: scribbles by the artist's son. The drawing was formerly on the same page as No. 284; its upper edge fits exactly with the lower edge of the other. See Note 25.

BIBLIOGRAPHY: Venturi No. 1176 ((a) only reproduced). Basel catalog, No. 71 (reproduced). Vollard, 1914 ((a) reproduced p. 38). Meier-Graefe, *Cézanne und sein Kreis*, Munich 1921 ((a) reproduced p. 45). Neumeyer, 1958, No. 5 (reproduced). Longstreet, 1964 (reproduced).

EXHIBITIONS: The Hague, 1956, No. 96 (reproduced). Zurich, 1956, No. 151 (reproduced).

COLLECTIONS: Cézanne *fils*, Paris. W. Feuz, Bern. Prof. Otto Fischer, then Curator of the Basel Museum. Kunstmuseum, Basel.

286. STUDY FOR *Afternoon in Naples*, 1872–76

$4\frac{1}{16} \times 6\frac{9}{16}$ inches—10,3 × 16,7 cm. Page from the sketchbook 10,3 × 17 cm. Pencil, corners damaged. Verso: No. 315.

(a) In the rectangle: study for *Afternoon in Naples*, with the whitish-colored figure of a man in a curious hat sitting at his ease in the foreground. The drawing is surrounded by strokes suggestive of a frame around a painting.—(b) Upper right: sketch of a cat or dog, the animal which is seen at the man's feet in (a).—(c) Next to (b): tubular object.—(d) Beneath the animal: sketch repeating the reclining woman.—(e) Lower right: plant in a pot; cf. the pot lower right in (a).

BIBLIOGRAPHY: Venturi, Vol. I, p. 350, *Oeuvres Inédites* (not reproduced). Basel catalog, No. 72 (reproduced).

COLLECTIONS: Cézanne *fils*, Paris. W. Feuz, Bern. Kunstmuseum, Basel.

287. STUDIES OF DRAPERY AND FIGURES; MEN 1870–73, drapery 1876–79
Pencil, stains. Verso: No. 567.

(a) Three figure sketches, studies for the men in the drawing No. 289 *The Woman taken by Surprise*. See also Nos. 290 and 417 of the same sketchbook.—(b) Study of drapery.

BIBLIOGRAPHY: Rewald, *Carnets*: C II, p. XXXIII (not reproduced). Schniewind, text p. 31 (reproduced). Andersen, *Sk.* (not reproduced).

288. TWO SKETCHES OF A MAN ON ALL FOURS, 1870–73

$4\frac{7}{8} \times 8\frac{9}{16}$ inches—12,4 × 21,7 cm. Page XXXVIII of the sketchbook A.I.C. Pencil, stains and smudges. Verso: No. 415.

(a) Top: sketch of a man leaning on his left thigh, preparing to crawl. Study for the subject *A Woman taken by Surprise*, see No. 289.—(b) Below: man on his knees, leaning over a woman; cf. Venturi No. 123 and our No. 254.—(c) Left: study of a face; a separate subject.

BIBLIOGRAPHY: Rewald, *Carnets*: C II, p. XXXVIII (not reproduced). Schniewind, text p. 32 (reproduced). Andersen, *Sk.* (not reproduced).

COLLECTIONS: Cézanne *fils*, Paris. M. Renou, Paris. Poyet, Lyons. M. Renou, Paris. Sam Salz, New York. Art Institute, Chicago.

289. *The Woman taken by Surprise*, 1870–73

$4\frac{7}{8} \times 8\frac{9}{16}$ inches—12,4 × 21,7 cm. Page XXXIII of the sketchbook A.I.C. Pencil, stains. Verso: No. 568.

The Woman taken by Surprise forms part of the erotic scenes of violence treated by the artist. The page is divided into two parts: (a) Right: isolated by a few strokes, a study in composition comprising three figures; the woman is drawn twice. Cf. Nos. 73, 125A, 126, 288, 290. Left: two or three male figures, repetition of the men throwing themselves on the woman. The one in the lower corner recalls the man in No. 254.

BIBLIOGRAPHY: Rewald, *Carnets*: C II, p. XXXIII (reproduced pl. 84). Schniewind, text p. 31 (reproduced). Andersen, *Sk.* (not reproduced).

COLLECTIONS: Cézanne *fils*, Paris. M. Renou, Paris. Poyet, Lyons. M. Renou, Paris. Sam Salz, New York. Art Institute, Chicago.

290. SCENE OF VIOLENCE: MEN THROWING THEMSELVES ON A WOMAN, 1870–73

$4\frac{7}{8} \times 8\frac{9}{16}$ inches—12,4 × 21,7 cm. Page XLVI verso of the sketchbook A.I.C. Pencil and pen. Verso: No. 708.

Several figures in movement, in a setting difficult to analyse. In the foreground a nude woman is defending herself from a kind of bearded satyr by pushing away his head; above the woman attacked, another woman can be seen fleeing. For the subject, cf. the different versions of *The Struggle of Love*, Venturi Nos. 379, 380, 897, and of *The Woman taken by Surprise*, our Nos. 125, 126, 162, 197, 254, 288, 289, 728 (c).

BIBLIOGRAPHY: Rewald, *Carnets*: C II, p. XLVI verso (reproduced pl. 85). Schniewind, text p. 33 (reproduced). Th. Rousseau Jr., *Paul Cézanne*, Paris, 1953 (reproduced pl. 8). Idem, Amsterdam, 1954 (reproduced pl. 8). Yvon Taillandier, *Paul Cézanne*, Paris, New York, Munich, 1961 and 1965 (reproduced p. 45). Andersen, *Sk.* (not reproduced).

COLLECTIONS: Cézanne *fils*, Paris. M. Renou, Paris. Poyet, Lyons. M. Renou, Paris. Sam Salz, New York. Art Institute, Chicago.

291. PORTRAIT OF DR. GACHET, AND EROTIC SCENE, 1872–74

$4\frac{1}{16} \times 6\frac{5}{8}$ inches—10,3 × 16,8 cm. Page from the sketchbook 10,3 × 17 cm. Pencil, small tear lower right, paper scraped in places. Verso: No. 256.

(a) Man sitting at a table, a pipe in his mouth: portrait of *Dr. Gachet*; cf. Nos. 292, 295.—(b) Right: study for the scene known as *Afternoon in Naples*: a nude man stretched out from left to right on a bed, a sheet hanging down in front; his left knee is bent, his right one raised (a first version shows it bent), and his hand caresses the shoulders of a woman who is leaning sideways against the edge of the bed. The curtain often shown in this type of scene is sketched higher up. The woman carrying a tray is summarily indicated. See Note 25.

BIBLIOGRAPHY: Basel catalog, No. 69 (reproduced).

COLLECTIONS: Cézanne *fils*, Paris. W. Feuz, Bern. Kunstmuseum, Basel.

292. DR. GACHET AND CÉZANNE: *Etching*, 1873

$8\frac{1}{16} \times 5\frac{3}{16}$ inches—20,4 × 13,2 cm. Pencil on laid writing paper of which the horizontal lines are apparent.

Dr. Gachet (pseudonym Van Ryssel) and Cézanne busy with the preparation of an etching. Paul Gachet wrote: "acid-bite manipulation, at Auvers, for the *Head of a Girl*." See Venturi No. 1160. This sketch shows the two friends as though observed by a third person. The doctor, in a cap, is on the right, watching the operations of his etching pupil.

BIBLIOGRAPHY: Venturi, Vol. I, p. 347, *Oeuvres Inédites* (not reproduced). Paul Gachet, *Cézanne à Auvers, Cézanne graveur*, Les Beaux-Arts, Paris, 1952 (reproduced).

COLLECTIONS: Dr. Gachet, Auvers. Paul Gachet, Auvers. Cabinet des Dessins of the Louvre, Gachet Donation (RF 29925).

293. TWO SEATED WOMEN, 1870–73

$6 \times 3\frac{15}{16}$ inches—15,3 × 9,9 cm. Pencil, light stains. Verso: No. 269.

One of the women is seen back view, the second in left profile. In front of her head and chest the legs of another figure seated further away are indicated. Study for No. 294. See Note 25.

BIBLIOGRAPHY: Venturi, Vol. I, p. 350, *Oeuvres Inédites* (not reproduced). Basel catalog, No. 81 (reproduced).

COLLECTIONS: Cézanne *fils*, Paris. W. Feuz, Bern. Kunstmuseum, Basel.

294. FAMILY IN A GARDEN, AND STUDIES, 1870–73

$9\frac{7}{8} \times 8\frac{1}{4}$ inches—25 × 21 cm. (Part reproduced by Venturi: $7\frac{1}{2} \times 5\frac{7}{8}$ inches—19 × 15 cm.) Pencil on white paper browned with age. Reverse side inaccessible.

(a) Group consisting of four women and two men. The man on the right reading a newspaper resembles the artist's father; cf. No. 413. John Rewald thinks it could as well be Dr. Gachet and his family. For the two women on the right, cf. No. 293. Lower left: some fruit and a straw hat. The young man sitting down seems to be drinking out of a bowl and the woman seated behind him has a basket on her knees. In the background: façade of a house, a tree and a mountain.—(b) Upper right: small portrait of Dr. Gachet; Venturi is mistaken in seeing it as a portrait of Victor Chocquet.—(c) Bottom of the page: unfinished sketch of a couple, similar in nature to the figures of *Afternoon in Naples*.

BIBLIOGRAPHY: Venturi No. 1200: (a) reproduced, (b) mentioned but not reproduced. G. Rivière, *Le Maître Paul Cézanne*, Paris, 1923 ((a) only reproduced, p. 127). Basel catalog ((a) only reproduced, fig. 30, in relation to pl. No. 81).

EXHIBITION: Kunsthalle, Basel, 1936, No. 156.

COLLECTIONS: Cézanne *fils*, Paris. W. Feuz, Bern. R. von Hirsch, Basel.

295. PORTRAIT OF DR. GACHET, circa 1873

$12\frac{11}{16} \times 8\frac{1}{2}$ inches—32,2 × 21,6 cm. Charcoal on gray-brown paper, holes in the upper corners. Verso: blank page (word written by an alien hand).

Portrait of Dr. Gachet holding a book; friendship is clearly expressed in this drawing. A cap on his head, the doctor is smoking a pipe; looking at him we expect to see a puff of smoke float off into the air. The darkest accent is on the lapel of his coat; his ear stands out against a light ground. Cf. Nos. 291, 292.

BIBLIOGRAPHY: Venturi, Vol. I, p. 347, *Oeuvres Inédites* (not reproduced). Paul Gachet, *Le Docteur Gachet et Murer*, Paris, 1956 (reproduced). *Cézanne*, Collection Génies et Réalités, Hachette, Paris, 1966, fig. 3 (reproduced p. 15).

COLLECTIONS: Dr. Gachet, Auvers. Paul Gachet, Auvers. Cabinet des Dessins of the Louvre, Gachet Donation (RF 29926).

296. DR. GACHET, SEEN BACK VIEW, 1873

$9\frac{1}{4} \times 7\frac{7}{8}$ inches—23,5 × 20 cm. Pencil on gray-blue paper (partly faded by sunlight). Verso: blank page.

Dr. Gachet in a cap, his back turned. At the lower edge the artist's signature: *P. Cézanne*.

BIBLIOGRAPHY: Venturi, Vol. I, p. 347, *Oeuvres Inédites* (not reproduced).

COLLECTIONS: Dr. Gachet, Auvers. Paul Gachet, Auvers. Galerie Daber, Paris.

297. VASE OF FLOWERS, 1873–74

$7\frac{11}{16} \times 6\frac{1}{8}$ inches—19,5 × 15,5 cm. Pastel and pencil. Verso: blank page.

Vase of flowers standing on a piece of furniture. A slight difference of levels in the horizontal line of the background may be noticed. This pastel is treated like an oil painting.

BIBLIOGRAPHY: Venturi, Vol. I, p. 347, *Oeuvres Inédites*, "collection Gachet, Vase de Fleurs." Th. Reff, *BurlM*, March 1960, p. 118 (reproduced fig. 25).

EXHIBITION: Wildenstein, New York, 1960.

COLLECTIONS: Dr. Gachet, Auvers. Paul Gachet, Auvers. Mr. and Mrs. Dunbar W. Bostwick, New York. Galerie Beyeler, Basel. Private collection, Switzerland.

298. PORTRAIT OF CAMILLE PISSARRO, circa 1873

$3\frac{7}{8} \times 3\frac{1}{8}$ inches—10 × 8 cm. Pencil on laid paper. Verso: blank page.

The painter Camille Pissarro, in profile. At the bottom of the page the inscription "*Portrait de C. Pissarro par Cézanne.*"

BIBLIOGRAPHY: Rewald, *Cézanne*, Paris, 1939 (reproduced fig. 34). Idem, *Camille Pissarro, Letters to his son Lucien*, London and New York, 1943 (reproduced No. 49). Idem, *Cézanne*, New York, 1948 (reproduced fig. 44). Idem, *The Ordeal of Paul Cézanne*, London, 1950 (reproduced fig. 33). Idem, *Cézanne*, Spring Books, London 1959 and 1965 (reproduced fig. 33). Idem, *History of Impressionism*, New York, 1961 (reproduced p. 312). Idem, *Briefe*, Diogenes, Zurich, 1962 (reproduced p. 161). Neumeyer, 1958, No. 28 (reproduced). *The World of Cézanne* (reproduced p. 68).

EXHIBITIONS: Wildenstein, New York, 1947, No. 87 (reproduced). Camille Pissarro, Toledo Museum of Art, 1949. Belvedere, Vienna, 1961, No. 86. Aix-en-Provence, 1961, No. 40. The Phillips Collection, Washington, D.C., Chicago, Boston, 1971, No. 66 (reproduced).

COLLECTIONS: Camille Pissarro, Paris. Lucien Pissarro, London. Leicester Galleries, London. Sir Hugh Walpole, London. The Art Collection of the late Sir Hugh Walpole, Exhibition and Sale, Leicester Galleries, London, 1945, No. 128. Dr. F. Sprinzels, Portinsale, Keswick, England. Mr. and Mrs. John Rewald, New York. Private collection, New York.

299. PORTRAIT OF PISSARRO, AND SKETCHES, 1874–78

$8\frac{9}{16} \times 5$ inches—21,7 × 12,6 cm. Page II verso of the sketchbook Leigh Block. Pencil. Verso: No. 770.

(a) Portrait of Camille Pissarro in a large straw hat. In Rewald's opinion this drawing was done at Auvers-sur-Oise.—(b) Lower left: portrait of Mme Cézanne, drawn later than (a) and (c).—(c) Lower right: head of a woman in a regional headdress; cf. No. 331 (a).

BIBLIOGRAPHY: Rewald, *Carnets*: C V, p. II verso (reproduced pl. 15).—Neumeyer, 1958, No. 30 (reproduced). H. Perruchot, *La Vie de Cézanne*, Paris, 1958 ((a) reproduced on the inside of the cover). Y. Taillandier, *Paul Cézanne*, Paris, New York, Munich, 1961 and 1965 (reproduced p. 6).

COLLECTIONS: Cézanne *fils*, Paris. Renou, Paris. Poyet, Lyons. M. Renou, Paris. Sam Salz, New York. Mr. and Mrs. Leigh Block, Chicago.

300. PISSARRO GOING OFF TO PAINT, 1874–77

$7\frac{11}{16} \times 4\frac{7}{16}$ inches—19,5 × 11,4 cm. Pencil. Verso: No. 758.

The painter Camille Pissarro on his way to work, drawn from a photograph taken at Pontoise. The light and shadow are skillfully rendered. In our permissive age, is one allowed a regret that Cézanne should have amused himself with an equivocal interpretation of a trouser fold?

BIBLIOGRAPHY: Venturi No. 1235. *La Renaissance*, 1928 (reproduced p. 507. *Parnassus*, April 1929, Vol. I (repro-

duced p. 13). J. Rewald, Sources d'Inspiration de Cézanne, *A.A.*, May 1936, p. 192, figs. 96, 97. Idem, *Cézanne et Zola* (thesis), Paris, 1936 (reproduced fig. 34). Idem, *History of Impressionism*, New York, 1961 (reproduced p. 296). Longstreet, 1964 (reproduced). Collection Génies et Réalités, *Cézanne*, Hachette, Paris, 1966 (reproduced fig. 107; in error as portrait of Cézanne by Pissarro). *Histoire universelle de l'Art*, Les Deux Coqs d'Or, Paris, and CEAM, Milano, Vol. III, p. 656 (reproduced).

EXHIBITIONS: Le Dessin français au XIXe et XXe siècles, Bucharest, 1931, No. 63 (reproduced). Dons et achats, Orangerie, Paris, 1933, No. 132. Orangerie, Paris, 1936, No. 144. Lyons, 1939, No. 58. Wildenstein, London, 1939, No. 77. Belvedere, Vienna, 1961, No. 88. Aix-en-Provence, 1961, No. 41.

COLLECTIONS: Camille Pissarro; Pissarro sale, Paris, December 3, 1928, No. 62 (reproduced). Cabinet des Dessins of the Louvre (RF 11995).

301. CAMILLE PISSARRO, SEEN FROM THE BACK, 1874–77

$4\frac{15}{16} \times 5\frac{15}{16}$ inches—12,5 × 15 cm. Pencil. Verso: blank page.

Head and shoulders of Camille Pissarro with a scarf around his neck. Inscription by an alien hand: "*Pissaro vu de dos par Cézanne.*" Sketch full of character and drawn from life.

BIBLIOGRAPHY: Venturi No. 1226.

COLLECTIONS: Camille Pissarro; Pissarro sale, Paris, Dec. 3, 1928, No. 61 (reproduced in the catalog). Tanner, Zurich. R. von Hirsch, Basel.

302. AFTER A SCULPTURE: CROUCHING FIGURE, 1872–75

$6\frac{11}{16} \times 4\frac{1}{16}$ inches—17 × 10,3 cm. Page from the sketchbook 10,3 × 17 cm. Pencil. Verso: blank page.

After the plaster cast of a crouching figure, or atlas, formerly attributed to Michelangelo. See fig. 41. The pencil technique is distinctive in that the curved hatching renders the rugosities of the casting. The authenticity of this drawing has been questioned, but I think the page comes from one of the artist's sketchbooks. Seen from a certain distance the sketch seems definitely by the hand of Cézanne. Cf. No. 303 and the etching *Guillaumin au pendu*, Venturi No. 1159.

BIBLIOGRAPHY: Basel catalog, Table VI, p. 27, where the drawing is mentioned. *Cézanne dessinateur* (reproduced fig. 31).

COLLECTIONS: Cézanne *fils*, Paris. J. Cailac, Paris. C. Aubry, Paris.

303. AFTER MICHELANGELO, A SLAVE, 1872–75

Pencil. Verso: blank page.

Sketch from Michelangelo's marble, *The Rebellious Slave*, in the Louvre, one of the figures intended for the tomb of Pope Julius II. See fig. 42. Four studies by Cézanne from this work are known: Nos. 589, 590, 679, and the present one.

BIBLIOGRAPHY: Th.Reff, in *AB*, June 1960, p. 145 (reproduced fig. 6).

COLLECTION: Present owner unknown.

304. AFTER AN ANTIQUE SCULPTURE: *Faun and Child*, 1872–75

$7\frac{1}{16} \times 4\frac{1}{2}$ inches—$18 \times 11,5$ cm. Page from a sketch-book (probably the Carnet I catalogued by Rewald). Pencil. Verso: watercolor sketch of foliage.

Bearded man leaning against a tree trunk, a little child in his arms. After the antique marble *Faun and Child* (or *Silenus carrying the child Bacchus*) in the Louvre; see fig. 43. It would seem natural to establish a link between the subject represented and the paternal sentiments manifested by the artist after the birth of his son Paul in 1872.

BIBLIOGRAPHY: Venturi, Vol. I, p. 349, *Oeuvres Inédites*, "Etudes (12×19 cm). Recto: feuilles . . ." (not reproduced).

COLLECTIONS: Kenneth Clark, London. R. von Hirsch, Basel.

305. AFTER PIGALLE: *Mercury*, 1873–76

$16\frac{1}{8} \times 10\frac{5}{8}$ inches—41×27 cm. Pencil. Verso: blank page.

After Jean-Baptiste Pigalle's statuette *Mercury Fastening his Heel Wings* (1740). The marble was in the Louvre and a plaster cast in the Trocadero. See fig. 44. Cf. other copies of the same subject, Nos. 973, 974, 975.

BIBLIOGRAPHY: Venturi No. 1451. Berthold, cat. No. 157 (reproduced). E. A. Jewell, *Cézanne*, New York, 1944–46 (reproduced).

EXHIBITIONS: Pennsylvania Museum of Art, Philadelphia, 1934, No. 57 San Francisco, 1937, No. 64 (in error as Venturi No. 1321 and wrong measurements; reprod.).

COLLECTIONS: Weyhe Gallery, New York. Present owner unknown.

FIG. 41. *Crouching Figure*, plaster cast of a sculpture formerly attributed to Michelangelo. The original is in the Galleria antica e moderna, Florence. *(Photograph: Brogi-Giraudon)*

FIG. 42. Michelangelo Buonarroti (1475–1564): *Slave*, marble originally destined for the tomb of Pope Julius II, now in the Louvre. Musée National du Louvre, *Catalogue des Sculptures* I, 1922, No. 697. Height: 2,09 m. *(Photograph: R. W. Ratcliffe)*

306. AFTER THE ANTIQUE: *Venus of Milo*, 1872–75

  $7\frac{11}{16} \times 4\frac{3}{4}$ inches—19,5 × 12 cm. Page XLI verso from the sketchbook CP I. Pencil. Verso: No. 440.

The *Vénus de Milo* in the Louvre, drawn from a plaster cast. Cf. Nos. 308, 634, 636, 637.

BIBLIOGRAPHY: Venturi, Vol. I, as verso of No. 1256 (mentioned, not reproduced). Berthold, cat. No. 17 (reproduced).

COLLECTION: Kenneth Clark, London.

FIG. 43. *Faun and Child*, also known as *Silenus carrying the child Bacchus*, antique marble in the Louvre (Inv. No. 709). See Salomon Reinach, *Répertoire de la Statuaire grecque et romaine*, 1897, Tome II, Vol. I, p. 169, pl. 333, No. 1556.

(Photograph: Giraudon)

FIG. 44. Jean-Baptiste Pigalle (1714–85): *Mercure attachant ses talonnières*, marble in the Louvre. Musée National du Louvre, *Catalogue des Sculptures* II, 1922, No. 1442. Height: 58 cm. Our reproduction shows a plaster cast; Cézanne could have seen one similar in the Trocadero.   *(Photograph: Chappuis)*

307. AFTER THE ANTIQUE: *Venus of Milo*, 1872–73

  $8\frac{5}{8} \times 4\frac{7}{8}$ inches—21,8 × 12,4 cm. Page XXXVIII from the sketchbook CP II. Pencil. Verso: No. 918.

From a plaster cast of the Greek marble *Vénus de Milo* in the Louvre, see fig. 45. (If Cézanne had drawn from the original he could not have chosen this angle of vision on account of the height of the pedestal). Of the artist's nine copies, this one alone shows the statue from the front; most of them show the figure in right three-quarter view.

BIBLIOGRAPHY: Venturi No. 1292. Berthold, cat. No. 10 (reproduced Abb. 85).

COLLECTIONS: Cézanne *fils*, Paris. Paul Guillaume, Paris. A. Chappuis, Tresserve. Private collection, Paris.

308. AFTER THE ANTIQUE: *Venus of Milo*, 1872–73

  $8\frac{5}{8} \times 4\frac{7}{8}$ inches—21,8 × 12,4 cm. Page XLVII from the sketchbook CP II. Pencil. Verso: No. 888.

See fig. 46. Study probably done from a plaster cast. Cf. Nos. 306, 310, 637. The right contour follows a movement repeated by the volumes of the body.

BIBLIOGRAPHY: Venturi No. 1296. Berthold, cat. No. 12 (reproduced). K. Pfister, *Cézanne*, Potsdam, 1927 (reproduced p. 31).

COLLECTIONS: Cézanne *fils*, Paris. Paul Guillaume, Paris. A. Chappuis, Tresserve. Private collection, Paris.

FIGS. 45 and 46. *Vénus de Milo*, antique marble in the Louvre. Musée National du Louvre, *Catalogue sommaire des marbres antiques*, 1922, No. 399.

309. AFTER THE ANTIQUE: *Venus of Milo*, 1873–75

$8\frac{9}{16} \times 4\frac{15}{16}$ inches—21,7 × 12,5 cm. Page XII from the sketchbook CP II. Pencil. Verso: No. 541.

The drawing of the torso is detailed, the drapery only sketched in. See fig. 46. Cf. our Nos. 306, 310, 637.

BIBLIOGRAPHY: Venturi No. 1285. Berthold, cat. No. 18 (reproduced Abb. 83).

COLLECTIONS: Cézanne *fils*, Paris. Paul Guillaume, Paris. A. Chappuis, Tresserve. Private collection, Paris.

310. AFTER THE ANTIQUE: *Venus of Milo*, 1873–75

$4\frac{3}{4}$ to $5\frac{1}{2} \times 4\frac{15}{16}$ inches—12 to 13,9 × 12,5 cm. Page XIII from the sketchbook CP II, part of the paper torn off. Pencil. Verso: No. 623.

After the antique marble in the Louvre, see fig. 46. Vigor-

ous drawing, with an architectural detail, in the background. Cf. No. 308.

BIBLIOGRAPHY: Venturi No. 1286. Berthold, cat. No. 13 (reproduced Abb. 84).

COLLECTIONS: Cézanne *fils*, Paris. Paul Guillaume, Paris. A. Chappuis, Tresserve. Private collection, Paris.

310bis. WOMAN GOING TO BED, HEAD OF A MAN, 1872–75

$4\frac{3}{4} \times 7\frac{7}{8}$ inches—12 × 20 cm. Pencil. Verso: the watercolor Venturi No. 866.

(a) Left: copy of an engraving by Porporati of *Le Coucher à l'italienne*, canvas by J. van Loo. See fig. 47. The forms of this nude resemble those of many bathing women figuring in the artist's paintings.—(b) Right, at right angles: head of a man with curly hair; a very fine sketch. Copy after an unidentified plaster cast.

COLLECTIONS: Bernheim-Jeune, Paris. Private collection, Paris.

FIG. 47. Engraving by Carlo Antonio Porporati (1741–1816), member of Paris Academy (1773), reproducing *Le Coucher à l'italienne,* canvas by Jacob van Loo (1614–70), now in the museum of Lyons. *(Photograph: Bibliothèque Nationale, Paris)*

311. AFTER RUBENS: *Christ on the Cross,* 1873–76

$11\frac{13}{16} \times 8\frac{1}{4}$ inches—30 × 21 cm. Pencil on laid paper. Verso: blank page.

After the figure of Christ in Rubens' painting *Christ on the Cross, Mary, John, and the Magdalene,* in the Louvre. See fig. 48.

BIBLIOGRAPHY: Venturi No. 1220. G. Rivière, *Le Maître Paul Cézanne,* Paris, 1923, cited p. 220 among the works executed in 1895 (reproduced p. 5). Berthold, cat. No. 228 (reproduced).

COLLECTIONS: Cézanne *fils,* Paris. Jean-Pierre Cézanne, Paris. Marianne Feilchenfeldt, Zurich.

312. MAN IN MOVEMENT, 1872–75

$6\frac{11}{16} \times 5$ inches—17 × 12,7 cm. Page XV from the second sketchbook Mrs. Enid A. Haupt. Pencil, touches of watercolor. The page seems to have been trimmed. Verso: No. 312A.

Sketch of a man in movement, his back turned. The diagonals form right angles, and the head, roughly sketched twice, prolongs the diagonal of the back. Eugène Delacroix's painting *Attila and the Barbarians treading Italy and the Arts underfoot* in the Palais Bourbon library (Robaut 897) shows an almost similar male figure in the foreground.

BIBLIOGRAPHY: Rewald, *Carnets:* C IV, page XV (not reproduced).

COLLECTIONS: Cézanne *fils,* Paris. M. Renou, Paris. Poyet, Lyons. M. Renou, Paris. Sam Salz, New York. Mrs. Enid A. Haupt, New York.

312A. HEAD OF A HORSE

Pencil; the inaccessible reverse side of No. 312.

BIBLIOGRAPHY: Rewald, *Carnets:* C IV, page XV verso, "Croquis d'une tête de cheval (copie d'un tableau?), voir carnet IV, page XXVII" (not reproduced). The latter drawing indicated by Rewald is our No. 1209. Berthold, cat. No. 225 (not reproduced).

313. SKETCH OF A NUDE, AND HEAD OF AN OLD MAN, 1872–77

$8\frac{1}{2} \times 5$ inches—21,6 × 12,7 cm. Page VII verso from the second sketchbook Mrs. Enid A. Haupt. Pencil. Verso: No. 471.

(a) Unfinished sketch of a nude. The figure is seen seated but as though on the point of rising. Confused indications on the left.—(b) Top right: head of an old man with a beard. This sketch is certainly a copy but the source has not been identified.

BIBLIOGRAPHY: Rewald, *Carnets:* C IV, p. VII verso (not reproduced). Berthold, cat. No. 298 (reproduced).

COLLECTIONS: Cézanne *fils,* Paris. M. Renou, Paris. Poyet, Lyons. M. Renou, Paris. Sam Salz, New York. Mrs. Enid A. Haupt, New York.

314. SKETCH OF TWO WOMEN BATHERS, 1873–75

$8\frac{9}{16} \times 5$ inches—21,7 × 12,6 cm. Page V of the sketchbook Leigh Block. Soft pencil, smudged counterproofs. Verso: No. 828.

FIG. 48. Peter Paul Rubens (1577–1640): *Christ on the Cross* (detail), in the Louvre, 3,33 m. × 2,82 m. Musée National du Louvre, *Catalogue des Peintures* III, 1922, No. 2082.

(Photograph: Archives photographiques, Paris)

One bather is seated, the other walking toward the left. A tree trunk on the right. Cf. No. 791.

BIBLIOGRAPHY: Rewald, *Carnets*: C V, p. V (not reproduced).

COLLECTIONS: Cézanne *fils*, Paris. M. Renou, Paris. Poyet, Lyons. M. Renou, Paris. Sam Salz, New York. Mr. and Mrs. Leigh Block, Chicago.

315. STUDY OF DRAPERY, circa 1873

$4\frac{1}{16} \times 6\frac{9}{16}$ inches—10,3 × 16,7 cm. Page from the sketchbook 10,3 × 17 cm. Pencil, a few stains. Verso: No. 286.

Study of a blanket or piece of cloth, the ensemble suggesting the form of a mountain. Cf. Nos. 316, 344.

BIBLIOGRAPHY: Venturi, Vol. I, p. 350, *Oeuvres Inédites* (not reproduced). Basel catalog, No. 65 (reproduced).

COLLECTIONS: Cézanne *fils*, Paris. W. Feuz, Bern. Kunstmuseum, Basel.

316. STUDY OF DRAPERY AND HEAD OF A HORSE, circa 1873

$6\frac{3}{4} \times 4\frac{1}{16}$ inches—17,1 × 10,3 cm. Page from the sketchbook 10,3 × 17 cm. Pencil, pink stain and small yellow stains. Verso: No. 129.

(a) Dress of a woman with her elbow lifted, seen from the back.—(b) Below and upside down: head of a horse, emerging from a square opening.

BIBLIOGRAPHY: Basel catalog, No. 64 (reproduced).

COLLECTIONS: Cézanne *fils*, Paris. W. Feuz, Bern. Kunstmuseum, Basel.

317. THE DANCE, 1869–71

$4\frac{13}{16} \times 8\frac{5}{8}$ inches—12,2 × 21,8 cm. Pencil on laid paper; transverse brushstrokes in the upper part. Verso: blank page.

The scene is a public dance hall: a woman with her arms raised and breasts bared is dancing, her ample gauze skirt spread out as she swirls. See the studies Nos. 263, 271 (g). Upper left: a violinist. Right foreground: man in a wheelchair pushed by a lackey. On the left, forming a contrast, a rustic lying on the ground smoking a pipe.

BIBLIOGRAPHY: Venturi No. 1203. Vollard, 1914 (reproduced p. 182). Meier-Graefe, *Cézanne und sein Kreis*, Munich, 1922 (reproduced p. 72).

COLLECTION: Albertina, Vienna (Inv. 24079).

318. IN THE COUNTRY, 1869–71

$6\frac{1}{8} \times 9\frac{7}{16}$ inches—15,5 × 24 cm. Pencil on white paper. Verso: print of boats at Etretat. Page trimmed at the upper edge.

Left: couple reclining. Behind them a man in a top hat, his back turned, holding a fishing rod. Right: couple in movement, the man clasping the woman. Cf. Nos. 138 (a), 935, 937. Three tree trunks. Study for a composition; its fanciful element remains enigmatic.

BIBLIOGRAPHY: Venturi No. 1201. Vollard, 1914 (reproduced p. 177). Meier-Graefe, *Cézanne und sein Kreis*, Munich, 1922 (reproduced p. 64).

COLLECTIONS: Kenneth Clark, London.

319. COUPLE IN A GARDEN, circa 1872

$6\frac{1}{8} \times 4\frac{1}{8}$ inches—15,5 × 10,5 cm. Pencil on laid paper. Verso: No. 702.

Couple seen back view looking toward a clump of trees in the distance. Curious foreground perspective. The movement of the woman's dress and hair should be remarked.

BIBLIOGRAPHY: Venturi No. 1228. Vollard, 1914 (reproduced p. 166). Meier-Graefe. *Cézanne und sein Kreis*, Munich 1922 (reproduced p. 100). Ikouma Arishima, Cézanne, *Ars*, 1926 (14th year Tai-Sho), reproduced pl. 31.

EXHIBITIONS: Kunsthalle, Basel, 1936, No. 114 (reproduced). Belvedere, Vienna, 1961, No. 84.

COLLECTION: Albertina, Vienna (Inv. 24086).

320. WOMAN AND LITTLE GIRL, EACH WITH ONE ARM RAISED, circa 1873

Pencil and india ink with white gouache on laid paper. Watermark: fragment of a scroll, cut off by the left edge of the page.

(a) Woman and little girl, seen back view, each gesticulating with one arm. The woman is drawn in pencil, the girl in ink. Study for No. 321 and for the painting Venturi No. 243.—(b) On the right, a list:

> *Chrome clair—un pot*
> *Jaune de Naples—idem*
> *Gomme gutte—tablette*
> *Bleu de Prusse—idem* (See Note 48)

BIBLIOGRAPHY: Venturi, Vol. I, p. 351, *Oeuvres Inédites* (not reproduced). Basel catalog, No. 67 (reproduced).

COLLECTIONS: Cézanne *fils*, Paris. W. Feuz, Bern. Kunstmuseum, Basel.

321. IMAGINARY SCENE, circa 1873

$3\frac{3}{8} \times 5\frac{11}{16}$ inches—8,5 × 14,5 cm. Pencil on ordinary paper, torn at the top. Entire sheet glued to thin paper. Verso: No. 322.

Compositional study for the painting Venturi No. 243. In the oil, the artist in a top hat in the left foreground is simply carrying a stick, whereas in our drawing he is standing in front of his easel. The group on the right is very different in the drawing and the landscape on the distant bank farther away.

BIBLIOGRAPHY: Venturi No. 1230. G. Rivière, *Le Maître Paul Cézanne*, Paris, 1923 (reproduced p. 167). *Dessins*, 1957, No. 20-21 (reproduced).

EXHIBITIONS: Orangerie, Paris, 1936, No. 143. Lyons, 1939, No. 59. Wildenstein, London, 1939, No. 76. Cézanne retrospective, Paris, No. 76.

COLLECTIONS: Cézanne *fils*, Paris. W. Feuz, Bern. W. Raeber, Basel. A. Chappuis, Tresserve.

322. STUDY OF A WOMAN AND FAUN, 1869–73

$3\frac{3}{8} \times 5\frac{11}{16}$ inches—8,5 × 14,5 cm. Pencil on ordinary paper covered with slightly transparent paper, torn. Verso: No. 321.

A framer having glued paper over this drawing, the subject cannot be described except for a seated woman in the company of a horned faun.

COLLECTIONS: Cézanne *fils*, Paris. W. Feuz, Bern. W. Raeber, Basel. A. Chappuis, Tresserve.

323. A PAIR OF LOVERS OUTDOORS, 1868–75

$6\frac{7}{8} \times 9\frac{1}{8}$ inches—17,5 × 23,1 cm. Page from the sketchbook 18 × 24 cm. Pencil; a strip of paper has been added to the lower edge and the drawing continues on it. Verso: No. 119.

Five versions of a pair of lovers lying on the grass near a tree.—(a) Top left, in a rectangle: love scene; further off is a man in a hat carrying a stick, perhaps a scarecrow. Max Dellis discovers the monogram PC in the round at the foot of the tree. Cf. No. 104 (b).—(b) Top right: the two lovers under a tree.—(c) Center right: the couple, without the tree.—(d) Lower right: the couple in the same attitude as in (a), with a tree as in (b).—(e) Just below the center of the page: study of the couple, larger and very beautiful; the composition forms a pyramid with symmetrical effects. The tree is indicated above them on the right.—The sketches (b), (c), and (d) seem to be anterior to (a) and (e), which date from 1871 at the earliest.

BIBLIOGRAPHY: Venturi does not reproduce the whole page, but only the following sketches, taken from Vollard, 1914: (a) No. 1216; (c) No. 1189; (e) No. 1182. Vollard, 1914: (a) (reproduced p. 137); (c) (reproduced p. 187); (e) (reproduced p. 188). Basel catalog, No. 62 (reproduced). E. d'Ors, *Cézanne*, Paris, 1930 ((a) reproduced p. 39). B. Dorival, *Cézanne*, Paris, 1948 ((c) reproduced p. 20). Max Dellis, *GBA,* March, 1971 ((a) reproduced p. 192).

EXHIBITIONS: The Hague, 1956, No. 97. Zurich, 1956, No. 149.

COLLECTIONS: Cézanne *fils*, Paris. W. Feuz, Bern. Kunstmuseum, Basel.

324. AENEAS MEETING DIDO IN CARTHAGE, 1873–76

9 × 12 inches—22,9 × 30,5 cm. Pencil on laid paper. Verso: the inscriptions "Affectueux souvenir de Paul Cézanne 1915" and "Don de Mr Bret 1922."

Copy after an unidentified work. Dido is seen seated like a goddess as Aeneas approaches her, accompanied by Achates who is still veiled with a shroud (see Virgil's *Aeneid*, Book I). Two figures standing in the background, and on the right, the ship at sea. In the lower left corner a man is sitting embracing a woman. Since the work Cézanne copied is unidentified, it is impossible to say whether this couple forms part of the scene or whether it was drawn in the corner of the page earlier, as its treatment would suggest; it can be compared with the couples in No. 323. Cf. also the watercolor Venturi No. 871 representing the same subject.

EXHIBITIONS: Baltimore Museum of Art, July–Aug. 1958. The Mr. and Mrs. Henry Pearlman Collection, Knoedler & Co., New York, Jan.–Feb. 1959, cat. No. 23 (reproduced). Idem, Detroit Institute of Arts, 1967, No. 9.

COLLECTIONS: Paul Cézanne *fils*, Paris. M. Bret, Paris. Dr. X, Paris. Galerie Baugin, Paris. Mr. and Mrs. Henry Pearlman, New York.

325. AFTER DELACROIX: HAMLET AND HORATIO, 1873

$10\frac{1}{16} \times 9\frac{7}{16}$ inches—25,5 × 24 cm. Black crayon. Verso: blank page.

After Eugéne Delacroix's lithograph *Hamlet contemplating the skull of Yorick*. See fig. 49. Dr. Gachet had a print of this lithograph in his house at Auvers, given him by the painter Armand Gautier. Cf. No. 326.

FIG. 49. Eugène Delacroix (1799–1863): *Hamlet contemplant le crâne de Yorick*, detail of lithograph (1828). 36 cm. × 27 cm.
(Photograph: Gabriel)

BIBLIOGRAPHY: Venturi, Vol. I, p. 347, *Oeuvres Inédites* (not reproduced). Venturi mistakenly calls it "Faust et Méphisto," whereas it is a lithograph from the series illustrating Shakespeare's *Hamlet*. Berthold, cat. No. 244 (reproduced); error as to title of lithograph. Paul Gachet mentions this drawing in: *Cézanne à Auvers, Cézanne graveur*, Les Beaux-Arts, Paris, 1952.

COLLECTIONS: Dr. Gachet, Auvers. Paul Gachet, Auvers. Galerie Daber, Paris.

326. AFTER DELACROIX: HAMLET AND HORATIO, 1873

$4\frac{7}{8} \times 6\frac{11}{16}$ inches—12,4 × 17 cm. Black crayon on bister paper. Verso: blank page.

After Eugène Delacroix's lithograph *Hamlet contemplating the skull of Yorick*. See fig. 49. According to Paul Gachet this is a smaller version of No. 325, drawn with a view to an etching which was never carried out.

BIBLIOGRAPHY: Venturi, Vol. I, p. 347, *Oeuvres Inédites* (not reproduced). Berthold, cat. No. 245 (reproduced). Paul Gachet, *Cézanne à Auvers, Cézanne graveur*, Les Beaux Arts, Paris, 1952 (reproduced).

COLLECTIONS: Dr. Gachet, Auvers. Paul Gachet, Auvers. Galerie Daber, Paris.

327. A WEDDING, 1873–76

$5 \times 6\frac{3}{16}$ inches—12,6 × 15,8 cm. Page XXXVIII of the sketchbook Leigh Block. Pencil. Verso: No. 333.

Civil marriage ceremony at the town hall. A couple standing in front of a bearded mayor who is reading out clauses from the marriage laws. Cf. No. 347 (b).

BIBLIOGRAPHY: Rewald, *Carnets:* C V, p. XXXVIII (reproduced pl. 88).

COLLECTIONS: Cézanne *fils*, Paris. M. Renou, Paris. Poyet, Lyons. M. Renou, Paris. Sam Salz, New York. Mr. and Mrs. Leigh Block, Chicago.

328. ORIENTALS SMOKING PIPES, 1873–76

$4\frac{1}{16} \times 6\frac{5}{8}$ inches—10,3 × 16,8 cm. Page from the sketchbook 10,3 × 17 cm. Pencil, upper corners damaged, stain, paper soiled. Verso: No. 255.

Right: (a) Man drawing at a pipe.—(b) Man with his elbows raised lighting a pipe.—(c) Center: rough sketch of a shoulder and head.—(d) Study for the gesture of lighting a pipe.—(e) Left: same subject.

BIBLIOGRAPHY: Basel catalog, No. 68 (reproduced).

COLLECTIONS: Cézanne *fils*, Paris. W. Feuz, Bern. Kunstmuseum, Basel.

329. WINE GLASS, STUDY OF A HEAD, NOTATIONS, 1873–76

$4\frac{7}{8} \times 8\frac{9}{16}$ inches—12,4 × 21,7 cm. Page II of the sketchbook A.I.C. Pencil, notations in ink, stains in the margin. Verso: scribbles by the artist's son.

(a) Left: a wine glass and its shadow.—(b) Page upright, right: head of the artist's little son, Paul.—(c) Across the page, covering the head: handwritten notations, in ink.— On top of (a): the name Cézanne written by the child.

BIBLIOGRAPHY: Rewald, *Carnets*: C II, p. II (not reproduced). Omission in the text of the number 3 in the notation: "boeuf plus [3] rognons." Schniewind, text p. 25, same omission of the number 3 (reproduced). W. V. Andersen, *Sk.*, (reproduced fig. 19b).

COLLECTIONS: Cézanne *fils*, Paris. M. Renou, Paris. Poyet, Lyons. M. Renou, Paris. Sam Salz, New York. Art Institute, Chicago.

330. FRAGMENT OF SCULPTURE, 1874–77

$7\frac{3}{16} \times 4\frac{9}{16}$ inches—18,2 × 11,6 cm. Page 41 verso from the first sketchbook Mrs. Enid A. Haupt. Pencil. Verso: blank page.

The subject of this sketch remains enigmatic. Judging from the hatching, the rounded part must be the top. It can be seen as a masculine torso, fragment of a sculpture.

BIBLIOGRAPHY: Rewald, *Carnets*: C I, page 41 verso "croquis d'un torse d'homme?" (not reproduced). Berthold, cat. No. 308 (reproduced). Th.Reff, *AB*, June 1960, p. 148, indicates a statue of Mercury in the Louvre as model: "Cat. sommaire des marbres antiques, Paris 1896, No. 573."

COLLECTIONS: Cézanne *fils*, Paris. M. Renou, Paris. Poyet, Lyons. M. Renou, Paris. Sam Salz, New York. Mrs. Enid A. Haupt, New York.

331. PEASANT WOMAN WEARING A COIF, HEAD OF A WOMAN, ROUND PITCHER, 1874–77

$8\frac{9}{16} \times 5$ inches—21,7 × 12,6 cm. Page III of the sketchbook Leigh Block. Pencil. Verso: No. 791.

(a) Head and shoulders of a peasant woman in a regional coif, her head tilted; cf. No. 299 (c). A downward shadow from the bridge of her nose is indicated.—(b) Lower right: head of Mme Cézanne, bent forward; drawn with a softer pencil.—(c) At right angles: small sketch of a round pitcher with handle.

BIBLIOGRAPHY: Rewald, *Carnets*: C V p. III (reproduced pl. 14).

COLLECTIONS: Cézanne *fils*, Paris. M. Renou, Paris. Poyet, Lyons. M. Renou, Paris. Sam Salz, New York. Mr. and Mrs. Leigh Block, Chicago.

332. BASE OF A LAMP, SUGAR BOWL, PROFILE OF A WOMAN, 1873–78

$4\frac{7}{8} \times 8\frac{9}{16}$ inches—12,4 × 21,7 cm. Page XXVII verso of the sketchbook A.I.C. Pencil, stains. Verso: No. 545.

(a) Left: incomplete sketch showing the base of a kerosene lamp.—(b) Sugar bowl with flattened corners, the lid topped with an acorn.—(c) At right angles: rapid sketch of a woman's head.

BIBLIOGRAPHY: Rewald, *Carnets*: C II, p. XXVII verso (not reproduced). Schniewind, text p. 30 (reproduced). W. V. Andersen, *Sk.* (not reproduced).

COLLECTIONS: Cézanne *fils*, Paris. M. Renou, Paris. Poyet, Lyons. M. Renou, Paris. Sam Salz, New York. Art Institute, Chicago.

333. BACK OF A CHAIR, 1874–77

$5 \times 6\frac{3}{16}$ inches—12,6 × 15,8 cm. Page XXXVIII verso of the sketchbook Leigh Block. Pencil. Verso: No. 327.

Chair seen from the back; its legs are not drawn. The three crossbars seem to be curved. Background indicated by dense, luminous hatching.

BIBLIOGRAPHY: Rewald, *Carnets*: C V, p. XXXVIII verso (not reproduced).

COLLECTIONS: Cézanne *fils*, Paris. M. Renou, Paris. Poyet, Lyons. M. Renou, Paris. Sam Salz, New York. Mr. and Mrs. Leigh Block, Chicago.

334. A CHAIR, 1874–77

$4\frac{7}{8} \times 8\frac{9}{16}$ inches—12,4 × 21,7 cm. Page XXX of the sketchbook A.I.C. Pencil, stains. Verso: No. 370.

(a) Left: rush-bottom chair with slightly curved back and three crossbars. There is a curious shadow between the uprights. In the background: a board.—(b) Right, upside down: rough draft of the son's head, crossed out. Cf. No. 698 (b).

BIBLIOGRAPHY: Rewald, *Carnets*: C II, p. XXX (reproduced pl. 80). Schniewind, text p. 30 (reproduced). Andersen, *Sk.* (not reproduced).

COLLECTIONS: Cézanne *fils*, Paris. M. Renou, Paris. Poyet, Lyons. M. Renou, Paris. Sam Salz, New York. Art Institute, Chicago.

335. TWO STUDIES: CHAIR AND BED, 1874–77

$8\frac{9}{16} \times 5$ inches—21,7 × 12,6 cm. Page XXXVII verso of the sketchbook Leigh Block. Pencil. Verso: No. 774.

(a) The back of a chair is seen behind the rectangle formed by a bedstead; indications of a bedspread.—(b) At right angles: two posts and transversal bar of the same iron bed. A cast shadow on the wall.

BIBLIOGRAPHY: Rewald, *Carnets:* C V, p. XXXVII verso (not reproduced).

COLLECTIONS: Cézanne *fils*, Paris. M. Renou, Paris. Poyet, Lyons. M. Renou, Paris. Sam Salz, New York. Mr. and Mrs. Leigh Block, Chicago.

336. IRON BEDPOST AND CHAIR BACK, 1874–77

$4\frac{9}{16} \times 7\frac{3}{16}$ inches—11,6 × 18,2 cm. Page 9 verso from the first sketchbook Mrs. Enid A. Haupt. Pencil. Verso: No. 824.

Fortuitous composition: study of two iron bedposts with rounded tops, connected by an ornamental headpiece leading in a diagonal to the right; behind, the back of a chair. Interplay of lines and surfaces. Cf. No. 339.

BIBLIOGRAPHY: Rewald, *Carnets:* C I, p. 9 verso (not reproduced).

COLLECTIONS: Cézanne *fils*, Paris. M. Renou, Paris. Poyet, Lyons. M. Renou, Paris. Sam Salz, New York. Mrs. Enid A. Haupt, New York.

337. BACK OF A CHAIR, 1876–79

$5 \times 4\frac{1}{4}$ inches—12,6 × 10,9 cm. Page X of the sketchbook Leigh Block. Pencil, stains upper left; part of page cut off. Verso: blank page.

The curved back of a chair. Shadows indicated by hatching.

BIBLIOGRAPHY: Rewald, *Carnets:* C V, p. X (not reproduced).

COLLECTIONS: Cézanne *fils*, Paris. M. Renou, Paris. Poyet, Lyons. M. Renou, Paris. Sam Salz, New York. Mr. and Mrs. Leigh Block, Chicago.

338. BACK OF A CHAIR, HILLS, 1876–81

$5 \times 8\frac{9}{16}$ inches—12,6 × 21,7 cm. Page XXXIV of the sketchbook Leigh Block. Pencil. Verso: No. 434.

(a) Bottom of the page: curved back of a chair; interior of a room indicated in the background, with hatching.—(b) Study of a chain of hills near Marseilles, seen across the sea from L'Estaque. Cf. the painting Venturi No. 429 in which these same hills are seen.

BIBLIOGRAPHY: Rewald, *Carnets:* C V, p. XXXIV (not reproduced).

COLLECTIONS: Cézanne *fils*, Paris. M. Renou, Paris. Poyet, Lyons. M. Renou, Paris. Sam Salz, New York. Mr. and Mrs. Leigh Block, Chicago.

339. BACK OF A CHAIR, 1876–79

$8\frac{9}{16} \times 5$ inches—21,7 × 12,6 cm. Page VIII of the sketchbook Leigh Block. Pencil. Verso: No. 754.

Chair with rounded back and double-curved crossbar. Of the seat, only the wooden frame is drawn, in an arc which forms a base for the sketch. One simple horizontal stroke indicates the background. Cf. the watercolor Venturi No. 850.

BIBLIOGRAPHY: Rewald, *Carnets:* C V, p. VIII (reproduced pl. 81).

COLLECTIONS: Cézanne *fils*, Paris. M. Renou, Paris. Poyet, Lyons. M. Renou, Paris. Sam Salz, New York. Mr. and Mrs. Leigh Block, Chicago.

340. MME CÉZANNE, TWO CHAIRS, 1876–80

$8\frac{9}{16} \times 5$ inches—21,7 × 12,6 cm. Page XLVI of the sketchbook Leigh Block. Pencil. Verso: No. 730.

(a) Top: head of Mme Cézanne, her eyelids lowered; hatching and a line indicate the background. Cf. No. 665. —(b) Below: two round-backed chairs in front of a wall. Cf. Nos. 333, 335, 339, 341.

BIBLIOGRAPHY: Rewald, *Carnets:* C V, p. XLVI (reproduced pl. 8).

COLLECTIONS: Cézanne *fils*, Paris. M. Renou, Paris. Poyet, Lyons. M. Renou, Paris. Sam Salz, New York. Mr. and Mrs. Leigh Block, Chicago.

341. CHAIR COVERED WITH A DUST SHEET, LAND-SCAPE, 1876–79

$5 \times 8\frac{9}{16}$ inches—12,6 × 21,7 cm. Page XLII of the sketchbook Leigh Block. Pencil. Verso: No. 749.

(a) Round-backed chair under a dust sheet; the chair rail of the room is indicated by horizontal strokes.—(b) Right, and at right angles: study of a landscape with steep cliffs, no doubt by the sea.

BIBLIOGRAPHY: Rewald, *Carnets:* C V, p. XLII (reproduced pl. 78).

COLLECTIONS: Cézanne *fils*, Paris. M. Renou, Paris. Poyet, Lyons. M. Renou, Paris. Sam Salz, New York. Mr. and Mrs. Leigh Block, Chicago.

342. CANDLESTICK WITH LIGHTED CANDLE, 1877–80

$8\frac{9}{16} \times 5$ inches—21,7 × 12,6 cm. Page XLIX of the sketchbook Leigh Block. Pencil. Verso: No. 837.

Stub of a candle, placed rather oddly in the candlestick, off-center to the right; the flame and holder assert their presence with remarkable emphasis.

BIBLIOGRAPHY: Rewald, *Carnets:* C V, p. XLIX (reproduced pl. 74).

COLLECTIONS: Cézanne *fils,* Paris. M. Renou, Paris. Poyet, Lyons. M. Renou, Paris. Sam Salz, New York. Mr. and Mrs. Leigh Block, Chicago.

343. KEROSENE LAMP, 1878–81

$9\frac{5}{16} \times 6$ inches—23,7 × 15,2 cm. Page VIII verso of the Album, Paul Mellon collection. Pencil. Verso: No. 1081.

Sketch of a kerosene lamp and shade, the base not finished. Cf. Nos. 955, 956: subjects similar but more complete.

BIBLIOGRAPHY: Venturi, Vol. I, under No. 1303 (not reproduced). *Album*, 1966 (reproduced).

COLLECTIONS: Cézanne *fils*, Paris. Paul Guillaume, Paris. A. Chappuis, Tresserve. Mr. and Mrs. Paul Mellon, Upperville, Va.

344. STUDY OF DRAPERY, 1877–80

$8\frac{9}{16} \times 4\frac{7}{8}$ inches—21,7 × 12,4 cm. Page XXXI of the sketchbook A.I.C. Pencil, stains. Verso: No. 915.

To examine this study, the page must no doubt be held vertically. The strokes are delicate, the hatching fine in texture, the contours closely observed.

BIBLIOGRAPHY: Rewald, *Carnets*: C II p. XXXI (not reproduced). Schniewind, text p. 31 (reproduced). Andersen, *Sk.* (not reproduced).

COLLECTIONS: Cézanne *fils*, Paris. M. Renou, Paris. Poyet, Lyons. M. Renou, Paris. Sam Salz, New York. Art Institute, Chicago.

345. WASHBOWL, FUNNEL, HANDWRITTEN NOTATIONS, 1878–81

$5 \times 8\frac{1}{16}$ inches—12,6 × 20,4 cm. Page I from the sketchbook BS III. Pencil, several stains. Verso: No. 552.

(a) Right: a funnel, with indications of background.— (b) Left: a washbowl.—Notations and numbers are spread over the page, partly covering the sketches: Notations: 2 *blanc d'argent*, 4 *terre verte*, 1 *petit Prusse*, 5 *petit chrome*, 1 *ombre naturelle, jaune brilliant*, 1 *ocre jaune*, 3 *blanc*, 2 *outremer*, 2 *terre verte*, 1 *vert véronèse—rue de la Monnaie*.

BIBLIOGRAPHY: Venturi No. 1398 (in error as: "on the inside of the cover [of the carnet]"). Basel catalog, No. 103 (reproduced).

COLLECTIONS: Cézanne *fils*, Paris. Paul Guillaume, Paris. W. Feuz, Bern. Kunstmuseum, Basel.

346. WOMAN SITTING ON A CHAIR WITH HER BACK TURNED, 1877–80

$8\frac{9}{16} \times 4\frac{7}{8}$ inches—21,7 × 12,4 cm. Page XLV verso of the sketchbook A.I.C. Pencil, light stains. Verso: No. 698.

Rapid sketch, but architectural and animated.

BIBLIOGRAPHY: Rewald, *Carnets*: C II, p. XLV verso (reproduced pl. 38). Schniewind, text, p. 33 (reproduced). Andersen, *Sk.* (not reproduced). Yvon Taillandier, *Paul Cézanne*, Paris, New York, Munich, 1961 and 1965 (reproduced p. 94).

COLLECTIONS: Cézanne *fils*, Paris. M. Renou, Paris. Poyet, Lyons. M. Renou, Paris. Sam Salz, New York. Art Institute, Chicago.

347. A CUP, CIVIL MARRIAGE CEREMONY, 1877–80

$5 \times 8\frac{9}{16}$ inches—12,6 × 21,7 cm. Page XLI verso of the sketchbook Leigh Block. Pencil. Verso: No. 797.

Page upright: (a) top, at right angles, cup with its handle in profile. The shadow against which the handle stands out and the ellipse of the cup's rim, retouched several times, should be noticed. A stroke in the center marks the vertical axis.—(b) Lower left, study of a civil marriage ceremony, same subject as No. 327.

BIBLIOGRAPHY: Rewald, *Carnets*: C V, p. XLI (reproduced pl. 79). Th.Reff, Cézanne's Drawings 1875–85, *BurlM*, May 1959, p. 171 (reproduced fig. 17).

COLLECTIONS: Cézanne *fils*, Paris. M. Renou, Paris. Poyet, Lyons. M. Renou, Paris. Sam Salz, New York. Mr. and Mrs. Leigh Block, Chicago.

348. STILL LIFE, 1877–80

$8\frac{5}{8} \times 4\frac{7}{8}$ inches—21,8 × 12,4 cm. Page L from the sketchbook CP II. Pencil. Verso: No. 631.

Rectangular mantel clock, a receptacle for potted plants on either side, indications of the mantelpiece. Cf. Nos. 349, 411. In the foreground, a sculptured ornament: the upper part of a chimney frame or divan. Cf. No. 662 (on the left).

BIBLIOGRAPHY: Venturi, Vol. I, under No. 1299 (not reproduced).

COLLECTIONS: Cézanne *fils*, Paris. Paul Guillaume, Paris. A. Chappuis, Tresserve.

349. MANTEL CLOCK, 1878–81

$5 \times 8\frac{9}{16}$ inches—12,6 × 21,7 cm. Page XXXVI of the sketchbook Leigh Block. Pencil. Verso: No. 884.

(a) Right: rectangular mantel clock and a vase or potted-plant receptacle. Cf. No. 411.—(b) Rough study of a head.

BIBLIOGRAPHY: Rewald, *Carnets*: C V, p. XXXVI (not reproduced).

COLLECTIONS: Cézanne *fils*, Paris. M. Renou, Paris. Poyet, Lyons. M. Renou, Paris. Sam Salz, New York. Mr. and Mrs. Leigh Block, Chicago.

350. PAGE OF STUDIES, INCLUDING A LANDSCAPE AND A LABORER, 1873–77

$11\frac{15}{16} \times 8\frac{1}{16}$ inches—30,4 × 20,5 cm. Pencil on gray-brown laid paper, small tear, a few stains. Verso: No. 610.

(a) Landscape of house, sunken road, bank strewn with boulders, and a twisted tree with three branches.—(b) A man working with an implement with handle, two heaps of gravel to his right; study for the painting *The Seine at Bercy*, Venturi No. 242. Cf. No. 351.—(c) Cut off by the right edge: legs of a man seen back view, after Michelangelo's *Soldiers at the Bathing Place*; see fig. 8. The rest of the figure is to be seen on No. 351, which formerly continued the present page.—(d) Upside down: contours of a seated man in right profile.—(e) Point of land which is cut off by the edge of the paper and continues on No. 351 (as does (c)). R. W. Ratcliffe, in 1956, was the first to observe that the present page and No. 351 originally formed one page.

BIBLIOGRAPHY: Venturi, Vol. I, as verso of No. 1478 (not reproduced). Berthold, (b) mentioned in the text of the catalog, Nos. 257 and 276 (not reproduced). Basel catalog, No. 66 (reproduced).

COLLECTIONS: Cézanne *fils*, Paris. W. Feuz, Bern. Kunstmuseum, Basel.

351. PAGE OF STUDIES, 1873–77

$11\frac{13}{16} \times 10\frac{1}{4}$ inches—30 × 26 cm. Pencil on laid paper. Verso: the watercolor Venturi No. 844.

Page of studies which originally formed one single sheet with No. 350.—(a) Upper left: copy after an engraving in Charles Blanc's *Ecole Espagnole*, portrait of the painter Navarrete, known as El Mudo. See fig. 50.—(b) Below: round platter, with apples.—(c) Upper right, upside down: laborer seen back view, study for the painting *The Seine at Bercy*, Venturi No. 242. Cf. No. 350.—(d) Beside it: the same figure with slight differences.—(e) At right angles: back of a nude man, after Marcantonio Raimondi's engraving reproducing *The Battle of Cascina*, by Michelangelo; see fig. 8. Cf. No. 364.—(f) Below:

FIG. 50. Portrait of the painter *Juan Fernando de Navarrete* (1526–79), known as *El Mudo*, wood engraving from Charles Blanc, *Ecole espagnole* (1869). *(Photograph: Kunstmuseum, Basel)*

bather standing with his hands on his hips, seen front view; cf. Nos. 946, 947, and Venturi Nos. 899, 1157.—(g) Between (b) and (f): two rough sketches.

BIBLIOGRAPHY: Venturi No. 1224. Berthold, cat. No. 257 (reproduced, (e) separately); cat. No. 276 ((a) reproduced). *Dessins*, 1957, No. 27 (reproduced).

COLLECTIONS: Ambroise Vollard, Paris. A. Chappuis, Tresserve.

352. GROUP BATHING, 1872–75

Measurements not known. Pencil, page trimmed on the left. Verso: unknown.

Five or six men at the river's edge, some nude, others clothed; composition conceived according to classical taste. Certain authors, including Venturi, are of the opinion that this sketch was drawn from nature: soldiers stationed in Aix bathing in the river Arc. To me this page lacks the spontaneity of a study from life.

BIBLIOGRAPHY: Venturi No. 1265. Vollard, 1914 (reproduced p. 166).

COLLECTIONS: Ambroise Vollard, Paris. Present owner unknown.

353. PAGE OF STUDIES: (a) circa 1878; (b) 1874–76; (c) circa 1873; (d) 1874–75; (e) 1874–76

$12\frac{3}{16} \times 17\frac{7}{16}$ inches—31 × 44,2 cm. Pencil, paper torn upper right, small stains. Verso: lithograph by Toussaint Duchemin, *Le Coucher*, after J.-B. Greuze.

(a) Head of the artist's son.—(b) *The Vagabond*, study for

the painting Venturi No. 248.—(c) Man wearing a curious hat seen in right profile, crouching; subject sketched twice. Study for the painting Venturi No. 243.—(d) Woman standing with her arm bent over her head; study for *The Temptation of St. Anthony* and more especially for our drawing No. 448.—(e) Two vagabonds in a landscape; the sequence formed by the cooking pot, the seated figure, and the standing figure should be noticed. The attitudes seem to be those of vagabonds; whether the seated figure is a woman, as H. R. Hoetink thinks, or a young man, in no way alters the feeling that the two form a pair. They may be compared with bathers in similar poses, for example Nos. 420, 421, 422. According to the dates specified, (c) is the first subject sketched and (a) the last; the vagabond scenes (b) and (e) are contemporaneous.

BIBLIOGRAPHY: Venturi No. 1218; date 1873. Vollard, 1914 ((b) reproduced p. 176, (e) p. 184). Frantisek Rachlik, *Cézanne*, Prague, 1948 ((e) reproduced pl. 6). Rewald, *The Ordeal of Paul Cézanne*, London, 1950 ((b) reproduced). Idem, *Paul Cézanne*, Spring Books, London, 1959 and 1965 ((b) reproduced p. 65). Th.Reff, *Bather*, ((b) mentioned p. 184). Idem, *Cézanne and Hercules*, *AB*, Vol. XLVIII, 1966 ((d) mentioned, see note 83, p. 41). H. R. Hoetink, *Franse Tekeningen uit de 19e Eeuw*, Rotterdam, 1968, No. 18 (reproduced); dates: (a) 1877–78, (b) circa 1875, (c) 1875–76, (d) circa 1875, (e) circa 1877; "impossible to say what relation exists between the seated woman and the man with his back turned."

EXHIBITIONS: Meisterzeichnungen französischer Künstler, Kunsthalle, Basel, 1935, No. 175. The Hague, 1956, No. 102. Zurich, 1956, No. 157. Munich, 1956, No. 120.

COLLECTIONS: Cassirer, Berlin. F. Koenigs, Haarlem. Boymans-van Beuningen Museum, Rotterdam (Inv. F II 117).

354. PAGE OF STUDIES, (a) and (b) 1874–75, (c) 1865–68, (d), (e), (f) 1868–71

$12\frac{3}{16} \times 9\frac{3}{8}$ inches—31 × 23,8 cm. Pencil on laid paper (three different kinds of pencil). Verso: No. 207.

(a) Head of Mme Cézanne against a background of hatching; a magnificent drawing.—(b) Framed by strokes: project for a canvas: a seated man, two women, and a child, in a park.—(c) Center: standing male nude with his arms outstretched in the pose of a dancer; drawn from either a live model or a bronze (near the man there is a study of one of his fingers). This figure is a little similar to the *Dancing Faun* in the Naples Museum, and later Cézanne used it, reversed, for *The Struggle of Love*, Venturi Nos. 379, 380, 897.—(d) Back view of a soldier bathing, after the engraving by Marcantonio Raimondi reproducing Michelangelo's cartoon, see fig. 8.—(e) Lower left: man fishing with the rod pointing down; his hat is noteworthy.—(f) Right: another man fishing, his rod raised; drawing reinforced with black crayon. For (e) and (f), cf. Nos. 148, 238, 777, 1123 (a).

BIBLIOGRAPHY: Venturi No. 1217 (in error as page from a sketchbook). Berthold, cat. No. 258 (reproduced). Neumeyer, New York, 1958, No. 14 (in error as a page from a sketchbook; reproduced). Longstreet, 1964 (reproduced). H. R. Hoetink, *Franse Tekeningen uit de 19e Eeuw*, Rotterdam, 1968, No. 19 (reproduced). Dates given: (a) circa 1874, (b) 1875–76, (c) and (d) 1873, (e) and (f) 1873–74.

COLLECTIONS: Cassirer, Berlin. F. Koenigs, Haarlem. Boymans-van Beuningen Museum, Rotterdam (Inv. F II 118).

355. AFTER JEAN FOUQUET: *portrait of a man*, 1871–74

$8\frac{5}{8} \times 4\frac{7}{8}$ inches—21,8 × 12,3 cm. Page from a sketch-book. Brown wash, pen, and pencil. Verso: blank page.

Head of a man wearing a curious skullcap. The wash of the background is paler than that of the headdress and collar; the light on the cap is noteworthy. Drawn from a reproduction of Jean Fouquet's *Portrait of a Man* in the Prince of Liechtenstein's collection, Vaduz. See fig. 51. Source identified by H. P. Landolt, professor at the University of Basel. For many years there was a tendency to see this drawing as a portrait of Mme Cézanne.

COLLECTIONS: A. Vollard, Paris. Paul Guillaume, Paris. Dr. Meller, Budapest. Count Seilern, Vienna. Galerie Zak, Paris. Kalebjan.

FIG. 51. Jean Fouquet (1415–80): *Portrait d'homme* (detail), dated 1436. Prince Liechtenstein collection, Vaduz.

(*Photograph: Giraudon*)

356. PAGE OF STUDIES: (a) 1875–78; (b) circa 1880; (c) circa 1873

About $8\frac{1}{4} \times 6\frac{1}{2}$ inches—21 × 16,5 cm. Pencil and wash. Verso of the lower part of this page: No. 357.

(a) Upper left, in pencil: soldier bathing, after Michelangelo's *Battle of Cascina*, reproduced in engraving by Marcantonio Raimondi. See fig. 8.—(b) Right: head of the artist's son, pencil sketch drawn about 1880, later than the others.—(c) Below: figures, in wash; study for the watercolors Venturi Nos. 875, 876, and for the right side of the canvas Venturi No. 234: *Déjeuner sur l'herbe*. The standing figure is repeated on the right; the woman seen back view on a folding stool may be compared with (c) of No. 138, though the latter is much earlier in date.

BIBLIOGRAPHY: Venturi No. 1225. Vollard, 1914 (reproduced p. 79). Berthold, cat. No. 260 ((a) reproduced). *Kunst und Künstler*, 1920–21, mentioned p. 516.

COLLECTIONS: Ambroise Vollard, Paris. Present owner unknown.

357. STUDIES: MEN AND LANDSCAPE; men, 1873–75; trees, 1880–85

$4\frac{1}{8} \times 6\frac{1}{2}$ inches—10,5 × 16,5 cm. Pencil, blue stains, paper torn right and bottom edges. Verso: the lower half only of No. 356.

(a) Right: standing man singing or declaiming, another man seated on his right, a third lying asleep on his left. Study for the figures in the watercolors Nos. 875, 876, and the painting Venturi No. 234. Notations by an alien hand: *tel* and a cross, see Note 25.—(b) Upside down: a few horizontal strokes and hatching indicate an unfinished landscape with two trees forming a V.

COLLECTIONS: Ambroise Vollard, Paris. Private collection, Paris. Norman Schlenoff, New York.

358. AFTER MICHELANGELO, TWO SOLDIERS, 1875–79

$8\frac{5}{8} \times 4\frac{7}{8}$ inches—21,8 × 12,4 cm. Page XLVIII verso from the sketchbook CP II. Pencil. Verso: No. 359.

Figures from *The Battle of Cascina* by Michelangelo, reproduced in engraving by Marcantonio Raimondi; see fig. 8. Cf. Nos. 87, 351, 354, 356.

BIBLIOGRAPHY: Venturi No. 1298. Berthold, cat. No. 255 (reproduced Abb. 89).

COLLECTIONS: Cézanne *fils*, Paris. Paul Guillaume, Paris. A. Chappuis, Tresserve. Private collection, Paris.

359. PAGE OF STUDIES, INCLUDING A FIGURE SKETCH AFTER MICHELANGELO, 1874–79

$8\frac{5}{8} \times 4\frac{7}{8}$ inches—21,8 × 12,4 cm. Page XLVIII from the sketchbook CP II. Pencil. Verso: No. 358.

(a) Below: male nude, kneeling, seen from in front in foreshortening, after an engraving by Marcantonio Raimondi of Michelangelo's *Battle of Cascina*; see fig. 8. Cf. No. 358. —(b) Top: head of a woman with her eyes half closed, the lower part of her face hidden by a piece of cloth.

BIBLIOGRAPHY: Venturi No. 1297. Berthold, cat. No. 256 (reproduced).

COLLECTIONS: Cézanne *fils*, Paris. Paul Guillaume, Paris. A. Chappuis, Tresserve. Private collection, Paris.

360. STUDIES: AN EAR, AND A MALE FIGURE, 1877–1880

$7\frac{5}{8} \times 4\frac{5}{8}$ inches—19,4 × 11,8 cm. Page LIII from the sketchbook CP I. Pencil. Verso: No. 675.

(a) Top: study of a right ear.—(b) Below: half-length study of a male nude, his arm raised as if to repel someone; copy after an unidentified engraving. Cf. No. 87. This study seems to have been utilized for the subject *Struggle of Love*; see Venturi Nos. 379, 380, 897, the male figure, in reverse, of the couple lower right.

BIBLIOGRAPHY: Venturi, Vol. I, under No. 1281 (not reproduced).

COLLECTIONS: Cézanne *fils*, Paris. Paul Guillaume, Paris. A. Chappuis, Tresserve. Private collection, Paris.

361. WOMAN BATHER, TWO MEN WRESTLING, BOY'S HEAD, 1871–78

$7\frac{3}{16} \times 10\frac{5}{16}$ inches—18,2 × 26,2 cm. Pencil, several tears at the edges, small stains. Verso: the upper part of a colored engraving taken out of *La Mode Illustrée*, 1870, No. 37 (reproduced in the Basel catalog, fig. 95).

(a) Left: woman bather seen in right lost profile; cf. Venturi No. 267.—(b) Right, drawn with rapid strokes: two men in shirtsleeves wrestling; cf. No. 318.—(c) Lower down and partly intermingled with (b): head of the artist's son; the edge of the paper cuts this sketch off at the level of the upper lip. Cf. No. 238.

Dates: these three sketches were drawn at successive periods, the reverse side providing a useful indication of the earliest date limit: 1870. (b) wrestlers: 1871–73. (a) woman bather: 1873–76. (c) son: circa 1878. Douglas Cooper, in his criticism of the Basel catalog, gives: wrestlers, and son: circa 1876; woman bather: 1877. The whole page: 1876–78.

BIBLIOGRAPHY: Basel catalog, No. 83 (reproduced). Douglas Cooper, in *Master Drawings*, Vol. 1, No. 4, 1963, p. 56.

COLLECTIONS: Cézanne *fils*, Paris. W. Feuz, Bern. Kunstmuseum, Basel.

362. MAN AND WOMAN, ROOF WITH CHIMNEYS, 1871–75

$5\frac{1}{4} \times 8\frac{3}{16}$ inches—13,3 × 20,8 cm. Pencil, ink, and watercolor, page torn in the margins and at the corners, red stain upper right. Verso: No. 376.

(a) A man approaching a nude woman, who is sitting on a divan leaning on her elbow.—(b) Upper right: repetition of the woman's face.—(c) Below these sketches and upside down: view of a roof with a row of small rounded chimneys; brush drawing in watercolor.

BIBLIOGRAPHY: Venturi, Vol. I, p. 351, *Oeuvres Inédites* (not reproduced). Basel catalog, No. 57 (reproduced). Longstreet, 1964 (reproduced).

COLLECTIONS: Cézanne *fils*, Paris. W. Feuz, Bern. Kunstmuseum, Basel.

363. PAGE OF STUDIES: (a) circa 1876; (b) circa 1883; (c) circa 1885

Pencil on laid paper. Verso: blank page.

FIG. 52. Augustin Pajou (1730–1809): *Psyché abandonnée*, marble in the Louvre. Musée National du Louvre, *Catalogue des Sculptures* II, 1922, No. 1433.　　(*Photograph: Giraudon*)

(a) Nude woman, half standing, half sitting; study after the marble *Psyche Abandoned* by Augustin Pajou, in the Louvre; see fig. 52.—(b) Head of the artist.—(c) Upside down: the artist's son in a large armchair, his head resting on his arm.

BIBLIOGRAPHY: Venturi No. 1479. Berthold, cat. No. 163 (reproduced). Collection Koenigs, Musée Boymans, Dessins de Pisanello à Cézanne, in *Art et Style*, 1952 (reproduced). A. Mongan, in Ira Moskowitz, *Great Drawings of all Time*, III, New York, 1962 (reproduced). M. Sérullaz, *Drawings of the Masters: French Impressionists*, London, 1963 (reproduced fig. 97). W. V. Andersen, A Cézanne Drawing after Couture, *Master Drawings*, Vol. 1, No. 4, 1963, p. 44 and note 7, p. 46. In (c) the author recognises the artist's son; date 1882–84. (a): circa 1882. Longstreet, 1964 (reproduced). *The World of Cézanne* (reproduced p. 103). H. R. Hoetink, *Franse Tekeningen uit de 19e Eeuw*, Rotterdam, 1968, No. 23 (reproduced); (b) dated circa 1883. J. Leymarie, *Dessins de la Période impressionniste*, Skira, Geneva, 1969 (reproduced p. 84).

EXHIBITIONS: Drawings from Ingres to Seurat, Boymans Museum, Rotterdam, 1933–34, No. 1 (reproduced).

Meisterzeichnungen französischer Künstler, Kunsthalle, Basel, 1935, No. 176. Kunsthalle, Basel, 1936, No. 126. Amsterdam, 1938, No. 23. Amsterdam, 1946, No. 9. Dessins du XVe au XIXe siècle [from the Boymans Museum, Rotterdam], Bibliothèque Nationale, Paris, 1952, No. 139. The Hague, 1956, No. 113. Zurich, 1956, No. 173. Munich, 1956, No. 133. Kunstverein, Hamburg, 1963, No. 27 (reproduced).

COLLECTIONS: F. Koenigs, Haarlem. Boymans-van Beuningen Museum, Rotterdam (Inv. F II 122).

364. PAGE OF STUDIES: (a), (b) and (d) 1871–74; (c) and (e) 1877–78

Pencil. Verso: No. 616.

(a) Left: encounter between a man and a woman; it is not clear whether the man is raising his hat to the woman or whether he is simply holding it out.—(b) Half-length study of a bather, or perhaps a repetition of the woman.—(c) Bather sitting at the foot of a tree.—(d) Woman bather standing with her elbow raised above her shoulder, a pose figuring in several paintings.—(e) Below, at right angles: sketch of the artist's son wearing a beret and schoolboy's pinafore.

BIBLIOGRAPHY: Venturi No. 1288 ((c) and (d) reproduced). Vollard, 1914 ((c) and (d) reproduced p. 118). *Dessins*, 1938, No. 2 (reproduced).

COLLECTIONS: Cézanne *fils*, Paris. Paul Guillaume, Paris. A. Chappuis, Tresserve.

365. THREE WOMAN BATHERS, 1874–78

$4\frac{5}{16} \times 5\frac{1}{2}$ inches—11 × 14 cm. Pencil, accentuated blacks. Verso: blank page.

Wooded landscape with a watercourse which is deep but not wide, recalling the canals around Aix. Left: a nude woman with abundant hair, standing in the same attitude as seen in *La Toilette*, Venturi No. 254; a hanging sheet forms a wide strip behind her. To the right, two women in the water, one with her back turned; the second has a she-faun's profile. This page is exceptionally detailed. Cf. No. 366.

BIBLIOGRAPHY: Venturi No. 1248. Vollard, 1914 (reproduced pl. 56). Ikouma Arishima, Cézanne, *Ars*, 1926 (14th year Tai-Sho—reproduced). *Paul Cézanne*, Takamizawa-Mokuhansha, Tokyo (reproduced between pls. 154 and 155). Kawakita Michiaki, *Cézanne*, Tokyo, 1957, Misuzu-shobô (reproduced p. 1).

COLLECTIONS: Ambroise Vollard, Paris. Maeda Seison (1923), Japan. Private collection, Odawara. Bridgestone Gallery, Tokyo.

366. THREE WOMEN BATHERS, 1874–78

Measurements not known. Pencil. Verso: unknown.

Three women bathers under an expanse of foliage. Study for the painting Venturi No. 269. Cf. also our No. 365.

BIBLIOGRAPHY: Venturi No. 1258. *Kunst und Künstler*, 1913 (reproduced p. 446).

COLLECTIONS: G. F. Reber, Lausanne. Present owner unknown.

367. CROUCHING WOMAN BATHER, 1874–78

$5\frac{13}{16} \times 9\frac{1}{8}$ inches—14,8 × 23,2 cm. Pencil. Verso: blank page.

Like No. 368, this sketch is a study for the watercolor Venturi No. 898 and the canvas Venturi No. 266. The woman is repelling a faun with her arm.

BIBLIOGRAPHY: Venturi No. 1253. Vollard, 1914 (reproduced p. 23).

EXHIBITION: Kunsthalle, Basel, 1936, No. 117.

COLLECTIONS: Meller, Budapest. A. Hahnloser, Winterthur. H. Hahnloser, Bern.

368. THREE WOMEN BATHERS, 1874–78

$4\frac{3}{44} \times 4\frac{3}{44}$ inches—12 × 12 cm. Pencil. Verso: blank page.

Group of three women bathers in a landscape, the one seated on the left repelling an approaching faun with her arm. Cf. the watercolor Venturi No. 898 and the canvas No. 266.

BIBLIOGRAPHY: *Dessins*, 1957, No. 41 (reproduced). *Cézanne*, Coll. Génies et Réalités, Hachette, Paris, 1966 (reproduced p. 243).

COLLECTIONS: Cézanne *fils*, Paris. M. Renou, Paris. Michel Grilichess, Paris.

369. AFTER RUBENS: NAIAD, 1873–77

$5\frac{1}{8} \times 7\frac{1}{2}$ inches—13 × 19 cm. Pencil. Verso: blank page.

After one of the naiads (the one on the right) in *Marie de Médicis landing in the Port of Marseilles* by Rubens, in the Louvre; see fig. 53. Cf. No. 455, and, for the pose only, No. 282.

BIBLIOGRAPHY: Berthold, cat. No. 217 (reproduced).

COLLECTIONS: Cézanne *fils*, Paris. L. Lichtenhan, Basel. Private collection, Paris.

370. TWO WOMEN IN A LANDSCAPE, 1874–78

$4\frac{7}{8} \times 8\frac{9}{16}$ inches—12,4 × 21,7 cm. Page XXX verso of the sketchbook A.I.C. Pencil, stains. Verso: No. 334.

Two women in a boat, one wearing a large hat, seated, the other standing with her right arm raised; there is a painting of the same subject. Right: a contour and sketchy strokes.

BIBLIOGRAPHY: Rewald, *Carnets*, C II, p. XXX verso (reproduced pl. 87). Berthold, cat. No. 303 (reproduced). Schniewind, text p. 31 (reproduced). Neumeyer, 1958, No. 7 (reproduced). Andersen, *Sk.* (not reproduced). Longstreet, 1964 (reproduced).

COLLECTIONS: Cézanne *fils*, Paris. M. Renou, Paris. Poyet, Lyons. M. Renou, Paris. Sam Salz, New York. Art Institute, Chicago.

371. THREE WOMEN BATHERS, 1873–77

$5 \times 8\frac{1}{16}$ inches—12,6 × 20,5 cm. Page XV from the sketchbook BS III. Pencil. Verso: No. 1142.

Left: a woman walking toward the background (a typical figure in Cézanne's work), a second woman, seated, and a

FIG. 53. Peter Paul Rubens (1577–1640): *Naiads*, detail from the canvas in the Medici series, *Débarquement de Marie de Médicis au port de Marseille*, painted between 1622 and 1625, now in the Louvre. 3,94 m.   2,95 m. Musée National du Louvre, *Catalogue des Peintures* III, No. 2090. These naiads had already attracted the attention of Delacroix, who had painted a copy of the same central figure represented in Cézanne's sketch (No. 1128). Delacroix's copy, 46,5 cm.   38 cm., is in the Kunstmuseum, Basel (Inv. 1953.396). On October 5, 1847, Delacroix noted in his diary: "With the habitual means, one has always to spoil one thing in order to obtain another. Rubens has slackened in his Naiads, to avoid losing his light and color." *(Photograph: Giraudon)*

third in the water up to her thighs. Background of trees. Cf. Nos. 649, 650, 971, and Venturi Nos. 539, 540. The standing figure was perhaps retouched later.

BIBLIOGRAPHY: Venturi No. 1417.

COLLECTIONS: Cézanne *fils*, Paris. Paul Guillaume, Paris. W. Feuz, Bern. R. Von Hirsch, Basel.

372. SEATED WOMAN BATHER, 1873–77

$7\frac{7}{8} \times 11\frac{13}{16}$ inches—20 × 30 cm. Pencil. Verso: No. 418.

Preliminary study for a painting; framed with strokes. Cf. Venturi Nos. 256, 258, and our Nos. 373, 374.

BIBLIOGRAPHY: Venturi, Vol. I, p. 350, *Oeuvres Inédites,*

under "Collection Ambroise Vollard"; mention "Verso: Baigneuse assise" (not reproduced).

COLLECTIONS: Ambroise Vollard, Paris. Present owner unknown.

373. PAGE OF STUDIES, WOMEN BATHERS, 1873–77

$7\frac{7}{8} \times 11\frac{7}{8}$ inches—20 × 30,1 cm. Pencil and pen on thin paper, stains, flyspecks, carmine blot lower left. Verso: No. 392.

(a) Upper left: study for a composition comprising four women bathers. The three figures to the right appear in several paintings; see Venturi Nos. 382-86, 547 etc. Cf. our Nos. 515, 516, 517. The woman seated in the center is looking at herself in a mirror held by the woman on the left.—(b) At right angles: another bather, sitting with her arms folded above her head; pencil reinforced with india ink. Cf. Venturi No. 258, and our Nos. 372, 374.—(c) Right: seated woman bather in a similar pose; pen drawing. Above: repetition of her head.—(d) Right: unfinished portrait of the artist and the peak of his cap.

BIBLIOGRAPHY: Venturi No. 1251. Vollard, 1914 ((a) reproduced p. 89, (b) reproduced p. 71, (c) reproduced p. 181). Basel catalog, No. 98 (reproduced). Meier-Graefe, *Cézanne und sein Kreis*, Munich, 1921 etc. ((a) reproduced p. 68). Idem, *Entwicklungsgeschichte der modernen Kunst,* 1904 ((b) reproduced p. 593). E. d'Ors, *Paul Cézanne*, Paris, 1930 ((c) reproduced p. 86). *A.A.*, 1920 ((c) reproduced p. 287).

EXHIBITIONS: The Hague, 1956, No. 100. Zurich, 1956, No. 155.

COLLECTIONS: Cézanne *fils*, Paris. W. Feuz, Bern. Kunstmuseum, Basel.

374. WOMAN BATHER, 1873–77

$3 \times 5\frac{11}{16}$ inches—7,5 × 14,5 cm. Pencil. Verso: blank page.

Woman bather, sitting at the foot of a tree, on a seat covered with a towel, her arms folded above her head and her hair falling down in a cascade to the left. Cf. our Nos. 372, 373, and Venturi Nos. 256, 258; our drawing is a version, a little rigid but sculptural and strong, of this same theme.

BIBLIOGRAPHY: Venturi, Vol. I, p. 349, *Oeuvres Inédites* (not reproduced).

COLLECTION: Kenneth Clark, London.

375. AFTER MICHELANGELO: *The Dying Slave*, 1875–78

$8\frac{1}{2} \times 5$ inches—21,6 × 12,7 cm. Page XLII verso from the second sketchbook Mrs. Enid A. Haupt. Pencil. Verso: blank page.

After Michelangelo's marble *Dying Slave* in the Louvre. See fig. 54. Retouches to the face. The drawing here is weaker than in the other three copies of the same work.

BIBLIOGRAPHY: Rewald, *Carnets*: C IV, p. XLII verso (reproduced pl. 124). Berthold, cat. No. 61 (reproduced).

COLLECTIONS: Cézanne *fils*, Paris. M. Renou, Paris. Poyet, Lyons. M. Renou, Paris. Sam Salz, New York. Mrs. Enid A. Haupt, New York.

376. HEAD OF A SLEEPING CHILD, 1873–76

$5\frac{1}{4} \times 8\frac{13}{16}$ inches—13,3 × 20,8 cm. Pencil and charcoal, notation in ink, small hole, paper torn. Verso: No. 362.

(a) Head of a child; the shadow below the chin shows that the head is in a horizontal position. Right (not visible in photograph): house, or lantern, by the artist's son. Notation in ink by an alien hand. See Note 25.

BIBLIOGRAPHY: Venturi, Vol. I, p. 351, *Oeuvres Inédites* (not reproduced). Basel catalog, No. 82 (reproduced). *Das Wort*, Literarische Beilage, Sept. 1962 (reproduced p. 64).

COLLECTIONS: Cézanne *fils*, Paris. W. Feuz, Bern. Kunstmuseum, Basel.

377. AFTER GÉROME: *Greek Interior*, circa 1874

$3\frac{7}{16} \times 5\frac{3}{16}$ inches—8,8 × 13,1 cm. Pencil. Verso: blank page.

Copied from the paintings *Greek Interior* (1851) and *Phryne before the Areopagus* (1861) by Jean-Léon Gérome (1824–1904). See figs. 55, 56. Cézanne had certainly seen the picture of Phyrne (letter to Huot, dated June 4, 1861). It is possible that he drew from reproductions (see for example the album of photographic reproductions entitled *Musée Goupil & Co.*, on sale from 1861 on); however, the lack of precision indicates rather that he reconstituted the subject from memory. Our drawing represents a group of nude women in a room furnished in Pompeian style, one of them reclining in the left foreground. R. W. Ratcliffe,

FIG. 54. Michelangelo Buonarroti (1475–1564): *Slave*, marble destined for the tomb of Pope Julius II, now in the Louvre. (Photograph from cast.) Height: 2,28 m. Musée National du Louvre, *Catalogue des Sculptures* I, 1922, No. 696.

FIG. 55. Jean-Léon Gérome (1824–1904): *Intérieur grec* (1851), painting in the Hamburg museum. A photograph had appeared in 1860 in the album *Musée Goupil & Cie.*, No. 857.
(Photograph: R. W. Ratcliffe)

FIG. 56. Also by Gérome: *Phryné devant l'Aréopage* (1861), from the album *Musée Goupil & Cie.* *(Photograph: R. W. Ratcliffe)*

who identified the originals, points out that this figure was used for the reclining bather in the painting Venturi No. 274. A standing woman, seen front view, was taken from the painting *Phryne before the Areopagus* and slightly modified.

BIBLIOGRAPHY: *Cézanne dessinateur*, p. 299 (reproduced fig. 15).

COLLECTIONS: Marignane, Paris. Present owner unknown.

378. ROUGH DRAFT OF A LETTER, AND SKETCHES OF BATHERS, 1874–77; rough draft circa 1878

$12\frac{5}{8} \times 7\frac{7}{8}$ inches—32 × 20 cm. Pencil and pen on gray laid paper, traces of folds. Verso: No. 239.

(a) Top: incomplete sketch of a bather with outstretched arms.—(b) Below: the same subject, less worked on.—(c) Rough draft of a letter, in ink, addressed to the writer Marius Roux (1838–1905); for the text, see letter No. LVII in the *Correspondance*. Cézanne speaks of himself here as an "impressionist painter."

BIBLIOGRAPHY: Venturi No. 1231. Vollard, 1914 (reproduced pp. 42-43). *Correspondance*, Letter No. LVII (reproduced fig. 24). Th.Reff, mention in *GBA*, 1962, p. 177. Jedlicka, *Cézanne Briefe*, Zurich, 1962, No. LVII.

COLLECTIONS: Cézanne *fils*, Paris. Paul Guillaume, Paris. A. Chappuis, Tresserve. Private collection, Paris.

379. PITCHER, BATHER, CANDLE SNUFFER, 1874–77

$4\frac{7}{8} \times 8\frac{9}{16}$ inches—12,4 × 21,7 cm. Page XXIII of the sketchbook A.I.C. Pencil, stains. Verso: No. 571.

(a) Left: pitcher, its handle toward the viewer.—(b) Standing bather, probably drawn from a model, the raised arm being held by a cord or stick. The lower end of this support joins the line indicating the edge of the table on which the pitcher stands.—(c) Upper right: candle snuffer, its shadow cast vertically.

BIBLIOGRAPHY: Rewald, *Carnets*: C II, p. XXIII (reproduced pl. 99). Schniewind, text p. 29 (reproduced). Andersen, *Sk.* (not reproduced). Th.Reff, *Bather* (not reproduced).

COLLECTIONS: Cézanne *fils*, Paris. M. Renou, Paris. Poyet, Lyons. M. Renou, Paris. Sam Salz, New York. Art Institute, Chicago.

380. SUGAR BOWL, STUDIES OF A BATHER, 1874–77

$8\frac{9}{16} \times 4\frac{7}{8}$ inches—21,7 × 12,4 cm. Page XXVI of the sketchbook A.I.C.

(a) Top: close view of a round sugar bowl.—(b) Below: bather with outstretched arms. Both the raised arm and the head are drawn in two different positions. Numerous studies of the arm.—(c) Right: two more studies of the head and arm.

BIBLIOGRAPHY: Rewald, *Carnets*: C II, p. XXVI (reproduced pl. 103). Schniewind, text p. 30 (reproduced). Andersen, *Sk.* (not reproduced). Th.Reff, *Bather* ((b) and (c) reproduced fig. 10).

COLLECTIONS: Cézanne *fils*, Paris. M. Renou, Paris. Poyet, Lyons. M. Renou, Paris. Sam Salz, New York. Art Institute, Chicago.

381. STUDY OF BATHERS, 1874–77

$8\frac{9}{16} \times 4\frac{7}{8}$ inches—21,7 × 12,4 cm. Page IX verso of the sketchbook A.I.C. Pencil, stains. Verso: No. 486.

(a) Bather seen front view, his arms outstretched, his head tilted backwards. Cf. Venturi No. 262.—(b) Half-length sketch of a bather under the stress of some violent emotion.—(c) Below: male nude looking down, the front of his head bald.

BIBLIOGRAPHY: Rewald, *Carnets*: C II, p. IX verso (reproduced pl. 90). Schniewind, text p. 27 (reproduced). Th.Reff, *Bather*, p. 173 (not reproduced). Andersen, *Sk.* (not reproduced).

COLLECTIONS: Cézanne *fils*, Paris. M. Renou, Paris. Poyet, Lyons. M. Renou, Paris. Sam Salz, New York. Art Institute, Chicago.

382. STANDING BATHER AND OTHER SKETCHES, 1874–77

$4\frac{7}{8} \times 8\frac{9}{16}$ inches—12,4 × 21,7 cm. Page XXII verso of the sketchbook A.I.C. Pencil, stain. Verso: No. 402.

(a) Bather with outstretched arms, his head tilted to the right.—(b) Below: repetition of the head.—(c) Right hand emerging from a sleeve, and to the right, a foot. My analysis of the page is as follows: in line with the bather (added later) is the arm of a seated figure, seen from above, one of his feet on the ground to the right, with a blanket covering the ankle and part of the foot. The figure is holding a book on his right knee and reading. The shaded part under the thumb represents the cover of the upright book. The figure is probably leaning back resting, so the chest is not seen. Cf. Nos. 626, 690, 855.

BIBLIOGRAPHY: Rewald, *Carnets:* C II, p. XXII verso (not reproduced). Schniewind, text p. 29 (reproduced). Andersen, *Sk.* (not reproduced).

COLLECTIONS: Cézanne *fils*, Paris. M. Renou, Paris. Poyet, Lyons. M. Renou, Paris. Sam Salz, New York. Art Institute, Chicago.

383. BATHER, SKETCHES OF A CAT, 1874–78
$4\frac{7}{8} \times 8\frac{9}{16}$ inches—12,4 × 21,7 cm. Page XVII of the sketchbook A.I.C. Pencil, stains. Verso: No. 810.

(a) Left: bather with outstretched arms. Near his groin are some forms recalling antique marbles.—(b) At right angles to the bather: two sketches of a somnolent cat. Cf. Nos. 475, 475 bis.

BIBLIOGRAPHY: Rewald, *Carnets:* C II, p. XVII (reproduced pl. 101). Schniewind, text p. 29 (reproduced). Andersen, *Sk.* (not reproduced).

COLLECTIONS: Cézanne *fils*, Paris. M. Renou, Paris. Poyet, Lyons. M. Renou, Paris. Sam Salz, New York. Art Institute, Chicago.

384. BATHER AND SMALL FIGURE, 1874–78
$4\frac{7}{8} \times 8\frac{9}{16}$ inches—12,4 × 21,7 cm. Page XVIII verso of the sketchbook A.I.C. Pencil, stains. Verso: No. 781.

(a) Left: a little person in a loose garment, in front of a seascape suggested by a few strokes.—(b) Right: bather with outstretched arms; he is surrounded by a landscape which is characteristic for this subject. Cf. the painting Venturi No. 259 and also 248, 271. Seen through the drawing of the bather: study of a straw hat, seen from much nearer, the ribbon around the crown visible near the bather's waist. Cf. No. 1176.

BIBLIOGRAPHY: Rewald, *Carnets:* C II, p. XVIII verso (reproduced pl. 100). Schniewind, text p. 29 (reproduced). Andersen, *Sk.* (not reproduced). Th.Reff, *Bather* (reproduced fig. 4).

COLLECTIONS: Cézanne *fils*, Paris. M. Renou, Paris. Poyet, Lyons. M. Renou, Paris. Sam Salz, New York, Art Institute, Chicago.

385. BATHER WITH OUTSTRETCHED ARMS, 1874–77
$5\frac{15}{16} \times 3\frac{15}{16}$ inches—15 × 10 cm. Pencil on laid paper. Verso: blank page.

In this sketch both arms are complete and the feet almost parallel. Landscape: diagonal slope becoming vertical near the figure's hips; sea and clouds.

BIBLIOGRAPHY: Venturi No. 1260. Else Cassirer, *Künstlerbriefe*, Berlin, 1923 (reproduced p. 602). G. Rivière, *Le Maître Paul Cézanne*, Paris, 1923 (reproduced p. 118).

EXHIBITION: Aquarelles et Baignades de Cézanne, Galerie Renou & Colle, Paris, 1935.

COLLECTIONS: Cézanne *fils*, Paris. Present owner unknown.

386. BATHER WITH OUTSTRETCHED ARMS, 1874–77
$6\frac{5}{16} \times 3\frac{3}{4}$ inches—16 × 9,5 cm. (or slightly larger). Pencil on laid paper. Verso: blank page.

The body is slender, the elements of the landscape conceived to stress the effect of contours and volumes. The line forming the bathing trunks is repeated at the neck, the left contour remarkable. An owl in flight is seen on the right.

BIBLIOGRAPHY: Venturi No. 1261. Vollard, 1914 (reproduced p. 9).

COLLECTIONS: Ambroise Vollard, Paris. Present owner unknown.

387. BATHER WITH OUTSTRETCHED ARMS, circa 1875
$4\frac{1}{16} \times 3\frac{1}{8}$ inches—10,3 × 8 cm. Pencil. Verso: blank page.

This drawing recalls the painting Venturi No. 259. Across the stretch of water, a distant shore and some clouds.

BIBLIOGRAPHY: Drawing mentioned by Th.Reff, *Bather*, p. 188, note 13.

EXHIBITION: Kunstnerforbundet, Oslo, 1954.

COLLECTIONS: Arnstein Arneberg, Oslo. Huguette Berès, Paris. Present owner unknown.

388. BATHER WITH OUTSTRETCHED ARMS, 1875–78
$6\frac{5}{16} \times 4\frac{5}{16}$ inches—16 × 11 cm. Pencil, round stains. Verso: blank page.

The head is bent low to the right; the expression on the face seems dramatic. Foreground and background are filled with details in curious hatching and spirals.

BIBLIOGRAPHY: Venturi No. 1262. Vollard, 1914 (reproduced p. 14).

COLLECTIONS: Ambroise Vollard, Paris. Present owner unknown.

389. TWO BATHERS, 1875–78
$8\frac{5}{8} \times 4\frac{7}{8}$ inches—21,8 × 12,4 cm. Page XLIX from the sketchbook CP II. Pencil. Verso: No. 481.

(a) A bather with outstretched arms, in a seascape. He is standing at the water's edge, as though preparing to dive.—(b) Seated man in an unusual pose: his right leg crossed over his left knee, his right hand on his right knee. Though the second figure is on a different scale and was drawn prior to (a), the two together form a composition.

BIBLIOGRAPHY: Venturi, Vol. I, under No. 1298 (not reproduced). *Dessins*, 1938, No. 35 (reproduced). Th.Reff, *Bather*, p. 173, and p. 188, note 13.

COLLECTIONS: Cézanne *fils*, Paris. Paul Guillaume, Paris. A. Chappuis, Tresserve. Private collection, Paris.

390. SKETCH OF A SEATED MAN, HANDWRITING, 1874–77
$8\frac{9}{16} \times 4\frac{7}{8}$ inches—21,7 × 12,4 cm. Page I verso of the sketchbook A.I.C. Pencil, numbers in ink, stains.

Verso: (not classified) rough draft of a letter, notations, unfinished sketch of a conical object, and sketch done by the son.

Old man with beard, bareheaded, in an overcoat. Slightly caricatural sketch which to a certain extent recalls the portrait of Achille Emperaire. Handwriting: end of the rough draft of a letter and a few numbers.

BIBLIOGRAPHY: Rewald, *Carnets*: C II, p. I verso (text of the rough draft of a letter, but drawing not reproduced). Schniewind, text p. 25 (reproduced). Andersen, *Sk.* (reproduced fig. 19a).

COLLECTIONS: Cézanne *fils*, Paris. M. Renou, Paris. Poyet, Lyons. M. Renou, Paris. Sam Salz, New York. Art Institute, Chicago.

391. AFTER PIERRE PUGET: ATLAS, 1874–77

$11\frac{7}{16} \times 9\frac{1}{4}$ inches—$29 \times 23,5$ cm. Pencil on laid paper. Verso: blank page.

Drawn from a plaster cast of Puget's atlas—that on the right—of the town hall in Toulon; see fig. 57. Cf. Nos. 689, 689A. Three sketches by Cézanne are known of this figure and one of the atlas on the left side; No. 838.

BIBLIOGRAPHY: Berthold, cat. No. 129 (reproduced). Rewald, *Paul Cézanne*, New York, 1948 (reproduced p. 152). Idem, *The Ordeal of Paul Cézanne*, London, 1950 (reproduced p. 165). Idem, *Paul Cézanne*, Spring Books, London, 1959 and 1965 (reproduced p. 87).

FIG. 57. Pierre Puget (1620–94): *Atlas* on the right side of the doorway of Toulon town hall, after a plaster cast in the Louvre from 1886 on, and later in the Trocadéro. *Catalogue du Musée de Sculpture comparée du Trocadéro* III, 1928, No. C 164.
(Photograph: Chappuis)

EXHIBITIONS: The Hague, 1956, No. 98 (reproduced). Zurich, 1956, No. 150 (reproduced). Munich, 1956, No. 116 (reproduced).

COLLECTIONS: G. H. Schick, Paris. Heidi Vollmoeller, Zurich.

392. HEADS AFTER VARIOUS OLD MASTERS, 1876–79

$7\frac{7}{8} \times 11\frac{7}{8}$ inches—20×30 cm. Pencil on thin paper, light stains. Verso: No. 373.

Six heads, drawn from unidentified reproductions of old masters.—(a) Upper left: head of a young man in a skullcap, his face framed with curls; after Pietro Perugino's *Head of a Boy* in the Uffizi Gallery, Florence (No. 416).—(b) Upper right: left three-quarter view of a man in a hat, after an etching attributed to Lucas van Leyden.—(c) Lower edge of the page, third sketch from the left: after a *self-portrait* by Gerard Dou in the Dresden Gallery (No. 1704).—(d) First on the left, upside down and crossed out: after the *Portrait of Masaccio*, formerly thought to be his self-portrait, now attributed to Filippino Lippi.—(e) The second sketch from the left, also crossed out, and (f), the fourth, are done after the same reproduction.

BIBLIOGRAPHY: Berthold, cat. No. 292 (reproduced). Basel catalog, No. 89 (reproduced). Longstreet, 1964 (reproduced).

COLLECTIONS: Cézanne *fils*, Paris. W. Feuz, Bern. Kunstmuseum, Basel.

393. LEFT EAR AND FRAGMENT OF AN ETCHING, 1874–76

$6 \times 8\frac{3}{8}$ inches—$15,3 \times 21,2$ cm. Pencil on yellowish paper, etching, tear repaired at lower edge, upper corner restored. Verso: No. 447.

Pencil sketch of a left ear. Lower part of an etching: portrait of *Dr. Gachet*, by Van Ryssel (Gachet himself). A print of this etching is conserved in the Cabinet des Estampes of the Bibliothèque Nationale, Paris, and is dated 1874.

BIBLIOGRAPHY: Basel catalog, No. 61 (reproduced).

COLLECTIONS: Cézanne *fils*, Paris. W. Feuz, Bern. Kunstmuseum, Basel.

394. PORTRAIT OF VICTOR CHOCQUET, 1875–77

$5\frac{1}{2} \times 3\frac{15}{16}$ inches—14×10 cm. Pencil. Verso: blank page.

Head and shoulders of Victor Chocquet, in left three-quarter view, the head seeming disproportionately large; background of hatching. Probably done from a photograph. This drawing has been cut out of a page of studies; the sketch of a tree, drawn earlier, can be seen upper left.

BIBLIOGRAPHY: Venturi No. 1241. Th. Reff, Cézanne's Drawings 1875–85, in *BurlM*, May 1959, p. 173 (reproduced fig. 20). W. V. Andersen, Cézanne, Tanguy, Chocquet, *AB*, Vol. XLIX, 1967, p. 137 (not reproduced). J. Rewald, Chocquet and Cézanne, *GBA*, July-Aug. 1969 (reproduced fig. 28).

COLLECTIONS: Ambroise Vollard, Paris. Baltimore Museum of Art: Mrs. Adelyn D. Breeskin Collection.

395. PORTRAIT OF VICTOR CHOCQUET, 1877–81
$3\frac{3}{16} \times 2\frac{15}{16}$ inches—8,1 × 7,5 cm. Pencil on laid paper. Verso: blank page.

Head and shoulders of Victor Chocquet, drawn from a photograph which is still in the possession of Cézanne's descendents. Cf. No. 398 (a).

BIBLIOGRAPHY: *Correspondance* (reproduced fig. 22). W. V. Andersen, Cézanne, Tanguy, Chocquet, *AB*, Vol. XLIX, p. 137 (reproduced fig. 8). J. Rewald, Chocquet and Cézanne. *GBA*, July-Aug. 1969 (reproduced fig. 27, date 1879–82).

EXHIBITIONS: Meisterzeichnungen, Kunsthalle, Basel, 1935, No. 174. Kunsthalle, Basel, 1936, No. 112. San Francisco, 1937, No. 55.

COLLECTIONS: Cézanne *fils*, Paris. Private collection, Basel.

395bis. MAN WITH A WIDE-BRIMMED HAT, 1867–72
$6\frac{11}{16} \times 8\frac{1}{4}$ inches—17 × 21 cm. Pencil. Verso: watercolor Venturi No. 895.

Small portrait on the verso of the watercolor *L'Eternel féminin*. It represents one of Cézanne's fellow-artists. There is a surprising likeness to Auguste Renoir; see the photographs reproduced in Rewald's *History of Impressionism* (New York, 1961) on pp. 74 and 358.

COLLECTIONS: Hazard, Orrouy. Sale Hazard, Paris, December 1-3, 1919, No. 259 (reproduced). Josse Hessel, Paris. Auguste Pellerin, Paris. J. V. Pellerin, Paris. Wildenstein & Co., New York.

396. PORTRAIT OF ANTOINE GUILLAUME, 1877–80
$3\frac{3}{4} \times 2\frac{9}{16}$ inches—9,5 × 6,5 cm. Pencil. Verso: blank page.

Antoine Guillaume, known as "le père Guillaume," was a shoemaker who around 1878 lived in the same house as Cézanne at No. 105, rue de Vaugirard, Paris. The Guillaume and Cézanne families were linked by a lasting friendship. According to Gerstle Mack, Mme Guillaume had known Hortense Fiquet for many years (see Gerstle Mack, *Paul Cézanne*, London, 1953, p. 232, and the French edition, Gallimard, Paris, 1938, p. 199; also the Basel catalog, p. 126, note 38). Cf. the portraits of Louis Guillaume, son of Antoine, Venturi Nos. 374, 552, and also No. 1573, which is our No. 940.

BIBLIOGRAPHY: Venturi No. 1239. Longstreet, 1964 (reproduced).

EXHIBITIONS: Zurich, 1956, No. 164 erroneously described as not mentioned by Venturi). Munich, 1956, No. 125 (erroneously described as not mentioned by Venturi).

COLLECTIONS: Cézanne *fils*, Paris. W. Feuz, Bern. Carl Roesch, Diessenhofen.

397. THE ARTIST'S MOTHER, 1877–80
$4\frac{7}{8} \times 7\frac{7}{8}$ inches—12,3 × 20 cm. Pencil, traces of a fold. Verso: unknown.

The artist's mother asleep in an armchair. Nothing is drawn in detail except Mme Cézanne's head, standing out against a vast chair back. In the background some wood paneling and round objects are indicated. A shadow on the sitter's chin seems inexplicable.

BIBLIOGRAPHY: *Correspondance* (reproduced fig. 30). Rewald, *Cézanne et Zola*, Paris, 1939 (reproduced fig. 58).

COLLECTIONS: Galerie Bénézit, Paris. Present owner unknown.

398. PAGE OF STUDIES, INCLUDING MME CÉZANNE SEWING, 1877–80
$7\frac{3}{4} \times 9\frac{1}{8}$ inches—19,7 × 23,2 cm. Pencil on beige paper. Verso: No. 701 bis.

(a) Portrait of Victor Chocquet, detailed preliminary drawing for the painting Venturi No. 532. Cf. our No. 395.—(b) Right: Mme Cézanne sewing, a table top in front of her; study for the canvas Venturi No. 291. Cf. Nos. 719, 728.—(c) Below, on a larger scale: Mme Cézanne's head leaning against a cushion.

BIBLIOGRAPHY: Venturi No. 1240. A. van Buren, Mme Cézanne's Fashions and the Dates of her Portraits, *The Art Quarterly*, Vol. XXIX, No. 2, 1966, p. 115 ff., Note 20. *Apollo*, March 1967 (reproduced p. 181). W. V. Andersen, Cézanne, Tanguy, Chocquet, *AB*, Vol. XLIX, 1967, p. 137 (reproduced fig. 7).

EXHIBITION: Belvedere, Vienna, 1961, No. 104.

COLLECTIONS: Kenneth Clark, London. Benjamin Sonnenberg, New York.

399. PORTRAIT OF A MAN, 1877–80
$4\frac{1}{2} \times 4\frac{3}{8}$ inches—11,5 × 11,2 cm. Pencil. Verso: blank page.

Rewald is right in not accepting this as a portrait of Cézanne as others have. The mustache, nose, forehead, and eyes are not those of the artist. It is more likely the head of some official or professor.

BIBLIOGRAPHY: *Correspondance* (reproduced fig. 23).

EXHIBITIONS: Meisterzeichnungen, Kunsthalle, Basel, 1935, No. 186. Kunsthalle, Basel, 1936, No. 132. San Francisco, 1937, No. 56.

COLLECTIONS: Cézanne *fils*, Paris. Private collection, Basel. Mr. and Mrs. I. H. Hume, San Francisco.

400. SELF-PORTRAIT OF THE ARTIST, circa 1875
6 × 5 inches—15,2 × 12,7 cm. Corners cut. Black crayon. Verso: blank page.

Head and shoulders of Cézanne, with a great deal of shadow, hatching, and stumping. In the right background a wine glass, with the ledge on which it rests, stands out light against the shadow. Signature lower left, of which the authenticity has been contested; the question remains open.

BIBLIOGRAPHY: Léo Larguier, Collectionneurs et collections: Emile Dunan, *L'Art vivant*, Paris, March 15, 1929 (reproduced). J. Rewald, *History of Impressionism*, New York, 1961 (reproduced p. 351).

EXHIBITION: Loan Exhibition of Modern Continental Paintings, Dublin, Aug. 1944, No. 16.

COLLECTIONS: Emile Dunan, Paris. Paul Guillaume, Paris. Derrick Morley, London.

401. SELF-PORTRAIT, circa 1875

Measurements not known. Charcoal on tinted paper, stains. Verso: blank page.

In this drawing the artist created initial effects by the use of stumping, influenced no doubt by a photograph (see *Correspondance*, fig. 1). He then heightened the portrait with vigorous strokes.

BIBLIOGRAPHY: René Huyghe, *Cézanne*, Aimery Somogy, Paris, 1957 (reproduced p. 30).

COLLECTIONS: Gustave Coquiot, Paris. Present owner unknown.

402. SELF-PORTRAIT, 1875–76

$8\frac{9}{16} \times 4\frac{7}{8}$ inches—21,7 × 12,4 cm. Page XXII of the sketchbook A.I.C. Pencil, stains. Verso: No. 382.

The expression on the face is singular, reminding me a little of certain portraits of Vincent van Gogh.

BIBLIOGRAPHY: Rewald, *Carnets:* C II, p. XXII (reproduced pl. 4). "This self-portrait is somewhat similar to the one painted by Cézanne from a photograph: see Venturi, No. 1519 and F. Novotny, *Cézanne und das Ende der wissenschaftlichen Perspektive*, Vienna, 1937 [reproduced pl. 48-49]." Schniewind, p. 29 (reproduced). Andersen, *Sk.* (not reproduced). Neumeyer, 1958, No. 31 (reproduced). Coll. Génies et Réalités, *Cézanne*, Hachette, Paris, 1966 (reproduced p. 170, fig. 124).

COLLECTIONS: Cézanne *fils*, Paris. M. Renou, Paris. Poyet, Lyons. M. Renou, Paris. Sam Salz, New York. Art Institute, Chicago.

403. SELF-PORTRAIT, circa 1878

$7\frac{15}{16} \times 5\frac{11}{16}$ inches—18,5 × 14,5 cm. Pencil. Verso: blank page.

Head of the artist, his lips in a thin line. The drawing finishes at the top by the rim of some kind of hat, which is not drawn. The sketch is all in the eyes, with their extraordinary, fixed look.

BIBLIOGRAPHY: Venturi No. 1238. *A.A.*, May 1936 (reproduced p. 159, fig. 1). René Huyghe, *Cézanne*, Aimery Somogy, Paris, 1957 (reproduced p. 66).

EXHIBITIONS: Art Français, Copenhagen, 1914, No. 231. Bibliothèque Nationale, Paris, 1933. Orangerie, Paris, 1936, No. 151.

COLLECTIONS: E. Blot, Paris; Blot sale, Paris, June 2, 1933, No. 6 (reproduced). Maurice Gobin, Paris.

404. PAGE OF STUDIES, INCLUDING BATHERS AND A SELF-PORTRAIT, 1875–78

$11\frac{5}{8} \times 9\frac{1}{8}$ inches—29,5 × 23,2 cm. Pencil on beige laid paper, trace of a fold, stains. Verso: fragment of a rocky landscape (cut off by the edge). See Bibliography.

Left part of a page which has been divided into two.—(a) Study of the artist in a hat, partly covered by later sketches; this portrait is rather similar to No. 611.—(b) Upside down: on the lower left, a study of bathers for the painting Venturi No. 275, which measures $5\frac{1}{2} \times 7\frac{1}{2}$ inches. The reclining figure seen back view is taken from the allegorical figure of a River by Eugène Delacroix; see fig. 27. Cf. No. 494. Cézanne has altered the shoulders and arms, while maintaining the curve described by the model's arm;

he has added a hump in the ground. The tree trunk screening the bather further back is indicated by a few strokes. Right background: a bush and rough sketch of women bathers.—(c) Lower right: study of a woman bather, who figures also in the painting.—(d) Upper left: study of the reclining bather and tree trunk.—Below, by the artist's son: crude sketch of the bather.—(e) Upper right: rough sketch of a bent arm. Upper right, by the son: confused sketch, with scribbles.—Written in an alien hand: the word *tel* (as is) three times, and *détacher les deux sujets*. See Note 25.

BIBLIOGRAPHY: Venturi, Vol. I, p. 349, *Oeuvres Inédites* (not reproduced). W. V. Andersen, Two Unpublished Cézanne self-portrait Drawings, *BurlM*, 1967, p. 475 (reproduced figs. 48 and 50; fig. 49 reproduces the reverse side of the page, not classified in our catalog.

EXHIBITION: The Mr. and Mrs. Henry Pearlman Collection, Detroit Institute of Arts, 1967, No. 7.

COLLECTIONS: Cézanne *fils*, Paris. Paul Guillaume, Paris. Kenneth Clark, London. Mr. and Mrs. Henry Pearlman, New York.

405. PAGE OF STUDIES, INCLUDING A PORTRAIT OF GOYA, 1877–80

$19\frac{11}{16} \times 11\frac{13}{16}$ inches—50 × 30 cm. Pencil, a few stains, fold across the page. Verso: No. 821.

(a) Upper left: copy of Goya's etched self-portrait, which figures at the head of the *Caprichos;* probably drawn by Cézanne from the reproduction printed in Charles Blanc's *Ecole Espagnole*, 1869. See fig. 58.—(b) Apple, casting a circular shadow.—(c) Upper right and upside down: woman bather walking away toward the background.—

FIG. 58. Francisco de Goya y Lucientes (1746–1828): *Portrait of the artist*; wood engraving in Charles Blanc, *Ecole espagnole* (1869), after Goya's etching for the headpiece of the "Caprichos." The etching measures 14,2 cm. × 11,7 cm.
(Photograph: Chappuis)

(d) Left: unfinished self-portrait.—(e) Man in a top hat: caricature in imitation of (a) ? Cf. Nos. 27, 31.—(f) Upside down again: reclining nude leaning on her elbow, a pose frequently studied by the artist.—(g) Compositional study: half-reclining couple, clothed and seen front view. See Note 25.

BIBLIOGRAPHY: Venturi No. 1474 ((d) only reproduced, after Vollard, 1914). Vollard, 1914 ((d) only reproduced, p. 13). Berthold, cat. No. 275 (reproduced). Meier-Graefe, *Cézanne und sein Kreis*, Munich, 1922 ((d) reproduced, p. 20). Idem, *Entwicklungsgeschichte*, Munich, 1927 ((d) reproduced, p. 593). *AA*, 1920, p. 286 ((d) reproduced). Frantisek Rachlik, *Cézanne*, Prague, 1948 ((d) reproduced pl. 1). Robert Rey, *Revue des Arts*, Paris, 1954 ((d) reproduced on the title page). Meyer Schapiro, The Apples of Cézanne, *Art News Annual* XXXIV, 1968 (reproduced p. 34).

EXHIBITIONS: Belvedere, Vienna, 1961, No. 105. Aix-en-Provence, 1961, No. 47 ((d) reproduced, frontispiece of catalog).

COLLECTION: Kenneth Clark, London.

406. SELF-PORTRAIT, 1880–84?

$6\frac{3}{4}$ to $6\frac{7}{8} \times 8\frac{15}{16}$ to 9 inches—17,1 to 17,4 × 22,6 to 22,9 cm. Pencil on laid paper, vertical fold, stains. Verso: blank page.

The artist's head, and on the right, an apple. See Note 49.

BIBLIOGRAPHY: Rewald, *Cézanne*, New York, 1948 (reproduced in reverse p. 163). Meyer Schapiro, The Apples of Cézanne, *Art News Annual* XXXIV, 1968 (reproduced p. 49).

EXHIBITIONS: San Francisco, 1937, No. 62 (reproduced). Charles E. Slatkin Gallery, New York, 1959, French Master Drawings XVI-XXth Centuries, No. 108 (reproduced).

COLLECTIONS: Ambroise Vollard, Paris. Theodor Schempff. Dr. Alyn C. Poole. Cincinnati Art Museum, gift of Miss Emily Poole.

407. HEAD OF THE ARTIST AND HEAD OF A WOMAN, 1881–84

$4\frac{7}{8} \times 8\frac{9}{16}$ inches—12,4 × 21,7 cm. Page XXXIX of the sketchbook A.I.C. Pencil, stains. Verso: No. 704.

(a) Left: unfinished self-portrait.—(b) Unfinished head of a woman.

BIBLIOGRAPHY: Rewald, *Carnets:* C II, p. XXXIX (not reproduced). Schniewind, text p. 32 (reproduced). Andersen, *Sk.*, (not reproduced).

COLLECTIONS: Cézanne *fils*, Paris. M. Renou, Paris. Poyet, Lyons. M. Renou, Paris. Sam Salz, New York. Art Institute, Chicago.

408. MAN SITTING READING A NEWSPAPER, 1874–77

$8\frac{9}{16} \times 4\frac{7}{8}$ inches—21,7 × 12,4 cm. Page XXIIII of the sketchbook A.I.C. Pencil, stain. Verso No. 694.

Sketch of a man seated sideways in an armchair, wearing a large straw hat and holding a newspaper. Below: foot in a slipper.

BIBLIOGRAPHY: Rewald, *Carnets:* C II, p. XXIIII (not reproduced). Schniewind, text p. 30 (reproduced). Andersen, *Sk.* (not reproduced).

COLLECTIONS: Cézanne *fils*, Paris. M. Renou, Paris. Poyet, Lyons. M. Renou, Paris. Sam Salz, New York. Art Institute, Chicago.

409. HEAD AND SHOULDERS OF THE ARTIST'S FATHER, 1877–80

$8\frac{9}{16} \times 4\frac{7}{8}$ inches—21,7 × 12,4 cm. Page XXIX of the sketchbook A.I.C. Pencil, stains. Verso: No. 453.

Louis-Auguste Cézanne, wearing a cap and reading a newspaper. The strokes rising toward the right indicate the top edge of the paper. Cf. Nos. 178, 410, 413, and Venturi Nos. 25, 91.

BIBLIOGRAPHY: Rewald, *Carnets:* C II, p. XXIX (reproduced pl. 10). Schniewind, text p. 30 (reproduced). Neumeyer, 1958, No. 40 (reproduced). Andersen, *Sk.* (not reproduced).

COLLECTIONS: Cézanne *fils*, Paris. M. Renou, Paris. Poyet, Lyons. M. Renou, Paris. Sam Salz, New York. Art Institute, Chicago.

410. THE FATHER AND THE SON OF THE ARTIST, 1877–80

$8\frac{9}{16} \times 4\frac{7}{8}$ inches—21,7 × 12,4 cm. Page XIX verso of the sketchbook A.I.C. Pencil, stains. Verso: No. 669.

Two sketches: (a) Louis-Auguste Cézanne half asleep, his eyes closed.—(b) Upside down: head of the artist's son, unfinished.

BIBLIOGRAPHY: Rewald, *Carnets:* C II, p. XIX verso (not reproduced). Schniewind, text p. 29 (reproduced). Andersen, *Sk.* (not reproduced).

COLLECTIONS: Cézanne *fils*, Paris. M. Renou, Paris. Poyet, Lyons. M. Renou, Paris. Sam Salz, New York. Art Institute, Chicago.

411. PAGE OF STUDIES, INCLUDING A MANTEL CLOCK, 1877–81

$4\frac{7}{8} \times 8\frac{5}{8}$ inches—12,4 × 21,8 cm. Page XL verso from the sketchbook CP II. Pencil. Verso: No. 614.

(a) On the mantelpiece of an apartment: a large clock and two potted plants with tapering leaves. This is not the same clock as that shown in the painting Venturi No. 69, *The Black Clock*. Cf. No. 349.—(b) Head of the artist's father in a cap, apparently by lamplight; cf. Nos. 409, 661, 662, 720. This sketch is later than (a).

BIBLIOGRAPHY: Venturi, Vol. I, under No. 1293 (not reproduced).

COLLECTIONS: Cézanne *fils*, Paris. Paul Guillaume, Paris. A. Chappuis, Tresserve. Private collection, Paris. Mr. and Mrs. Paul Mellon, Upperville, Va.

412. PORTRAIT OF LOUIS-AUGUSTE CÉZANNE, 1879–81

$8\frac{11}{16} \times 9\frac{7}{8}$ inches—22 × 25 cm. Black crayon on laid paper. Verso: blank page.

Head and shoulders of the artist's father, the head standing out light against a dark background. A certain solemnity pervades this work.

BIBLIOGRAPHY: Venturi No. 1234.

COLLECTIONS: Cézanne *fils*, Paris. Jean-Pierre Cézanne, Paris. Emery Reves, U.S.A.

413. PORTRAIT OF LOUIS-AUGUSTE CÉZANNE, 1879–82

$8\frac{1}{8} \times 4\frac{15}{16}$ inches—20,7 × 12,5 cm. Page III verso from the sketchbook BS III. Pencil. Verso: No. 527.

The artist's father, sitting in an enormous armchair reading a newspaper. The left leg is crossed over the right, whereas in the oil portrait, Venturi No. 91, only the feet are crossed.

BIBLIOGRAPHY: Venturi No. 1403. Rewald, *Cézanne et Zola*, Paris, 1936 (reproduced fig. 48). Idem, *Cézanne et Zola*, Paris, 1939 (reproduced fig. 59). Idem, *The Ordeal of Paul Cézanne*, London, 1950 (reproduced). Idem, *Paul Cézanne*, Spring Books, London, 1959 and 1965 (reproduced p. 98). Neumeyer, 1958, No. 27 (reproduced). Yvon Taillandier, *Paul Cézanne*, 1965 (reproduced p. 33). Coll. Génies et Réalités, *Cézanne*, Hachette, Paris, 1966 (reproduced p. 57).

EXHIBITION: Kunsthalle, Basel, 1936, No. 153.

COLLECTIONS: Cézanne *fils*, Paris. Paul Guillaume, Paris. W. Feuz, Bern. R. von Hirsch, Basel.

414. AFTER C. PISSARRO: WOMAN SEWING, 1881–83

$5 \times 8\frac{9}{16}$ inches—12,6 × 21,7 cm. Page IV of the sketchbook. Leigh Block. Pencil. Verso: No. 759.

After the gouache by Camille Pissarro, *Woman Sewing*, signed and dated 1881. See *Camille Pissarro, son art, son oeuvre*, by Ludovic Pissarro and Lionello Venturi, Paris, 1939, No. 1356.

BIBLIOGRAPHY: Rewald, *Carnets*: C V, p. IV (reproduced pl. 39). Th. Reff, *Cézanne's Drawings 1875–85*, *BurlM*, May 1959, p. 173 (reproduced fig. 21); "Cézanne must have seen the gouache when staying at Pontoise from May to October 1881."

COLLECTIONS: Cézanne *fils*, Paris. M. Renou, Paris. Poyet, Lyons. M. Renou, Paris. Sam Salz, New York. Mr. and Mrs. Leigh Block, Chicago.

415. THE ARTIST'S FATHER, AND ANOTHER HEAD, 1882–85

$8\frac{9}{16} \times 4\frac{7}{8}$ inches—21,7 × 12,4 cm. Page XXXVIII verso of the sketchbook A.I.C. Pencil, stains. Verso: No. 288.

(a) Top: portrait of the artist's father, asleep.—(b) Below: head in left profile, bent forward; cf. Nos. 416, 417.

BIBLIOGRAPHY: Rewald, *Carnets*: C II, p. XXXVIII verso (reproduced pl. 11). Schniewind, text p. 32 (reproduced). Andersen, *Sk.* (not reproduced).

COLLECTIONS: Cézanne *fils*, Paris. M. Renou, Paris. Poyet, Lyons. M. Renou, Paris. Sam Salz, New York. Art Institute, Chicago.

416. TWO SKETCHES OF HEADS, 1882–85

$8\frac{9}{16} \times 4\frac{7}{8}$ inches—21,7 × 12,4 cm. Page XXXVI verso of the sketchbook A.I.C. Pencil, stains. Verso: No. 573.

(a) Top: head seen in left profile, the mouth half open; the chin is left blank. Cf. Nos. 415 (b), 417 (a).—(b) Below: head bent forward: I think that it represents the artist's son in a beret; others see it as a woman, her chignon tied round with a ribbon. Cf. No. 665.

BIBLIOGRAPHY: Rewald, *Carnets*: C II, p. XXXVI verso (not reproduced); (b) "possibly Mme Cézanne." Schniewind, text p. 31; (b) "might be Mme Cézanne" (reproduced). Andersen, *Sk.* (not reproduced).

COLLECTIONS: Cézanne *fils*, Paris. M. Renou, Paris. Poyet, Lyons. M. Renou, Paris. Sam Salz, New York. Art Institute, Chicago.

417. HEAD AND SKETCH; sketch, 1870–73; head, 1882–85

$4\frac{7}{8} \times 8\frac{9}{16}$ inches—12,4 × 21,7 cm. Page XXXV of the sketchbook A.I.C. Pencil, stains. Verso: No. 485.

(a) Two rough studies and the sketch of a moving figure, the latter related to the subject of *The Woman taken by Surprise*, see No. 289.—(b) Head bent forward, a collar turned up against the nape of the neck; see the same figure in Nos. 415 (b) and 416 (a). Schniewind and others see it as the profile of a woman, but it could as well be a young man.

BIBLIOGRAPHY: Rewald, *Carnets*: C II, p. XXXV (not reproduced). Schniewind, text p. 31 (reproduced). Andersen, *Sk.* (not reproduced).

COLLECTIONS: Cézanne *fils*, Paris. M. Renou, Paris. Poyet, Lyons. M. Renou, Paris. Sam Salz, New York. Art Institute, Chicago.

418. PAGE OF STUDIES, INCLUDING BATHERS, 1872–76

$7\frac{7}{8} \times 11\frac{3}{16}$ inches—20 × 30 cm. Pencil, accidental touches of watercolor, a few numbers. Verso: No. 372.

Three subjects appear on this page.—(a) The earliest in date is the sketch upper right: man seen in profile, holding a feather or arrow; copy. Date 1867–70. The drapery over his left arm hangs down into the composition of bathers.—(b) Study, framed with strokes, for the small canvas *Bathers*, Venturi No. 268. At the lower edge of the page, the words *entier* and *tel*, see Note 25.—(c) Right: repetition of the seated bather.—(d) Upper right corner: a rectangle, crossed out.—(e) Above (b): half-length sketch of a bather with arms crossed, study for one of the figures in the water.—At right angles: (f) left, repetition of the bather standing on the right in (b).—(g) Head of (e), repeated.—(h) The second man, emerging from the water; in the painting as in the sketch (b) he is hidden by the legs of the bather on the right.—(i) Repetition of the bather seen back view.—Upside down and on a larger scale: (k) upper part of *L'Ecorché* (see fig. 36) seen from the back. It seems difficult to attribute a date to this sketch; in spite of the inclination to consider it as later than the others, a close scrutiny of the strokes (which follow the curving motions of the model) establishes it as contemporary with the bathers.

BIBLIOGRAPHY: Venturi, Vol. I, p. 350, *Oeuvres Inédites*, "Collection Vollard: Baigneurs (dessin 20 × 30 cm.). Recto: Etude de plusieurs baigneurs . . ." Berthold, cat. No. 82 (reproduced Abb. 42).

COLLECTIONS: A. Vollard, Paris. Present owner unknown.

419. TWO BATHERS, 1873–76

$12\frac{3}{16} \times 9\frac{7}{16}$ inches—31 × 24 cm. Pencil on laid paper, paper torn, traces of folds, stain. Verso: rough sketch of a landscape (not classified).

(a) Left: bather holding a towel, seen back view; cf. No. 428. The pose corresponds to that of the statue known as *The Roman Orator* (see fig. 59), but the proportions, more compact, suggest that the artist drew from a live model or photograph. The landscape is detailed. — (b) Right: study of a bather standing with his arms crossed behind his neck. — (c) Lower right, behind (b): back and arm of a bather bending down.

EXHIBITION: Kunsthalle, Basel, 1936, No. 107. Sammlung Hahnloser, Lucerne, 1940, No. 166. Zurich, 1956, No. 212. Munich, 1956, No. 130. Europäische Meisterwerke aus Schweizer Sammlungen, Munich, 1969, catalog by Gisela Hopp, No. 24 (reproduced Abb. 22).

COLLECTIONS: Meller, Budapest. A. Hahnloser, Winterthur. H. R. Hahnloser, Bern.

420. TWO BATHERS, 1873–76

$8\frac{1}{2} \times 5$ inches—21,6 × 12,7 cm. Page XLVI verso of the second sketchbook Mrs. Enid A. Haupt. Pencil, smudging on the right side of the page. Verso: No. 420A.

Left: unfinished sketch of two bathers, one seated, the other standing, and together forming a composition. The sketch of a bather going down into the water can be seen beneath the smudging.

BIBLIOGRAPHY: Rewald, *Carnets:* C IV, p. XLVI verso (not reproduced).

COLLECTIONS: Cézanne *fils*, Paris. M. Renou, Paris. Poyet, Lyons. M. Renou, Paris. Sam Salz, New York. Mrs. Enid A. Haupt, New York.

420A. STUDY OF A HAND

Inaccessible reverse side of No. 420 (not reproduced).

BIBLIOGRAPHY: Rewald, *Carnets:* C IV, p. XLVI "study of a hand" (not reproduced).

421. THREE BATHERS, 1875–78

$5 \times 8\frac{1}{2}$ inches—12,7 × 21,6 cm. Page XLIX verso from the second sketchbook Mrs. Enid A. Haupt. Pencil. Verso: No. 436.

(a) Two bathers, one seated, the other (unfinished) standing. Landscape with a tree in leaf, a stretch of water, and a mountain in the background. — (b) Right: bather with his back turned, of the type based on the figure of *The Roman Orator*, see fig. 59.

BIBLIOGRAPHY: Rewald, *Carnets:* C IV, p. XLIX verso (reproduced pl. 108).

COLLECTIONS: Cézanne *fils*, Paris. M. Renou, Paris. Poyet, Lyons. M. Renou, Paris. Sam Salz, New York. Mrs. Enid A. Haupt, New York.

422. BATHERS, 1875–78

$4\frac{3}{4} \times 4\frac{5}{16}$ inches—12 × 11 cm. Half page from a sketchbook. Pencil, stamp of the Rignault collection (Lugt 2218), as on Nos. 102, 155.

Left: seated bather; right: legs and back of a bather standing with his back turned. One of the numerous studies for the group seen on the left in the paintings of *Bathers*.

COLLECTIONS: Joseph Rignault, Paris and Avignon. Musée Calvet, Avignon (No. 22.305).

423. THREE BATHERS, HANDWRITTEN NOTATIONS, 1875–78

$7\frac{3}{16} \times 4\frac{9}{16}$ inches—18,2 × 11,6 cm. Page 47 verso from the first sketchbook Mrs. Enid A. Haupt. Pencil. Verso: handwritten notations.

(a) One bather is standing in the center, another in the water on the right; of the third, on the left, only the legs are visible. All three correspond to types of bathers often portrayed by Cézanne; see for example Venturi No. 541. In his commentary, Rewald notes that the central bather was inspired by Signorelli's drawing *The Live carrying the Dead* (see fig. 22). The observation is correct, and, with regard to the left arm and the head, *The Roman Orator*, seen back view (see fig. 59), should also be mentioned. — (b) Upside down: study of a glass, covered by handwriting: various numbers, 17 *Boulevard St-Germain/rue Chanez*, 15.

BIBLIOGRAPHY: Rewald, *Carnets:* C I, p. 47 verso, enumeration of a series of works in which there is a figure similar to this central bather (reproduced pl. 106).

COLLECTIONS: Cézanne *fils*, Paris. M. Renou, Paris. Poyet, Lyons. M. Renou, Paris. Sam Salz, New York. Mrs. Enid A. Haupt, New York.

424. BATHER SEEN BACK VIEW, 1875–78

$8\frac{5}{8} \times 4\frac{7}{8}$ inches—21,8 × 12,4 cm. Page XXVIII verso from the sketchbook CP II. Pencil on pale blue paper. Verso: blank page.

The attitude corresponds to that of *The Roman Orator*, marble in the Louvre; see fig. 59. However in our drawing the pose is shown in reverse, and certain differences in the form of the body seem to show that Cézanne drew from a live model, or with no model. Analogies can also be noted to *The Live carrying the Dead*, drawing by Signorelli. Cf. Nos. 182, 426.

BIBLIOGRAPHY: Venturi, Vol. I, under No. 1289 (not reproduced). *Dessins*, 1938, No. 33 (reproduced).

COLLECTIONS: Cézanne *fils*, Paris. Paul Guillaume, Paris. A. Chappuis, Tresserve. Private collection, Paris. H. Purrmann, Montagnola. Dr. R. Purrmann, Starnberg.

425. STUDY OF BATHERS, 1875–78

$7\frac{7}{8} \times 5\frac{1}{8}$ inches—20 × 13 cm. Pencil on laid paper, tear at upper edge; page cut from a larger sheet. Verso: blank page.

(a) Sketch of a seated bather with a towel around his head; cf. Venturi Nos. 389, 390, also 260, 892; and our Nos. 431, 433. The quality of this sketch is inferior to that of (b) and I think it is not going too far to suppose that another hand has intervened. — (b) Bather standing with his back turned, his head in left lost profile; cf. Venturi No. 903, and our Nos. 396, 398.

EXHIBITION: Bernheim-Jeune, Paris, 1952–53, Cent cinquante ans de dessins.

COLLECTIONS: Albert Sarraut, Paris. Catalog of the Albert Sarraut sale, Paris (Maître Ader), Dec. 3, 1964, No. 6 (reproduced). Present owner unknown.

426. BATHER SEEN BACK VIEW, 1875–78

$8\frac{1}{2} \times 5$ inches—21,6 × 12,7 cm. Page XXXIIII verso from the second sketchbook Mrs. Enid A. Haupt. Pencil. Verso: No. 438.

FIG. 59. The antique marble known as *L'Orateur romain* in the Louvre, seen from the back. See fig. 88 for the statue seen front view, and text.

Pose partially influenced by that of *The Roman Orator*, marble in the Louvre; see fig. 59. Three and even four contours in some places. Curious retouches under the left elbow. Cf. particularly No. 428.

BIBLIOGRAPHY: Rewald, *Carnets:* C IV, p. XXXIIII verso (reproduced pl. 107).

COLLECTIONS: Cézanne *fils*, Paris. M. Renou, Paris. Poyet, Lyons. M. Renou, Paris. Sam Salz, New York. Mrs. Enid A. Haupt, New York.

427. TWO STANDING BATHERS, 1876–79

$5 \times 8\frac{1}{2}$ inches—12,7 × 21,6 cm. Page L from the second sketchbook Mrs. Enid A. Haupt. Pencil. Verso: No. 689A.

(a) Page upright, top left: study of an undefinable object. —(b) Page lengthwise, right: two standing bathers. The figure to the right, which seems to be a later version, is a finer, more expressive drawing; cf. especially Nos. 426, 428.

BIBLIOGRAPHY: Rewald, *Carnets:* C IV, p. L (reproduced pl. 109).

COLLECTIONS: Cézanne *fils*, Paris. M. Renou, Paris. Poyet, Lyons. M. Renou, Paris. Sam Salz, New York. Mrs. Enid A. Haupt, New York.

428. BATHER SEEN BACK VIEW, 1877–80

$7\frac{15}{16} \times 4\frac{7}{8}$ inches—20,1 × 12,4 cm. Page XXVII from the sketchbook BS III. Pencil and pen, traces of oil color, stain upper left. Verso: blank page.

Rather free version of the type of bather influenced by the statue *The Roman Orator*, see fig. 59. The ink drawing tends to make this sketch look earlier; its date corresponds to that of No. 429. Cf. also No. 419.

BIBLIOGRAPHY: Venturi No. 1433. Basel catalog, No. 111 (reproduced). Douglas Cooper, in *Master Drawings*, Vol. 1, No. 4, 1963, p. 56.

COLLECTIONS: Cézanne *fils*, Paris. Paul Guillaume, Paris. W. Feuz, Bern. Kunstmuseum, Basel.

429. BATHER SEEN BACK VIEW, 1877–80

$4\frac{3}{4} \times 7$ inches—12,1 × 17,9 cm. Page XVIII from the sketchbook BS III. Pencil, stain on the edge of the paper. Verso: blank page.

The attitude of the figure is one rarely studied by Cézanne. Cf. Venturi No. 587, and our No. 78.

BIBLIOGRAPHY: Venturi No. 1420. Basel catalog, No. 112 (reproduced). Douglas Cooper, in *Master Drawings*, Vol. 1, No. 4, 1963, p. 56.

COLLECTIONS: Cézanne *fils*, Paris. Paul Guillaume, Paris. W. Feuz, Bern. Kunstmuseum, Basel.

430. BATHER STANDING WITH BACK TURNED, 1877–80

$9\frac{1}{16} \times 5\frac{7}{8}$ inches—23 × 15 cm. Pencil. Verso: blank page.

(a) Pose similar to that of *The Roman Orator* seen from the back; see fig. 59. On the left, sketch of the legs and one hand of a seated bather.—(b) Earlier studies drawn with a light pencil: near the bather's head and at right angles, a head with the hair covering the ears; another sketch is covered by the bather.

BIBLIOGRAPHY: *Correspondance* (reproduced fig. 18, error in the measurements). F. Novotny, *Cézanne als Zeichner, Wiener Jahrbuch für Kunstgeschichte*, 1950 (reproduced fig. 115). Idem, *Ueber das Elementare in der Kunstgeschichte und andere Aufsätze*, Vienna, 1968 (reproduced fig. 48).

COLLECTIONS: Cézanne *fils*, Paris. Present owner unknown.

431. BATHER SITTING AT WATER'S EDGE, 1877–80

$5\frac{13}{16} \times 7\frac{3}{4}$ inches—14,7 × 19,6 cm. Pencil, hole restored in the lower margin. Verso: blank page.

(a) Bather with a towel wrapped around his head sitting at the water's edge; a landscape stretches out to the right. For the head, cf. No. 946 (c); for the figure and landscape, cf. Venturi Nos. 260 (the feet are differently placed) and 892.—(b) Below: rough sketch of an arm.

BIBLIOGRAPHY: Venturi No. 1263. Vollard, 1914 (reproduced p. 83). Basel catalog, No. 97 (reproduced). Douglas Cooper, *Master Drawings*, Vol. 1, No. 4, 1963, p. 56; dated circa 1881. R. Cogniat, *Cézanne*, Flammarion, Paris, 1967 (reproduced p. 45).

EXHIBITION: Meisterzeichnungen französischer Künstler, Kunsthalle, Basel, 1935, No. 195.

COLLECTIONS: Cézanne *fils*, Paris. W. Feuz, Bern. Kunstmuseum, Basel.

432. TWO BATHERS, 1878–81

$5 \times 8\frac{1}{2}$ inches—12,7 × 21,6 cm. Page XLV verso from the second sketchbook Mrs. Enid A. Haupt. Pencil. Verso: No. 855.

(a) Left: nude bather sitting at the foot of a tree.—(b) At right angles: standing bather of the type deriving from *The Roman Orator*, as seen from the back; see fig. 59.

BIBLIOGRAPHY: Rewald, *Carnets*: C IV, p. XLV verso (reproduced pl 110).

COLLECTIONS: Cézanne *fils*, Paris. M. Renou, Paris. Poyet, Lyons. M. Renou, Paris. Sam Salz, New York. Mrs. Enid A. Haupt, New York.

433. SEATED BATHER 1878–81

$7\frac{5}{8} \times 4\frac{5}{8}$ inches—19,4 × 11,8 cm. Page XXX verso from the sketchbook CP I. Pencil on ocher paper. Verso: No. 675.

Young bather sitting up straight, supported by his right hand on the grassy ground behind him, his left hand on his knee; the attitude suggests someone who has just finished speaking. A horizontal line in the foreground indicates water. This study seems close to the watercolor Venturi No. 892. Cf. our No. 422.

BIBLIOGRAPHY: Venturi, Vol. I, under No. 1282, erroneously listed as without pagination (not reproduced). *Dessins*, 1938, No. 20 (reproduced).

COLLECTIONS: Cézanne *fils*, Paris. Paul Guillaume, Paris. A. Chappuis, Tresserve.

434. TWO STANDING BATHERS AND TWO SAILBOATS, 1877–81.

$5 \times 8\frac{9}{16}$ inches—12,5 × 21,7 cm. Page XXXIV verso of the sketchbook Leigh Block. Pencil. Verso: No. 338.

(a) Page lengthwise: partly covering (b), two standing bathers, one in three-quarter view, the other in right profile, each with his right arm bent over his head; a tree on the left. Studies of the type of bather seen in the painting Venturi No. 261.—(b) Page upright: two sailboats at anchor in a river basin. In the foreground, a plank fixed edgeways near a corner.

BIBLIOGRAPHY: Rewald, *Carnets*: C V, p. XXXIV verso (not reproduced).

COLLECTIONS: Cézanne *fils*, Paris. M. Renou, Paris. Poyet, Lyons. M. Renou, Paris. Sam Salz, New York. Mr. and Mrs. Leigh Block, Chicago.

435. STANDING BATHER AND VARIOUS SKETCHES, 1875–80

$8\frac{9}{16} \times 4\frac{7}{8}$ inches—21,7 × 12,4 cm. Page XXVIII of the sketchbook A.I.C. Pencil, stains. Verso: No. 565.

Page upright: (a) Framed by a rectangle, a standing bather seen in right three-quarter view near a tree, his arm bent over his head; cf. No. 434 and Venturi No. 261.—Page lengthwise: (b) Parallel to the upper strokes of the frame of (a): unfinished sketch, interpreted by Rewald and Schniewind as a candlestick, but I believe it is a copy, by the artist's son, of the base of the lamp seen on the adjoining page, our No. 332 (a).—Upside down to (b): (c) Two sketches of a figure hurrying off to the right; these are variants of one of the men participating in the scenes of violence. See the same sketchbook, p. XXXIII (our No. 289) and also No. 937.

BIBLIOGRAPHY: Rewald, *Carnets*, C II, p. XXVIII (reproduced pl. 102). Schniewind, text p. 30 (reproduced). Andersen, *Sk.* (not reproduced). Th. Reff, *Bather* (not reproduced).

COLLECTIONS: Cézanne *fils*, Paris. M. Renou, Paris. Poyet, Lyons. M. Renou, Paris. Sam Salz, New York. Art Institute, Chicago.

436. STANDING BATHER, 1877–80

$8\frac{1}{2} \times 5$ inches—21,6 × 12,7 cm. Page XLIX from the second sketchbook Mrs. Enid A. Haupt. Pencil. Verso: No. 421.

Standing nude bather, his left elbow lifted vertically, his right horizontally. Type of bather frequently portrayed and in this case studied with a view to the watercolor Venturi No. 900.

BIBLIOGRAPHY: Rewald, *Carnets*: C IV, p. XLIX (not reproduced). Berthold (reproduced Abb. 54).

COLLECTIONS: Cézanne *fils*, Paris. M. Renou, Paris. Poyet, Lyons. M. Renou, Paris. Sam Salz, New York. Mrs. Enid A. Haupt, New York.

437. BATHER, DOG LYING DOWN, 1877–80

$8\frac{1}{2} \times 5$ inches—21,6 × 12,7 cm. Page XXXVIII from the second sketchbook Mrs. Enid A. Haupt. Pencil. Verso: No. 951.

(a) Bather standing with his hands behind his head, taking a step forward; cf. No. 1217.—Lower right and at right angles: (b) Dog lying down; cf. Nos. 251, 477, 1074,

BIBLIOGRAPHY: Rewald, *Carnets*: C IV, p. XXXVIII; enumeration at similar types of bathers, mainly in paintings, for comparison (reproduced pl. 112).

COLLECTIONS: Cézanne *fils*, Paris. M. Renou, Paris. Poyet, Lyons. M. Renou, Paris. Sam Salz, New York. Mrs. Enid A. Haupt, New York...

438. BATHER WITH HIS ARMS RAISED, SEEN BACK VIEW, 1877–80

$8\frac{1}{2} \times 5$ inches—21,6 × 12,7 cm. Page XXXIIII from the second sketchbook Mrs. Enid A. Haupt. Pencil. Verso: No. 426.

Nude model (guided by a cord) turned toward the left background; cf. No. 994.

BIBLIOGRAPHY: Rewald, *Carnets:* C IV, p. XXXIIII (reproduced pl. 111). Yvon Taillandier, *Paul Cézanne*, Paris, New York, Munich, 1961 and 1965 (reproduced p. 59).

COLLECTIONS: Cézanne *fils*, Paris. M. Renou, Paris. Poyet, Lyons. M. Renou, Paris. Sam Salz, New York. Mrs. Enid A. Haupt, New York.

439. STUDIES AND NOTATIONS, 1876–80

$10\frac{11}{16} \times 4\frac{9}{16}$ inches—27,2 × 11,6 cm. Page 44 (fragment) and page 43 verso from the first sketchbook Mrs. Enid A. Haupt. Pencil, notation in ink. Verso of the fragment of p. 44: feet of the bather No. 442 (not reproduced because inaccessible); on back of p. 43 verso: inaccessible sketch (not reproduced).

(a) Buttocks and legs of a bather seen in left profile.—(b) Study of a woman bather with her arms crossed behind her head; pose similar to that of the central figure in Venturi No. 726. This, however, is also a frequent academy pose. The wide difference in dates does not permit a definite affirmation of a link between the two.—(c) Man, or boy, sitting at a table, seen front view.—Handwritten notation in ink: *Mlle Aimée Broquet rue Ponchet*, 45.

BIBLIOGRAPHY: Rewald, *Carnets*, C I, pp. 43 verso and 44 (not reproduced).

COLLECTIONS: Cézanne *fils*, Paris. M. Renou, Paris. M. Renou, Paris. Sam Salz, New York. Mrs. Enid A. Haupt, New York.

440. TWO STUDIES OF BATHERS, 1877–80

$4\frac{3}{4} \times 7\frac{11}{16}$ inches—12 × 19,5 cm. Page XLI from the sketchbook CP I. Pencil and pen. Verso: No. 306.

(a) Left: two bathers, one standing with his arms behind his head, the other in the water, washing his face. These poses are repeated together in the painting Venturi No. 582.—(b) Right: study of a bather stepping down into the water (see description of this type of figure, No. 524). The drawing was later heightened in ink.

BIBLIOGRAPHY: Venturi No. 1256.

COLLECTION: Kenneth Clark, London.

441. STANDING BATHER, 1879–82

$8\frac{1}{4} \times 5\frac{1}{8}$ inches—21 × 13 cm. Page from the sketchbook Basel I. Pencil. Verso: the watercolor Venturi No. 905.

Study of a bather standing up with his hands behind his head; cf. No. 440 (a). The watercolor on the reverse side shows a bather stepping down into the water.

BIBLIOGRAPHY: Venturi No. 1257.

COLLECTIONS: Cézanne *fils*, Paris. Private collection, Paris. G. Wildenstein, Paris. Mr. and Mrs. Ira Haupt, New York.

442. STANDING BATHER, 1879–82

$5 \times 4\frac{9}{16}$ inches—12,6 × 11,6 cm. Fragment of p. 45 from the first sketchbook Mrs. Enid A. Haupt. Pencil, handwritten notation in ink. Verso: No. 524.

A study in form. The bather's arms are crossed behind his head; the conception of the whole contrasts with naturalistic vision. Cf. Nos. 437, 441, 443, 1217.—Handwritten notations: *Mademoiselle Marie Louise 7 Villa Monceau*.

BIBLIOGRAPHY: Rewald, *Carnets:* C I, p. 45 (not reproduced). Rewald adds "this drawing stretches on to p. 44 verso"; today this part is inaccessible, p. 44 being framed with p. 43 verso (our No. 439).

COLLECTIONS: Cézanne *fils*, Paris. M. Renou, Paris. Poyet, Lyons. M. Renou, Paris. Sam Salz, New York. Mrs. Enid A. Haupt, New York.

443. STANDING BATHER, 1881–84

$8\frac{1}{2} \times 5$ inches—21,6 × 12,7 cm. Page XLIII verso from the second sketchbook Mrs. Enid A. Haupt. Pencil. Verso: blank page.

For the pose, cf. Nos. 437, 1217. Compared with similar studies, this one is distinctive in the fluidity of the drawing of trunk and thighs; these appear to be taken from a live model, whereas the head and arms are rather a study in form. The arms seem somewhat short, and the head, tilted forward, produces the effect of a head added to a sculpture.

BIBLIOGRAPHY: Rewald, *Carnets:* C IV, p. XLIII verso (reproduced pl. 113).

COLLECTIONS: Cézanne *fils*, Paris. M. Renou, Paris. Poyet, Lyons. M. Renou, Paris. Sam Salz, New York. Mrs. Enid A. Haupt, New York.

444. *The Temptation of St. Anthony*, and sketch, 1869–73

$6\frac{3}{4} \times 4\frac{1}{16}$ inches—17,1 × 10,3 cm. Page from the sketchbook 10,3 × 17 cm. Pencil, corners damaged. Verso: No. 198.

(a) Seated man, summarily drawn, both his arms stretched out toward a nude woman on the right; he holds a crucifix in his left hand. The gesture and crucifix suggest that it represents the temptation of St. Anthony. Cf. especially the watercolored drawing reproduced in *Cézanne dessinateur*, fig. 39, and our No. 445. The sketch is partly crossed out in pencil.—(b) Head of a woman, tilted forward, a scarf around her neck; this sketch is vigorously crossed out.

BIBLIOGRAPHY: Venturi, Vol. I, p. 350, *Oeuvres Inédites* (not reproduced). Basel catalog, No. 43 (reproduced, but the crucifix is hidden by the mount around the original drawing). Th. Reff, in *BurlM*, Aug. 1963, p. 375, and Douglas Cooper, in *Master Drawings*, Vol. 1, No. 4, 1963, p. 55; the latter two authors are of the opinion that the man is not St. Anthony repelling a woman, but a libertine beckoning to one.

COLLECTIONS: Cézanne *fils*, Paris. W. Feuz, Bern. Kunstmuseum, Basel.

445. STUDIES FOR *The Temptation of St. Anthony*, 1869–72

$5\frac{5}{16} \times 8\frac{1}{2}$ inches—13,5 × 21,5 cm. Page from a sketchbook. Pencil, traces of three folds. Verso: ?

(a) Upper left: St. Anthony, one knee on the ground, his hands stretched out in front of him, his face turned away.—(b) Right: the saint and the devil, the latter standing with one hand on the saint's shoulder, the other hand pointing toward the woman's apparition. Cf. No. 448.—

(c) Lower left: half-length study of the tempter, in a flowing garment, leaning over the saint.

BIBLIOGRAPHY: Venturi, Vol. I, p. 352, *Oeuvres Inédites* (not reproduced). Th. Reff, Cézanne, Flaubert, St. Anthony, and the Queen of Sheba, *AB*, June 1962, p. 113 (reproduced fig. 6).

COLLECTIONS: Pierre Loeb, Paris. Present owner unknown.

446. STUDY FOR *The Temptation of St. Anthony*, BRIGAND HOLDING A BLUNDERBUSS; pen, 1857–58; pencil, 1869–72

$4\frac{1}{2} \times 8$ inches—11,5 × 20,3 cm. Page 24 (or 14) verso from the sketchbook 11,5 × 20,3 cm. Pencil, pen, wash. Verso: No. 90.

(a) Right, in pencil: rapid study of movement, St. Anthony repelling the apparition of the temptress; cf. the paintings Venturi Nos. 240, 241, and our Nos. 445, 448.— (b) Page upright, lower left: brigand of the Roman campagna, seen in right profile holding a blunderbuss, his right foot on a higher level than his left; pen and wash sketch.

COLLECTIONS: Cézanne *fils*, Paris. Jean-Pierre Cézanne, Paris. Private collection, Paris. Sale, Parke-Bernet, New York, Dec. 13, 1967, verso of No. 4 of sale, which is our No. 90. Samuel J. Lefrak, Forest Hills, N.Y.

447. GOBLET, AND STUDY FOR *The Temptation of St. Anthony*, 1870–73

$6 \times 8\frac{3}{8}$ inches—15,3 × 21,2 cm. Pencil on yellowish paper, tear restored at lower edge, upper right corner renewed. Verso: No. 393.

(a) Left: cut-glass goblet, drawn with observation of the ridges and planes of the glass.— (b) Right: man, seen front view in a dramatic attitude; this is a study for the tempter as he places his hand on St. Anthony's shoulder. Cf. Nos. 445, 449, 450, 452, 453, 1108.

BIBLIOGRAPHY: Venturi, Vol. I, p. 351, *Oeuvres Inédites*, "actor in old-time dress" (not reproduced). Basel catalog, No. 60, "goblet and actor" (reproduced). Th. Reff, *Bather*, p. 185 ((b) reproduced, fig. 13). Idem, Cézanne and Hercules, *AB*, Vol. XLVIII, 1966, p. 41, note 83.

COLLECTIONS: Cézanne *fils*, Paris. W. Feuz, Bern. Kunstmuseum, Basel.

448. STUDY FOR *The Temptation of St. Anthony*, 1873–75

$5\frac{1}{8} \times 8\frac{1}{4}$ inches—13 × 21 cm. Pencil. Verso: ?

Preliminary study for the paintings Venturi Nos. 240, 241. Left: the saint in an attitude of dramatic renunciation before the temptress who, surrounded by more or less impertinent little cupids, is unveiling her nudity. A hand, that of the tempter, weighs heavily on the saint's shoulder: *il lui met le grappin dessus* (he has him in his clutches). For this gesture, cf. No. 445. Top center: an owl. This is the most complete of the pencil drawings of the subject; the following sketches may be compared, either for the whole or for certain details: Nos. 65, 263, 353 (d), 444, 449, 450, 452, 967.

BIBLIOGRAPHY: Venturi No. 1214. Vollard, 1914 (reproduced p. 39). G. Rivière, *Le Maître Paul Cézanne*, Paris,

1923 (reproduced p. 25). Meier-Graefe, *Cézanne und sein Kreis*, Munich, 1922 (reproduced p. 112). Th. Reff, Cézanne, Flaubert, St. Anthony, and the Queen of Sheba, *AB*, June 1962, p. 113 (reproduced fig. 5).

COLLECTIONS: Cézanne *fils*, Paris. Present owner unknown.

449. STUDY FOR *The Temptation of St. Anthony*, 1875–78

$7\frac{5}{8} \times 4\frac{5}{8}$ inches—19,4 × 11,8 cm. Page L verso from the sketchbook CP I. Pencil. Verso: blank page.

Study for the tempter in the painting *The Temptation of St. Anthony*, Venturi No. 241. Cf. Nos. 445, 447, 453.

BIBLIOGRAPHY: Venturi, Vol. I, under the No. 1280 (not reproduced). *Dessins*, 1938, No. 19 (reproduced). Th. Reff, Cézanne, Flaubert, St. Anthony, and the Queen of Sheba, *AB*, 1962, pp. 113-125. Idem, Cézanne and Hercules, *AB*, 1966, p. 41, note 83.

COLLECTIONS: Cézanne *fils*, Paris. Paul Guillaume, Paris. A. Chappuis, Tresserve. H. Purrmann, Montagnola. Dr. R. Purrmann, Starnberg.

450. STUDY FOR *The Temptation of St. Anthony*, man, 1875–78; head, circa 1885

$4\frac{5}{8} \times 7\frac{5}{8}$ inches—11,8 × 19,4 cm. Page XLII verso from the sketchbook CP I. Pencil. Verso: No. 1098.

(a) Left: sketch of a man leaning forward, his legs apart, a lock of hair or a horn protruding from each temple. Cf. the figure of the tempter in the canvas Venturi No. 241, and our Nos. 445, 447, 449, 452, 453.— (b) Right: unfinished sketch of a round object, seen from above. The best way to interpret the drawing is to hold the page upright, with (a) below: one sees the head of the artist's son, bent forward; the strokes around it indicate the clothing behind the neck; cf. Nos. 847, 870.

BIBLIOGRAPHY: Venturi, Vol. I; no mention of it under No. 1275 as verso of p. XLII.

COLLECTIONS: Cézanne *fils*, Paris. Paul Guillaume, Paris. A. Chappuis, Tresserve.

451. STUDIES, INCLUDING TWO NUDE CHILDREN, 1875–78

$5\frac{1}{8} \times 3\frac{15}{16}$ inches—13 × 10 cm. Pencil, page smudged and soiled; scribbles by another hand. Verso: No. 460.

Disregarding the scribbles scattered over the page, there are three subjects:— (a) Left: sketch of a nude child seen in left lost profile.— (b) Right: a similar nude but with the body leaning backward, forming a diagonal rising to the right from foot to head; the pose corresponds to that of a putto in *The Temptation of St. Anthony*, Venturi No. 880 and also No. 241.— (c) At right angles and covered by the first two sketches: study of a poplar tree, with another tree to the right. This drawing, although defaced, reveals a simple charm.— In the upper left corner is written 68 *PH*: notation by an alien hand indicating that the reverse side was photographed.

COLLECTIONS: Mouradian & Vallotton, Paris. Present owner unknown.

452. STUDY FOR *The Temptation of St. Anthony*, 1875–78

$4\frac{5}{8} \times 7\frac{5}{8}$ inches—11,8 × 19,4 cm. Page XVII of the sketchbook CP I. Pencil and pen. Verso: No. 793.

Compositional study for the canvas Venturi No. 241. Left, pen: the saint kneeling; his arm stretched out to the right is drawn twice. The curious rectangle on his back probably indicates a patch of light. Above this figure, a rough sketch of the tempter. Right: sketch of the woman, standing with her right arm raised and her left arm, partly retouched in pencil, in a line with her body. Center: indication of a putto, important element in the composition. Further right, pencil: study of a leg.

BIBLIOGRAPHY: Venturi, Vol. I, under No. 1273, erroneously described as p. XVIbis, instead of p. XVII (not reproduced). Th. Reff, *Cézanne and Hercules, AB*, Vol. XLVIII, 1966, p. 41, note 83.

COLLECTIONS: Cézanne *fils*, Paris. Paul Guillaume, Paris. A. Chappuis, Tresserve. Private collection, Paris. H. Purrmann, Montagnola. Dr. R. Purrmann, Starnberg.

453. YOUNG MAN IN MOVEMENT, BESET BY RATS, 1875–78

$8\frac{9}{16} \times 4\frac{7}{8}$ inches—21,7 × 12,4 cm. Page XXIX verso of the sketchbook A.I.C. Pencil, stains. Verso: No. 409.

(a) Bottom of the page: a young man, his hair and shirt flowing in the wind; cf. Nos. 447, 449, 450, 452, studies for *The Temptation of St. Anthony*. On the left, four rats and a big lizard are leaping in the air.—(b) Top: rapid sketch of the same figure's head, surrounded by a semi-circular stroke.—(c) Beside it: head seen full face.

BIBLIOGRAPHY: Rewald, *Carnets*: C II, p. XXIX verso (reproduced pl. 91). Schniewind, text p. 30: the author notes the influence of Daumier and Delacroix (reproduced). Th. Reff, *Bather*, text p. 185 (reproduced fig. 14). Andersen, *Sk.* (not reproduced). Longstreet, 1964 (reproduced).

COLLECTIONS: Cézanne *fils*, Paris. M. Renou, Paris. Poyet, Lyons. M. Renou, Paris. Sam Salz, New York. Art Institute, Chicago.

454. MAN WALKING, PRECEDED BY A DOG, 1876–79

$5\frac{1}{8} \times 7\frac{1}{2}$ inches—13 × 19 cm. Page II verso from the sketchbook BS III (page also marked XLIX). Pencil, smudges. Verso: No. 1104.

The man, in a smock and round hat, is carrying over his shoulder a stick with a bag on the end. An animated little scene.

BIBLIOGRAPHY: Venturi No. 1401. Longstreet, 1964 (reproduced).

EXHIBITIONS: Zurich, 1956, No. 198. Munich, 1956, No. 150.

COLLECTIONS: Cézanne *fils*, Paris. Paul Guillaume, Paris. W. Feuz, Bern. Carl Roesch, Diessenhofen.

455. AFTER RUBENS: THREE NAIADS, 1876–79

$12\frac{3}{16} \times 17\frac{3}{4}$ inches—31 × 45 cm. Pencil. Verso: blank page.

Copy of a detail showing three naiads (or nereids) in *Marie de Médicis Landing in the Port of Marseilles*, painting by Rubens in the Louvre. See fig. 53. It has been said, and it seems likely, that this drawing was done from a photograph in the artist's possession. Cf. Nos. 369, 457, 1128.

BIBLIOGRAPHY: Venturi No. 1625. Berthold, cat. No. 214 (reproduced Abb. 103). J. Rewald, *Cézanne au Louvre, AA*, Oct. 1935, mention p. 288. Th. Rousseau, Jr., *Paul Cézanne*, Paris, 1953 (reproduced pl. 6). Idem, Amsterdam, 1954 (reproduced pl. 6). A. Neumeyer, *Cézanne Drawings*, New York, 1958, No. 10 (reproduced). *The World of Cézanne*, 1968 (reproduced p. 146).

EXHIBITIONS: Aquarelles et Baignades de Cézanne, Renou & Colle, Paris, 1935. Orangerie, Paris, 1936, No. 154. Phillips Collection, Washington, D.C., Chicago, Boston, 1971, No. 67 (reproduced).

COLLECTIONS: Cézanne *fils*, Paris. Marianne Feilchenfeldt, Zurich.

456. AFTER RUBENS: NAIAD, 1876–79

About $8\frac{1}{16} \times 4\frac{3}{4}$ inches—20,5 × 12 cm. Pencil. Verso: childish drawings of houses, etc., not by the artist.

This page from a sketchbook was given to Maurice Renou by Cézanne *fils*, together with Nos. 130 and 144. Renou told me this himself when he showed me the drawings on October 12, 1959. The present sketch is drawn after the naiad (or siren) on the left of Rubens' painting *Marie de Médicis Landing in the Port of Marseilles*, in the Louvre. See fig. 53, and cf. our Nos. 455, 457. Cézanne possessed a photograph of this group of naiads (see Gasquet, 1926, p. 74). As reproduced, the sketch has been partially extricated from the scribbles covering it, an operation which seems to have led to retouches.

COLLECTIONS: Cézanne *fils*, Paris. M. Renou, Paris. M. X, auctioneer, Paris. Present owner unknown.

457. PAGE OF STUDIES, INCLUDING A CLOCK, AND A NAIAD, 1876–79

$11\frac{7}{16} \times 15\frac{3}{4}$ inches—29 × 40 cm. Pencil on gray laid paper. Verso: blank page.

(a) Left: woman seated beside the dial of a clock, copied from an ornamental mantel clock in Charles X style. The model remains untraced, although Cézanne drew it several times: cf. No. 458. Beside the clock is a vase.—(b) Right: one of the naiads of *Marie de Médicis Landing in the Port of Marseilles* by Rubens, in the Louvre. See fig. 53. The detail shows the naiad on the left and the triton blowing into a conch; both figures are partly traced. It is known that Cézanne possessed a photograph of this painting. Cf. No. 455.

BIBLIOGRAPHY: Venturi No. 1449. Berthold, cat. Nos. 215 and 325 (reproduced Abb. 30). Th. Reff, *AB*, June 1961, p. 148, note 34, where models for (a) are indicated. Longstreet, 1964 (reproduced).

EXHIBITIONS: Zurich, 1956, No. 172. Munich, 1956, No. 132.

COLLECTIONS: Cézanne *fils*, Paris. W. Feuz, Bern. Sale, Stuttgarter Kunstkabinett, R. N. Ketterer, Stuttgart, No. 114, 1959. Carl Roesch, Diessenhofen.

458. STUDIES, INCLUDING A CLOCK, 1876–79

$9\frac{5}{8} \times 12$ inches—24,5 × 30,5 cm. Pencil. Verso: No. 721.

(a) Part of a mantel clock: a woman sitting with her elbow against the frame of a clock dial. The original model seems to be in Charles X style and has not been identified. This drawing being the most complete of the eleven copies known to date (Berthold catalogues six of them), this seems the most appropriate place to enumerate the entire series: Nos. 457, 458, 459, 579, 580, 581, 582, 583, 713, 721, 821. —(b) Head of the artist's son, a developed study.—(c) Unfinished sketch of the same head, smaller.—Handwritten notations: *tel* and a cross; see Note 25.

BIBLIOGRAPHY: Venturi, Vol. I, p. 349, *Oeuvres Inédites* "Coll. Kenneth Clark. Etudes, 23 × 29 cm." (not reproduced). There is a difference of $\frac{5}{8}$ inch (1.5 cm.) in both height and length between our measurements and those of Venturi. The drawing was framed, which also explains why Venturi made no mention of the sketches on the reverse side. Berthold, cat. No. 337 (not reproduced).

COLLECTIONS: Kenneth Clark, London. E. Katzenellenbogen, Santa Monica, Calif.

459. PAGE OF STUDIES, 1876–79

12 × 19$\frac{1}{4}$ inches—30,5 × 49 cm. Pencil on grayish-yellow paper. Verso: inaccessible.

(a) Left, seated woman in a loose, draped garment, her elbow leaning against the frame of a clock; after an unidentified mantel clock studied several times by the artist; see text No. 458.—(b) Top: detailed sketch of a piece of pastry dough in the shape of a cabbage; shadows and background indicated by hatching.—(c) Right: half-length study of a woman arranging her hair, after Eugène Delacroix's *Le Lever* (Robaut 1165). See fig. 60.—(d) Less complete sketch of the same subject.

BIBLIOGRAPHY: Venturi, Vol. I, p. 348, *Oeuvres Inédites* (not reproduced). Berthold, cat. No. 341 (not reproduced). *Cézanne dessinateur*, p. 301 ((b) (c) (d) reproduced fig. 23).

COLLECTIONS: Kenneth Clark, London. H. Burg, London.

460. STUDIES FOR *Afternoon in Naples*, 1877–79

5$\frac{1}{8}$ × 3$\frac{15}{16}$ inches—13 × 10 cm. Page trimmed. Pencil and pen. Verso: No. 451.

None of these three studies for the subject *Afternoon in Naples* has direct reference to any of the oils or watercolors known.—(a) Upper left: woman carrying the tray; the pen drawing (c) covers her arms and the tray. An overemphasized stroke under her nose is accompanied by strokes crossing out the head.—(b) Below: more detailed study of the same figure, the face again crossed out. A striped curtain can be seen on the left. A bowl containing various objects is sketched in on the tray.—(c) Top right: nude woman lying on her back, fragment of a pen sketch with a few pencil contours; drawn later than (a). Cf. No. 461 (a).

COLLECTIONS: Mouradian & Vallotton, Paris. Kelekian, Paris. Present owner unknown.

461. STUDIES FOR *Afternoon in Naples*, 1877–79

4$\frac{1}{8}$ × 6$\frac{11}{16}$ inches—10,5 × 17 cm. Pencil, top left corner missing. Verso: page of a review dated May 20, 1877.

Disregarding the scribbles, there are three studies on this page, and a handwritten note.—(a) Upper left: nude woman lying on her back, her head leaning to the left; cf. the watercolor Venturi No. 820 and our No. 460 (c). The

nonchalant and rather unusual attitude of this figure is worth noting.—(b) Below, also on the left: woman lying face down; cf. the watercolor Venturi No. 822 which, though different, elucidates this pose. It is even more important to note the similarity of this sketch to the nude

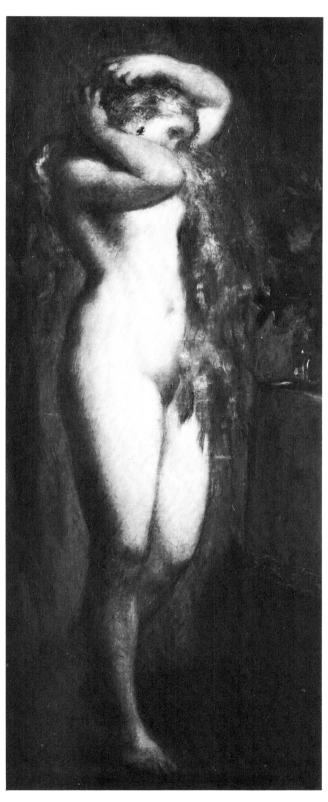

FIG. 60. Eugène Delacroix (1799–1863): *Le Lever* (detail), canvas, 47 cm. × 38 cm. (1850). Collection of Mme. M. David-Weill, Paris. *Mémorial de l'exposition Delacroix*, by M. Sérullaz, Paris, 1963, No. 409.

figures, also lying face down, which play a certain part in the late compositions of *Women Bathers*. (Melvin Wald-fogel deals with this subject in A Problem in Cézanne's Grandes Baigneuses, *BurlM*, May 1962, p. 203).—(c) Right, and at right angles: the three figures of *Afternoon in Naples*, sketched rapidly and with numerous retouches; cf. Venturi No. 820 for the servant and the man smoking a pipe.—(d) Note written across the page: "*Je suis allé chez Tanguy/à ce soir sept heures 7 h./je laisse tout chez la rôtisseuse.*" It will be objected that the word is written *allée*, giving the feminine form: *Je suis allée . . .* However I prefer to read it as *allé*, in the masculine, because I believe this note to be by the hand of Cézanne and it was not unusual for him to add flourishes to the end of his words. (See for example the draft of a letter to Marius Roux, No. 378, line 8, where the word *camarade* finishes with a flourish and could be read *camaradee*, or *camarades*. See also the word *idem*(e) on No. 320, and *foncé*(e) on No. 963.) With refer-ence to the handwritten note cited above, a remark at the end of a letter from Cézanne to Zola, dated Aug. 28, 1877, should be quoted: "Yesterday evening when I called in on my color dealer, rue Clauzel, I found our good friend Emperaire there." (*Correspondance*, letter No. XXXVII. Bibliothèque Nationale, Manuscrits, Nouvelles acquisi-tions françaises, Vol. 24516, feuillets 510, 511.)

COLLECTIONS: Mouradian & Vallotton, Paris. Private collection, Paris. Present owner unknown.

462. STUDY OF A RECLINING FEMALE NUDE, 1877–79

$8\frac{1}{4} \times 7\frac{3}{8}$ inches—21 × 18,7 cm. Pencil, upper corners restored, paper slightly torn on the left. Pale pink stain on the figure's abdomen. Verso: blank page, entirely covered with transparent Japan paper.

Nude woman reclining on her back, her legs toward the right. Vigorous, flaky strokes; study for the watercolor Venturi No. 886, *Le Réveil*.

BIBLIOGRAPHY: Venturi, Vol. I, p. 352, *Oeuvres Inédites* (not reproduced). Basel catalog, No. 177 (reproduced).

COLLECTIONS: Cézanne *fils*, Paris. W. Feuz, Bern. Kunst-museum, Basel.

463. STUDY FOR *Bathsheba*, 1877–79

$15\frac{5}{16} \times 7\frac{9}{16}$ inches—38,8 × 19,2 cm. Pencil, edges of the paper slightly torn and pieces missing upper left renewed. Verso: blank page, entirely covered with transparent Japan paper.

Four studies for *Bathsheba*, subject taken from the story of King David (II Samuel 2:2).—(a) Upper left: nude woman, sitting rather than reclining, with her servant.—(b) To the right, and at right angles: same subject, the drawing more lively and less distinct.—(c) Below (a), lower center: similar composition, except for the attitude of the legs; to the left, a repetition of the head and bust. These three studies are related to the painting Venturi No. 252.—(d) In the center of the page: reclining woman, similar to the one of No. 462 and to the watercolor Venturi No. 886, known as *Le Réveil*. The head is sketched successively in four different ways.—(e) To the left: cursory sketch of a half-length figure. Cf. Nos. 461, 513, 1101.

BIBLIOGRAPHY: Venturi, Vol. I, p. 352, *Oeuvres Inédites* (not reproduced). Basel catalog, No. 176, dated 1880–90, "certain features in common with the painting by Eugène Delacroix, *St. Sebastian tended by the Holy Women*, Robaut

No. 627." (Reproduced.) Th. Reff, *BurlM*, Aug. 1963, shares Lawrence Gowing's opinion that the Bacchante of Poussin's *Education of Bacchus* in the Louvre was the model for this female figure.

EXHIBITION: Meisterzeichnungen französischer Künstler, Kunsthalle, Basel, 1935, No. 264.

COLLECTIONS: Cézanne *fils*, Paris. W. Feuz, Bern. Kunst-museum, Basel.

464. PAGE OF STUDIES, INCLUDING ONE OF *Bathsheba*, 1877–79

$11\frac{13}{16} \times 16\frac{15}{16}$ inches—30 × 43 cm. Pencil on laid paper, various stains, trace of a fold lower left. Verso: an unidentified watercolor or drawing.

(a) Left: study for the theme of *Bathsheba*; for this, see No. 463. The mistress is sitting in a large round-backed arm-chair, with the servant occupied at her side, a round basin near them on the ground.—(b) Right: study for *The Eternal Feminine*, Venturi No. 247; see also Venturi No. 904 and our No. 257. The scene shows the woman enthroned under a kind of tent, like an idol, with a throng of adorers crowding at her feet. This sketch, framed with strokes, is related to the watercolor Venturi No. 895.—(c) Above: the woman's head and shoulders are repeated, seen as in Venturi No. 895.

COLLECTIONS: Mouradian & Vallotton, Paris. John Wyeth, New York.

465. BATHER, STUDY FOR *Bathsheba*; pencil, 1876–79; pen, circa 1890

$4\frac{5}{8} \times 7\frac{1}{2}$ inches—11,8 × 19 cm. Page XXVII from the sketchbook CP I. Pencil and pen on pale blue paper. Verso: blank page.

(a) Page lengthwise, pen drawing: standing bather, turn-ing to the right.—(b) Page upright: two women, one of them leaning forward, the other rubbing her back. Vari-ant for the subject *Bathsheba*, see Venturi No. 252. Experi-mental study of an unusual pose.

BIBLIOGRAPHY: Venturi, Vol. I, under No. 1273 (not re-produced). *XXe siècle*, Paris, March 1938 (reproduced).

EXHIBITIONS: Kunsthalle, Basel, 1936, No. 115. Aix-en-Provence, 1961, No. 55.

COLLECTIONS: Cézanne *fils*, Paris. Paul Guillaume, Paris. A. Chappuis, Tresserve. Sale, Palais Galliera, Paris, March 23, 1965. Present owner unknown.

466. TWO STUDIES OF A WOMAN BATHER, 1876–79

$4\frac{5}{8} \times 7\frac{5}{8}$ inches—11,8 × 19,4 cm. Page VIII verso from the sketchbook CP I. Pencil, Verso: No. 261.

(a) Left: sketch of a standing woman bather seen in lost profile, leaning forward from the waist; her right arm seems to be leaning on a prop, which is not drawn.—(b) Right: more detailed but freely drawn sketch of a similar figure, almost in right profile, holding a towel and sur-rounded by vegetation. Several renderings of the right arm; cf. No. 515. Neither (a) nor (b) portray a body in movement. For (b), cf. Venturi No. 538 and our No. 366.

BIBLIOGRAPHY: Venturi, Vol. I, under No. 1270; errone-ously described as page VIIIbis instead of VIII verso (not reproduced).

COLLECTIONS: Cézanne *fils*, Paris. Paul Guillaume, Paris. A. Chappuis, Tresserve.

466bis. Two studies of women bathers; left, 1876–79; right, 1879–82

$4\frac{5}{8} \times 7\frac{3}{4}$ inches—11,8 × 19,7 cm. Page from the sketchbook CP I. Pencil. Verso: No. 909bis.

(a) Left: woman bather of the short, squat type.—(b) Right: woman bather of the classical type. Both are facing toward the right background and starting to move away. Although one may be inclined to consider these two sketches as contemporaneous, which is possible, they nevertheless express two ways of seeing that followed one another in time, and this has to be indicated by successive dates.

COLLECTIONS: Cézanne *fils*, Paris. Private collection, Paris. Dr. W. Raeber, Basel. Private collection, Basel.

467. Two studies for *La Toilette*, 1878–81

$5 \times 8\frac{1}{8}$ inches—12,6 × 20,6 cm. Page VI from the sketchbook BS III. Pencil. Verso: blank page.

(a) Left half of page, separated from the right half by vertical strokes: nude woman standing with her hands behind her neck, seen in left three-quarter view. To the right a small sketch, probably a repetition of the arm, and below this, the summit of a mountain.—(b) Right half of the page: the same woman occupied with her toilet, a servant kneeling beside her. In the background: vegetation, and indication of a mountain as in (a). These studies, no longer on one sheet, are in relation to the subject *La Toilette*, after Delacroix (cf. Venturi No. 254); also *Bathsheba* (cf. Venturi Nos. 252, 253, 255). Cf. our Nos. 439 (b), 459, and Rewald, *Cézanne et Zola*, Paris, 1939, fig. 84.

BIBLIOGRAPHY: Venturi, No. 1407. Berthold (reproduced Abb. 52). Basel catalog, No. 141 ((a) only reproduced). Longstreet, 1964 ((b) reproduced).

COLLECTIONS: Cézanne *fils*, Paris. Paul Guillaume, Paris. W. Feuz, Bern. Left half: Kunstmuseum, Basel. Right half: Nelly and Werner Baer, Zurich.

468. Tracing of an engraving after Caravaggio, 1877–80

$5\frac{3}{4} \times 4\frac{1}{8}$ inches—14,5 × 10,5 cm. Pencil on ordinary paper. Verso: blank page.

Tracing made from an engraving by Pauquet reproducing Caravaggio's *Entombment*, painting in the Pinacoteca Vaticana. See fig. 61; cf. the watercolor Venturi No. 869 of the same subject.

BIBLIOGRAPHY: Berthold, cat. No. 270 (reproduced Abb. 95, with identification of the original source).

COLLECTIONS: Cézanne *fils*, Paris. Paul Guillaume, Paris. A. Chappuis, Tresserve.

469. After Hans Holbein: *The family of the artist*, 1877–80

$6\frac{11}{16} \times 7\frac{1}{2}$ inches—17 × 19 cm. Pencil. Verso: blank page.

This sketch, a mother with two children, is after the painting by Hans Holbein the Younger in the Basel Museum (Inv. No. 325) portraying the artist's family. Cézanne did not copy the original but a reproduction printed in *Le Magasin Pittoresque*, 1845, p. 133. See fig. 62.

BIBLIOGRAPHY: Berthold, cat No. 277 (reproduced). Rewald, in *Renaissance*, March-April 1937 (reproduced). *Cézanne dessinateur* (reproduced fig. 5).

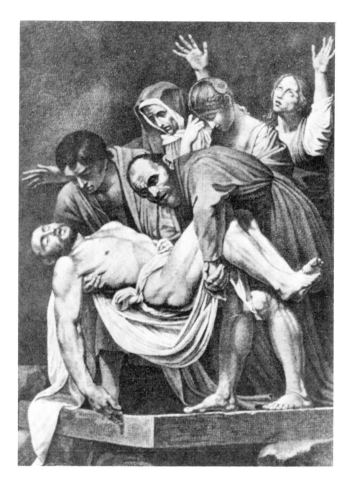

FIG. 61. After Caravaggio (1573–1610): *The Entombment*, painting in the Pinacoteca Vaticana, Rome. Engraved by Pauquet after a drawing by Bourdon. 14,8 cm. × 10,7 cm. Bibliothèque Nationale, Estampes, Vol. 8, in folio 12.
(Photograph: Bibliothèque Nationale, Paris)

FIG. 62. After Hans Holbein the Younger (1498–1543): *The Family of the Artist*. Wood engraving printed in *Le Magasin Pittoresque*, 1845, p. 183, reproducing the painting in the Basel museum.
(Photograph: Chappuis)

EXHIBITIONS: Europäische Meisterwerke aus Schweizer Sammlungen, Munich, 1969, No. 25 (reproduced Abb. 23).

COLLECTIONS: Galerie Würthle, Vienna. W. Raeber, Basel. R. von Hirsch, Basel.

470. AFTER MERCIÉ: *David*, 1877–80

$8\frac{1}{2} \times 4\frac{7}{8}$ inches—21,5 × 12,4 cm. Page XXXVII from the sketchbook CP II. Pencil. Verso: No. 851.

After Antonin Mercié's bronze *David* in the Louvre. See fig. 63. This statue was first exhibited in the Salon of 1872, then in the Luxembourg Museum. It is seen in almost three-quarter right view; the two other copies by Cézanne show it in left three-quarter view; see Nos. 471, 472.

BIBLIOGRAPHY: Venturi No. 1291. Berthold, cat. No. 176 (reproduced Abb. 82).

COLLECTIONS: Cézanne *fils*, Paris. Paul Guillaume, Paris. A. Chappuis, Tresserve. Musée National de la Ville de Paris, Petit Palais (Inv. D. 3288).

471. AFTER MERCIÉ: *David*, 1877–80

$8\frac{1}{2} \times 5$ inches—21,6 × 12,7 cm. Page VII from the second sketchbook Mrs. Enid A. Haupt. Pencil. Verso: No. 313.

After Antonin Mercié's bronze statue of *David* in the Louvre, see fig. 63. Cf. Nos. 470, 472.

BIBLIOGRAPHY: Rewald, *Carnets:* C IV, p. VII (reproduced pl. 132). Berthold, cat. No. 174 (reproduced).

COLLECTIONS: Cézanne *fils*, Paris. M. Renou, Paris. Poyet, Lyons. M. Renou, Paris. Sam Salz, New York. Mrs. Enid A. Haupt, New York.

472. AFTER MERCIÉ: *David*, 1879–82

$7\frac{5}{8} \times 4\frac{5}{8}$ inches—19,4 × 11,8 cm. Page III from the sketchbook CP I. Pencil, small violet watercolor stain at the bottom of the page. Verso: blank page.

After Antonin Mercié's bronze *David* in the Louvre. See fig. 63. This statue was exhibited in the Salon of 1872. Auguste Renoir remarked to Vollard: "When you see Mercié's David sheathing his sword, you want to give him a hand to get it in; whereas with the artists of antiquity the sword is sheathed but you have the feeling that it may come out." See Note 50. Two other copies exist by Cézanne after the same bronze: Nos. 470, 471.

BIBLIOGRAPHY: Venturi No. 1267. Berthold, cat. No. 175 (reproduced).

COLLECTIONS: Cézanne *fils*, Paris. Paul Guillaume, Paris. A. Chappuis, Tresserve. Private collection, Paris. Private collection, New York.

473. AFTER MICHELANGELO: SLAVE, 1879–82

$7\frac{5}{8} \times 4\frac{5}{8}$ inches—19,4 × 11,8 cm. Page XLIX verso from the sketchbook CPI. Pencil, Verso: blank page.

After the marble known as *The Dying Slave*, by Michelangelo, in the Louvre. See fig. 64. Cf. No. 678.

BIBLIOGRAPHY: Venturi, No. 1278; in error as p. XLVII verso. Berthold, cat. No. 63 (reproduced).

COLLECTIONS: Cézanne *fils*, Paris. Paul Guillaume, Paris. A. Chappuis, Tresserve.

474. STANDING MAN, AFTER AN UNIDENTIFIED WORK, 1879–82

$7\frac{3}{16} \times 4\frac{9}{16}$ inches—18,2 × 11,6 cm. Page 12 verso from the first sketchbook Mrs. Enid A. Haupt. Pencil. Verso: No. 474A.

Man in a headdress with two feathers or little wings; a strap across his naked chest holds up a skin draping his hips. Th. Reff (see Bibliography) is of the opinion that this sketch represents one of the terms decorating the periphery of the Parterre de Latone in the park at Versailles. I cannot agree with this since I see too many differences; also I think that Cézanne copied a painting rather than a sculpture.

BIBLIOGRAPHY: Rewald, *Carnets*, C I, p. 12 verso (not reproduced). Berthold, cat. No. 278, original not identified (reproduced). Th. Reff, *AB*, June 1960, p. 148: "Berthold cat. 278 represents a *Term with Hercules* by Leconte from the Park at Versailles (Note 22): See Frantz Marcou: *Album du Musée de Sculpture Comparée (Palais du Trocadéro)*, Paris, no date, V, pl. 17."

COLLECTIONS: Cézanne *fils*, Paris. M, Renou, Paris. Poyet, Lyons. M. Renou, Paris. Sam Salz, New York. Mrs. Enid A. Haupt, New York.

FIG. 63. Antonin Mercié (1845–1916): *David*, bronze exhibited in the 1872 Salon and subsequently in the Musée du Luxembourg and the Louvre. Height: 1,88 m. Musée National du Louvre, *Catalogue des Sculptures*, supplément 1933, No. 1844. *(Photograph: Bulloz)*

474A. SKETCH OF FOLIAGE

This sketch, verso of No. 474, is inaccessible on account of the frame. (Not reproduced.)

BIBLIOGRAPHY: Rewald, *Carnets*: C I, p. 12 "croquis de feuillage" (not reproduced).

475. SKETCHES OF A CAT, 1879–82

$5 \times 8\frac{1}{8}$ inches—12,6 × 20,6 cm. Page XXII verso from the sketchbook BS III. Pencil. Verso: No. 510.

Three unfinished sketches of a cat; cf. Nos. 383, 475bis.

BIBLIOGRAPHY: Venturi No. 1428. Basel catalog, No. 120 (reproduced).

COLLECTIONS: Cézanne *fils*, Paris. Paul Guillaume, Paris. W. Feuz, Bern. Kunstmuseum, Basel.

476. HEAD AND FORELEG OF A DOG, 1876–78

$6\frac{11}{16} \times 9\frac{1}{16}$ inches—17 × 23 cm. Page from the sketchbook 18 × 24 cm. Pencil. Verso: No. 172.

Study showing the head and foreleg of a sleeping dog. This drawing subtly expresses the sympathy Cézanne felt for the trusty animal. A dog called Black is mentioned in letters to Numa Coste (*Correspondance*, Letter XV, 1863).

BIBLIOGRAPHY: Venturi, Vol. I, p. 349, *Oeuvres Inédites* (not reproduced).

COLLECTIONS: Kenneth Clark, London. Sale, Galerie Motte, Geneva, 1967, and Nov. 16, 1968 No. 304. Private collection, Switzerland.

477. SLEEPING DOG, 1876–78

$8\frac{11}{16} \times 11\frac{13}{16}$ inches—22 × 30 cm. Pencil, upper corners damaged, attenuated stains. Verso: No. 757.

(a) The animal lying down, his eyes half closed.—(b) Below: head only of the dog asleep. Cf. Nos. 476, 1074.

BIBLIOGRAPHY: Venturi, No. 1583. Basel catalog, No. 95 (reproduced). Longstreet, 1964 (reproduced).

COLLECTIONS: Cézanne *fils*, Paris. W. Feuz, Bern. Kunstmuseum, Basel.

478. SKETCHES OF A COW, 1877–80

$18\frac{7}{8} \times 11\frac{13}{16}$ inches—48 × 30 cm. Pencil on laid paper. Watermark: M. Verso: No. 648.

Three unfinished studies.—(a) Upper right: profile of a cow's head.—(b) Below: hindquarters of a cow, the right hindleg particularly worked on. The light strokes over the animal's back (roof of a chalet) and upper left (landscape) form part of the same sketch.—(c) Left: repetition of the hindleg in (b).

COLLECTIONS: Mouradian & Vallotton, Paris. Kelekian, Paris. Sale, Hôtel Drouot, Paris, Nov. 22, 1968 No. 96. Present owner unknown.

479. SKETCH OF PELICANS, 1877–80

$9\frac{5}{16} \times 6$ inches—23,7 × 15,2 cm. Page XXX verso of the Album, Paul Mellon Collection. Pencil. Verso: No. 1023.

The sketch shows two pelicans and, upper left, an outline of the bird's neck; the pelican on the right has its beak

tucked under its wing. This study might be assumed to be a copy, but Berthold makes no mention of it. Subjects of this kind are unusual with Cézanne, though a comparison may be made to the swan in our No. 484 and Venturi No. 550, and to another in our No. 1134 (c). In Venturi No.

FIG. 64. *Slave* by Michelangelo. See fig. 54.

494 a painting of birds, similar, though in different positions, is shown hanging on the wall; Venturi No. 494 was painted at Pontoise and the picture on the wall could well be by another artist there at the time.

BIBLIOGRAPHY: Venturi, Vol. I, under No. 1309 (not reproduced). *Album* 1966 (reproduced).

COLLECTIONS: Cézanne *fils*, Paris. Paul Guillaume, Paris. A. Chappuis, Tresserve. Mr. and Mrs. Paul Mellon, Upperville, Va.

480. AFTER RAPHAEL: *Venus and Psyche*, 1877–80

$8\frac{9}{16} \times 4\frac{15}{16}$ inches—21,7 × 12,5 cm. Page VIII from the sketchbook CP II. Pencil. Verso: blank page.

After a drawing by Raphael in the Cabinet des Dessins of the Louvre, showing Psyche offering Venus a flask containing water from the Styx, there is a painting of the same subject by Raphael in the Farnesina, Rome. See fig. 7. Another copy by Cézanne: our No. 85 (Venus pouting: Apuleius, *Metamorphoses*, Book, VI, XVI.)

BIBLIOGRAPHY: Venturi No. 1284. Berthold, cat. No. 264 (reproduced Abb. 93).

EXHIBITION: Aix-en-Provence, 1961, No. 60.

COLLECTIONS: Cézanne *fils*, Paris. Paul Guillaume, Paris. A. Chappuis, Tresserve.

481. AFTER MARCANTONIO RAIMONDI: CARYATID, 1877–80

$8\frac{5}{8} \times 4\frac{7}{8}$ inches—21,8 × 12,4 cm. Page XLIX verso from the sketchbook CP II. Pencil. Verso: No. 389.

Study of the figure on the left in Marcantonio's engraving representing an incense-burner held up by three caryatids; see fig. 65. Cf. Nos. 631, 715 (b). Th. Reff believes that this figure served as model for the temptress in *The Temptation of St. Anthony*; see Venturi Nos. 240, 241, and our Nos. 263 (d), 353 (d), 448.

BIBLIOGRAPHY: Venturi No. 1299. Berthold, cat. No. 262 (reproduced Abb. 92). Th. Reff, Cézanne, Flaubert, St. Anthony, and the Queen of Sheba, *AB*, June 1962, p. 121, note 77.

COLLECTIONS: Cézanne *fils*, Paris. Paul Guillaume, Paris. A. Chappuis, Tresserve.

482. AFTER BARYE: JAGUAR, 1877–80

$4\frac{15}{16} \times 8\frac{9}{16}$ inches—12,5 × 21,7 cm. Page V verso from the sketchbook CP II. Pencil. Verso: No. 1020.

Study after a bronze *Jaguar moving forward* by Antoine-Louis Barye (1796-1875). The bronze (height about 5 inches) is scarcely larger than the drawing. The animal is drawn in left profile. Venturi describes the volumes of this sketch as "terrible."

BIBLIOGRAPHY: Venturi No. 1283. Berthold, cat. No. 170, source identified (reproduced).

COLLECTIONS: Cézanne *fils*, Paris. Paul Guillaume, Paris. A. Chappuis, Tresserve. Private collection, Paris. Private collection, New York.

482A. ROCKS AT BIBÉMUS, date uncertain

$8\frac{9}{16} \times 4\frac{15}{16}$ inches—21,7 × 12,5 cm. Page VII from the sketchbook CP II. Pencil. Verso: No. 482B. (Not reproduced.)

Roughly sketched study of rocks, probably at Bibémus quarry. Not reproduced.

BIBLIOGRAPHY: Venturi, Vol. I, under No. 1283 (not reproduced).

COLLECTIONS: Cézanne *fils*, Paris. Paul Guillaume, Paris. B. Remund, Théméricourt.

482B. SKETCH OF THE ARTIST'S YOUNG SON, PAUL, 1878–81

$8\frac{9}{16} \times 4\frac{15}{16}$ inches—21,7 × 12,5 cm. Page VII verso from the sketchbook CP II. Pencil. Verso: No. 482A. (Not reproduced.)

Head of the artist's son, seen in right profile; unfinished but characteristic sketch. Not reproduced.

BIBLIOGRAPHY: Venturi, Vol. I, under No. 1283 (not reproduced).

COLLECTIONS: Cézanne *fils*, Paris. Paul Guillaume, Paris. B. Remund, Théméricourt.

FIG. 65. Marcantonio Raimondi (1475–1530): *La Cassolette*. Engraving (burin), 31,2 cm. × 18,8 cm. Two female figures supporting an incense burner. Proofs of this copperplate were printed in 1865 in the *Gazette des Beaux-Arts*, Paris. Bartsch 489. Passavant 278. (*Photograph: Bibliothèque Nationale, Paris*)

483. STUDY FOR *Leda*, 1876–79

$4\frac{9}{16} \times 7\frac{3}{16}$ inches—11,6 × 18,2 cm. Page 6 from the first sketchbook Mrs. Enid A. Haupt. Pencil. Verso: No. 583.

Nude woman stretched out on a couch leaning on one elbow, a flute of champagne in the opposite hand. This drawing is similar to the small painting Venturi No. 111 ($6\frac{11}{16} \times 8\frac{11}{16}$ inches) in which a hand mirror takes the place of the flute. Venturi Nos. 550 and 551 shows a woman in the same attitude, with a swan, as does our No. 484, which is the reason for alluding to the mythological subject of *Leda and the Swan*. It is probable that our drawing was directly inspired by a photograph or some unidentified work.

BIBLIOGRAPHY: Rewald, *Carnets*, C I, p. 6 (reproduced pl. 83). Berthold, cat. No. 301 "after an unidentified work" (reproduced).

COLLECTIONS: Cézanne *fils*, Paris. M. Renou, Paris. Poyet, Lyons. M. Renou, Paris. Sam Salz, New York. Mrs. Enid A. Haupt, New York.

484. STUDIES FOR *Leda and the Swan*; Leda: 1877–82, head: 1880–82

$4\frac{7}{8} \times 8\frac{5}{8}$ inches—12,4 × 21,8 cm. Page XXXVI verso from the sketchbook CP II. Pencil. Verso: No. 831.

(a) Right, framed with strokes: a study for the painting Venturi No. 550: *Leda and the Swan*. The woman is lying on a couch, her raised body supported by one elbow, her other arm stretched out to the swan as it comes into view. The similarity between No. 483 and this drawing is noteworthy: both were probably inspired by an unidentified engraving. The present study is a later version, amplified by the addition of the swan.—(b) Left, at right angles: study of a head and ear, the face not drawn; cf. No. 734. It may be remarked that the swan's wing in the canvas Venturi No. 550 describes a curve similar to that of the head in this drawing.

BIBLIOGRAPHY: Venturi, Vol. I, under No. 1290 (not reproduced). Berthold, cat. No. 300 (reproduced). *Dessins*, 1938, No. 9 (reproduced). For an account of the subject's origin, see Vollard, 1914, p. 31.

COLLECTIONS: Cézanne *fils*, Paris. Paul Guillaume, Paris. A. Chappuis, Tresserve.

485. TWO HEADS, 1877–80

$8\frac{9}{16} \times 4\frac{7}{8}$ inches—21,7 × 12,4 cm. Page XXXV verso of the sketchbook A.I.C. Pencil, stains. Verso: No. 417.

(a) Page upright: head of a woman seen full face, her eyes half closed and her head covered with a fichu of which one corner falls down over her forehead. A very fine drawing. —(b) Page lengthwise: head of an old woman, her eyelids lowered and chin hidden, expressing grief.

BIBLIOGRAPHY: Rewald, *Carnets*: C II, p. XXXV verso (not reproduced). Schniewind, text p. 31 (reproduced). Andersen, *Sk*. (not reproduced).

COLLECTIONS: Cézanne *fils*, Paris. M. Renou, Paris. Poyet, Lyons. M. Renou, Paris. Sam Salz, New York. Art Institute, Chicago.

486. HEAD OF A YOUNG MAN (AND A CHILD'S DRAWINGS), 1877–78

$8\frac{9}{16} \times 4\frac{7}{8}$ inches—21,7 × 12,4 cm. Page IX of the sketchbook A.I.C. Pencil, stains. Verso: No. 381.

Unfinished sketch of the head of a young man; the forehead is confined within a curious rectangle.

BIBLIOGRAPHY: Rewald, *Carnets*: C II, p. IX (not reproduced). Schniewind, p. 27 (reproduced). Andersen, *Sk*. (reproduced fig. 25b).

COLLECTIONS: Cézanne *fils*, Paris. M. Renou, Paris. Poyet, Lyons. M. Renou, Paris. Sam Salz, New York. Art Institute, Chicago.

487. NUDE WOMAN, SEEN BACK VIEW, 1879–82

Measurements not known. Pencil. Verso: ?

Back view of a female nude, her elbows held tight against her waist. Drawn in contours with very few inner shadows. Only Vollard's reproduction of this drawing is known. Venturi believes it to be a copy after the *Capitoline Venus*; Berthold thinks that Cézanne copied some other marble; I myself (with Vollard) am of the opinion that it is a study from a live model. The woman's hands must have been touching a prop to allow her to hold this pose, inspired by the antique.

BIBLIOGRAPHY: Venturi No. 1442. Vollard, 1914, p. 149 (reproduced). Berthold, cat. No. 49 "after a marble in the Louvre; Cat. sommaire des Marbres antiques, 1922, No. 316 or 373" (reproduced).

COLLECTIONS: Cézanne *fils*, Paris. Ambroise Vollard, Paris. Present owner unknown.

488. STUDY OF A NUDE, AND FOLIAGE, 1879–82

$9\frac{5}{16} \times 6$ inches—23,7 × 15,2 cm. Page XXXI verso of the Album, Paul Mellon Collection. Pencil. Verso: No. 1082.

Two subjects.—(a) Top: sketch of the figure seen back view in Luca Signorelli's drawing *The Live carrying the Dead* in the Cabinet des Dessins of the Louvre. See fig. 22. Cf. Nos. 182, 675.—(b) Study of foliage with compact, thin, tapering leaves; cf. No. 644.

BIBLIOGRAPHY: Venturi, Vol. I, under No. 1309 (not reproduced). Berthold, cat. No. 250 (reproduced). *Album*, 1966 (reproduced).

COLLECTIONS: Cézanne *fils*, Paris. Paul Guillaume, Paris. A. Chappuis, Tresserve. Mr. and Mrs. Paul Mellon, Upperville, Va.

489. AFTER RUBENS: BELLONA, 1879–82

$17\frac{3}{4} \times 10\frac{1}{4}$ inches—45 × 26 cm. Pencil on laid paper. Verso: blank page.

After the allegorical figure of Bellona in Rubens' painting *The Apotheosis of Henry IV* in the Louvre. See fig. 9. Cf. especially Nos. 489bis, 490.

BIBLIOGRAPHY: Venturi No. 1455. Berthold, cat. No. 204 (reproduced Abb. 4 and Abb. 104). J. Gasquet, *Cézanne*, Paris, 1921 & 1926 (reproduced p. 184). Meier-Graefe, *Cézanne und sein Kreis*, Munich, 1922 (reproduced p. 141).

EXHIBITIONS: Kunsthalle, Basel, 1936, No. 171. Zurich, 1956, No. 214A.

COLLECTIONS: Bernheim-Jeune, Paris. R. von Hirsch, Basel.

489bis. AFTER RUBENS: BELLONA, 1879–82

$8\frac{3}{4} \times 5\frac{1}{2}$ inches—22,2 × 14 cm. Pencil on laid paper.
Verso: No. 701ter.

After the allegorical figure of Bellona in Rubens' painting *The Apotheosis of Henri IV* in the Louvre. See fig. 9.

BIBLIOGRAPHY: Venturi, Vol. I, p. 349, *Oeuvres Inédites*, measurements 23 × 15 cm. (not reproduced). Berthold, cat. No. 213 (not reproduced).

COLLECTIONS: Kenneth Clark, London. Private collection, London.

490. AFTER RUBENS: BELLONA, 1879–82

$9\frac{5}{16} \times 6$ inches—23,7 × 15,2 cm. Page XXV verso of the Album, Paul Mellon Collection. Pencil. Verso: No. 576.

Unfinished study after the allegorical figure of Bellona in Rubens painting *The Apotheosis of Henri IV* in the Louvre; see fig. 9. The artist drew nine other copies after this same model: Nos. 489, 489bis, 598, 627, 1007, 1138, 1139, 1140, 1215.

BIBLIOGRAPHY: Venturi No. 1307; in error as page XXVI. Berthold, cat. No. 206, text p. 18 (reproduced). *Album* 1966 (reproduced).

EXHIBITION: Kunsthalle, Basel, 1936, No. 138.

COLLECTIONS: Cézanne *fils*, Paris. Paul Guillaume, Paris. A. Chappuis, Tresserve. Mr. and Mrs. Paul Mellon, Upperville, Va.

491. AFTER PISANELLO AND LEONARDO DA VINCI: HEAD OF A MULE AND PROFILE OF A CHILD, 1878–81

$8\frac{9}{16} \times 4\frac{7}{8}$ inches—21,7 × 12,4 cm. Page XI verso of the sketchbook A.I.C. Pencil, stains. Verso: No. 566.

(a) Head of a mule, magnificently harnesssed.—(b) Head of a child in left profile. Both are drawn from prints published in *Le Magasin Pittoresque* of 1858, pp. 12 and 13, reproducing (a) a drawing by Pisanello, *The Prelate's Mule*, and (b) a drawing by Leonardo da Vinci, both in the Cabinet des Dessins of the Louvre. See figs. 66, 67. R. W. Ratcliffe was the first (1956) to draw attention to these prints as the models of our sketches.

FIG. 66. After Pisanello (1395–1450): *The Prelate's Mule*, drawing in the Cabinet des Dessins of the Louvre. Wood engraving printed in *Le Magasin Pittoresque*, 1858, p. 12.
(Photograph: R. W. Ratcliffe)

FIG. 67. After Leonardo da Vinci (1452–1519): *Profile of a Child*, drawing in the Cabinet des Dessins of the Louvre. Wood engraving printed in *Le Magasin Pittoresque*, 1858, p. 12.
(Photograph: R. W. Ratcliffe)

BIBLIOGRAPHY: Rewald, *Carnets:* C II, p. XI verso (not reproduced). Schniewind, text pp. 27/28 (reproduced). Th. Reff, *AB*, June 1960, p. 148, add. 3. Andersen, *Sk.* (not reproduced). *Cézanne dessinateur* (reproduced fig. 1).

COLLECTIONS: Cézanne *fils*, Paris. M. Renou, Paris. Poyet, Lyons. M. Renou, Paris. Sam Salz, New York. Art Institute, Chicago.

492. AFTER LEONARDO DA VINCI: CHILD'S HEAD (fragment), 1878–81

$4 \times 4\frac{7}{8}$ inches—10,1 × 12,4 cm. Page XII verso of the sketchbook A.I.C. Pencil. Verso: No. 769. The outer half of the page has been cut off.

Lower part of a child's head, copied from a print in *Le Magasin Pottoresque* of 1858, p. 13, reproducing three studies of a child's head drawn by Leonardo da Vinci, now in the Cabinet des Dessins of the Louvre. See fig. 68. Cf. No. 491 and its commentary.

BIBLIOGRAPHY: Rewald, *Carnets:* C I, p. XII verso (not reproduced). Schniewind, text p. 28 (reproduced). Andersen, *Sk.* (not reproduced). *Cézanne dessinateur* (reproduced fig. 3).

COLLECTIONS: Cézanne *fils*, Paris. M. Renou, Paris. Poyet, Lyons. M. Renou, Paris. Sam Salz, New York. Art Institute, Chicago.

493. AFTER CH.-A. COYSEVOX: CROUCHING VENUS, 1878–81

$18\frac{1}{2} \times 12\frac{3}{16}$ inches—47 × 31 cm. Pencil on laid paper. Verso: blank page.

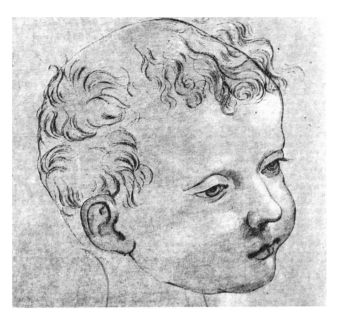

FIG. 68. After Leonardo da Vinci (1452–1519): *Head of a Child*, drawing in the Cabinet des Dessins of the Louvre. Wood engraving printed in *Le Magasin Pittoresque*, 1858, p. 12.
(Photograph: R. W. Ratcliffe)

FIG. 69. Charles-Antoine Coysevox (1640–1720): *Vénus accroupie*, marble (1686) exhibited in the Tuileries, 1871, and in the Louvre from 1873 on. Musée National du Louvre, *Catalogue des Sculptures* II, 1922, No. 1117.

After Charles-Antoine Coysevox's marble (height 6 ft.) in the Louvre. See fig. 69.

BIBLIOGRAPHY: Venturi, No. 1440; in error as "after the Vienna Venus." Berthold, cat. No. 148, the correct model identified (reproduced). Meier-Graefe, *Cézanne und seine Ahnen*, Munich, 1921 (reproduced pl. 15).

EXHIBITION: Galerie A. Flechtheim, Berlin, 1927, No. 60.

COLLECTIONS: Frau Paul Huldschinsky, Bad Kreuth. Present owner unknown.

494. AFTER DELACROIX: ALLEGORICAL FIGURE OF A RIVER, 1878–81

$4\frac{7}{8} \times 8\frac{9}{16}$ inches—12,4 × 21,7 cm. Page IIII of the sketchbook A.I.C. Pencil, stains. Verso: a child's scribbles.

Male nude lying on his left side, seen in foreshortening, his feet toward the background. Rather finished copy of the figure of a River from the Apollo Ceiling by Eugène Delacroix, in the Louvre; see fig. 27. Other copies of this figure: Nos. 181, 195 (d). Cf. Venturi Nos. 272, 275, and our No. 404 (b).

BIBLIOGRAPHY: Rewald, *Carnets*: C II, p. IIII (reproduced pl. 142). Berthold, cat. No. 240 (reproduced Abb. 101). Schniewind, text p. 26 (reproduced). Andersen, *Sk.* (reproduced fig. 22b). *Selearte*, No. 52, July-Aug. 1961 (reproduced fig. 10).

COLLECTIONS: Cézanne *fils*, Paris. M. Renou, Paris. Poyet, Lyons. M. Renou, Paris. Sam Salz, New York. Art Institute, Chicago.

495. AFTER DELACROIX: *Spartan girls wrestling*, 1880–83

$10\frac{1}{16} \times 15\frac{3}{8}$ inches—25,5 × 39 cm. Pencil on laid paper, stain, traces of folds. Verso: No. 496.

After a painstaking investigation, Miss Sara Lichtenstein (see Bibliography) concludes that three preliminary drawings by Delacroix for a pendentive in the Palais Bourbon library may be the source of this study. However, Cézanne probably knew only two of these drawings, through reproductions, and it is uncertain that he ever saw the third. The two former are almost similar: one (Robaut 811), having been reproduced by Quantin in 1881, was acquired by the Cabinet des Dessins of the Louvre in 1908 (RF 3713) (see fig. 70); the other (Robaut 810) is now lost, but was reproduced by Robaut in 1865. The third of Delacroix's drawings is different from the other two and was acquired by the Cabinet des Dessins in 1927 (RF 9403); according to Miss Lichtenstein it may also be considered as the source, though it is not known how Cézanne could have seen it.—Our drawing: (a) Copy of the whole subject, roughly sketched, and framed by strokes corresponding to the shape of Delacroix's project.—(b) Lower left: sketch of the seated girl.—(c) Upper right: contours of the woman wrestler on the right.—(d) Below: wrestler on the left.—(e) Sketch of the group seen in the left background of the original.—Cézanne used these studies for the couples at the back and right center in *The Struggle of Love*, Venturi Nos. 379, 380, 879.

BIBLIOGRAPHY: *Cézanne dessinateur*, date 1878–80. (Error: the number of the original model reproduced fig. 26 is not RF 9403, but RF 3713). Reproduced fig. 25. Sara Lichtenstein, A Sheet of Cézanne Copies after Delacroix, *Master*

[149]

FIG. 70. Eugène Delacroix (1799–1863): *Jeunes Filles de Sparte s'exerçant à la lutte;* in the Cabinet des Dessins of the Louvre (RF 3713).

FIG. 71. August Préault (1800–79): statue of *Clémence Isaure,* erected in the Luxembourg Gardens of Paris in 1848. *Inventaire des Richesses d'Art de la France,* Paris, Monuments civils, Vol. 3, 1902, pp. 417–18, No. 57.

(*Photograph: R. W. Ratcliffe*)

Drawings, Vol. 5, No. 2, 1967, p. 182, date 1875–85 (reproduced pl. 34); two drawings by Delacroix reproduced pls. 35 and 36.

COLLECTIONS: Mouradian & Vallotton, Paris. Private collection, Paris. P. Cailac, Paris. Private collection, Paris.

496. STUDIES AFTER DELACROIX, 1880–83

$10\frac{1}{16} \times 15\frac{3}{8}$ inches—25,5 × 39 cm. Pencil on laid paper, traces of folds. Verso: No. 495.

Lightly drawn sketches after two subjects by Eugène Delacroix.—(a) Left: copy of group seen in left background of Delacroix's drawing *Spartan girls wrestling,* see fig. 70. Cf. No. 495.—(b) Man crouching, seen in left profile, holding shears in his right hand. A copy (the source was identified by Miss Sara Lichtenstein) after Delacroix's *Samson and Delilah* (Robaut 1238), now in the O. Reinhart Collection, Winterthur; formerly owned by Charles Daubigny and after 1878 by his widow.

BIBLIOGRAPHY: Sara Lichtenstein. A Sheet of Cézanne Copies after Delacroix, *Master Drawings,* No. 2, 1967, p. 184 (reproduced pl. 37).

COLLECTIONS: Mouradian & Vallotton, Paris. Private collection, Paris. P. Cailac, Paris. Private collection, Paris.

497. AFTER A.-A. PRÉAULT: *Clémence Isaure,* 1880–83

$7\frac{5}{8} \times 4\frac{5}{8}$ inches—19,4 × 11,8 cm. Page VII of the sketchbook CP I. Pencil. Verso: No. 547.

Sketch after the statue of *Clémence Isaure* by Antoine-Auguste Préault, which was erected in the Luxembourg Gardens, Paris, in 1848; see fig. 71. Cf. No. 498.

BIBLIOGRAPHY: Venturi No. 1270. Berthold, cat. No. 172 (reproduced Abb. 108). *Dessins,* 1957, No. 50 (reproduced).

COLLECTIONS: Cézanne *fils,* Paris. Paul Guillaume, Paris. A. Chappuis, Tresserve.

498. AFTER A.-A. PRÉAULT: *Clémence Isaure,* 1880–83

$8\frac{1}{4} \times 4\frac{3}{4}$ inches—20,9 × 12,1 cm. Page XXXV from the sketchbook BS II. Pencil. Verso: blank page.

Sketch after the statue of *Clémence Isaure* by Antoine-Auguste Préault, which was erected in the Luxembourg Gardens, Paris, in 1848; see fig. 71. Cf. No. 497.

BIBLIOGRAPHY: Venturi No. 1370. Berthold, cat. No. 173 (reproduced Abb. 109). Basel catalog, No. 116 (reproduced).

COLLECTIONS: Cézanne *fils,* Paris. Paul Guillaume, Paris. W. Feuz, Bern. Kunstmuseum, Basel.

499. AFTER PUGET: *Perseus rescuing Andromeda,* 1879–82

$18\frac{1}{2} \times 12$ inches—47 × 30,5 cm. Pencil. Verso: blank page.

After the marble *Perseus rescuing Andromeda* by Pierre Puget, in the Louvre; see fig. 6. Andromeda is in chains and Perseus climbing onto the rock. Once again Cézanne represents a figure with the arm bent over the shoulder. Lower left: a cupid.

FIG. 72. *Centaur tamed by Love*, antique marble in the Louvre
(Inv. No. A.562).   *(Photograph: Giraudon)*

FIG. 73. Jean-Baptiste Pigalle (1714–85): *L'Amour et l'Amitié*,
marble in the Louvre since 1879. Musée National du Louvre,
Catalogue des Sculptures II, 1922, No. 1445. Our photograph
was taken from a plaster cast in the Musée des Monuments
français (ex-Trocadero).

BIBLIOGRAPHY: Venturi No. 1445. Berthold, cat. No. 126
(reproduced). J. Gasquet, *Cézanne*, Paris, 1926, p. 191:
"Cézanne on the sculpture of Puget."

EXHIBITIONS: The catalogues of the exhibitions in The
Hague, Zurich, and Munich in 1956 mention this drawing erroneously, since the drawing shown was our No. 83,
the same subject.

COLLECTIONS: Bernheim-Jeune, Paris. Sale, Paris, Dec. 21,
1929. Galerie Arnold, Dresden. Present owner unknown.

500. PAGE OF STUDIES, INCLUDING A CENTAUR AFTER
    THE ANTIQUE, 1879–82.

$13\frac{7}{8} \times 11\frac{1}{16}$ inches—35,2 × 28,1 cm. Pencil on laid
paper. Verso: blank page.

(a) Study after the antique marble known as *The Centaur
tamed by Love*, in the Louvre; see fig. 72. Two almost vertical strokes indicate the direction of the two legs that are
not drawn.—(b) Below the Centaur, to the right: sketch
of three apples with two cast shadows.—(c) Left, and upside down: sketch of a woman bather walking toward the
background.

BIBLIOGRAPHY: Berthold, cat. No. 290 (reproduced).
Cézanne dessinateur, p. 304 (reproduced fig. 33).

EXHIBITIONS: Kunsthalle, Basel, 1936, No. 135. Meisterwerke aus Frankreichs Museen, Vienna, 1950, No. 252.
Belvedere, Vienna, 1961, No. 96; date 1880–85.

COLLECTION: Albertina, Vienna (Inv. 24084).

501. AFTER PIGALLE: *Love and Friendship*, 1879–82

$8\frac{3}{16} \times 5\frac{3}{16}$ inches—20,8 × 13,1 cm. Page XI from the
sketchbook BS I. Pencil. Verso: blank page.

After Jean-Baptiste Pigalle's marble *Love and Friendship* in
the Louvre. See fig. 73. For the subject, cf. our Nos. 1044,
1045, 1046, 1047.

BIBLIOGRAPHY: Venturi No. 1334. Berthold, cat. No. 159
(reproduced).

COLLECTIONS: Cézanne *fils*, Paris. Paul Guillaume, Paris.
W. Feuz, Bern. R. von Hirsch, Basel.

502. AFTER PUGET: *Milo of Crotona*, 1877–80

$8\frac{1}{16}$ to $8\frac{1}{4} \times 5\frac{13}{16}$ inches—20,5 to 21 × 14,8 cm. Pencil
on laid paper; watermark: a stylized design cut off in
part by the lower edge of the paper. Verso: blank
page.

After Pierre Puget's marble *Milo of Crotona* in the Louvre.
See fig. 30.

BIBLIOGRAPHY: Venturi No. 1447. Berthold, cat. No. 96
(reproduced). G. Rivière, *Le Maître Paul Cézanne*, Paris,
1923 (reproduced p. 107).

COLLECTIONS: Cézanne *fils*, Paris. Wertheimer, Paris.
J. Hohl, Basel. Frau von Braun, Hannover.

503. AFTER PUGET: *Milo of Crotona*, 1880–83

$9\frac{5}{16} \times 6$ inches—23,7 × 15,2 cm. Page XXXV verso
of the Album, Paul Mellon Collection. Pencil. Verso
No. 1130.

After Pierre Puget's marble *Milo of Crotona* in the Louvre.
See fig. 30.

BIBLIOGRAPHY: Venturi No. 1311. Berthold, cat. No. 101 (reproduced). *Album*, 1966 (reproduced).

COLLECTIONS: Cézanne *fils*, Paris. Paul Guillaume, Paris. A. Chappuis, Tresserve. Mr. and Mrs. Paul Mellon, Upperville, Va.

504. AFTER PUGET: *Milo of Crotona*, 1880–83

$8\frac{5}{8} \times 5\frac{1}{8}$ inches—$21,8 \times 13$ cm. Page XXIII from the sketchbook BS I. Pencil. Verso: blank page.

After Pierre Puget's marble *Milo of Crotona* in the Louvre. See fig. 30.

BIBLIOGRAPHY: Venturi No. 1348; in error as "au Musée de Bâle." Berthold, cat. No. 100 (reproduced).

COLLECTIONS: Cézanne *fils*, Paris. Paul Guillaume, Paris. W. Feuz, Bern. Unknown collection. Sale Kornfeld & Klipstein, Bern, June 13, 1968, No. 138 (reproduced). Kunsthalle, Bremen (Inv. 68/373).

505. AFTER PUGET: *Milo of Crotona*, 1882–85

$7\frac{5}{8} \times 4\frac{5}{8}$ inches—$19,4 \times 11,8$ cm. Page XLVII from the sketchbook CP I. Pencil. Verso: blank page.

After Pierre Puget's marble *Milo of Crotona* in the Louvre. See fig. 30.

BIBLIOGRAPHY: Venturi No. 1277. Berthold, cat. No. 97 (reproduced).

COLLECTIONS: Cézanne *fils*, Paris. Paul Guillaume, Paris. A. Chappuis, Tresserve. Private collection, Paris.

506. AFTER PUGET: *Milo of Crotona*, 1882–85

$8\frac{15}{16} \times 4\frac{3}{4}$ inches—$21,1 \times 12,1$ cm. Page I from the sketchbook BS II. Pencil, tear restored upper left. Verso: blank page.

Study after Pierre Puget's marble *Milo of Crotona* in the Louvre, See fig. 30.

BIBLIOGRAPHY: Venturi No. 1358. Berthold, cat. No. 102 (reproduced). Basel catalog, No. 195 (reproduced); eleven copies after the *Milo* are enumerated, instead of twelve. Longstreet, 1964 (reproduced).

EXHIBITION: Belvedere, Vienna, 1961, No. 94.

COLLECTIONS: Cézanne *fils*, Paris. Paul Guillaume, Paris. W. Feuz, Bern. Kunstmuseum, Basel.

507. SKETCH, BENEATH HANDWRITTEN NOTATIONS, 1875–78

$8\frac{1}{2} \times 5$ inches—$21,6 \times 12,7$ cm. Page I from the second sketchbook Mrs. Enid A. Haupt. Pencil, stains. Verso: blank page.

Beneath the handwriting: sketch in simple outline of a figure seen in right profile, standing with one foot on a step; an academy pose. Cf. No. 508. Notations: *Cobalt 4/ Bleu minéral 1/Jaune brillant 5/Ocre jaune 2–No. 6/Emeraude 1/Terre verte 5/Blanc d'argent 5/Laque garance foncée 1/Laque fine/Terre verte/Jan Davidz du Heem Ecole Hollandaise/Blanc d'Argent 4/Brun rouge 1/Laque fine 2/Bleu cobalt 2/Bleu outremer 4/Sienne naturelle 1/Terre verte 4/Vert Véronèse 2/32–41/ Edouard/Vermillon français/Noir pêche/Pincelier/Palette.*

BIBLIOGRAPHY: Rewald, *Carnets:* C IV, p. 1 (not reproduced).

COLLECTIONS: Cézanne *fils*, Paris. M. Renou, Paris. Poyet, Lyons. M. Renou, Paris. Sam Salz, New York. Mrs. Enid A. Haupt, New York.

508. WOMAN BATHER, HER HAND REACHING DOWN TO HER ANKLE, 1875–78

$5\frac{5}{16} \times 3\frac{1}{8}$ inches—$13,5 \times 8$ cm. Pencil on ordinary ruled paper, tear in the left margin, fold lower left. Verso: blank page.

Small academy study: woman seen in profile, one foot on a step at a level with her other knee, her right hand touching her ankle. If the left leg seems rather short this is probably intentional, the dynamism of the sketch being thoroughly studied. The pose is the classical one of the marble *Jason*, or *Hermes fastening his Sandal*. Cf. No. 683, and the different pose of the figure on the left in No. 373.

EXHIBITION: Kunstnerforbundet, Oslo, 1954.

COLLECTIONS: Arnstein Arneberg, Oslo. Huguette Berès, Paris. Present owner unknown.

509. HEAD OF A WOMAN ASLEEP, 1876–79

$7\frac{1}{16} \times 11$ inches—18×28 cm. Pencil. Verso: No. 1089.

This drawing, placed in the upper left corner of a large page, seems to be unfinished; it is a study in detail. The half-closed hand is expressive and great tenderness is expressed in the whole. From a distance, the sketch calls to mind *Young Ladies on the Banks of the Seine* (1856), by Gustave Courbet.

COLLECTIONS: Edgar Degas, Paris. Degas sale, Paris, March 26-27, 1918. Léon Bollag, Zurich. Bollag sale, Zurich, April 3, 1925, verso of No. 32 (not reproduced). Mr. and Mrs. H. Goldschmidt, Zurich.

510. WOMAN BATHER AND LANDSCAPE, 1876–79

$5 \times 8\frac{9}{16}$ inches—$12,6 \times 21,7$ cm. Page I of the sketchbook Leigh Block. Pencil, a few small spots. Verso: No. 826.

(a) Left: standing woman bather seen in right lost profile; cf. Nos. 511, 963.—(b) At right angles: sketch showing a road leading to a house, with trees on the left and right.— (c) Unfinished sketch of a man's head, which covers part of the landscape.—(d) Handwritten notations: *Le Bar(c) de Bouteville, La Bodinière* (see Note 51) *Dilater les yeux/4 rue St. Rustique.*

BIBLIOGRAPHY: Rewald, *Carnets:* C V, p. 1 (not reproduced).

COLLECTIONS: Cézanne *fils*, Paris. M. Renou, Paris. Poyet, Lyons. M. Renou, Paris. Sam Salz, New York. Mr. and Mrs. Leigh Block, Chicago.

511. WOMAN BATHER, 1876–79

$8\frac{9}{16} \times 5$ inches—$21,7 \times 12,6$ cm. Page L of the sketchbook Leigh Block. Pencil. Verso: No. 581.

Woman bather with her right arm outstretched, walking toward the background; higher up a second position of the forearm is sketched in lighter strokes. This type of figure was often both painted and sketched in pencil by the artist. Rewald cites the paintings Venturi Nos. 257, 381-

86, 538, 539, 540, 547; the arm movement corresponds most nearly to that in the canvas Venturi No. 385. Other variants are seen in the watercolors Venturi Nos. 1103, 1104, 1107. For the subject, cf. the drawings Nos. 510 (a), 514, 517, 649, 963. This fine study in movement is surrounded by a simple landscape: water, plain, hill.

BIBLIOGRAPHY: Rewald, *Carnets:* C V, p. L (reproduced pl. 94).

COLLECTIONS: Cézanne *fils*, Paris. M. Renou, Paris. Poyet, Lyons. M. Renou, Paris. Sam Salz, New York. Mr. and Mrs. Leigh Block, Chicago.

512. GROUP OF FOUR WOMEN BATHERS, 1879–82

$4\frac{9}{16} \times 7\frac{3}{16}$ inches—11,6 × 18 cm. Endpaper on the back cover of the first sketchbook Mrs. Enid A. Haupt. Pencil. Verso: back cover.

Project for part of a composition: a central group consisting of four women bathers, each in a pose typical of Cézanne's work. See for example the paintings Venturi Nos. 382-86. This page is somewhat reminiscent of certain decorative bas-reliefs on ancient sarcophagi.

BIBLIOGRAPHY: Rewald, *Carnets:* C I, "envers de la couverture" (reproduced pl. 95).

COLLECTIONS: Cézanne *fils*, Paris. M. Renou, Paris. Poyet, Lyons. M. Renou, Paris. Sam Salz, New York. Mrs. Enid A. Haupt, New York.

513. SEATED WOMAN BATHER, 1879–82

$8\frac{1}{8} \times 5\frac{1}{8}$ inches—20,6 × 13 cm. Pencil. Verso: blank page.

The model is sitting on a low prop, her forearm hanging down between her bent knees; a classical academy pose. Study in composition for *Four Women Bathers*, Venturi Nos. 383, 386. Cf. our No. 514.

BIBLIOGRAPHY: Venturi No. 1250. Atzuoji Zeisho, *Paul Cézanne*, 1921 (first year Tai-Sho), (reproduced pl. 4). Neumeyer, New York, 1958, No. 9 (reproduced). Idem, *Paul Cézanne, die Badenden*, Stuttgart, 1959 (reproduced fig. 3). Longstreet, 1964 (reproduced). H. R. Hoetink, *Franse Tekeningen uit de 19e Eeuw*, Rotterdam, 1968, No. 17 (reproduced).

EXHIBITIONS: *Meisterzeichnungen französischer Künstler*, Kunsthalle, Basel, 1935, No. 178. Haarlem, 1935, No. 32. Amsterdam, 1946, No. 5. The Hague, 1956, No. III (reproduced). Zurich, 1956, No. 168. Munich, 1956, No. 129 (reproduced).

COLLECTIONS: Romanelli, Paris. P. Cassirer. F. Koenigs, Haarlem. Boymans-van Beuningen Museum, Rotterdam (Inv. F II 116).

514. FOUR WOMEN BATHERS, 1879–82

$8 \times 8\frac{13}{16}$ inches—20,3 × 22,3 cm. Pencil. Verso: blank page.

This is one of the most important drawings grouping the different types of women bathers studied by Cézanne. See Venturi No. 386. Cf. our Nos. 513, 515, 517. There is a series of oil paintings in which the artist grouped sometimes four, sometimes five of these figures.

BIBLIOGRAPHY: Venturi No. 1264. A. Vollard, Paris, 1914 (reproduced on the cover). Catalog of the exhibitions Chicago-New York, 1952, No. 27 (reproduced although not exhibited). Haverkamp Begemann, 1957, No. 85 (reproduced). M. Waldvogel, *The Bathers of Paul Cézanne*, thesis, Harvard University, 1961, pp. 76, 145, 151, 153 (reproduced fig. 48). F. Mathey, *Les Impressionnistes*, Paris, 1959, and *The Impressionists*, New York, 1961, p. 139 (reproduced). W. Haftmann, *Meisteraquarelle des 20. Jahrhunderts*, Keulen, 1964 (reproduced p. 41). Longstreet, 1964 (reproduced). H. R. Hoetink, *Franse Tekeningen uit de 19e Eeuw*, Rotterdam, 1968, No. 27, date circa 1879 (reproduced). *The World of Cézanne*, 1968 (reproduced p. 174).

EXHIBITIONS: Galerie Vollard, Paris, 1898 (reproduced on the invitation card which served also as catalog). Rotterdam, 1933-34, No. 2 (reproduced). Haarlem, 1935, No. 35. Kunsthalle, Basel, Meisterzeichnungen, 1935, No. 177. Kunsthalle, Basel, 1936, No. 125. Amsterdam, 1946, No. 11. Bibliothèque Nationale, Paris, 1952, No. 131 (reproduced). The Hague, 1956, No. 112 (reproduced). Zurich, 1956, No. 171 (reproduced). Munich. 1956, No. 131 (reproduced). Hamburg, 1963, No. 26 (reproduced).

COLLECTIONS: A. Vollard, Paris. Count Kessler, Weimar. P. Cassirer. F. Koenigs, Haarlem. Boymans-van Beuningen Museum, Rotterdam (Inv. F II 192).

515. WOMEN BATHERS, 1879–82

$5\frac{15}{16} \times 5\frac{1}{8}$ inches—15 × 13 cm. Pencil, right side of page cut off. Verso: No. 516.

Compositional study for the group of *Five Women Bathers*, Venturi No. 542. Cf. our Nos. 373, 517; also the versions Venturi Nos. 382-86, 547, and our No. 514. Only three women are seen on the present page, but a fourth, the central figure, is drawn on the reverse side. The variant No. 517 is probably later. Special note should be made of the bather walking toward the background holding a towel in her left hand, her right forearm sketched in three positions; in the lowest of these renderings she seems also to be holding a towel. This triple research helped the artist to the final solution: the left hand above the right. Another study of this type: No. 465 (b).

BIBLIOGRAPHY: Venturi, Vol. I, p. 349, *Oeuvres Inédites*, "Groupe de baigneurs" (not reproduced).

COLLECTIONS: Kenneth Clark, London. Henry Moore, Much Hadham (Herts.).

516. WOMAN BATHER, 1879–82

$5\frac{1}{8} \times 5\frac{15}{16}$ inches—13 × 15 cm. Pencil. Verso: No. 515.

This is the central figure missing in the compositional study No. 515 on the other side of the page. Cf. No. 517 and the painting Venturi No. 542, *Five Women Bathers*. The general aspect of this sketch led Venturi to see it as the figure of a man and not a woman: however, the hair seen to the right above this shoulder and continuing down to the waist is that of a woman. The attitude of the arms may well be compared with those of Nos. 374, 459, 946 (b).

BIBLIOGRAPHY: Venturi, Vol. I, p. 349, Oeuvres Inédites, "Baigneur seul, vu de face" (not reproduced).

COLLECTIONS: Kenneth Clark, London. Henry Moore, Much Hadham (Herts.).

517. Five women bathers, 1879–82

About $5\frac{5}{16} \times 5\frac{1}{8}$ inches—13,5 × 13 cm. Pencil. Verso: blank page.

Compositional study for the painting *Five Women Bathers*, Venturi No. 542, in the Basel Museum. The drawing is squared, which is exceptional for Cézanne. Cf. Nos. 373, 514, 515, 516.

BIBLIOGRAPHY: Venturi No. 1490. Vollard, 1914 (reproduced p. 174).

COLLECTIONS: Ambroise Vollard, Paris. Richard S. Davis, Minneapolis. E. V. Thaw, New York. Mrs. H. J. Heinz III, Pittsburgh.

518. Study of a woman bather drying herself, 1879–82

$9\frac{1}{16} \times 11$ inches—23 × 28 cm. Pencil on yellowish paper, torn in places, lower left corner damaged, brown stains. Verso: print of *The Education of the Virgin* after Eugène Delacroix (Robaut 1193), engraved by Hédouin (Robaut 752) and published in *L'Artiste*, 1845. The page is fixed to cardboard.

Study of a standing bather, placed diagonally on the page, drying herself with a towel. Study for the central figure in several paintings, notably Venturi Nos. 382–86, 547. Cf. our Nos. 373, 514, 516, 519, 520, 521. A cross and the word *tel*, by an alien hand. See Note 25.

BIBLIOGRAPHY: Venturi, No. 1254. Basel catalog, No. 94 (reproduced).

COLLECTIONS: Cézanne *fils*, Paris. W. Feuz, Bern. Kunstmuseum, Basel.

519. Study of women bathers, 1879–82

$4\frac{15}{16} \times 8\frac{9}{16}$ inches—12,5 × 21,7 cm. Page XIV from the sketchbook CP II. Pencil. Verso: No. 537.

(a) Beneath the figures: seascape comprising horizontal lines and a distant mountain.—(b) Left: sketch of a nude bather seen back view with her arms raised.—(c) Above: the head and shoulders repeated cursively, twice.—(d) Center: bather walking toward the background with a towel in her left hand; cf. Venturi No. 382 and our Nos. 361, 963 (b).—(e) Right: bather drying her arm; cf. Nos. 518, 520.

BIBLIOGRAPHY: Venturi, Vol. I, under No. 1286 (not reproduced).

COLLECTIONS: Cézanne *fils*, Paris. Paul Guillaume, Paris. A. Chappuis, Tresserve.

520. Woman bather drying herself, and head of Mme Cézanne; bather: 1879–82; head: 1883–85

$4\frac{7}{8} \times 17\frac{1}{8}$ inches—12,4 × 43,6 cm. Pages XLIV verso and XLV from the sketchbook CP II. Pencil. Verso: Nos. 655 and 952; the present drawing spreads over two pages: XLIV verso and XLV recto.

From left to right: (a) Sketch of the head, in left profile, of the bather drying herself.—(b) The same head in left three-quarter view, bent forward.—(c) The head in left three-quarter view, raised.—(d) The whole figure, in left three-quarter view, drawn to below the knee; she is hold-

ing a towel and her hair falls in profusion down her back. —(e) The same figure, without a towel, her back arched. —(f) Same figure drawn more sketchily, the body erect.— (g) Rapid sketch from abdomen to thighs.—(h) More complete study down to the knee, the head almost in profile and the hair seen on either side of the shoulders.—(i) Head of Mme Cézanne; study for the portrait Venturi No. 229, drawn some years later than (a) to (h). Cf. Nos. 518, 519, 736.

BIBLIOGRAPHY: Venturi No. 1295: "La baigneuse, figure centrale des Nos. 383, 385, 386, est étudiée d'après nature."

COLLECTIONS: Cézanne *fils*, Paris. Paul Guillaume, Paris. A. Chappuis, Tresserve.

521. Three studies of a woman bather, 1882–85

$8\frac{9}{16} \times 5$ inches—21,7 × 12,6 cm. Page XLVII of the sketchbook Leigh Block. Pencil. Verso: No. 522.

Standing nude woman, drying her right arm. The second is a study of only the abdomen and thighs, while the third shows the whole figure again but with legs and body in a different attitude. Rewald refers to the oil paintings Venturi Nos. 382, 383, 384, 385, 386, 547; cf. also our Nos. 514, 518, 520, 522.

BIBLIOGRAPHY: Rewald, *Carnets*: C V, p. XLVII (reproduced pl. 93).

COLLECTIONS: Cézanne *fils*, Paris. M. Renou, Paris. Poyet, Lyons. M. Renou, Paris. Sam Salz, New York. Mr. and Mrs. Leigh Block, Chicago.

522. Two women bathers, study of drapery, 1882–85

$8\frac{9}{16} \times 5$ inches—21,7 × 12,6 cm. Page XLVII verso of the sketchbook Leigh Block. Pencil. Verso: No. 521.

Lower left: standing woman bather; study similar to No. 521 on the reverse side of the page.—(b) Lower right: seated woman bather. The contours of the head, roughly sketched in (though retouched), are covered by part of the drapery (c), which hangs down on this side. The result is disconcerting. Seeking to understand Cézanne's purpose, we observe that this pose is very similar to that of No. 513, except for the head, which is here in left profile and resembles that of the central figure in the canvas Venturi No. 383; this latter, according to Nos. 31 and 94 of the Basel catalog, is based on one of the *Women of Algiers* by Delacroix. In the painting Venturi No. 383 the woman bather seated on the right (corresponding to our study) is also seen in left profile, but the head is different. In the present sketch Cézanne has made the experiment of placing the head of the central figure in the canvas on the figure of the seated woman.—(c) Top: fine study of drapery, later than the bather sketches. On the right are three accentuated shadows, the lower one covering the head of (b).

BIBLIOGRAPHY: Rewald, *Carnets*: C V, p. XLVII verso (reproduced pl. 92).

COLLECTIONS: Cézanne *fils*, Paris. M. Renou, Paris. Poyet, Lyons. M. Renou, Paris. Sam Salz, New York. Mr. and Mrs. Leigh Block, Chicago.

523. SEATED WOMAN BATHER, STUDIES, 1882–85

$4\frac{5}{16} \times 8\frac{9}{16}$ inches—12,5 × 21,7 cm. Page XIIIbis verso from the sketchbook CP II. Pencil. Verso: No. 535.

(a) Beneath the figures the elements of a seascape can be seen: the Château d'If (beneath the calf of the leg) and the Ile de Retonneau as seen from L'Estaque.—(b) Three sketches showing a woman bather sitting in shallow water; repetition of just the head in the center. Cf. Venturi Nos. 385, 386, 542, and our Nos. 373, 514, 517.

BIBLIOGRAPHY: Venturi, Vol. I, under No. 1286 (not reproduced). *Dessins*, 1938, No. 16 (reproduced).

COLLECTIONS: Cézanne *fils*, Paris. Paul Guillaume, Paris. A. Chappuis, Tresserve. Private collection, Paris. Private collection, New York.

524. AFTER ALONSO CANO: *The Dead Christ*, 1877–80

$4\frac{5}{8} \times 7\frac{3}{8}$ inches—18,2 × 11,6 cm. Page 45 verso from the first sketchbook Mrs. Enid A. Haupt. Pencil, handwritten notation in ink, dabs of watercolor. Verso: No. 442.

Copy of an engraving representing *The Dead Christ*, after a painting by Alonso Cano. The engraving was reproduced in Charles Blanc's *Ecole Espagnole* (1869), in a chapter devoted to Cano; see fig. 74. Berthold is right in observing that the attitude of the dead Christ inspired Cézanne for his "bathers going down into the water."—Notation in ink: *Soccio, 7 rue Maître Albert*.

BIBLIOGRAPHY: Rewald, *Carnets:* C I, p. 45 verso; in error as after a Christ in Limbo (not reproduced). Berthold, cat. No. 273 (reproduced Abb. 50, where the original source is indicated).

COLLECTIONS: Cézanne *fils*, Paris. M. Renou, Paris. Poyet, Lyons. M. Renou, Paris. Sam Salz, New York. Mrs. Enid A. Haupt, New York.

525. THREE WOMEN BATHERS, 1878–81

$5 \times 5\frac{5}{8}$ inches—12,7 × 14,2 cm. Fragment of a page from the second sketchbook Mrs. Enid A. Haupt. Pencil, part of the page torn off. Verso: No. 525A.

Summary sketch of three women bathers seen back view, in a row on the same plane, the legs not drawn; a tree on the right. Cf. No. 313 (a).

BIBLIOGRAPHY: Rewald, *Carnets:* C IV, p. X verso (not reproduced).

COLLECTIONS: Cézanne *fils*, Paris. M. Renou, Paris. Poyet, Lyons. M. Renou, Paris. Sam Salz, New York. Mrs. Enid A. Haupt, New York.

525A. SKETCH OF A FLOWER

Pencil. Inaccessible reverse side of No. 525 (not reproduced).

BIBLIOGRAPHY: Rewald, *Carnets:* C IV, p. X "croquis d'une fleur" (the part, measuring $5 \times 5\frac{5}{8}$ inches—12,7 × 14,2 cm., torn out from the page).

FIG. 74. After Alonso Cano (1601–67): *The Dead Christ*, wood engraving printed in Charles Blanc, *Ecole espagnole* (1869). *(Photograph: Chappuis)*

526. SKETCH OF A BATHER GOING DOWN INTO THE WATER, 1878–81

$4\frac{15}{16} \times 8\frac{1}{8}$ inches—12,5 × 20,7 cm. Page X verso from the sketchbook BS III. Pencil. Verso: No. 1066.

Type of bather frequently studied by Cézanne and used in his paintings; cf. Nos. 440 (b), 527, 1066 (b), 1218.

BIBLIOGRAPHY: Venturi No. 1412.

COLLECTIONS: Cézanne *fils*, Paris. Paul Guillaume, Paris. W. Feuz, Bern. R. von Hirsch, Basel.

527. PAGE OF STUDIES, INCLUDING BATHERS AND VEGETATION, 1878–81

$8\frac{1}{8} \times 4\frac{15}{16}$ inches—20,7 × 12,5 cm. Page III from the sketchbook BS III. Pencil, trial dabs of watercolor. Verso: No. 413.

(a) Page upright, left: foliage of trees with shadows.—(b) Page lengthwise: three studies of bathers, one standing in left three-quarter view, his arms held straight down in front of him; cf. Nos. 659, 965. Seated bather and, above, similar figure with retouches to the head and legs; the feet are crossed.

BIBLIOGRAPHY: Venturi No. 1402.

COLLECTIONS: Cézanne *fils*, Paris. Paul Guillaume, Paris. W. Feuz, Bern. R. von Hirsch, Basel.

528. BATHER GOING DOWN INTO THE WATER, 1878–81

$8\frac{1}{2} \times 5$ inches—21,6 × 12,7 cm. First endpaper from the second sketchbook Mrs. Enid A. Haupt. Pencil. Verso: the cover of the sketchbook.

Fine sketch of this figure often studied by Cézanne; he resembles a Michelangelo *ignudo*. Cf. No. 524. Notations: *Malle/No.* 7 (by an alien hand, indicating the number of this sketchbook). Below: *Ocre jaune.*

BIBLIOGRAPHY: Rewald, *Carnets:* C IV, "verso de la couverture"; described erroneously as No. 17 for No. 7, and "Signature," for "Ocre jaune." (Not reproduced).

COLLECTIONS: Cézanne *fils,* Paris. M. Renou, Paris. Poyet, Lyons. M. Renou, Paris. Sam Salz, New York. Mrs. Enid A. Haupt, New York.

529. SEATED MAN WEARING A TOP HAT, 1879–82

$5 \times 3\frac{15}{16}$ inches—12,7 × 9,9 cm. Page II verso from the sketchbook BS I. Page trimmed. Pencil. Verso: blank page.

Rapid sketch of a man in a top hat, seated like a coachman.

BIBLIOGRAPHY: Venturi No. 1325. Basel catalog, No. 134 (reproduced).

COLLECTIONS: Cézanne *fils,* Paris. Paul Guillaume, Paris. W. Feuz, Bern. Kunstmuseum, Basel.

530. SKETCH OF A MAN SEEN BACK VIEW, 1880–83

$9\frac{15}{16} \times 6$ inches—23,7 × 15,2 cm. Page XXXIbis verso of the Album, Paul Mellon Collection. Pencil. Verso: No. 841.

(a) Top: sketch of a man wearing a little round hat, in the attitude of an artisan or artist at work.—(b) Below: sketch of an unrecognizable object.

BIBLIOGRAPHY: Venturi, Vol. I, under No. 1309 (not reproduced). *Album,* 1966 (reproduced).

COLLECTIONS: Cézanne *fils,* Paris. Paul Guillaume, Paris. A. Chappuis, Tresserve. Mr. and Mrs. Paul Mellon, Upperville, Va.

531. HEAD OF A DONKEY, AND NOTATIONS, 1880–83

$5 \times 8\frac{9}{16}$ inches—12,6 × 21,7 cm. Page VII verso of the sketchbook Leigh Block. Pencil. Verso: No. 802.

Head of a donkey drawn twice; a pair of ears. Cf. the donkey in No. 532; for observations on Cézanne and donkeys, see No. 761.—Notations: *Calicot/coke/fil blanc/coton rouge/ pièces pour le caraco/chemises de nuit/couverture/pâtes/tilleul/ fauteuil/tapisserie.*

BIBLIOGRAPHY: Rewald, *Carnets:* C V, p. VII verso (not reproduced).

COLLECTIONS: Cézanne *fils,* Paris. M. Renou, Paris. Poyet, Lyons. M. Renou, Paris. Sam Salz, New York. Mr. and Mrs. Leigh Block, Chicago.

532. CART AND DONKEY; DRAPERY, cart: 1880–83, drapery: circa 1888

$8\frac{9}{16} \times 5$ inches—21,7 × 12,6 cm. Page VI verso of the sketchbook Leigh Block. Pencil. Verso: No. 803.

(a) Below: farm cart with two large wheels, half-hiding a donkey waiting unharnessed, only his hindquarters visible. Cf. the donkey's head, No. 531; for observations on Cézanne and donkeys, see No. 761.—(b) Top: study of drapery.

BIBLIOGRAPHY: Rewald, *Carnets:* C V, p. VI verso (not reproduced).

COLLECTIONS: Cézanne *fils,* Paris. M. Renou, Paris. Poyet, Lyons. M. Renou, Paris. Sam Salz, New York. Mr. and Mrs. Leigh Block, Chicago.

533. NOTATIONS AND SKETCHES, 1877–80

$7\frac{5}{8} \times 4\frac{5}{8}$ inches—19,4 × 11,8 cm. Page I from the sketchbook CP I. Pencil. Verso: No. 829.

Page covered with notations and two addition sums; an address: *Félix Brousse Pélissane (B.d.Rh.)/Prendre la mesure du chevalet.* Partly covered by these notations: (a) Sketch with a right angle that is difficult to interpret.—(b) Chair seen from the front, the back consisting of a rectangular frame dotted with round marks.—(c) Unfinished study of a pitcher; cf. No. 379 (a).

BIBLIOGRAPHY: Venturi, Vol. I, p. 304, under No. 1266 (not reproduced).

COLLECTIONS: Cézanne *fils,* Paris. Paul Guillaume, Paris. A. Chappuis, Tresserve.

534. STUDY OF AN UPRIGHT WITH CROSSBAR, 1877–80

$4\frac{7}{8} \times 8\frac{5}{8}$ inches—12,4 × 21,8 cm. Page XXX verso from the sketchbook CP II. Pencil on ocher paper. Verso: No. 727.

An upright supporting a round crossbar: detail of some domestic article, a drying-rail or carpet-beater. Study almost exclusively in vertical and horizontal lines, with hatching.

BIBLIOGRAPHY: Venturi, Vol. I, under No. 1290 (not reproduced).

COLLECTIONS: Cézanne *fils,* Paris. Paul Guillaume, Paris. A. Chappuis, Tresserve.

535. WASHBOWL AND BOTTLE, 1877–81

$4\frac{15}{16} \times 8\frac{9}{16}$ inches—12,5 × 21,7 cm. Page XIIIbis from the sketchbook CP II. Pencil. Verso: No. 523.

On a washstand: a small glass bottle and a washbowl with a decorative design of large dots, casting a shadow on its left. Cf. Nos. 542, 952, and for the subject, Venturi No. 1151.

BIBLIOGRAPHY: Venturi, Vol. I, under No. 1286 (not reproduced). *Dessins,* 1957, No. 17 (reproduced).

COLLECTIONS: Cézanne *fils,* Paris. Paul Guillaume, Paris. A. Chappuis, Tresserve. Private collection, Paris. Private collection, New York.

536. CORNER OF A STUDIO, 1877–81

$8\frac{9}{16} \times 4\frac{7}{8}$ inches—21,7 × 12,4 cm. Page XLI from the sketchbook CP II. Pencil, two round stains. Verso: No. 720.

A picture in a wide frame is seen on the left and a drapery lower right. In the background there is a wall with wainscoting, and a large roller. This work has been hailed as one of the forerunners of Cubism; as far as Cézanne is concerned, it is remarkable for the pencil gradations.

BIBLIOGRAPHY: Venturi, Vol. I, under No. 1293 (not reproduced). M. Raynal, Dessins de Cézanne, *Arts et Métiers graphiques*, 1936, No. 54, pp. 46-52 (reproduced).

COLLECTIONS: Cézanne *fils*, Paris. Paul Guillaume, Paris. A. Chappuis, Tresserve. O. Wertheimer, Paris. Fogg Art Museum, Cambridge, Mass. (Inv. 1962.24).

537. TABLE AND BOX, FLOWERSTAND, 1879–82

$4\frac{15}{16} \times 8\frac{9}{16}$ inches—12,5 × 21,7 cm. Page XIV verso from the sketchbook CP II. Pencil, four trial dabs of watercolor. Verso: No. 519.

(a) Top: massive oval table, covered with a cloth which accentuates its form. On the table, a long box or beam, hatching in the background; cf. No. 833.—(b) Below: study of a flower stand. The artist has treated the same object, but in more detail, in the watercolor Venturi No. 1539A.

BIBLIOGRAPHY: Venturi, Vol. I, under No. 1286 (not reproduced).

COLLECTIONS: Cézanne *fils*, Paris. Paul Guillaume, Paris. A. Chappuis, Tresserve.

538. STUDY OF A DECORATIVE ORNAMENT, 1879–82

$9\frac{15}{16} \times 6$ inches—23,7 × 15,2 cm. Page XII of the Album, Paul Mellon Collection. Pencil. Verso: No. 827.

Elaborate study of a carved ornament as seen on the corners of console tables, armchairs, etc. The original model has not been traced; it was no doubt an imitation Louis XIV decorative element.

BIBLIOGRAPHY: Venturi, Vol. I, under No. 1304 "écusson rococo" (not reproduced). Berthold, cat. No. 335 (reproduced). *Dessins*, 1938 (reproduced pl. 48). *Album*, 1966 (reproduced).

COLLECTIONS: Cézanne *fils*, Paris. Paul Guillaume, Paris. A. Chappuis, Tresserve. Mr. and Mrs. Paul Mellon, Upperville, Va.

539. SMALL SKETCHES: POT AND SUGAR BOWL, 1879–82

$7\frac{11}{16} \times 4\frac{5}{8}$ inches—19,5 × 11,8 cm. Back endpaper of the sketchbook CP I. Pencil. Pagination: LIV × 2, meaning 54 double-sided leaves in this sketchbook. Verso: cloth of the cover.

(a) At the top and partly covered by the number 8 written in blue crayon: pot decorated with tongue-shaped grooves. Right: the number 6, by an alien hand, like the number 8 mentioned above. Light contours of a sugar bowl with a lid; cf. Venturi Nos. 496, 497, 594.

COLLECTIONS: Cézanne *fils*, Paris. Paul Guillaume, Paris. A. Chappuis, Tresserve.

539A. HANDWRITTEN NOTATIONS, 1877–85

$8\frac{1}{2} \times 4\frac{15}{16}$ inches—21,6 × 12,5 cm. Front endpaper of the sketchbook CP II. Pencil. Verso: cloth of the cover. (Not reproduced.)

On the white endpaper of the sketchbook: handwritten notations and some dense hatching not composing a drawing. Label of the seller of the sketchbook: *Couleurs et vernis*

SALES 25 *Boulevard Montparnasse* (illegible) *registres*. (illegible).—In Cézanne's handwriting: *De la lumière et de la couleur chez les maîtres anciens, par Régnier. Blanc 5/Naples 2/ Brillant 2-2/Ocre jaune 5/Jaune de chrome 3/Vermillon 3/Vert Véronèse 5/Vert émeraude 2/Outremer Guimet 2-2/Terre verte 6/ Laque fine 2-2/Remède/pinceaux.*—There are also two small addition sums, almost obliterated.

BIBLIOGRAPHY: Venturi, Vol. I, under No. 1282 (handwritten notations quoted—not reproduced). J. de Beucken, *Un Portrait de Cézanne*, Paris, 1955, p. 304 (the author says that he saw Cézanne's copy of the Régnier book in the house of the artist's grandson). R. W. Ratcliffe, *Cézanne's Working Methods and their Theoretical Background*, London, 1960; typewritten doctoral thesis, filed at London University, pp. 330 ff. The author studies the influence on Cézanne of Régnier's book, published in Paris in 1865, and after comparing the handwriting of the present note on Régnier with that of the artist's letters to Zola, he dates the note circa 1880: widest possible margin, 1877–85.

COLLECTIONS: Cézanne *fils*, Paris. Paul Guillaume, Paris. A. Chappuis, Tresserve.

540. SPIRIT-STOVE AND MILK PITCHER, 1879–82

$7\frac{5}{8} \times 4\frac{5}{8}$ inches—19,4 × 11,8 cm. Page IV verso from the sketchbook CP I. Pencil. Verso: No. 578.

Spirit-stove with a straight handle on a table, and beside it a hook. Right background: porcelain milk pitcher, its grooved surface decorated with a floral design. The same pitcher figures in the oils Venturi Nos. 593, 619, 735, 736, 750 and the watercolors Nos. 1146, 1147. Cézanne also drew another spirit-stove with differently shaped uprights; see Nos. 552, 553.

BIBLIOGRAPHY: Venturi, Vol. I as verso of No. 1268 (not reproduced). *Dessins*, 1938, No. 27 (reproduced).

EXHIBITION: Orangerie, Paris, 1936, No. 158.

COLLECTIONS: Cézanne *fils*, Paris. Paul Guillaume, Paris. A. Chappuis, Tresserve. H. Berggruen, Paris.

541. WATER-JUG, 1879–82

$4\frac{15}{16} \times 8\frac{9}{16}$ inches—12,5 × 21,7 cm. Page XII verso from the sketchbook CP II. Pencil. Verso: No. 309.

The contours are indicated by multiple juxtaposed strokes, as are the shadows. Both the handle and wide lip of the jug are seen in foreshortening, as mentioned by Venturi, and we would like to stress the interplay between volume and paper surface. Cf. Nos. 535, 542, 952, and for the subject, Venturi No. 1151.

BIBLIOGRAPHY: Venturi, Vol. I, under No. 1285 (not reproduced).

COLLECTIONS: Cézanne *fils*, Paris. Paul Guillaume, Paris. A. Chappuis, Tresserve.

542. TOILET ARTICLES, 1879–82

$4\frac{7}{8} \times 8\frac{5}{8}$ inches—12,4 × 21,8 cm. Page XXXIX verso from the sketchbook CP II. Pencil. Verso: No. 747.

From left to right on a dressing table: a comb, a glass of water, a pitcher, a bottle behind, and a long object in front of the pitcher, then a washbowl, and a small bottle. For the objects, cf. Nos. 535, 541, 952, and Venturi No. 1151.

BIBLIOGRAPHY: Venturi, Vol. I, under No. 1292 (not reproduced). *Dessins*, 1938, No. 15 (reproduced).

EXHIBITION: Phillips Collection, Washington, D.C., Chicago, Boston, 1971, No. 70 (reproduced).

COLLECTIONS: Cézanne *fils*, Paris. Paul Guillaume, Paris. A. Chappuis, Tresserve. Private collection, Paris. Private collection, New York.

543. PAGE OF STUDIES, 1880–83

$9\frac{7}{16} \times 12\frac{3}{16}$ inches—24 × 31 cm. Pencil on beige paper. Verso: No. 543A.

(a) Top left: spirit-stove with its cast shadow.—(b) Right: head of a woman, her eyelids lowered.—(c) Lower left: earthenware pan, its handle seen in foreshortening.—(d) Study of drapery or paper.

BIBLIOGRAPHY: Venturi, Vol. I, p. 348, *Oeuvres Inédites* "Coll. Kenneth Clark" (not reproduced).

COLLECTIONS: Kenneth Clark, London. Marlborough Gallery, London. Oswald T. Falk, Oxford.

543A. ELEMENTS OF STATUES

Verso of No. 543. (Not reproduced.)

BIBLIOGRAPHY: Venturi, Vol. I, p. 348, *Oeuvres Inédites*: "Coll. Kenneth Clark. Eléments de statues" (not reproduced).

544. BELLOWS, BOTTLE, PROFILE OF A WOMAN, 1880–83

$4\frac{7}{8} \times 8\frac{9}{16}$ inches—12,4 21,7 cm. Page XXVI verso of the sketchbook A.I.C.

(a) Left: hearth bellows, standing open; cf. No. 953.—(b) Squat milk bottle with a wide cork, in front of a piece of furniture with round marks on its top; the effects of whiteness and volume are noteworthy.—(c) Unfinished sketch of a woman's head; cf. No. 610 (b).

BIBLIOGRAPHY: Rewald, *Carnets*: C II, p. XXVI verso (reproduced pl. 73). Schniewind, text p. 30 (reproduced). Andersen, *Sk.* (not reproduced).

COLLECTIONS: Cézanne *fils*, Paris. M. Renou, Paris. Poyet, Lyons. M. Renou, Paris. Sam Salz, New York. Art Institute, Chicago.

545. A CARAFE, HOT-WATER JUG, AND LOGS, 1880–83

$4\frac{7}{8} \times 8\frac{9}{16}$ inches—12,4 × 21,7 cm. Page XXVII of the sketchbook A.I.C. Pencil, stains. Verso: No. 332.

(a) Left: a half-filled carafe decorated with grooves or facets.—(b) Right: small hot-water jug standing near some logs and a stick.

BIBLIOGRAPHY: Rewald, *Carnets*: C II, p. XXVII (reproduced pl. 72). Schniewind, text p. 30 (reproduced). Andersen, *Sk.* (not reproduced).

COLLECTIONS: Cézanne *fils*, Paris. M. Renou, Paris. Poyet, Lyons. M. Renou, Paris. Sam Salz, New York. Art Institute, Chicago.

546. CHAIR AND DRESSER, 1880–83

$6 \times 9\frac{15}{16}$ inches—15,2 × 23,7 cm. Page LII of the Album, Paul Mellon Collection. Pencil. Verso: No. 635.

Chair, its rush-bottom seat summarily indicated. For the dresser behind, cf. Venturi No. 496. There is a certain distance between the two pieces of furniture.

BIBLIOGRAPHY: Venturi, Vol. I, under No. 1314 (not reproduced); by error "chaise et personnage." *Album*, 1966 (reproduced).

COLLECTIONS: Cézanne *fils*, Paris. Paul Guillaume, Paris. A. Chappuis, Tresserve. Mr. and Mrs. Paul Mellon, Upperville, Va.

547. A CUP, 1880–83

$7\frac{5}{8} \times 4\frac{5}{8}$ inches—19,4 × 11,8 cm. Page VII verso from the sketchbook CP I. Pencil. Verso: No. 497.

A rustic cup, with its saucer, standing on a table; the cup handle is in profile. The corner of a napkin covers part of the saucer and the whiteness of the object mingles with the whiteness of the paper below. With light falling from the right, the cup casts a shadow shaped like a tower. The play of ellipses is important: the handle and rim of the cup and two curves on the left, the lower one arresting the movement of the saucer's edge while at the same time repeating the form of the handle.

BIBLIOGRAPHY: Venturi, Vol. I, under No. 1270 (not reproduced). *Dessins*, 1938, No. 25 (reproduced). *Dessins*, 1957 (reproduced on the back of the cover).

COLLECTIONS: Cézanne *fils*, Paris. Paul Guillaume, Paris. A. Chappuis, Tresserve. Private collection, Paris.

548. STUDY OF DRAPERY, 1881–84

$5 \times 8\frac{1}{2}$ inches—12,7 × 21,6 cm. Page III from the second sketchbook Mrs. Enid A. Haupt. Pencil. Verso: blank page.

In the foreground, the fabric with its dark shadows swells like a wave; in the background it is draped in the form of a mountain.

BIBLIOGRAPHY: Rewald, *Carnets*: C IV, page III (not reproduced).

COLLECTIONS: Cézanne *fils*, Paris. M. Renou, Paris. Poyet, Lyons. M. Renou, Paris. Sam Salz, New York. Mrs. Enid A. Haupt, New York.

549. STUDY OF DRAPERY, 1881–84

$8\frac{9}{16} \times 4\frac{7}{8}$ inches—21,7 × 12,4 cm. Page XXI verso of the sketchbook A.I.C. Pencil, stains. Verso: No. 615.

Schniewind says: "study of a hanging coat"; I think it is a work-jacket thrown over the back of a chair. The lower part of the sketch is on the side of the sketchbook binding. A kind of gaping open pocket can be distinguished and, upper right, the end of some protruding object. Cf. Nos. 131, 1076.

BIBLIOGRAPHY: Rewald, *Carnets*: C II, p. XXI verso (not reproduced). Schniewind, text p. 29 (reproduced). Andersen, *Sk.* (not reproduced).

COLLECTIONS: Cézanne *fils*, Paris. M. Renou, Paris. Poyet, Lyons. M. Renou, Paris. Sam Salz, New York. Art Institute, Chicago.

550. STUDY OF A SUIT OF ARMOR, 1881–84

$8\frac{9}{16} \times 5$ inches—21,7 × 12,6 cm. Page XIII of the sketchbook Leigh Block. Pencil. Verso: No. 626.

Study of a heavy suit of armor: European, dating from the second half of the sixteenth century. See Note 52. It is standing on a pedestal, one of the gauntlets supported by a pike. Rewald thinks that Cézanne may have seen this armor in one of Emile Zola's homes. Three suits of occidental armor figured in the Zola sale (1903). See Note 53.

BIBLIOGRAPHY: Rewald, *Carnets*: C V, p. XIII (reproduced pl. 141). Berthold, cat. No. 333 (reproduced).

COLLECTIONS: Cézanne *fils*, Paris. M. Renou, Paris. Poyet, Lyons. M. Renou, Paris. Sam Salz, New York. Mr. and Mrs. Leigh Block, Chicago.

551. PIECE OF FURNITURE WITH VASE, AND HEAD, 1881–84

$8\frac{9}{16} \times 5$ inches—21,7 × 12,6 cm. Page XVI of the sketchbook Leigh Block. Pencil. Verso: No. 625.

Top part of a piece of furniture, carved asymmetrically in the Oriental style. A vase with two or three porcelain pots stand above the ornamental curve. At the bottom of the page: a kind of caryatid placed horizontally and held up by a hand; the other arm, bent, is seen above. Rewald is of the opinion that Cézanne may have drawn this piece of furniture at Emile Zola's house. I would add that it gives one a feeling of the boredom of a rainy day.

BIBLIOGRAPHY: Rewald, *Carnets*: C V, p. XVI (reproduced pl. 70).

COLLECTIONS: Cézanne *fils*, Paris. M. Renou, Paris. Poyet, Lyons. M. Renou, Paris. Sam Salz, New York. Mr. and Mrs. Leigh Block, Chicago.

552. SPIRIT-STOVE, 1881–84 (see Note 54)

$5 \times 8\frac{1}{16}$ inches—12,6 × 20,4 cm. Page I verso from the sketchbook BS III. Pencil, touches of watercolor, stains. Verso: No. 345.

(a) Spirit-stove with three T-shaped uprights: the background is indicated by hatching.—(b) Left: sketch of an unrecognizable object. Notation: *Louis Leclerc aux Sapeurs —Melun—*.

BIBLIOGRAPHY: Venturi, No. 1399; in error as page I recto. Basel catalog, No. 105 (reproduced). Douglas Cooper, in *Master Drawings*, Vol. 1, No. 4, p. 56; date proposed 1896–1900.

COLLECTIONS: Cézanne *fils*, Paris. Paul Guillaume, Paris. W. Feuz, Bern. Kunstmuseum, Basel.

553. STILL LIFE WITH CANDLESTICK, 1881–84 (see Note 54)

$4\frac{15}{16} \times 7\frac{3}{4}$ inches—12,5 × 19,6 cm. Page XVII from the sketchbook BS III. Pencil. Verso: blank page.

Still life with a candlestick, a spirit-stove, a tureen ornamented with flowers, and a round pot.

BIBLIOGRAPHY: Venturi No. 1419. Basel catalog, No. 104 (reproduced). Yvon Taillandier, *Paul Cézanne*, Paris, New York, Munich, 1961 and 1965 (reproduced p. 36).

EXHIBITIONS: The Hague, 1956, No. 132 (reproduced). Zurich, 1956, No. 201 (reproduced pl. 78).

COLLECTIONS: Cézanne *fils*, Paris. Paul Guillaume, Paris. W. Feuz, Bern. Kunstmuseum, Basel.

554. STILL LIFE WITH CARAFE, 1881–84 (see Note 54)

$7\frac{13}{16} \times 4\frac{3}{4}$ inches—19,9 × 12 cm. Page XXIII from the sketchbook BS II. Pencil. Verso: blank page.

Partly-filled carafe on a table, with a glass on the right. The artist stresses the round volumes and obtains a monumental effect. The affinity between the strokes of this drawing and the one following should be noted.

BIBLIOGRAPHY: Venturi, No. 1368. Basel catalog, No. 106, dated 1882–92 (reproduced). *Le Dessin français au XIXe siècle*, Mermod, Lausanne, 1948, p. 104 (reproduced). Th. Reff, *BurlM*, Aug. 1963, p. 376, date "probably after 1900." Douglas Cooper, in *Master Drawings*, Vol. 1, No. 4, 1963, p. 56, date 1896–1900.

EXHIBITIONS: The Hague, 1956, No. 129. Zurich, 1956, No. 195.

COLLECTIONS: Cézanne *fils*, Paris. Paul Guillaume, Paris. W. Feuz, Bern. Kunstmuseum, Basel.

555. AFTER B. DA MAIANO: *Pietro Mellini*, 1881–84

$8\frac{1}{8} \times 4\frac{13}{16}$ inches—20,7 × 12,2 cm. Page XXXVII from the sketchbook BS II. Pencil. Verso: blank page.

FIG. 75. Benedetto da Maiano (1442–97): bust (1474) of *Pietro Mellini*, a Florentine merchant. Our photograph was taken from a plaster cast in the Victoria and Albert Museum, London. The cast from which Cézanne drew, formerly in the Musée de Sculpture comparée of the Trocadéro, Paris, is now in the collection of the Faculty of Letters of the University of Lyons. The original marble is in the National Museum (Bargello), Florence. Height: 50 cm. *Catalogue général du Musée de Sculpture comparée du Trocadéro* III, 1928, No. I 190.
(Photograph: R. W. Ratcliffe)

After a plaster cast of Benedetto da Maiano's bust of *Pietro Mellini*. See fig. 75.

BIBLIOGRAPHY: Venturi, No. 1372. Berthold, cat. No. 87 (reproduced Abb. 105). Basel catalog, No. 113 (reproduced).

EXHIBITIONS: Meisterzeichnungen französischer Künstler, Kunsthalle, Basel, 1935, No. 198. Belvedere, Vienna, 1961, No. 95.

COLLECTIONS: Cézanne *fils*, Paris. Paul Guillaume, Paris. W. Feuz, Bern. Kunstmuseum, Basel.

556. AFTER B. DA MAIANO: *Filippo Strozzi*, 1881–84

$8\frac{1}{2} \times 5$ inches—21,6 × 12,7 cm. Page XXVIII verso from the second sketchbook Mrs. Enid A. Haupt. Pencil. Verso: No. 641.

Head of *Filippo Strozzi* seen in right three-quarter view and from below. After Benedetto da Maiano's marble bust in the Louvre. See fig. 76. Cf. No. 724.

BIBLIOGRAPHY: Rewald, *Carnets:* C IV, p. XXVIII verso (reproduced pl. 146). Berthold, catalog No. 85 (reproduced).

COLLECTIONS: Cézanne *fils*, Paris. M. Renou, Paris. Poyet, Lyons. M. Renou, Paris. Sam Salz, New York. Mrs. Enid A. Haupt, New York.

557. AFTER B. DA MAIANO: *Filippo Strozzi*, 1881–84

$8\frac{1}{2} \times 5$ inches—21,6 × 12,7 cm. Page XXX from the second sketchbook Mrs. Enid A. Haupt. Pencil. Verso: No. 968.

(a) Head of *Filippo Strozzi* seen in right three-quarter view, after Benedetto da Maiano's bust in the Louvre. See fig. 77.—(b) Below: study of an animal's paw, or the foot of a statue, in foreshortening.

BIBLIOGRAPHY: Rewald, *Carnets:* C IV, p. XXX (reproduced pl. 145). Berthold, cat. No. 86 (reproduced). Th. Reff, Cézanne's Drawings 1875–85, *BurlM*, May 1959, p. 173 (reproduced fig. 22).

COLLECTIONS: Cézanne *fils*, Paris. M. Renou, Paris. Poyet, Lyon. M. Renou, Paris. Sam Salz, New York. Mrs. Enid A. Haupt, New York.

558. AFTER B. DA MAIANO: *Filippo Strozzi,* 1881–84

$7\frac{3}{16} \times 4\frac{9}{16}$ inches—18,2 × 11,6 cm. Page 23 verso from the first sketchbook Mrs. Enid A. Haupt. Pencil. Verso: No. 600.

After Benedetto da Maiano's marble bust of *Filippo Strozzi*, in the Louvre. See fig. 76. The head is seen in left profile.

BIBLIOGRAPHY: Rewald, *Carnets:* C I, p. 23 verso (reproduced pl. 147). Berthold, cat. No. 83 (reproduced).

COLLECTIONS: Cézanne *fils*, Paris. M. Renou, Paris. Poyet, Lyons. M. Renou, Paris. Sam Salz, New York. Mrs. Enid A. Haupt, New York.

559. AFTER B. DA MAIANO: *Filippo Strozzi*, 1881–84

$8\frac{7}{16} \times 5\frac{3}{16}$ inches—21,4 × 13,1 cm. Page III verso from the sketchbook BS I. Pencil. Verso: blank page.

After Benedetto da Maiano's marble bust of *Filippo Strozzi* in the Louvre. See fig. 77. Cf. Nos. 556, 557, 558. Indications of background with the leg of another statue on a square pedestal—according to Berthold, a *Slave* by Michelangelo.

BIBLIOGRAPHY: Venturi, No. 1327. Berthold, cat. No. 84 (reproduced). Basel catalog No. 115 (reproduced). *Dessins*, 1957, No. 54 (reproduced). Yvon Taillandier, *Paul Cézanne*, Paris, New York, Munich, 1961 and 1965 (reproduced p. 22). R. Cogniat, *Cézanne*, Flammarion, Paris 1967 (reproduced p. 28).

COLLECTIONS: Cézanne *fils*, Paris. Paul Guillaume, Paris. W. Feuz, Bern. Kunstmuseum, Basel.

560. AFTER MINO DA FIESOLE: *Giovanni de' Medici*, 1881–84

$8\frac{1}{8} \times 5\frac{3}{16}$ inches—20,7 × 13,1 cm. Page XXI from the sketchbook BS I. Pencil. Verso: blank page.

After a plaster cast from Mino da Fiesole's bust of *Giovanni de' Medici* (died 1463); the shoulders are covered by a V-necked garment. See fig. 78.

BIBLIOGRAPHY: Venturi, No. 1346 "buste de Filippo Strozzi." Berthold, cat. No. 94 "bust of Rinaldo della Luna" (reproduced Abb. 107). Basel catalog, No. 114 (reproduced). Fritz Novotny, Cézanne als Zeichner, *Wiener Jahrbuch für Kunstgeschichte,* 1950, p. 233. Longstreet, 1964 (reproduced).

COLLECTIONS: Cézanne *fils*, Paris. Paul Guillaume, Paris. W. Feuz, Bern. Kunstmuseum, Basel.

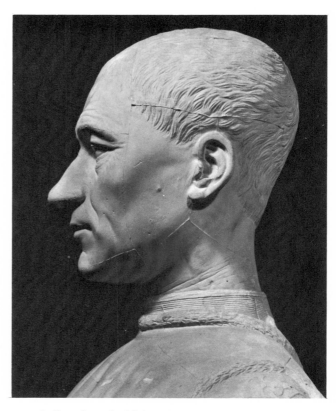

FIG. 76. Benedetto da Maiano (1442–97): bust of *Filippo Strozzi* (1426–91), a Florentine banker renowned for the Palazzo which he began building in 1489. Marble (1491) in the Louvre, acquired in 1878; height: 52 cm. Our photograph was taken from a plaster cast. Musée National du Louvre, *Catalogue des Sculptures* I, 1922, No. 693.

FIG. 77. The same bust as fig. 76, but here the photograph was taken from the marble. *(Photograph: R. W. Ratcliffe)*

561. AFTER THE ANTIQUE: *Young man removing a thorn from his foot*, 1882–85

    Pencil. Verso: No. 1051.

The *Young Man removing a Thorn from his Foot* is an antique bronze, of which there is an original in the Naples Museum. See fig. 79. Cézanne could have done this drawing from a plaster cast or from the bronze replica in the Louvre. Cf. No. 562.

BIBLIOGRAPHY: Venturi, Vol. I, p. 349, *Oeuvres Inédites* (not reproduced). Berthold, cat. No. 36 (reproduced).

COLLECTION: Kenneth Clark, London.

562. AFTER THE ANTIQUE: *Young man removing a thorn from his foot*, 1883–86

    $8\frac{1}{2} \times 5$ inches—21,6 × 12,7 cm. Page XIII verso from the second sketchbook Mrs. Enid A. Haupt. Pencil. Verso: blank page.

After the statue *Young Man removing a Thorn from his Foot*, seen here in left profile, whereas No. 561 shows the figure in right profile. See fig. 80.

BIBLIOGRAPHY: Rewald, *Carnets:* C IV, p. XIII verso (reproduced pl. 129). Berthold, cat. No. 35 (reproduced Abb. 120).

COLLECTIONS: Cézanne *fils*, Paris. M. Renou, Paris. Poyet, Lyons. M. Renou, Paris. Sam Salz, New York. Mrs. Enid A. Haupt, New York.

563. AFTER THE ANTIQUE: *Bacchus,* 1882–85

    $7\frac{3}{16} \times 4\frac{9}{16}$ inches—18,2 × 11,6 cm. Page 1 from the first sketchbook Mrs. Enid A. Haupt. Pencil. Verso: No. 1031.

The antique marble known as *The Versailles Bacchus* is in the Louvre. See fig. 81. In the figure's stability, movement is suggested.

BIBLIOGRAPHY: Rewald, *Carnets:* C I, p. 1 (not reproduced). Berthold, cat. No. 47, original model identified (reproduced). Th. Reff, *Bather* (reproduced fig. 7).

COLLECTIONS: Cézanne *fils*, Paris. M. Renou, Paris. Poyet, Lyons. M. Renou, Paris. Sam Salz, New York. Mrs. Enid A. Haupt, New York.

FIG. 78. Mino da Fiesole (1431–84): marble bust of *Giovanni de' Medici* (1463) in the National Museum (Bargello), Florence. Our reproduction shows the plaster cast, formerly in the Musée de Sculpture comparée du Trocadéro, photographed by Gertrude Berthold in the Faculty of Letters of Lyons. *(Photograph: G. Berthold)*

FIG. 79. *Young Man removing a Thorn from his Foot.* An antique bronze (Spinario) is in the Naples Museum, and a bronze cast is in the Louvre (Musée National du Louvre, *Catalogue des Sculptures* I, 1922, No. 823). Our photograph was taken from a plaster cast. It cannot be said with certainty whether Cézanne drew from the bronze or a plaster cast; however, No. 561 may have been done after the bronze and No. 562 after a cast. *(Photograph: Skulpturhalle, Basel)*

FIG. 80. The same statue as in fig. 79, seen here in left profile. *(Photograph: Skulpturhalle, Basel)*

FIG. 81. *Bacchus* of Versailles, antique marble in the Louvre. Musée national du Louvre, *Catalogue sommaire des Marbres antiques*, 1922, No. 337. *(Photograph: Alinari)*

564. SKETCH OF A HAND AND NOTATIONS, 1879–82

$8\frac{9}{16} \times 5$ inches—21,7 × 12,6 cm. Front endpaper of the sketchbook Leigh Block. Pencil, a few stains. Verso: the cloth of the cover.

(a) Sketch of a hand, perhaps the artist's left hand.—(b) Handwritten notations (my reading): *Blanc d'argent* 5-15/ *jaune brillant* 6-10/*ocre jaune* -6/*vermillon* 2-4/*garance foncée* -1/*vert véronèse* 8-10/*outremer* 5-6/*vert émeraude* 2-0/*terre verte* 5-0/*chrome clair* 1-2/*pinceaux putois* -2 *douzaines No.* 8-9-10.— Childish scribbles here and there that obscure the text; also Cézanne altered certain numerals himself on top of the original ones.

BIBLIOGRAPHY: Rewald, *Carnets:* C V, p. 51 (not reproduced).

EXHIBITIONS: The whole sketchbook was exhibited at the Art Institute, Chicago, in 1952, and at the Metropolitan Museum, New York, 1952, under the number 91. Further reference to these exhibitions will be omitted in our notices for other pages of this same sketchbook that were *not* reproduced in the catalogs of these exhibitions.

COLLECTIONS: Cézanne *fils*, Paris. M. Renou, Paris. Poyet, Lyons. M. Renou, Paris. Sam Salz, New York. Mr. and Mrs. Leigh Block, Chicago.

565. After *l'Ecorché*, 1877–80

$8\frac{9}{16} \times 4\frac{7}{8}$ inches—21,7 × 12,4 cm. Page XXVIII verso of the sketchbook A.I.C. Pencil, stains. Verso: No. 435.

Rough study after the plaster cast owned by the artist. See fig. 36. The sketchbook belonging to the Art Institute of Chicago contains nine studies after this little cast: our Nos. 565-73.

BIBLIOGRAPHY: Rewald, *Carnets*: C II, p. XXVIII verso (not reproduced). Berthold, cat. No. 76 (reproduced). Schniewind, text p. 30 (reproduced). Andersen, *Sk.* (not reproduced).

COLLECTIONS: Cézanne *fils*, Paris. M. Renou, Paris. Poyet, Lyons. M. Renou, Paris. Sam Salz, New York. Art Institute, Chicago.

566. After *l'Ecorché*, 1877–80

$8\frac{9}{16} \times 4\frac{7}{8}$ inches—21,7 × 12,4 cm. Page XI of the sketchbook A.I.C. Pencil, stains. Verso: No. 491.

The plaster cast seen front view. See fig. 36. Strokes and hatching are both exceptionally delicate.

BIBLIOGRAPHY: Rewald, *Carnets*: C II, p. XI (not reproduced). Berthold, cat. No. 67 (reproduced Abb. 98). Schniewind, text p. 27 (reproduced). Andersen, *Sk.* (not reproduced).

COLLECTIONS: Cézanne *fils*, Paris. M. Renou, Paris. Poyet, Lyons. M. Renou, Paris. Sam Salz, New York, Art Institute, Chicago.

567. After *l'Ecorché*, 1879–82

$8\frac{9}{16} \times 4\frac{7}{8}$ inches—21,7 × 12,4 cm. Page XXXIIII verso of the sketchbook A.I.C. Pencil, stains. Verso: No. 287.

Study after the plaster cast owned by the artist. See fig. 36. The sketch is little developed but remarkable for the fluidity of the contours.

BIBLIOGRAPHY: Rewald, *Carnets*: C II, p. XXXIIII verso (reproduced pl. 156). Berthold, cat. No. 70 (reproduced Abb. 99). Schniewind, text p. 31 (reproduced). Andersen, *Sk.* (not reproduced).

EXHIBITIONS: Art Institute, Chicago, 1952, and Metropolitan Museum, New York, 1952, No. 90 (reproduced).

COLLECTIONS: Cézanne *fils*, Paris. M. Renou, Paris. Poyet, Lyons. M. Renou, Paris. Sam Salz, New York. Art Institute, Chicago.

568. After *l'Ecorché*, 1879–82

$8\frac{9}{16} \times 4\frac{7}{8}$ inches—21,7 × 12,4 cm. Page XXXIII verso of the sketchbook A.I.C. Pencil, stains. Verso: No. 289.

Study after the plaster cast owned by the artist. See fig. 36.

BIBLIOGRAPHY: Rewald, *Carnets*: C II, p. XXXIII verso (reproduced pl. 158). Berthold, cat. No. 75 (reproduced). Schniewind, text p. 31 (reproduced). Andersen *Sk.* (not reproduced).

COLLECTIONS: Cézanne *fils*, Paris. M. Renou, Paris. Poyet, Lyons. M. Renou, Paris. Sam Salz, New York. Art Institute, Chicago.

569. After *l'Ecorché*, 1879–82

$8\frac{9}{16} \times 4\frac{7}{8}$ inches—21,7 × 12,4 cm. Page XIX of the sketchbook A.I.C. Pencil, stains. Verso: No. 410.

Study, part quite finished, part incomplete, after the plaster cast owned by the artist. See fig. 36. Cf. especially Nos. 566, 570.

BIBLIOGRAPHY: Rewald, *Carnets*: C II, p. XIX (reproduced pl. 159). Berthold, cat. No. 69 (reproduced Abb. 97). Schniewind, text p. 29 (reproduced). Andersen, *Sk.* (not reproduced).

COLLECTIONS: Cézanne *fils*, Paris. M. Renou, Paris. Poyet, Lyons. M. Renou, Paris. Sam Salz, New York. Art Institute, Chicago.

570. After *l'Ecorché* 1879–82

$8\frac{9}{16} \times 4\frac{7}{8}$ inches—21,7 × 12,4 cm. Page XX of the sketchbook A.I.C. Pencil, stains. Verso: No. 772.

Complete study after the plaster cast owned by the artist. See fig. 36. The figure is seen front view. Cf. especially Nos. 566, 569.

BIBLIOGRAPHY: Rewald, *Carnets*: C II, p. XX (reproduced pl. 160). Berthold, cat. No. 68 (reproduced). Schniewind, text p. 29 (reproduced). Andersen, *Sk.* (not reproduced). Th. Rousseau Jr., *Paul Cézanne*, Flammarion, Paris, 1953 (reproduced pl. 3). Idem, Amsterdam, 1954 (reproduced pl. 3). *L'Encyclopédie des Arts illustrée*, Flammarion; Golden Press Inc., New York, 1961 (reproduced No. 438). Idem, Edition des Deux Coqs, Paris, 1964 (reproduced No. 438).

COLLECTIONS: Cézanne *fils*, Paris. M. Renou, Paris. Poyet, Lyons. M. Renou, Paris. Sam Salz, New York. Art Institute, Chicago.

571. After *l'Ecorché*, 1879–82

$8\frac{9}{16} \times 4\frac{7}{8}$ inches—21,7 × 12,4 cm. Page XXIII verso of the sketchbook A.I.C. Pencil, stains. Verso: No. 379.

Study, much worked on, after the plaster cast owned by the artist. See fig. 36. The shadows form magnificent contrasts to the white parts. The movement goes upward on the right, down on the left, and then surges up again toward the head.

BIBLIOGRAPHY: Rewald, *Carnets*: C II, p. XXIII verso (reproduced pl. 157). Berthold, cat. No. 71 (reproduced). Schniewind, text p. 30 (reproduced). Andersen, *Sk.* (not reproduced).

COLLECTIONS: Cézanne *fils*, Paris. M. Renou, Paris. Poyet, Lyons. M. Renou, Paris. Sam Salz, New York. Art Institute, Chicago.

572. After *l'Ecorché*, 1879–82

$8\frac{9}{16} \times 4\frac{7}{8}$ inches—21,7 × 12,4 cm. Page XXXVII verso of the sketchbook A.I.C. Pencil, stains. Verso: No. 617.

Study after the plaster cast owned by the artist. See fig. 36. Firm drawing, with a background of hatching. Subtle contrasts of black, white, and gray.

BIBLIOGRAPHY: Rewald, *Carnets*: C II, p. XXXVII verso (reproduced pl. 154). Berthold, cat. No. 79 (reproduced Abb. 100). Schniewind, text p. 32(reproduced). Andersen, *Sk.* (not reproduced).

COLLECTIONS: Cézanne *fils*, Paris. M. Renou, Paris. Poyet, Lyons. M. Renou, Paris. Sam Salz, New York. Art Institute, Chicago.

573. AFTER *l'Ecorché*, 1879–82
$8\frac{9}{16} \times 4\frac{7}{8}$ inches—21,7 × 12,4 cm. Page XXXVI of the sketchbook A.I.C. Pencil, stains. Verso: No. 416.
Study after the plaster cast owned by the artist. See fig. 36. Cf. especially No. 574.
BIBLIOGRAPHY: Rewald, *Carnets*: C II, p. XXXVI (not reproduced). Berthold, cat. No. 78 (reproduced Abb. 13). Schniewind, text p. 31 (reproduced). Andersen, *Sk.* (not reproduced).
COLLECTIONS: Cézanne *fils*, Paris. M. Renou, Paris. Poyet, Lyons. M. Renou, Paris. Sam Salz, New York. Art Institute, Chicago.

574. AFTER *l'Ecorché*, 1881–84
$7\frac{15}{16} \times 5$ inches—20,2 × 12,7 cm. Page from a sketchbook. Pencil. Verso: blank page.
After the plaster cast owned by the artist. See fig. 36. In the background: vertical surface with horizontal joins, dense hatching. Cf. No. 573.
BIBLIOGRAPHY: Berthold, cat. No. 80 (reproduced).
EXHIBITION: Fine Arts Associates, New York, 1952, No. 3 (reproduced).
COLLECTION: Leonard C. Hanna, Jr., New York.

575. AFTER PUGET: *Hercules resting*, 1872–75
Measurements not known. Pencil. Verso: blank page.
Study after Pierre Puget's marble *Hercules resting* in the Louvre. See figs. 6 and 82. The head of the figure is seen here in left lost profile; this is the only one of the studies known which shows it from this angle.
COLLECTIONS: J. Wyeth, New York. Present owner unknown.

576. AFTER PUGET: *Hercules resting*, circa 1879
$6 \times 9\frac{5}{16}$ inches—15,2 × 23,7 cm. Page XXV of the Album, Paul Mellon Collection. Pencil. Verso: No. 490.
Study after Pierre Puget's marble *Hercules resting*, in the Louvre. See fig. 82. Cf. No. 578.
BIBLIOGRAPHY: Venturi, under No. 1306; by error: "Milon de Crotone" (not reproduced). Berthold, cat. No. 118 (not reproduced). Th. Reff, in *AB*, June 1960 (reproduced fig. 7). *Album*, 1966 (reproduced).
COLLECTIONS: Cézanne *fils*, Paris. Paul Guillaume, Paris. A. Chappuis, Tresserve. Mr. and Mrs. Paul Mellon, Upperville, Va.

577. AFTER PUGET: *Hercules resting*, 1881–84
$5 \times 8\frac{1}{2}$ inches—12,7 × 21,6 cm. Page XLIIII verso from the second sketchbook Mrs. Enid A. Haupt. Pencil. Verso: No. 668.
After Pierre Puget's marble *Hercules resting*, in the Louvre. See fig. 82. Cf. No. 1006.

BIBLIOGRAPHY: Rewald, *Carnets*: C IV, p. XLIIII verso (not reproduced). Berthold, cat. No. 111 (reproduced).
COLLECTIONS: Cézanne *fils*, Paris. M. Renou, Paris. Poyet, Lyons. M. Renou, Paris. Sam Salz, New York. Mrs. Enid A. Haupt, New York.

578. AFTER PUGET: *Hercules resting*, 1884–87
$4\frac{5}{8} \times 7\frac{5}{8}$ inches—11,8 × 19,4 cm. Page IV from the sketchbook CP I. Pencil. Verso: No. 540.
Study after Pierre Puget's marble *Hercules resting*, in the Louvre. See fig. 82. In the lower part of the right background the frame of a door is shown (the marble pedestal is unusually high, the statue having been originally intended for a park).
BIBLIOGRAPHY: Venturi, No. 1268. Berthold, cat. No. 119 (reproduced). J. Rewald, Cézanne au Louvre, *AA*, 1935, p. 287 (drawing and original model reproduced).
COLLECTIONS: Cézanne *fils*, Paris. Paul Guillaume, Paris. A. Chappuis, Tresserve. Private collection, Paris.

579. FIGURE ORNAMENTING A CLOCK, 1877–80
$5\frac{5}{8} \times 4\frac{5}{8}$ inches—14,2 × 11,7 cm. (sight). Pencil on gray paper, small stains. Verso: blank page.
Sketch cut out of a larger page of studies. It shows a decorative figure of a Charles X style clock; the original model has not been identified. Cf. No. 458.

FIG. 82. Pierre Puget (1620–94): *Hercules au repos*, formerly in the park of the Château de Sceaux (1660), now in the Louvre. Musée National du Louvre, *Catalogue des Sculptures* II, 1922, No. 1465.   (*Photograph: R. W. Ratcliffe*)

BIBLIOGRAPHY: Berthold, cat. No. 327 (reproduced). The author is mistaken in saying that this drawing is mentioned by Venturi, Vol. I, "Coll. Pierre Loeb," p. 352, *Oeuvres Inédites*. Venturi's reference is to our No. 582.

COLLECTIONS: Ambroise Vollard, Paris. Private collection, New York.

580. FIGURE ORNAMENTING A CLOCK, 1879–82

$8\frac{9}{16} \times 5$ inches—21,7 × 12,6 cm. Page XXXII verso of the sketchbook Leigh Block. Pencil. Verso: blank page.

Figure of a seated woman resting her elbow against the frame of a mantel clock. After a Charles X style clock: the original model has not been identified. Cf. No. 458.

BIBLIOGRAPHY: Rewald, *Carnets*: C V, p. XXXII verso (reproduced pl. 134). Berthold, cat. No. 326 (reproduced). Th. Reff, in *AB*, June 1960, p. 148, note 34, where he indicates a model which does not seem to me the authentic one.

COLLECTIONS: Cézanne *fils*, Paris. M. Renou, Paris. Poyet, Lyons. M. Renou, Paris. Sam Salz, New York. Mr. and Mrs. Leigh Block, Chicago.

581. FIGURE ORNAMENTING A CLOCK, VIEW OF THE PANTHEON, 1879–82

$8\frac{3}{8} \times 5$ inches—21,8 × 12,6 cm. Page L verso of the sketchbook Leigh Block. Pencil. Verso: No. 511.

(a) Top: head of a woman drawn from a figure ornamenting a clock; cf. No. 458.—(b) View of the Pantheon in Paris seen across the roof tops; cf. Nos. 801, 807. On the right of the dome can be seen the Tour Saint-Jacques du Haut-Pas.—(c) Upside down, handwritten notations: *Cassis/Gâteau de marrons/Bannettes* (a "bannette" is a small basket made of wicker, reed, or wood shavings). Three childish scribbles by the artist's son.

BIBLIOGRAPHY: Rewald, *Carnets*: C V, p. L verso (not reproduced). Berthold, cat. No. 329 (reproduced). Th. Reff, Cézanne's Drawings 1875–85, *BurlM*, May 1959, p. 171 (reproduced fig. 26).

COLLECTIONS: Cézanne *fils*, Paris. M. Renou, Paris. Poyet, Lyons. M. Renou, Paris. Sam Salz, New York. Mr. and Mrs. Leigh Block, Chicago.

582. FIGURE ORNAMENTING CLOCK, 1881–84

$11\frac{13}{16} \times 9\frac{7}{8}$ inches—30 × 25 cm. Pencil. Verso: blank page.

Seated woman leaning her elbow against the frame of a mantel clock; the frame however is not drawn; cf. No. 458. The classicistic treatment might make a later date seem probable, circa 1890 for example. But this is not so.

BIBLIOGRAPHY: Venturi, Vol. I, p. 352, *Oeuvres Inédites* (not reproduced). Berthold, reference (inexact) under cat. No. 327.

EXHIBITION: San Francisco, 1937, No. 58.

COLLECTIONS: Pierre Loeb, Paris. J. Wyeth, New York. Present owner unknown.

583. FIGURE ORNAMENTING A CLOCK, 1881–84

$7\frac{3}{16} \times 4\frac{9}{16}$ inches—18,2 × 11,6 cm. Page 6 verso from the first sketchbook Mrs. Enid A. Haupt. Pencil. Verso: No. 483.

Head and forearm of a woman, after a figure decorating a mantel clock; the original model has not been identified. Cf. No. 458.

BIBLIOGRAPHY: Rewald, *Carnets*: C I, p. 6 verso (not reproduced); error in the reference to Venturi: read 1449 for 1446. Berthold, cat. No. 330 (reproduced). *Dessins*, 1957, No. 9 (reproduced).

COLLECTIONS: Cézanne *fils*, Paris. M. Renou, Paris. Poyet, Lyons. M. Renou, Paris. Sam Salz, New York. Mrs. Enid A. Haupt.

584. AFTER THE ANTIQUE: *The Lycian Apollo*, 1881–84

$8\frac{1}{4} \times 4\frac{3}{4}$ inches—20,9 × 12,1 cm. Page LII from the sketchbook BS II. Pencil. Verso: No. 667.

Standing man, drawn from the knee up, with one hand resting on his head. After the marble known as *The Lycian Apollo* in the Louvre. See fig. 83.

BIBLIOGRAPHY: Venturi, No. 1396. Berthold, cat. No. 43 (reproduced). Basel catalog, No. 107 (reproduced).

COLLECTIONS: Cézanne *fils*, Paris. Paul Guillaume, Paris. W. Feuz, Bern. Kunstmuseum, Basel.

585. AFTER G. PILON: *The Three Graces*, 1881–84

$18\frac{11}{16} \times 12$ inches—47,5 × 30,6 cm. Pencil heightened with white, brown stains; on laid paper with the watermark MBM. Verso: blank page.

Study after a monument comprising three female figures standing back to back: *The Three Graces* by Germain Pilon, part of the funeral monument of King Henri II, marble now in the Louvre. See fig. 84. Cf. Nos. 672, 1112, 1113. This drawing differs from the others in its measurements and in the white highlights on the inner parts, added with the intention of imitating marble. The result is a wooly appearance, surprising from Cézanne.

COLLECTIONS: Pierre Loeb, Paris. H. Gomès, Paris. M. Bousquet, Paris. H. Gomès, Paris.

586. AFTER THE ANTIQUE: *The Borghese Mars*, 1879–82

$12\frac{3}{16} \times 9\frac{1}{4}$ inches—31 × 23,5 cm. Pencil on laid paper. Verso: blank page.

After *Ares*, known as *The Borghese Mars*, antique marble in the Louvre; the figure is seen in right profile. See fig. 85. Cf. Nos. 587, 588.

BIBLIOGRAPHY: Berthold, cat. No. 7 (reproduced).

COLLECTIONS: Private collection, Paris. Present owner unknown.

587. AFTER THE ANTIQUE: *The Borghese Mars*, 1879–82

$8\frac{1}{2} \times 5$ inches—21,6 × 12,7 cm. Page VIII from the second sketchbook Mrs. Enid A. Haupt. Pencil. Verso: No. 225.

After *Ares*, known as *The Borghese Mars*, antique marble in the Louvre. See fig. 85.

FIG. 83. *The Lycian Apollo,* antique replica of an original of the School of Praxiteles; marble in the Louvre. Musée National du Louvre, *Catalogue sommaire des Marbres antiques,* 1922, No. 928. The province of Lycia in Asia Minor was distinguished by its cult of Apollo. There is a sanctuary in the ancient town of Patara. *(Photograph: R. W. Ratcliffe)*

BIBLIOGRAPHY: Rewald, *Carnets:* C IV, p. VIII (reproduced pl. 120). Berthold, cat. No. 8 (reproduced).

COLLECTIONS: Cézanne *fils,* Paris. M. Renou, Paris. Poyet, Lyons. M. Renou, Paris. Sam Salz, New York. Mrs. Enid A. Haupt, New York.

588. AFTER THE ANTIQUE: *The Borghese Mars,* 1881–84
$8\frac{1}{4} \times 4\frac{13}{16}$ inches—20,9 × 12,2 cm. Page XLII verso from the sketchbook BS II. Pencil. Verso: No. 1009.

After *Ares,* known as *The Borghese Mars,* antique marble in the Louvre. See fig. 85. Cf. No. 586.

BIBLIOGRAPHY: Venturi No. 1379. Berthold, cat. No. 6 (reproduced). Basel catalog, No. 159 (reproduced).

COLLECTIONS: Cézanne *fils,* Paris. Paul Guillaume, Paris. W. Feuz, Bern. Kunstmuseum, Basel.

FIG. 84. Germain Pilon (about 1535–90): *Les Trois Grâces* from the mausoleum containing the heart of Henri II, in the Louvre. The figures were hewn from a single block of marble; height: 1,50 m. Work commissioned by Catherine de' Medici in 1559; conserved in Les Celestins until 1792, then in the Musée des Petits-Augustins, it entered the Louvre in 1916. Musée National du Louvre, *Catalogue des Sculptures* I, 1922, No. 413. *(Photograph: R. W. Ratcliffe)*

FIG. 85. *Ares*, known also as the *Borghese Mars*, antique replica of a statue dating from the fifth century B.C. attributed to Alcamenes. Marble in the Louvre with a mechanism which allows it to be turned on its pedestal. As shown in right profile, the curve of the back is seen in an unusual way because the left elbow appears above the buttocks. The elbow has been consolidated with plaster; the hands are restored in marble. Musée National du Louvre, *Catalogue sommaire des Marbres antiques*, 1922, No. 866. (*Photograph: R. W. Ratcliffe*)

589. AFTER MICHELANGELO: *Slave*, 1881–84

$10\frac{3}{4} \times 8\frac{5}{16}$ inches—27,3 × 21,1 cm. Page LXXVI from the sketchbook CP IV. Pencil. Verso: No. 1166.

After Michelangelo's marble in the Louvre. See fig. 42. Cf. Nos. 303, 590, 679.

BIBLIOGRAPHY: Venturi No. 1319. Berthold, cat. 60 (reproduced Abb. 116). J. Rewald, Cézanne au Louvre, *AA*, 1935, p. 284 (reproduced). Elie Faure, *Cézanne*, Collection des Maîtres, Braun, Paris 1936 (reproduced fig. 60). *Dessins*, 1957, No. 48 (reproduced).

COLLECTIONS: Cézanne *fils*, Paris. Paul Guillaume, Paris. A. Chappuis, Tresserve. Private collection, Paris. Private collection, New York.

590. AFTER MICHELANGELO: *Slave*, 1883–86

$7\frac{5}{8} \times 4\frac{5}{8}$ inches—19,4 × 11,8 cm. Page XLVIII from the sketchbook CP I. Pencil. Verso: No. 665.

After Michelangelo's marble in the Louvre. See fig. 42.

BIBLIOGRAPHY: Venturi No. 1279. Berthold, cat. No. 59 (reproduced Abb. 115). Mentioned by Rewald in *A.A.*, 1935, p. 288, note 14.

EXHIBITIONS: Orangerie, Paris, 1936, No. 162 (error: Venturi No. 1280; the Album Braun reproduction, fig. 60, on the right, is cited incorrectly). San Francisco, 1937, No. 60. Wildenstein, London, 1939, No. 84. Aix-en-Provence, 1961, No. 59.

COLLECTIONS: Cézanne *fils*, Paris. Paul Guillaume, Paris. A. Chappuis, Tresserve.

591. AFTER COYSEVOX: *Faun playing the transverse flute*, 1883–86

$16\frac{1}{4} \times 12\frac{1}{4}$ inches—41,2 × 31,2 cm. Pencil on laid paper. Verso: blank page.

After the marble by Charles-Antoine Coysevox in the Louvre. See fig. 86. Cf. No. 592.

BIBLIOGRAPHY: Swiss review *DU*, November 1959, where the original model was identified (reproduced). Berthold, cat. No. 149 (reproduced).

EXHIBITIONS: Galerie A. Flechtheim, Berlin, 1929, No. 33. Kunsthalle, Basel, 1936, No. 129. Lucerne, 1940, Hauptwerke der Sammlung Hahnloser, Winterthur, No. 165 (reproduced).

COLLECTIONS: Simon Meller, Budapest. A. Hahnloser, Winterthur. H. R. Hahnloser, Bern.

FIG. 86. Charles-Antoine Coysevox (1640–1720): *Faune jouant de la flûte traversière* (1709), marble in the Louvre. Height: 1,84 m. Musée National du Louvre, *Catalogue des Sculptures* II, 1922, No. 1119. *Adonis* (see fig. 160) is a pendant to this figure. The two were commissioned for a grove at Marly. In the Louvre since 1870, formerly in the Tuileries Gardens.

(Photograph: Giraudon)

592. AFTER COYSEVOX: *Faun playing the transverse flute,* 1887–90

$7\frac{3}{16} \times 4\frac{9}{16}$ inches—18,2 × 11,6 cm. Page 18 from the first sketchbook Mrs. Enid A. Haupt. Pencil. Verso: No. 944.

After the marble by Charles-Antoine Coysevox in the Louvre. See fig. 86. The faun's fingers are spread out on the flute, which traces a diagonal on the page. One could imagine it to be a sketch from life. Another copy: No. 591.

BIBLIOGRAPHY: Rewald, *Carnets:* C I, p. 18 (not reproduced). Berthold, cat. No. 149, indicates the original (reproduced).

COLLECTIONS: Cézanne *fils*, Paris. M. Renou, Paris. Poyet, Lyons. M. Renou, Paris. Sam Salz, New York. Mrs. Enid A. Haupt, New York.

593. AFTER RUBENS: ALLEGORICAL FIGURE REPRE-SENTING HEALTH, 1880–83

$8\frac{9}{16} \times 5$ inches—21,7 × 12,6 cm. Page XXXI verso of the sketchbook Leigh Block. Pencil. Verso: blank page.

Standing man draped in a loincloth with a woman laying a newborn baby in his arms. Indications of wings on the man's back and of a snake coiling round his hips. After the allegorical figure of Health in Rubens' painting *The Birth of Louis XIII* in the Medici Gallery of the Louvre. It

is sometimes called *Aesculapius*. See fig. 155. Other copies by Cézanne: Nos. 594, 595, 1130.

BIBLIOGRAPHY: Rewald, *Carnets:* C V, p. XXXI verso (reproduced pl. 139). Berthold, cat. No. 220; error: p. XXXIV instead of XXXI (reproduced). Th. Reff, in *AB*, June 1960, p. 145, note 2.

COLLECTIONS: Cézanne *fils*, Paris. M. Renou, Paris. Poyet, Lyons. M. Renou, Paris. Sam Salz, New York. Mr. and Mrs. Leigh Block, Chicago.

594. AFTER RUBENS: ALLEGORICAL FIGURE REPRE-SENTING HEALTH, 1880–83

$7\frac{3}{16} \times 4\frac{9}{16}$ inches—18,2 × 11,6 cm. Page 14 verso from the first sketchbook Mrs. Enid A. Haupt. Pencil. Verso: No. 597.

Standing man, after the figure representing Health (also Aesculapius) in Rubens' painting *The Birth of Louis XIII* in the Louvre. See fig. 155: the spirit of Health receiving the newborn baby in his arms.

BIBLIOGRAPHY: Rewald, *Carnets:* C I, p. 14 verso (reproduced pl. 138). Berthold, cat. No. 219, "Esculape" (reproduced).

COLLECTIONS: Cézanne *fils*, Paris. M. Renou, Paris. Poyet, Lyons. M. Renou, Paris. Sam Salz, New York. Mrs. Enid A. Haupt, New York.

595. AFTER RUBENS: ALLEGORICAL FIGURE REPRE-SENTING HEALTH, 1882–85

$9\frac{5}{16} \times 6$ inches—23,7 × 15,2 cm. Page XIII verso of the Album, Paul Mellon Collection. Pencil. Verso: No. 1189.

Unfinished sketch of the allegorical figure in Rubens' painting *The Birth of Louis XIII* in the Louvre. See fig. 155.

BIBLIOGRAPHY: Venturi, Vol. I, under No. 1304 (not reproduced). Berthold, cat. No. 221 (not reproduced). *Album*, 1966 (reproduced).

COLLECTIONS: Cézanne *fils*, Paris. Paul Guillaume, Paris. A. Chappuis, Tresserve. Mr. and Mrs. Paul Mellon, Upperville, Va.

596. AFTER RUBENS: ALLEGORICAL FIGURE REPRE-SENTING FRANCE, 1882–85

$9\frac{5}{16} \times 6$ inches—23,7 × 15,2 cm. Page XXVI of the Album, Paul Mellon Collection. Pencil heightened with ink. Verso: No. 1024.

Helmeted and armed figure personifying France, making a gesture of welcome. After Rubens' painting *The Exchange of the Two Princesses*, in the Louvre (fig. 87); cf. No. 597. Cézanne obtains a graphic effect by the play of the gray pencil strokes and black India ink against the white of the paper. We may suppose that he drew in pencil from the painting in the museum and heightened the sketch afterwards.

BIBLIOGRAPHY: Venturi, No. 1308. Berthold, cat. No. 222 (reproduced). *Album*, 1966 (reproduced).

COLLECTIONS: Cézanne *fils*, Paris. Paul Guillaume, Paris. A. Chappuis, Tresserve. Mr. and Mrs. Paul Mellon, Upperville, Va.

FIG. 87. Peter Paul Rubens (1577–1640): Allegorical figure of *La France*, detail from *L'Echange des Princesses à Hendaye*, painting (1615) in the Medici series in the Louvre. Musée National du Louvre, *Catalogue des Peintures* III, 1922, No. 2098.
(*Photograph: Giraudon*)

597. AFTER RUBENS: FIGURE REPRESENTING FRANCE, 1882–85

$7\frac{3}{16} \times 4\frac{9}{16}$ inches—18,2 × 11,6 cm. Page 14 from the first sketchbook Mrs. Enid A. Haupt. Pencil. Verso: No. 594.

After the allegorical figure of France in Rubens' painting *Exchange of the Two Princesses*, in the Louvre. See fig. 87. This figure was studied twice by Cézanne; see No. 596.

BIBLIOGRAPHY: Rewald, *Carnets*: C I, p. 14 (reproduced pl. 136). Berthold, cat. No. 223 (reproduced).

COLLECTIONS: Cézanne *fils*, Paris. M, Renou, Paris. Poyet, Lyons. M. Renou, Paris. Sam Salz, New York. Mrs. Enid A. Haupt, New York.

598. AFTER RUBENS: BELLONA, 1883–86

$9\frac{5}{16} \times 6$ inches—23,7 × 15,2 cm. Page L verso of the Album, Paul Mellon Collection. Pencil. Verso: blank page.

After the allegorical figure of Bellona in Rubens' painting *The Apotheosis of King Henri IV*, in the Louvre (fig. 9).

BIBLIOGRAPHY: Venturi, No. 1314. Berthold, cat. No. 205

(reproduced). B. Dorival, 1948 (reproduced pl. XVI); described erroneously as belonging to the Louvre and having figured in the Kunsthalle Exhibition, Basel, 1936. *Album*, 1966 (reproduced).

COLLECTIONS: Cézanne *fils*, Paris. Paul Guillaume, Paris. A. Chappuis, Tresserve. Mr. and Mrs. Paul Mellon, Upperville, Va.

599. AFTER THE ANTIQUE: *The Roman Orator*, 1883–86

$9\frac{5}{16} \times 6$ inches—23,7 × 15,2 cm. Page XLIX verso of the Album, Paul Mellon Collection. Pencil. Verso: No. 889.

Head, shoulders, and raised hand of the figure known as *The Roman Orator* (or *Germanicus*), marble in the Louvre. See fig. 88. Cf. No. 993.

FIG. 88. *L'Orateur romain*, or *Germanicus*. Roman nobleman representing Hermes, protector of Eloquence; known also as *Mercure orateur*. Marble from Paros (40–30 B.C.) signed Cleomenes, in the Louvre. The thumb and index finger of the left hand are restored. Statue discovered in the Villa Montalto-Negroni, Rome, and later placed in the long gallery of Versailles. Height: 1,95 m. Musée National du Louvre, *Catalogue sommaire des Marbres antiques*, 1922, No. 2207. (See fig. 59 for back view.)
(*Photograph: R. W. Ratcliffe*)

BIBLIOGRAPHY: Venturi, Vol. I, under No. 1313. Berthold, cat. No. 30 (not reproduced). Th. Reff, *AB*, June 1960 (reproduced). *Album*, 1966 (reproduced).

COLLECTIONS: Cézanne *fils*, Paris. Paul Guillaume, Paris. A. Chappuis, Tresserve. Mr. and Mrs. Paul Mellon, Upperville, Va.

600. HEAD, AFTER A BUST, 1883–86

$7\frac{3}{16} \times 4\frac{9}{16}$ inches—18,2 × 11,6 cm. Page 23 from the first sketchbook Mrs. Enid A. Haupt. Pencil. Verso: No. 558.

Oval head seen in left three-quarter view. The face is young and the hair, parted in the middle, falls down to the nape of the neck.

BIBLIOGRAPHY: Rewald, *Carnets:* C I, p. 23 "tête de femme; d'après un buste?" (not reproduced). Berthold, cat. No. 202 (reproduced), designates as probable model the bust of Racine, by L. S. Boizot, in the Comédie Française, Paris. Th. Reff, in *AB*, June 1960, p. 147 suggests a bust of Orbiana in the Louvre; see Bernoulli, *Die Bildnisse der Römischen Kaiser*, Stuttgart, 1882, II, 3, pl. XXXIa.

COLLECTIONS: Cézanne *fils*, Paris. M. Renou, Paris. Poyet, Lyons. M. Renou, Paris. Sam Salz, New York. Mrs. Enid A. Haupt, New York.

601. AFTER POLLAIUOLO: *Young Florentine*, 1883–86

$8\frac{1}{4} \times 5\frac{1}{8}$ inches—21 × 13 cm. Page I from the sketchbook BS I. Pencil. Verso: blank page.

FIG. 90. *Diane chasseresse*, or *Diane de Versailles*, antique replica of a work dating from the end of the fourth century B.C. Marble in the Louvre. Musée National du Louvre, *Catalogue sommaire des Marbres antiques*, 1922, No. 589. A marble replica ornaments the Luxembourg Gardens.

(Photograph: Musées nationaux)

The expression on the face denotes both vanity and character. Drawn after a plaster cast formerly in the Trocadéro, now in the Faculté des Lettres of Lyons. The original *Bust of a Young Florentine* by Antonio del Pollaiuolo is in Florence. See fig. 89.

BIBLIOGRAPHY: Venturi No. 1323. Berthold, cat. No. 88 (reproduced). Longstreet, 1964 (reproduced).

EXHIBITIONS: Zurich, 1956, No. 189. Munich, 1956, No. 145.

COLLECTIONS: Cézanne *fils*, Paris. Paul Guillaume, Paris. W. Feuz, Bern. Carl Roesch, Diessenhofen.

602. AFTER THE ANTIQUE: *Diana the Huntress*, 1882–85

$7\frac{5}{8} \times 4\frac{5}{8}$ inches—19,4 × 11,8 cm. Page XVI from the sketchbook CP I. Pencil. Verso: No. 603.

After a replica of *The Diana of Versailles*, also known as *Diana the Huntress*, or *Diana and the Doe*, marble in the Louvre. See fig. 90. Cézanne seems to have drawn from the replica in the Luxembourg Gardens in Paris. Cf. No. 603.

BIBLIOGRAPHY: Venturi No. 1272. Berthold, cat. No. 28 (reproduced Abb. 111). J. Rewald, Cézanne au Louvre, *AA*, Oct. 1935, reference p. 288.

FIG. 89. Antonio del Pollaiuolo (1429–98): *Young Florentine*, detail of bust in the National Museum (Bargello), Florence. The original is reproduced here in left three-quarter view since it was not possible to procure a more adequate photograph. Cézanne drew after a plaster cast: *Catalogue Général du Musée de Sculpture comparée du Trocadéro* III, 1928, No. I, 161. The cast was on exhibition from 1880 on, but today is lost.

(Photograph: Alinari-Giraudon)

COLLECTIONS: Cézanne *fils*, Paris. Paul Guillaume, Paris. A. Chappuis, Tresserve. Sale, Maître M. Rheims, Palais Galliera, Paris, March 23, 1965, No. 12 (not reproduced). Present owner unknown.

603. AFTER THE ANTIQUE: *Diana the huntress*, 1882–85

$7\frac{5}{8} \times 4\frac{5}{8}$ inches—19,4 × 11,8 cm. Page XVI verso from the sketchbook CP I. Pencil. Verso: No. 602.

After a replica of *The Diana of Versailles*, also known as *Diana the Huntress* or *Diana and the Doe*, marble in the Louvre. See fig. 90.

BIBLIOGRAPHY: Venturi No. 1273. Berthold, cat. No. 29 (reproduced). J. Rewald, *Cézanne au Louvre, AA*, Oct. 1935, reference p. 288.

COLLECTIONS: Cézanne *fils*, Paris. Paul Guillaume, Paris. A. Chappuis, Tresserve. Sale, Maître M. Rheims, Palais Galliera, Paris, March 23, 1965, No. 12 (reproduced).

604. AFTER THE ANTIQUE: *Diana the Huntress*, 1882–85

$7\frac{5}{8} \times 4\frac{5}{8}$ inches—19,4 × 11,8 cm. Page XV from the sketchbook CP I. Pencil. Verso: No. 967.

After a replica of *The Diana of Versailles*, also known as *Diana the Huntress* or *Diana and the Doe*, marble in the Louvre. See fig. 90. The drawing shows trees and a branch, from which I deduce that it was done from the replica in the Luxembourg Gardens in Paris. Cézanne has accentuated the dynamism of the statue.

BIBLIOGRAPHY: Venturi No. 1271. Berthold, cat. No. 27 (reproduced Abb. 110). J. Rewald, *Cézanne au Louvre, AA*, Oct. 1935, reference p. 288.

EXHIBITIONS: Lyons, 1939, No. 60. Wildenstein, London, 1939, No. 80.

COLLECTIONS: Cézanne *fils*, Paris. Paul Guillaume, Paris. A. Chappuis, Tresserve.

605. AFTER P. JULIEN: *The Nymph Amalthaea*, 1882–85

$8\frac{1}{4} \times 4\frac{13}{16}$ inches—20,9 × 12,2 cm. Page XLVIII verso from the sketchbook BS II. Pencil. Verso: No. 1013.

After Pierre Julien's *The Nymph Amalthaea*. See fig. 91. During Cézanne's lifetime this marble was in the Louvre, now it again decorates a fountain at the Château de Rambouillet, its original destination.

BIBLIOGRAPHY: Venturi No. 1389. Berthold, cat. No. 165 (reproduced). Basel catalog, No. 108 (reproduced).

COLLECTIONS: Cézanne *fils*, Paris. Paul Guillaume, Paris. W. Feuz, Bern. Kunstmuseum, Basel.

606. AFTER MURILLO: *Beggar Boy*, 1882–85

$7\frac{5}{8} \times 4\frac{5}{8}$ inches—19,4 × 11,8 cm. Page V from the sketchbook CP I. Pencil. Verso: blank page.

(a) Sketch after the painting *A Beggar Boy* by Bartolomé Estebán Murillo, in the Louvre. See fig. 92. Cf. the watercolor Venturi No. 866.—(b) Above: lightly-drawn sketch of the boy's head. Charles Blanc reproduced Murillo's canvas in his *Ecole Espagnole*, but Cézanne drew from the original.

BIBLIOGRAPHY: Venturi No. 1269. Berthold, cat. No. 274 (reproduced Abb. 113). J. Rewald, *Cézanne au Louvre, AA*, 1935, p. 288, reference note 4.

EXHIBITION: Orangerie, Paris, 1936, No. 159.

COLLECTIONS: Cézanne *fils*, Paris. Paul Guillaume, Paris. A. Chappuis, Tresserve. Private collection, Paris.

607. AFTER THE ANTIQUE: *Marsyas*, 1882–85

$7\frac{3}{16} \times 4\frac{9}{16}$ inches—18,2 × 11,6 cm. Page 34 verso from the first sketchbook Mrs. Enid A. Haupt. Pencil. Verso: blank page.

FIG. 91. Pierre Julien (1731–1804): *Nymphe Amalthée avec la chèvre*. Our photograph shows a plaster cast in the Musée de Sculpture comparée of the Trocadéro, Paris. Destined to be placed near the pool filled from a spring at the Château de Rambouillet, the original marble is now in the castle dairy. Height: 1,74 m.; exhibited in the Salon of 1791. In Cézanne's day this marble was in the Louvre. Musée National du Louvre, *Catalogue des Sculptures* II, 1922, No. 1388. Concerning the mythological subject: Zeus as a newborn babe is secretly committed to the care of the nymph Amalthea, who brings him up on the milk of her goat (for this reason goats are sometimes given the name of Amalthea). It was from the horn of this excellent wet-nurse that Zeus was later to create the horn of Abundance. *(Photograph: R. W. Ratcliffe)*

FIG. 92. Bartolomé Esteban Murillo (1618–82): *A Beggar Boy*, canvas in the Louvre. Musée National du Louvre, *Catalogue des Peintures* II, 1926, No. 1717. *(Photograph: Giraudon)*

After the antique marble representing *Marsyas,* in the Louvre. The background is indicated on the left by parallel hatching.

BIBLIOGRAPHY: Rewald, *Carnets:* C I, p. 34 verso (not reproduced). Berthold, cat. No. 46 (reproduced).

COLLECTIONS: Cézanne *fils,* Paris. M. Renou, Paris. Poyet, Lyons. M. Renou, Paris. Sam Salz, New York. Mrs. Enid A. Haupt, New York.

608. LANDSCAPE AT THE JAS DE BOUFFAN, AND PORTRAIT OF A YOUNG MAN, 1882–85

$5 \times 8\frac{9}{16}$ inches—12,6 × 21,7 cm. Page XVI from the CP II (not page XVI from the sketchbook Leigh Block, same measurements, which is not missing). Pencil. Stamp of F. Koenigs collection. Verso: the watercolor Venturi No. 870.

(a) Landscape: outbuildings of the Jas de Bouffan; cf. Nos. 737, 880, 916, and Venturi Nos. 462, 463.—(b) Head of a young man wearing a beret, after a reproduction of the painting in the Louvre formerly designated as a *Self-Portrait* by Raphael, now attributed to Bacchiacca; cf. the same subject, No. 272 and fig. 40. Cézanne may have seen the reproduction printed in *Le Magasin Pittoresque* of 1845, p. 9, but the artist's two drawings resemble each other more than they resemble this print, or indeed the painting in the Louvre.—(c) Page upright: rough sketch of a head.

BIBLIOGRAPHY: Venturi, Vol. I, mentioned as the verso of No. 870 (not reproduced). H. R. Hoetink, *Franse Tekeningen uit de 19e Eeuw,* Rotterdam, 1968, No. 29 verso, dates: (a) circa 1885, (b) circa 1882 (reproduced).

COLLECTIONS: Cézanne *fils,* Paris. P. Cassirer. F. Koenigs,

Haarlem. Boymans-van Beuningen Museum, Rotterdam (Inv. F II 211).

609. HEAD OF A YOUNG WOMAN, circa 1880

$9\frac{5}{16} \times 6$ inches—23,7 × 15,2 cm. Page XI verso of the Album, Paul Mellon Collection. Pencil. Verso: rough sketch of the nape of a neck, not classified in our catalog but reproduced in the Album, 1966, p. XI.

Head of a young woman with the light falling from the right, a round collar around the base of the neck. The eyes are small and look straight at the viewer. It is rare to be confronted with such youth and charm in a Cézanne portrait. Cf. No. 273. With regard to the date: in the Album, 1966, I dated this drawing 1890–95; here I date it circa 1880 and must give my reasons. The former date had in fact never entirely satisfied me: compared with other portraits drawn between 1890 and 1900, this head, in spite of its attraction, lacks presence and volume. It seems to me that cohesion is achieved here by static rather than dynamic graphism: the oval of the face, the circle of the collar, the symmetry. In the years following 1890 the artist no longer attained unity in this way. A drawing of 1890–1900 is felt immediately as a whole, the volume evoked is alive, present; at the same time the image creates no illusion but remains surface-and-pencil stroke, inimitable in its clarity. In this domain it is, alas! most difficult to prove what each individual must feel on looking at it and to discriminate between impressions. Anne van Buren, in her article, Madame Cézanne's Fashions and the Dates of her Portraits (*The Art Quarterly,* Vol. XXIX, No. 2, 1966), dates certain works according to the fashion chronicles of the period. For all the portraits of women wearing round collars she proposes 1886 as the earliest date. The study is mainly concerned with the oil portraits of Mme Cézanne and presupposes that for dress she followed the Paris fashion magazines. But this drawing shows a country girl, not a young lady of Paris, and she could well be wearing a linen waist or a round-collared bodice cut according to regional custom. Although this drawing is not cited in the article, I must assume that Anne van Buren would date it 1886–88.

BIBLIOGRAPHY: Venturi, Vol. I, under No. 1304 (not reproduced). *Dessins,* 1938 (reproduced pl. 26). *The Studio,* London, March 1939 (reproduced). *Album,* 1966, dated 1890–95 (reproduced).

COLLECTIONS: Cézanne *fils,* Paris. Paul Guillaume, Paris. A. Chappuis, Tresserve. Mr. and Mrs. Paul Mellon, Upperville, Va.

610. SELF-PORTRAIT, circa 1880

$11\frac{15}{16} \times 8\frac{1}{16}$ inches—30,4 × 20,5 cm. Pencil on gray-brown laid paper, small tear restored, small brown stain. Verso: No. 350.

(a) Self-portrait of the artist, his head turned slightly to the right, shoulders and collar indicated.—(b) Below, at right angles: sketch of a woman's head leaning forward and covered by a sort of veil; cf. Nos. 417 (a), 485, 544 (c). Formerly this portrait and the watercolor Venturi No. 844 were together on one sheet.

BIBLIOGRAPHY: Venturi No. 1478. Vollard, 1914 (reproduced p. 171). Basel catalog, No. 93 (reproduced).

EXHIBITIONS: The Hague, 1956, No. 115. Zurich, 1956, No. 175.

COLLECTIONS: Cézanne *fils*, Paris. W. Feuz, Bern. Kunstmuseum, Basel.

611. SELF-PORTRAIT, circa 1880

$11\frac{13}{16} \times 9\frac{7}{8}$ inches—30 × 25 cm. Pencil, paper renewed upper left above the ear. Verso: No. 789.

This fine portrait shows the artist in right three-quarter view; the ear protrudes rather more than in other portraits. His look is optimistic, confident. Formerly there were light sketches in blue crayon on the page, near the chest; traces can still be seen on the reproduction in Meier-Graefe's *Cézanne und seine Ahnen*, 1921.

BIBLIOGRAPHY: Venturi No. 1237. Meier-Graefe, *Cézanne und seine Ahnen*, Munich, 1921, No. VII (reproduced). *Le Dessin français au XIXe siècle*, Mermod, Lausanne, 1948 (reproduced p. 100). Genthon, Istvan, *Cézanne*, Budapest, 1964 (reproduced as frontispiece). Longstreet, 1964 (reproduced).

EXHIBITION: De Majovsky, Budapest, 1935, No. 76.

COLLECTIONS: De Majovsky, Budapest. Museum of Fine Arts, Budapest.

612. SELF-PORTRAIT, circa 1880

$13 \times 10\frac{3}{4}$ inches—33 × 27,3 cm. Pencil on laid paper. Verso: blank page.

The artist himself, looking at the viewer.

BIBLIOGRAPHY: J. Rewald, Paul Cézanne, New Documents for the Year 1870–71, *BurlM*, April 1939, p. 167. Idem, *Cézanne*, Paris, 1939 (reproduced fig. 31). Idem, *Letters*, London, 1941 (reproduced pl. 20). Idem, *Paul Cézanne*, New York, 1948 (reproduced pl. 39). Idem, *The Ordeal of Paul Cézanne*, London, 1950 (reproduced pl. 27). *Paul Cézanne*, Spring Books, London 1959 and 1965 (reproduced fig. 27).

EXHIBITIONS: Masterpieces of Drawing, Philadelphia Museum of Art, 1950–51, No. 103 (reproduced). Cézanne, Art Institute of Chicago, and Metropolitan Museum of Art, New York, 1952, No. 40 (reproduced). Cinquantenaire de la mort de Cézanne, Pavillon de Vendôme, Aix-en-Provence, 1956, No. 88 (reproduced). De Clouet à Matisse, Musée de l'Orangerie, Paris, 1958–59, No. 150 (reproduced).

COLLECTIONS: Ambroise Vollard, Paris. Reid & Lefevre, London. Walter C. Baker, New York.

613. SELF-PORTRAIT, circa 1880

$18\frac{1}{2} \times 12\frac{3}{16}$ inches—47 × 31 cm. Page cut out of a sheet of studies. Pencil. Verso: No. 1183.

Portrait of the artist; the play of light down the cheek on the left produces an unusual contour. Seen from a distance this portrait seems suggestive of a painting.

COLLECTIONS: Jaufret, Aix-en-Provence. Private collection, Paris. Private collection, Switzerland.

614. SELF-PORTRAIT, 1880–82

$8\frac{5}{8} \times 4\frac{7}{8}$ inches—21,8 × 12,4 cm. Page XL from the sketchbook CP II. Pencil. Verso: No. 411.

Head of Cézanne, almost bald, the eyes looking straight at the viewer; study for the portrait Venturi No. 367. There is extraordinary intensity in this drawing.

BIBLIOGRAPHY: Venturi, No. 1293. J. Rewald, Un épisode inconnu de la vie de Cézanne, *Marianne*, Oct. 20, 1937 (reproduced p. 8). Idem (in German), *Neue Zürcher Zeitung*, Feb. 6, 1938. *L'Oeuvre*, Paris, Jan. 8, 1939 (reproduced). *Dessins*, 1938, No. 1 (reproduced). *Dessins*, 1957, No. 30 (reproduced). H. Perruchot, *La vie de Cézanne*, Paris, 1958 (reproduced p. 398). *Correspondance de Cézanne*, edited by Rewald, translated into Japanese by Chuji Ikegami, Tokyo, 1967 (reproduced on the first page).

COLLECTIONS: Cézanne *fils*, Paris. Paul Guillaume, Paris. A. Chappuis, Tresserve. Private collection, Paris. Private collection, New York.

615. SELF-PORTRAIT, AND PORTRAIT OF THE ARTIST'S SON, 1880–82

$8\frac{9}{16} \times 4\frac{7}{8}$ inches—21,7 × 12,4 cm. Page XXI of the sketchbook A.I.C. Pencil, stains. Verso: No. 549.

(a) Page upright: head of Cézanne, detailed drawing. The expression is calm but enigmatic, the look extraordinary. —(b) Page lengthwise: head and shoulder of the young Paul; his hair is longer here than in other portraits.

BIBLIOGRAPHY: Rewald, *Carnets:* C II, p. XXI (reproduced pl. 3). Schniewind, text p. 29 (reproduced). Andersen, *Sk.* (not reproduced).

COLLECTIONS: Cézanne *fils*, Paris. M. Renou, Paris. Poyet, Lyons. M. Renou, Paris. Sam Salz, New York. Art Institute, Chicago.

616. SELF-PORTRAIT, 1882–83

$8\frac{9}{16} \times 4\frac{15}{16}$ inches—21,7 × 12,5 cm. Page XVII from the sketchbook CP II. Pencil. Verso: No. 364.

Head and shoulders of the artist in an open-necked shirt; his look, directed at the viewer, is calm.

BIBLIOGRAPHY: Venturi No. 1287. Vollard, 1914 (reproduced p. 54).

EXHIBITIONS: Meisterwerke aus Frankreichs Museen, Albertina, Vienna, 1950, No. 251, Francouzské Umění, Prague, 1956, No. 64 (reproduced). Aix-en-Provence, 1961, No. 52. Phillips Collection, Washington, D.C., Chicago, Boston, 1971, No. 71 (reproduced).

COLLECTIONS: Cézanne *fils*, Paris. Paul Guillaume, Paris. A. Chappuis, Tresserve.

617. SELF-PORTRAIT, circa 1883

$8\frac{9}{16} \times 4\frac{7}{8}$ inches—21,7 × 12,4 cm. Page XXXVII of the sketchbook A.I.C. Pencil, stains. Verso: No. 572.

On that day Cézanne was suffering from a stye on his eye, which is what gives his look such a very human expression of distress. For this reason the drawing is often reproduced.

BIBLIOGRAPHY: Rewald, *Carnets:* C II, p. XXXVII (reproduced pl. 1). Schniewind, text p. 32 (reproduced; reproduction also on the cardboard case). Meyer Schapiro, *Paul Cézanne*, New York, 1952 (reproduced p. 18). Th. Rousseau Jr., *Paul Cézanne*, Paris, 1953 (reproduced pl. 1). Idem, Amsterdam, 1954 (reproduced pl. 1). A. Neumeyer, 1958, No. 33 (reproduced). Yvon Taillandier, *Paul Cézanne*, Paris, New York, Munich, 1961 and 1965 (reproduced p. 78). Basil Taylor, *Cézanne*, London, 1961 (reproduced as frontispiece). J. Leymarie, *Dessins de la Période impressionniste*, Skira, Geneva, 1969 (reproduced p. 86).

COLLECTIONS: Cézanne *fils*, Paris. M. Renou, Paris. Poyet, Lyons. M. Renou, Paris. Sam Salz, New York. Art Institute, Chicago.

618. SELF-PORTRAIT, circa 1883

$8\frac{9}{16} \times 4\frac{7}{8}$ inches—21,7 × 12,4 cm. Page VII verso of the sketchbook A.I.C. Pencil, stains. Verso: No. 740.

One of the five self-portraits in the Art Institute of Chicago sketchbook. The artist looks at the viewer with a rather skeptical expression. The zones of light and the curved hatching are noteworthy.

BIBLIOGRAPHY: Rewald, *Carnets:* C II, p. VII verso (reproduced pl. 2). Schniewind, text p. 26 (reproduced). A. Neumeyer, 1958, No. 32 (reproduced). Andersen, *Sk.* (not reproduced).

COLLECTIONS: Cézanne *fils*, Paris. M. Renou, Paris. Poyet, Lyons. M. Renou, Paris. Sam Salz, New York. Art Institute, Chicago.

619. AFTER A DELACROIX SELF-PORTRAIT, 1882–85

$11\frac{7}{16} \times 7\frac{1}{2}$ inches—29 × 19 cm. Pencil on laid paper. Verso: blank page.

Head and shoulders of Eugène Delacroix in left three-quarter view, after Delacroix's oil self-portrait in the Louvre. See fig. 93.

BIBLIOGRAPHY: Venturi No. 1623; in error, Venturi refers

FIG. 93. Eugène Delacroix (1799–1863): *Portrait de l'artiste* (detail), painting in the Louvre. Musée National du Louvre, *Catalogue des Peintures* I, 1924, No. 214. Jenny Le Guillou bequest, 1872.   (*Photograph: Giraudon*)

to this drawing once again among the Oeuvres Inédites as belonging to the Basel Museum; see Venturi, Vol. I, p. 352. Berthold cat. No. 238 (reproduced). Sara Lichtenstein. An unpublished Portrait of Delacroix and some Figure Sketches by Cézanne, *Master Drawings*, Vol. 4, No. 1, 1966 (reproduced p. 41).

EXHIBITIONS: Kunsthalle, Basel, 1936, No. 164. Zurich, 1956, No. 170.

COLLECTIONS: Cézanne *fils*, Paris. R. von Hirsch, Basel.

620. SELF-PORTRAIT, BUSTS, 1882–85

$5 \times 8\frac{9}{16}$ inches—12,6 × 21,7 cm. Page XIV verso of the sketchbook Leigh Block. Pencil. Verso: No. 643.

(a) Portrait of the artist; the expression of perplexed scrutiny on the face is unusual. The painterly effects of the pencil strokes in the shadow on the shoulder are noteworthy.—(b) Left, at right angles: sketches of two busts. The first, in right profile, represents an old bearded sailor; the second, seen front view, shows a stern face, cut in half by the edge of the page. They look like plaster casts in an overcrowded exhibition hall; the original models have not been identified.

BIBLIOGRAPHY: Rewald, *Carnets:* C V, p. XIV verso (reproduced pl. 13). Berthold, cat. No. 322 ((b) only reproduced).

COLLECTIONS: Cézanne *fils*, Paris. M. Renou, Paris. Poyet, Lyons. M. Renou, Paris. Sam Salz, New York. Mr. and Mrs. Leigh Block, Chicago.

621. HEAD AND SHOULDERS OF A BEARDED MAN, 1881–84

$8\frac{9}{16} \times 4\frac{15}{16}$ inches—21,7 × 12,5 cm. Page XI verso from the sketchbook CP II. Pencil. Verso: No. 621A.

The man's eyelids are lowered and his right hand is on a table (note the foreshortening of the thumb). In the left background is a piece of furniture with a flat top, and on it a scroll-like object, seen in perspective. In other words: a cylinder; the oval volume of the head of which only the right side is irregular; and in addition a triangle under the chin and triangular nose. Seen from a distance, the diagonals of the drawing dominate. A concern for expressing volume on a flat surface is more evident than usual.—Th. Reff considers this to be a portrait of Emile Zola. It seems to me that this sketch and our No. 622 show two different people.

BIBLIOGRAPHY: Venturi, Vol. I, under No. 1284 (not reproduced); "même personnage qu'à la page X." (Page X is our No. 622). *Dessins*, 1938, No. 40 (reproduced). Th. Reff, Cézanne's Drawings 1875–85, *BurlM*, May 1959, p. 176 (reproduced fig. 28) "Portrait of Zola."

COLLECTIONS: Cézanne *fils*, Paris. Paul Guillaume, Paris. A. Chappuis, Tresserve. O. Wertheimer, Paris. Knoedler & Co., New York. Private collection, New York.

621A. ARMCHAIR

Pencil. Verso of No. 621. (Not reproduced.)

Rapid sketch of an armchair, with heavy proportions and rectangular lines.

BIBLIOGRAPHY: Venturi, Vol. I, under No. 1284, "Page XI. Grand fauteuil, vu de profil" (not reproduced).

622. EMILE ZOLA READING, 1881–84

$8\frac{9}{16} \times 4\frac{15}{16}$ inches—21,7 × 12,5 cm. Page X from the sketchbook CP II. Pencil. Verso: No. 732.

Half-length study of a bearded man sitting at a writing table, his eyelids lowered and one hand on the table. Th. Reff thinks that the drawing represents Emile Zola reading or studying, and this seems probable. Cf. No. 624.

BIBLIOGRAPHY: Venturi, Vol. I, under No. 1284 (not reproduced). *Dessins*, 1938, No. 38 (reproduced). Th. Reff, Cézanne's Drawings 1875–85, *BurlM*, May 1959, p. 176. Jean Adhémar, Le Cabinet de Travail de Zola, *GBA*, July 1960, p. 285.

EXHIBITION: Orangerie, Paris, 1936, No. 163.

COLLECTIONS: Cézanne *fils*, Paris. Paul Guillaume, Paris. A. Chappuis, Tresserve. Private collection, Paris.

623. SKETCH OF A HEAD (FRAGMENT), 1881–84

$4\frac{3}{4}$ ($5\frac{1}{2}$ at the point of the tear) $\times 4\frac{15}{16}$ inches—12 (13,9) × 12,5 cm. Page XIII verso from the sketchbook CP II. Pencil on a torn page. Verso: No. 310.

Head of a man seen full face, the head tilted to the right; only part of the drawing, showing the lower part of the face, remains. Traces of gum.

COLLECTIONS: Cézanne *fils*, Paris. Paul Guillaume, Paris. A. Chappuis, Tresserve.

624. PORTRAITS OF EMILE ZOLA, 1882–85

$8\frac{9}{16} \times 5$ inches—21,7 × 12,6 cm. Page XV of the sketchbook Leigh Block. Pencil. Verso: No. 645.

(a) Top: Emile Zola sitting at a writing table, his head bent over his left hand on the table in front of him.—(b) Below: same subject, but without the hand; the head is rounder and the expression different. Cf. No. 622.

BIBLIOGRAPHY: Rewald, *Carnets*: C V, p. 53 (reproduced pl. 12). Th. Rousseau Jr., *Paul Cézanne*, Paris, 1953, and Amsterdam, 1954 (reproduced pl. 36).

COLLECTIONS: Cézanne *fils*, Paris. M. Renou, Paris. Poyet, Lyons. M. Renou, Paris. Sam Salz, New York. Mr. and Mrs. Leigh Block, Chicago.

625. EMILE ZOLA, HEAD AND SHOULDERS OF A MAN, BATHER, 1882–85

$5 \times 8\frac{9}{16}$ inches—12,6 × 21,7 cm. Page XVI verso of the sketchbook Leigh Block. Pencil. Verso: No. 551.

(a) Left: portrait of Emile Zola in profile (behind his head there is an unfinished rough sketch); cf. No. 624.—(b) Head and shoulders of a dignitary wearing a wig, copied from an unidentified monument; cf. No. 626 and the watercolor Venturi No. 870.—(c) Lower right: male figure of the type *Bather with his Hands on his Hips*: rapid sketch with elements of a landscape (this is the latest in date of the drawings on this page); cf. Nos. 946, 947.

BIBLIOGRAPHY: Rewalds, *Carnets*: C V, p. XVI verso (not reproduced). Berthold, cat. No. 318 (reproduced).

COLLECTIONS: Cézanne *fils*, Paris. M. Renou, Paris. Poyet, Lyons. M. Renou, Paris. Sam Salz, New York. Mr. and Mrs. Leigh Block, Chicago.

626. PERSONAGE IN A WIG, SKETCH OF A MAN READING, 1883–86

$8\frac{9}{16} \times 5$ inches—21,7 × 12,6 cm. Page XIII verso of the sketchbook Leigh Block. Pencil. Verso: No. 550.

(a) Below: dignitary wearing a wig, seen front view, his hands joined; copy after an unidentified monument. Cf. the same subject No. 625, and the watercolor Venturi No. 870 (on another page of this same sketchbook), which shows the full-length figure.—(b) Above: incomplete sketch in foreshortening of a man sitting on a bed or divan. His left foot is crossed over his right leg in the foreground, while further back his bent right arm holds a book or magazine that screens his head; cf. the similar subjects No. 382 (c), 663, 690, 855.

BIBLIOGRAPHY: Rewald, *Carnets*: C V, p. XIII verso (reproduced pl. 32). Berthold, cat. No. 305 (reproduced). R. Cogniat, Paris, 1967 (reproduced p. 36).

COLLECTIONS: Cézanne *fils*, Paris. M. Renou, Paris. Poyet, Lyons. M. Renou, Paris. Sam Salz, New York. Mr. and Mrs. Leigh Block, Chicago.

627. AFTER RUBENS: BELLONA, 1883–86

$6\frac{1}{2} \times 4\frac{9}{16}$ inches—16,5 × 11,6 cm. Page 13 verso from the first sketchbook Mrs. Enid A. Haupt. Pencil. Verso: No. 627A.

After the allegorical figure of Bellona, goddess of War, in Rubens' painting *The Apotheosis of King Henri IV* in the Louvre. See fig. 9. Of the ten known copies of this figure, this is one of the finest. Cf. No. 490.

BIBLIOGRAPHY: Rewald, *Carnets*: C I, p. 13 verso (not reproduced). Berthold, cat. No. 207 "figure of Victory" (reproduced).

EXHIBITIONS: New York, 1952, No. 4 (reproduced). Aix-en-Provence, Nice, Grenoble, 1953, No. 38. Los Angeles, No. 15. Wildenstein Galleries, New York, 1959, No. 62.

COLLECTIONS: Cézanne *fils*, Paris. M. Renou, Paris. Poyet, Lyons. M. Renou, Paris. J. Rewald, New York. Sale, Sotheby's, London, 1960. Private collection, England. Mr. and Mrs. E. V. Thaw, Scarborough, New York.

627A. SEATED BATHER

Pencil. Verso of No. 627. (Not reproduced.)

BIBLIOGRAPHY: Rewald, *Carnets*: C I, p. 13 (not reproduced): "Croquis de baigneur assis, correspondant au personnage de gauche dans Venturi Nos. 580, 581, 902 et 1114."

628. SKETCH OF A HEAD, 1883–86

$4\frac{9}{16} \times 7\frac{3}{16}$ inches—11,6 × 18,2 cm. Page 22 from the first sketchbook Mrs. Enid A. Haupt. Pencil. Verso: No. 977.

Head of a woman or young man, tilted forward; indications of a round collar. This study has something more than the charm of an unfinished sketch.—Impossible to say whether it is a copy or not.

BIBLIOGRAPHY: Rewald, *Carnets*: C I, p. 22 (not reproduced).

COLLECTIONS: Cézanne *fils*, Paris. M. Renou, Paris. Poyet, Lyons. M. Renou, Paris. Sam Salz, New York. Mrs. Enid A. Haupt, New York.

629. BATHER, CANISTER, AND HANDWRITTEN NOTATIONS, 1883–86

$8\frac{1}{16} \times 5$ inches—20,5 × 12,6 cm. Page XXX from the sketchbook BS III. Pencil, blue crayon, pen with black and violet inks, watercolor. Dab of oil color, other stains. Verso: copy of a letter (see Basel catalog No. 167).

(a) Bather seen front view (pencil, ink, watercolor); cf. the bather in the background of the canvas Venturi No. 582.—(b) Above and at right angles: a round canister with lid and on it a little bread loaf (pen, with violet ink). —(c) Notations: *chez Marie*. In blue crayon and with no relation to the preceding: *A demain donc, ce n'est qu'un plaisir différé—et le désir s'accroît quand l'effet se recule*. The second part of this sentence is a quotation from Pierre Corneille (*Polyeucte* I, 1, verse 42). Cézanne had known the citation since his adolescence; students and artists give it an obscene double meaning by linking the last syllables. Addition sum, in pencil.

BIBLIOGRAPHY: Venturi No. 1436. Basel catalog, No. 133 (reproduced).

COLLECTIONS: Cézanne *fils*, Paris. Paul Guillaume, Paris. W. Feuz, Bern. Kunstmuseum, Basel.

630. BATHER WITH OUTSTRETCHED ARMS, 1883–86

$8\frac{9}{16} \times 4\frac{15}{16}$ inches—21,7 × 12,5 cm. Page IX verso from the sketchbook CP II. Pencil. Verso: No. 794.

Young man standing on a little promontory at the water's edge; retouches to one foot. In the right background: a cliff with towers on the heights. The bather's outstretched arms form a diagonal downward to the right.

BIBLIOGRAPHY: Venturi, Vol. I, under No. 1284 (not reproduced). *Dessins*, 1957, No. 23 (reproduced). Th. Reff, *Bather*, p. 188, note 13.

EXHIBITIONS: Meisterwerke aus Frankreichs Museen, Albertina, Vienna, 1950, No. 248. Prague, 1956, No. 63. Aix-en-Provence, 1961, No. 56.

COLLECTIONS: Cézanne *fils*, Paris. Paul Guillaume, Paris. A. Chappuis, Tresserve. Private collection, Paris.

631. BATHERS, CARYATID, 1883–86

$4\frac{7}{8} \times 8\frac{5}{8}$ inches—12,4 × 21,8 cm. Page L verso from the sketchbook CP II. Pencil. Verso: No. 348.

(a) Left: bather with outstretched arms; no indication of landscape.—(b) At right angles, in light strokes: sketch of a caryatid after the engraving by Marcantonio Raimondi; see fig. 65. Cf. No. 481, the upper part only of the figure.—(c) Study of the left leg of (a), on a larger scale.— (d) Right: a nude bather with outstretched arms in a seascape near L'Estaque, showing the Château d'If.

BIBLIOGRAPHY: Venturi, Vol. I, under No. 1299 (not reproduced). Th. Reff, *Bather*, p. 181 (reproduced fig. 8).

COLLECTIONS: Cézanne *fils*, Paris. Paul Guillaume, Paris. A. Chappuis, Tresserve.

632. STILL LIFE, 1881–84

$13\frac{3}{4} \times 9\frac{3}{4}$ inches—34,9 × 24,8 cm. Pencil on laid paper. Verso: blank page.

Study for the painting Venturi No. 498. From left to right: a round dish with a few cherries, a vase, and a plate with fruit, its rim covered on the right by the folds of a napkin; all grouped together on a table of which the far edge is horizontal. Another plate is roughly indicated in the near foreground.

BIBLIOGRAPHY: Venturi No. 1491. Meier-Graefe, Cézanne und seine Ahnen, Mappe der Marées-Gesellschaft, Munich, 1921 (reproduced only in the first French and in the English editions).

EXHIBITION: Galerie Alfred Flechtheim, Berlin, 1927, No. 47.

COLLECTIONS: Hugo Perls, Berlin. Knoedler and Co., New York.

633. TWO BOTTLES ON A TABLE, 1881–84

$8\frac{9}{16} \times 5\frac{3}{16}$ inches—21,7 × 13,1 cm. Page from a sketchbook (BS I ?). Pencil on white paper. Verso: a watercolor not classified by Venturi.

The table edges are indicated and also a light cast shadow. Still life apparently simple but revealing rich discoveries in perspective.

COLLECTION: Kenneth Clark, London.

634. AFTER THE ANTIQUE: *Venus of Milo*, 1880–83

$18\frac{11}{16} \times 11$ inches—47,5 × 28 cm. Pencil. Verso: blank page.

The Venus of Milo, marble in the Louvre. See figs. 45, 46. We know nine studies of this statue by Cézanne, this one being the largest.

BIBLIOGRAPHY: Berthold, cat. No. 16 (reproduced). J. Rewald, *Paul Cézanne*, New York, 1948 (reproduced pl. 96).

EXHIBITION: Rétrospective du Centenaire, Paris, 1939, No. 43.

COLLECTIONS: Mrs. Jean Douglas, London. Curt Valentin, New York. Jacques Lipchitz, Hastings-on-Hudson, N.Y.

635. AFTER THE ANTIQUE: *Venus of Milo*, 1881–84

$9\frac{5}{16} \times 6$ inches—23,7 × 15,2 cm. Page LII verso of the Album, Paul Mellon Collection. Pencil. Verso: No. 546.

After the marble statue in the Louvre. See fig. 45, 46.

BIBLIOGRAPHY: Venturi No. 1315. Berthold, cat. No. 11 (reproduced Abb. 112). *Album*, 1966 (reproduced).

EXHIBITIONS: Meisterwerke aus Frankreichs Museen, Albertina, Vienna, 1950, No. 254. Francouzské Umění, Prague, 1956, No. 66.

COLLECTIONS: Cézanne *fils*, Paris. Paul Guillaume, Paris. A. Chappuis, Tresserve. Mr. and Mrs. Paul Mellon, Upperville, Va.

636. AFTER THE ANTIQUE: *Venus of Milo*, 1883–86

$7\frac{3}{16} \times 4\frac{9}{16}$ inches—18,2 × 11,6 cm. Page 27 verso from the first sketchbook Mrs. Enid A. Haupt. Pencil. Verso: blank page.

After *The Venus of Milo*, antique marble in the Louvre. See figs. 45, 46. The face is crossed out.

BIBLIOGRAPHY: Rewald, *Carnets*: C I, p. 27 verso (not reproduced). (p. 27 recto: blank page). Berthold, cat. No. 15 (reproduced).

COLLECTIONS: Cézanne *fils,* Paris. M. Renou, Paris. Poyet, Lyons. M. Renou, Paris. Sam Salz, New York. Mrs. Enid A. Haupt, New York.

637. AFTER THE ANTIQUE: *Venus of Milo,* 1883–86

$10\frac{5}{8} \times 9\frac{1}{16}$ (formerly $12\frac{3}{16} \times 10\frac{1}{4}$) inches—27 × 23 cm. (31 × 26 cm.). Pencil. Verso: blank page.

After the antique marble in the Louvre. See figs. 45, 46. Since the statue is not seen from below, we must conclude that Cézanne did this sketch from a plaster cast.

BIBLIOGRAPHY: Venturi, Vol. I, p. 352, Oeuvres Inédites, (not reproduced). Berthold, cat. No. 14 (reproduced). *Correspondance* (reproduced fig. 38). Jedlicka, *Paul Cézanne, Briefe,* Zurich, 1962 (reproduced).

EXHIBITIONS: Paul Cassirer, Berlin, 1921. Belvedere, Vienna, 1961, No. 101. Aix-en-Provence, 1961, No. 46.

COLLECTIONS: J. Meier-Graefe, Berlin. Leo von König, Berlin. Pierre Loeb, Paris. Stuttgarter Kunstkabinett Ketterer, 32. Auktion 1958, No. 146 (reproduced). Galerie Würthle, Vienna. Sale, Kornfeld & Klipstein, Bern, June 13, 1968, No. 139 (reproduced). Kunsthalle, Bremen (Inv. 68/374).

638. AFTER THOMAS COUTURE: HALF-LENGTH SKETCH OF A WOMAN, 1883–86

$7\frac{3}{16} \times 4\frac{9}{16}$ inches—18,2 × 11,6 cm. Page removed from the first sketchbook Mrs. Enid A. Haupt. Soft pencil on white paper. Verso: the watercolor Venturi No. 850.

Study after the nude figure in the upper center of Thomas Couture's painting *The Romans of the Decadence,* in the Louvre. See fig. 94. On the left, opposite the face: the contour of a vase that also figures in the painting. Cf. No. 639, another copy of the same subject.

BIBLIOGRAPHY: Wayne V. Andersen, A Cézanne Drawing after Couture, *Master Drawings,* Vol. I, No. 4, 1963, pp. 44-46.

COLLECTION: Kenneth Clark, London.

639. TWO SKETCHES: WOMEN, 1883–86

$7\frac{5}{8} \times 4\frac{5}{8}$ inches—19,4 × 11,8 cm. Page II from the sketchbook CP I. Pencil. Verso: blank page.

FIG. 94. Thomas Couture (1815–79): *Romains de la Décadence* (1847), painting in the Louvre.
(Photograph: Archives photographiques, Paris)

(a) Head and shoulders of a woman, her head leaning forward; after Thomas Couture's painting *The Romans of the Decadence* in the Louvre. See fig. 94. Cf. No. 638. Below: woman seen in left three-quarter view, carrying something in her arms. Probably copied from some unidentified source.

BIBLIOGRAPHY: Venturi, Vol. I, p. 304, under No. 1266 (not reproduced).

COLLECTIONS: Cézanne *fils,* Paris. Paul Guillaume, Paris. A. Chappuis, Tresserve. R. W. Ratcliffe, London.

640. MAN WITH A LARGE HEAD, 1883–86

$9\frac{5}{16} \times 6$ inches—23,7 × 15,2 cm. Page XXXIIII verso of the Album, Paul Mellon Collection. Pencil. Verso: blank page.

Youngish man, his head bent forward to the left. On the right the folds of a garment leave his neck bare to its base. Cf. No. 865. This is a fine drawing but its interpretation remains obscure. Possibly a copy.

BIBLIOGRAPHY: Venturi, Vol. I, under No. 1309. Berthold, cat. No. 271 (not reproduced); the author alludes to Caravaggio's *Narcissus,* but in spite of quite striking analogies, this supposition does not seem convincing. *Album,* 1966 (reproduced).

COLLECTIONS: Cézanne *fils,* Paris. Paul Guillaume, Paris. A. Chappuis, Tresserve. Mr. and Mrs. Paul Mellon, Upperville, Va.

641. WOMEN SITTING IN A PARK, 1883–86

$5 \times 8\frac{9}{16}$ inches—12,7 × 21,7 cm. Page XXVIII from the second sketchbook Mrs. Enid A. Haupt. Pencil. Verso: No. 556.

Left: sitting on a bench and seen in perspective, two women under a parasol, one holding a baby on her knees. Further back, a baby-carriage and on the right two more seated women.

BIBLIOGRAPHY: Rewald, *Carnets:* C IV, p. XXVIII (reproduced pl. 86). *Dessins,* 1957, No. 12 (reproduced).

COLLECTIONS: Cézanne *fils,* Paris. M. Renou, Paris. Poyet, Lyons. M. Renou, Paris. Sam Salz, New York. Mrs. Enid A. Haupt, New York.

642. ENTRANCE TO ZOLA'S HOUSE IN MÉDAN, 1883–85

$16\frac{3}{4} \times 11\frac{3}{8}$ inches—42,5 × 28,8 cm. Pencil on laid paper. Verso: blank page.

Left: the branches of an oleander. In the background: a garden chair in front of the wall of a small roofed outbuilding. Right: steps with iron balustrades leading up to the house entrance and a little balcony on either side of the door, which is not visible.

BIBLIOGRAPHY: *Correspondance:* "L'entrée du jardin de la première maison de Zola à Médan" (reproduced fig. 34).

COLLECTIONS: Kenneth Clark, London. William Walton, England. Sale, London, March 3, 1939, "Entrée de Jardin." Hortense Anda-Bührle, St. Anton, Vorarlberg.

643. FLOWER STAND WITH PLANT, 1882–85

$5 \times 8\frac{9}{16}$ inches—12,6 × 21,7 cm. Page XIV of the sketchbook Leigh Block. Pencil. Verso: No. 620.

Unfinished sketch of an indoor flowerpot receptacle with a metal stem; indications of a fan-shaped plant. No. 644 does not represent the same object.

BIBLIOGRAPHY: Rewald, *Carnets:* C V, p. XIV (not reproduced).

COLLECTIONS: Cézanne *fils*, Paris. M. Renou, Paris. Poyet, Lyons. M. Renou, Paris. Sam Salz, New York. Mr. and Mrs. Leigh Block, Chicago.

644. PLANTS IN A FLOWER STAND, 1882–85

$8\frac{9}{16} \times 5$ inches—21,7 × 12,6 cm. Page XII verso of the sketchbook Leigh Block. Pencil. Verso: No. 779.

Upright plants and spreading palm leaves in a round flower stand with decorative volutes and a metal stem; a fine, detailed drawing. Cf. No. 643. Rewald thinks that Cézanne did this drawing at Zola's house in Médan, which seems likely. "Fifty-seven vases, porcelain jars, and flower stands" figured in the Zola sale, 1903. See Note 53.

BIBLIOGRAPHY: Rewald, *Carnets:* C V, p. XII verso (reproduced pl. 68).

COLLECTIONS: Cézanne *fils*, Paris. M. Renou, Paris. Poyet, Lyons. M. Renou, Paris. Sam Salz, New York. Mr. and Mrs. Leigh Block, Chicago.

645. FLOWERS IN A VASE, 1883–86

$8\frac{9}{16} \times 5$ inches—21,7 × 12,6 cm. Page XV verso of the sketchbook Leigh Block. Pencil. Verso: No. 624.

Vase shaped like a bottle with no neck, filled with two or three roses and their leaves; cast shadow at its base, and further back a second shadow from a half-hidden object. Cf. No. 646.

BIBLIOGRAPHY: Rewald, *Carnets:* C V, p. XV verso (reproduced pl. 71).

COLLECTIONS: Cézanne *fils*, Paris. M. Renou, Paris. Poyet, Lyons. M. Renou, Paris. Sam Salz, New York. Mr. and Mrs. Leigh Block, Chicago.

646. ROSES IN A VASE, 1883–86

$11\frac{1}{2} \times 8$ inches—29,2 × 20,3 cm. Pencil. Verso: No. 786.

Vase shaped like a bottle with no neck; on the right a light cast shadow. Cf. No. 645 and the watercolor Venturi No. 1542. It is a good drawing but it diffuses a curious sensation of boredom.

BIBLIOGRAPHY: Venturi No. 1492.

EXHIBITIONS: Paul Cassirer, London, 1939, No. 6. Phillips Collection, Washington, D.C., Chicago, Boston, 1971, No. 72 (reproduced).

COLLECTIONS: Cézanne *fils*, Paris. Galerie Quatre-Chemins, Paris. Private collection, Holland. Mr. and Mrs. Leigh Block, Chicago.

647. STUDY OF FLOWERS, 1883–86

$4\frac{7}{8} \times 8\frac{9}{16}$ inches—12,4 × 21,7 cm. Page XXXII of the sketchbook A.I.C. Pencil, stains. Verso: No. 901.

This study of flowers spreading over the whole page like an arabesque unfortunately remains confused in spite of the luxuriant plant life portrayed.

BIBLIOGRAPHY: Rewald, *Carnets:* C II, p. XXXII (not reproduced). Schniewind, text p. 31 (reproduced). Andersen, *Sk.* (not reproduced).

COLLECTIONS: Cézanne *fils*, Paris. M. Renou, Paris. Poyet, Lyons. M. Renou, Paris. Sam Salz, New York. Art Institute, Chicago.

648. FLOWER WITH FOLIAGE, 1883–86

$18\frac{7}{8} \times 12\frac{3}{8}$ inches—48 × 31,5 cm. Pencil on laid paper with the watermark: MRM; a few stains and flyspecks. Verso: No. 478.

This drawing was perhaps done as a preliminary sketch for a watercolor. It represents a hydrangea flower partly hidden by its leaves, the contours obtained by several juxtaposed strokes. Cf. the watercolor Venturi No. 1100, a similar subject.

COLLECTIONS: Mouradian & Vallotton, Paris. Kelekian, Paris. Sale, Hôtel Drouot, Paris, Maître M. Rheims, Nov. 22, 1968, No. 96 (not reproduced). Present owner unknown.

649. FIVE WOMEN BATHERS, 1883–86

$5 \times 8\frac{9}{16}$ inches—12,7 × 21,7 cm. Page XXXV from the second sketchbook Mrs. Enid A. Haupt. Pencil. Verso: No. 991.

Five women bathers in a rapidly sketched landscape; the central figure is the only one whose face is shown. The composition has the rhythmic quality of a frieze. All five attitudes correspond to one or another of those frequent in Cézanne's work.

BIBLIOGRAPHY: Venturi, No. 1255. Vollard, 1914 (reproduced p. 65). Rewald, *Carnets:* C IV, p. XXXV (reproduced pl. 96). *Dessins*, 1957, No. 36 (reproduced).

COLLECTIONS: Cézanne *fils*, Paris. M. Renou, Paris. Poyet, Lyons. M. Renou, Paris. Sam Salz, New York. Mrs. Enid A. Haupt, New York.

650. WOMEN BATHERS IN A LANDSCAPE, 1883–86

$5 \times 8\frac{1}{2}$ inches—12,7 × 21,6 cm. Page XXXVII from the second sketchbook Mrs. Enid A. Haupt. Pencil. Verso: No. 1041.

Two seated women bathers, a third standing, and on the left, the leg and arm of a fourth. Landscape of bushes and trees with a stream flowing across the middle ground. Retouches, mainly to the thigh of the figure on the left. Successful, important drawing.

BIBLIOGRAPHY: Venturi No. 1249. Vollard, 1914 (reproduced p. 67). Rewald, *Carnets:* C IV, p. XXXVII (reproduced pl. 97). Th. Rousseau, *Paul Cézanne*, Paris, 1953 (reproduced pl. 37). Idem, Amsterdam, 1954 (reproduced pl. 37). *Dessins*, 1957, No. 40 (reproduced); error in the note. Yvon Taillandier, *Paul Cézanne*, 1965 (reproduced p. 47).

COLLECTIONS: Cézanne *fils*, Paris. M. Renou, Paris. Poyet, Lyons. M. Renou, Paris. Sam Salz, New York. Mrs. Enid A. Haupt, New York.

651. PAGE OF STUDIES, INCLUDING WOMEN BATHERS: ROLL OF PAPER, 1882–85; BATHERS, 1894–99

$6 \times 9\frac{5}{16}$ inches—15,2 × 23,7 cm. Page XXIII of the Album, Paul Mellon Collection. Pencil. Verso: No. 847.

(a) Right: rapid sketch of two women bathers and a tree. —(b) Left: unfinished sketch of an object that seems to be a roll of paper lying on a table.

BIBLIOGRAPHY: Venturi, Vol. I, under No. 1306 "esquisse de deux baigneurs" (not reproduced). *Album*, 1966 (reproduced).

COLLECTIONS: Cézanne *fils*, Paris. Paul Guillaume, Paris. A. Chappuis, Tresserve. Mr. and Mrs. Paul Mellon, Upperville, Va.

652. MALE NUDE WITH HIS ARM RAISED, 1882–85

$8\frac{1}{4} \times 4\frac{3}{4}$ inches—21×12 cm. Page XXXVI from the sketchbook BS II. Pencil. Verso: blank page.

Half-length study of a model with his one visible arm stretched up high in front of him to grip a cord. Indications of some ill-defined objects in the background.

BIBLIOGRAPHY: Venturi No. 1371. Berthold, cat. No. 307 (reproduced); the author thinks it is probably a copy. Basel catalog, No. 142 (reproduced).

COLLECTIONS: Cézanne *fils*, Paris. Paul Guillaume, Paris. W. Feuz, Bern. Kunstmuseum, Basel.

653. MAN IN A BOWLER HAT, 1882–85

$8\frac{9}{16} \times 5$ inches—$21,7 \times 12,6$ cm. Page XLIV of the sketchbook Leigh Block. Pencil. Verso: No. 760.

Young man in a jacket with two buttons at the back, standing. Numerous strokes from the knee down denote successive renderings. The identity of the model is not known; the date of execution precludes the idea of its being the artist's son.

BIBLIOGRAPHY: Rewald, *Carnets*: C V, p. XLIV (reproduced pl. 37).

COLLECTIONS: Cézanne *fils*, Paris. M. Renou, Paris. Poyet, Lyons. M. Renou, Paris. Sam Salz, New York. Mr. and Mrs. Leigh Block, Chicago.

654. PAGE OF STUDIES, INCLUDING A BATHER WITH OUTSTRETCHED ARMS, 1883–86

$8\frac{5}{8} \times 4\frac{7}{8}$ inches—$21,8 \times 12,4$ cm. Page XLII from the sketchbook CP II. Pencil. Verso: No. 835.

(a) Below: young bather in a seascape.—(b) Above and at right angles: half-length sketch of a fully-clothed man with his arm raised. Perhaps a preliminary study for the watercolors Venturi Nos. 875, 876.

BIBLIOGRAPHY: Venturi No. 1294. Th. Reff, *Bather*, p. 188, note 13.

EXHIBITION: Les 30 ans de la Galerie Max Kaganovitch, Paris, 1966, No. 16 (reproduced).

COLLECTIONS: Cézanne *fils*, Paris. Paul Guillaume, Paris. A. Chappuis, Tresserve. Sale, Maître M. Rheims, Palais Galliera, Paris, March 23, 1965, No. 15 (not reproduced). Private collection, Paris. Sale, Galerie Motte, Geneva, June 12, 1970, No. 33 (reproduced).

655. FIGURE SEEN FROM THE BACK, 1883–86

$8\frac{5}{8} \times 4\frac{7}{8}$ inches—$21,8 \times 12,4$ cm. Page XLIV from the sketchbook CP II. Pencil. Verso: No. 520.

Top: rapid half-length sketch of a figure, seen from the back, wearing a garment with vertical stripes. Beside it

the notation 43 *chez Vollard* written in blue crayon, probably by Cézanne *fils*. The fragment of page 43 (XLIII) remaining attached shows that it bore a watercolor, but it has not been identified.

BIBLIOGRAPHY: Venturi, Vol. I, under No. 1294 (not reproduced).

COLLECTIONS: Cézanne *fils*, Paris. Paul Guillaume, Paris. A. Chappuis, Tresserve.

656. HEAD OF LOUIS GUILLAUME, 1883–86

$8\frac{9}{16} \times 4\frac{7}{8}$ inches—$21,7 \times 12,4$ cm. Page VIII of the sketchbook A.I.C. Pencil, stains. Verso: a child's scribbles.

Portrait of Louis Guillaume, friend of the artist's son. Cf. the painting Venturi No. 374 and our No. 940: Louis Guillaume in Pierrot costume.

BIBLIOGRAPHY: Rewald, *Carnets*: C II, p. VIII (not reproduced). Schniewind, text p. 26 (reproduced). Andersen, *Sk.* (not reproduced).

COLLECTIONS: Cézanne *fils*, Paris. M. Renou, Paris. Poyet, Lyons. M. Renou, Paris. Sam Salz, New York. Art Institute, Chicago.

657. STUDY OF SPANISH DANCERS, 1883–86

$6 \times 9\frac{5}{16}$ inches—$15,2 \times 23,7$ cm. Page XXVIII verso of the Album, Paul Mellon Collection. Pencil. Verso: No. 658.

(a) Right: a woman dancing, seen front view; vivid movement of the arms, legs, and skirt.—(b) Left: study of a male dancer jumping onto one foot as though running toward the left. Next to the dancer is a rough repetition of figure (a), the two figures together forming a couple.—It is possible that these sketches are copies.

BIBLIOGRAPHY: Venturi, Vol. I, under No. 1309: "deux Bacchantes dansant furieusement" (not reproduced). *Album*, 1966 (reproduced).

COLLECTIONS: Cézanne *fils*, Paris. Paul Guillaume, Paris. A. Chappuis, Tresserve. Mr. and Mrs. Paul Mellon, Upperville, Va.

658. TWO STUDIES FOR *The Judgment of Paris* OR *The Amorous Shepherd*, 1883–86

$6 \times 9\frac{5}{16}$ inches—$15,2 \times 23,7$ cm. Page XXVIII of the Album, Paul Mellon Collection. Pencil. Verso: No. 657.

(a) Left, framed by strokes: a sketch, with retouches, of four women, two of them stretching out their arms to the right while the other two are walking in that direction.—(b) Right: three nude women, two of them crouching back to back while the third, standing behind them, welcomes Paris, who is lightly sketched in on the right. The trunk of a tree on the far left covers the buttocks of an unfinished figure and its branches curve over the group.—Neither (a) nor (b) corresponds exactly to the composition Venturi No. 537 nor to our drawing No. 659.

BIBLIOGRAPHY: Venturi, Vol. I, under No. 1309 (not reproduced). Th. Reff, Cézanne and Hercules, *AB*, Vol. XLVIII, p. 38 et sqq. (reproduced fig. 7). *Album*, 1966 (reproduced). Meyer Schapiro, The Apples of Cézanne, *Art News Annual*, XXXIV, 1968 (reproduced p. 37); title proposed: *The Amorous Shepherd* (Le Berger amoureux).

COLLECTIONS: Cézanne *fils*, Paris. Paul Guillaume, Paris. A. Chappuis, Tresserve. Mr. and Mrs. Paul Mellon, Upperville, Va.

659. STUDY FOR *The Judgment of Paris*, OR *The Amorous Shepherd*, 1883–86

$6 \times 9\frac{5}{16}$ inches—15,2 × 23,7 cm. Page XXIX of the Album, Paul Mellon Collection. Pencil. Verso: a watercolor, study for *Homage to Delacroix* (reproduced in the Album, 1966, and in J. Rewald, Cézanne and Chocquet, *GBA*, July-Aug. 1969, fig. 33).

This compositional study was followed quite closely in the painting Venturi No. 537, although the style is not the same. Apart from the group of three goddesses, behind and to the right of Paris the silhouette of a fourth woman is seen, walking away. This figure is surprising, since according to tradition one would expect to see Mercury-Hermes. It is possible that the title of the subject has been wrongly chosen.—Cf. for the women: No. 658; for Paris: the bather No. 1218 and the figure of Aeneas in No. 324.

BIBLIOGRAPHY: Venturi, Vol. I, under No. 1309 (not reproduced). *Dessins*, 1938 (reproduced pl. 7). Th. Reff, Cézanne and Hercules, *AB*, Vol. XLVIII, 1966, p. 39, note 60. *Album*, 1966 (reproduced). Meyer Schapiro, The Apples of Cézanne, *Art News Annual*, XXXIV, 1968, p. 50, note 3: the author proposes the title *The Amorous Shepherd*.

COLLECTIONS: Cézanne *fils*, Paris. Paul Guillaume, Paris. A. Chappuis, Tresserve. Mr. and Mrs. Paul Mellon, Upperville, Va.

660. HEAD OF A MAN AND HANDWRITTEN NOTATIONS, 1883–86

$8\frac{1}{2} \times 5$ inches—21,6 × 12,7 cm. Page LII verso from the second sketchbook Mrs. Enid A. Haupt. Pencil. Verso: blank page.

(a) Head of a young man with thick hair and one eye closed on account of a swollen eyelid; the expression on the face is rather sullen. Cf. No. 860.—(b) Notations: *Glace/table/Buffet/2 chaises/1 tabouret/Espadrilles/outremer/ châssis de 150 (. . . illegible), Jan Fyt Ecole flamande/Jan Weenix Ecole Hollandaise.*

BIBLIOGRAPHY: Rewald, *Carnets*: C IV, p. LII verso (reproduced pl. 30).

COLLECTIONS: Cézanne *fils*, Paris. M. Renou, Paris. Poyet, Lyons. M. Renou, Paris. Sam Salz, New York. Mrs. Enid A. Haupt, New York.

661. HEAD OF LOUIS-AUGUSTE CÉZANNE, sketch, 1883–86

$4\frac{7}{8} \times 8\frac{5}{8}$ inches—12,4 × 21.8 cm. Page XXXI verso from the sketchbook CP II. Pencil on gray paper. Verso: No. 767.

Reclining head, seen in left lost profile. No doubt the artist's father, Louis-Auguste, asleep. Cf. No. 410 (a).

COLLECTIONS: Cézanne *fils*, Paris. Paul Guillaume, Paris. A. Chappuis, Tresserve.

662. PAGE OF STUDIES, 1883–86

$8\frac{5}{8} \times 4\frac{7}{8}$ inches—21,8 × 12,4 cm. Page XXXIV verso from the sketchbook CP II. Pencil. Verso: No. 800.

(a) Top: half-length sketch of the artist's father reading, his forearms on a table; the peak of his cap hides his face. Left background: the back of a divan (or perhaps a screen); cf. No. 348.—(b) Below: straight side and ledge of a fireplace; to the left, the arm of the chair habitually used by the artist's father is sketched in.—(c) Upside down: sketch of a head in right three-quarter view, bent forward. The drawings (b) and (c) are intermingled: (c) seems to be earlier than (b).

BIBLIOGRAPHY: Venturi, Vol. I, under No. 1290 (not reproduced).

COLLECTIONS: Cézanne *fils*, Paris. Paul Guillaume, Paris. A. Chappuis, Tresserve.

662bis. STUDIES OF THE ARTIST'S FATHER, 1883–86

$10\frac{5}{8} \times 6\frac{7}{8}$ inches—27 × 17,5 cm. Pencil. Verso: No. 1087bis.

(a) Unfinished portrait. The artist's father sitting beside a fireplace, the back of his armchair higher than his head.—(b) Lower left: repetition of the cap and the shadow of the eyes.—(c) Hands holding a book.—(d) Cap, ear, and coat collar. Cf. No. 662.

COLLECTIONS: Cézanne *fils*, Paris. Paul Guillaume, Paris. Michael Sadler, Oxford. Leicester Galleries, London. Edward le Bas, R.A., London. Sale, Christie's, Geneva, Nov. 6, 1969, No. 154 (reproduced); Error in designation of recto/verso. Dr. Armand Hammer, Los Angeles.

663. FIGURE READING, 1883–86

$8\frac{9}{16} \times 5$ inches—21,7 × 12,6 cm. Page XXVII verso of the sketchbook Leigh Block. Pencil on gray paper. Verso: No. 789.

Seated figure seen in left three-quarter view, the head plunged into a book held with both hands, partly hiding the face. The arm of the seat indicated on the right could be that of a train compartment. Cf., for the subject, Nos. 382, 626, 690, 855.

BIBLIOGRAPHY: Rewald, *Carnets*: C V, p. XXVII verso (reproduced pl. 33). Yvon Taillandier, *Paul Cézanne*, Paris, New York, Munich, 1961 and 1965 (reproduced p. 23).

COLLECTIONS: Cézanne *fils*, Paris. M. Renou, Paris. Poyet, Lyons. M. Renou, Paris. Sam Salz, New York. Mr. and Mrs. Leigh Block, Chicago.

664. TWO HEADS OF WOMEN, 1883–86

$7\frac{5}{8} \times 4\frac{5}{8}$ inches—19,4 × 11,8 cm. Page XLIII from the sketchbook CP I. Pencil. Verso: No. 873.

(a) Top: head, tilted forward, of a woman—probably Mme Cézanne; cf. No. 665. This sketch appears unfinished, no doubt abandoned, judging from the erasures and repetitions of contour.—(b) Smaller head of a woman, copy after an unidentified source.

BIBLIOGRAPHY: Venturi, Vol. I, under No. 1275 (not reproduced).

COLLECTIONS: Cézanne *fils*, Paris. Paul Guillaume, Paris. A. Chappuis, Tresserve. H. Berggruen, Paris.

665. MME CÉZANNE, 1884–87

$7\frac{5}{8} \times 4\frac{5}{8}$ inches—19,4 × 11,8 cm. Page XLVIII verso from the sketchbook CP I. Pencil. Verso: No. 590.

The ordonnance of this drawing is purposeful, with its light horizontal bands on the left, the black collar, and the strokes stressing the features of the face. The graphic quality of the whites, grays, and blacks is remarkable.

BIBLIOGRAPHY: Venturi No. 1280.

COLLECTIONS: Cézanne *fils*, Paris. Paul Guillaume, Paris. A. Chappuis, Tresserve.

666. STUDIES, INCLUDING A HEAD OF MME CÉZANNE, 1884–87

$9\frac{5}{16} \times 6$ inches—23,7 × 15,2 cm. Page LI verso of the Album, Paul Mellon Collection. Pencil. Verso: blank page.

(a) Top: head of Mme Cézanne, seen in left three-quarter view leaning forward.—(b) Upside down: carnival scene, a man seizing a woman; cf. Nos. 935, 936, 937.

BIBLIOGRAPHY: Venturi, Vol. I, under No. 1314 (not reproduced). *Album*, 1966 (reproduced).

COLLECTIONS: Cézanne *fils*, Paris. Paul Guillaume, Paris. A. Chappuis, Tresserve. Mr. and Mrs. Paul Mellon, Upperville, Va.

667. AFTER LOUIS LE NAIN: WOMAN IN A BONNET, 1884–87

$8\frac{1}{4} \times 4\frac{3}{4}$ inches—20,9 × 12,1 cm. Page LII verso from the sketchbook BS II. Pencil. Verso: No. 362.

(a) Head of a woman wearing a bonnet, detail from Louis Le Nain's painting *Blacksmith in front of his Forge* in the Louvre. See fig. 95.—(b) Handwritten notations partially

FIG. 95. Louis Le Nain (1593–1648): *Maréchal devant sa Forge* (detail). Oil on canvas in the Louvre, painted in 1641. Musée National du Louvre, *Catalogue des Peintures* I, 1924, No. 540.
(Photograph: Giraudon)

FIG. 96. Guillaume Coustou (1677–1746): bust of *Pierre-François Darerès de La Tour*, Superior of the Oratorian Order. The name was also written *d'Arères de La Tour*, and this is the Père de La Tour of whom Saint-Simon wrote in his memoirs. Terra-cotta bust, seen front view, signed, dated 1733. In the Louvre; height: 39 cm. For the same bust seen in left profile, see fig. 150. There is a marble version in the Lycée de Tournon (Ardèche). Musée National du Louvre, *Catalogue des Sculptures* II, 1922, No. 1091.
(Photograph: R. W. Ratcliffe)

covering the drawing: *Brillant 2 Sienne naturelle 2 Blanc d'argent Laque brulée.*—Upside down: 39, *rue de Latour d'Auvergne—Lubin Jean—Ibels—Vuillard—Prozio* (Prosio corrected to Prozio).

BIBLIOGRAPHY: Venturi, No. 1397; in error as inside of the cover. Basel catalog, No. 109 (reproduced).

COLLECTIONS: Cézanne *fils*, Paris. Paul Guillaume, Paris. W. Feuz, Bern. Kunstmuseum, Basel.

668. AFTER G. COUSTOU: *Father de La Tour*, 1882–85

$8\frac{1}{2} \times 5$ inches—21,6 × 12,7 cm. Page XLIIII from the second sketchbook Mrs. Enid A. Haupt. Pencil. Verso: No. 577.

After the terracotta bust of *Pierre-François Darerès de La Tour* by Guillaume Coustou, in the Louvre. See fig. 96. We know seven studies by Cézanne after this bust of Father de La Tour, Superior of the Oratorian Order.

BIBLIOGRAPHY: Rewald, *Carnets:* C IV, p. XLIIII (reproduced pl. 149). Berthold, cat. No. 190 (reproduced).

COLLECTIONS: Cézanne *fils*, Paris. M. Renou, Paris. Poyet, Lyons. M. Renou, Paris. Sam Salz, New York. Mrs. Enid A. Haupt, New York.

669. AFTER G. COUSTOU: *Father de La Tour*, 1882–85
$8\frac{1}{2} \times 5$ inches—21,6 × 12,7 cm. Page IIII from the second sketchbook Mrs. Enid A. Haupt. Pencil. Verso: blank page.

(a) Top: head of *Pierre-François Darerès de La Tour*, after the terracotta bust by Guillaume Coustou, in the Louvre. See fig. 96.—(b) Below and upside down: head of a boy seen from above in foreshortening; unfinished sketch, earlier than (a); cf. No. 870.

BIBLIOGRAPHY: Rewald, *Carnets*: C IV, p. IIII "buste de G. de la Tour, au Louvre . . . et croquis d'un bol" (reproduced pl. 148). Berthold, cat. No. 189 (reproduced).

COLLECTIONS: Cézanne *fils*, Paris. M. Renou, Paris. Poyet, Lyons. M. Renou, Paris. Sam Salz, New York. Mrs. Enid A. Haupt, New York.

670. AFTER G. COUSTOU: *Father de La Tour*, 1884–87
$8\frac{1}{2} \times 5$ inches—21,6 × 12,7 cm. Page XII verso from the second sketchbook Mrs. Enid A. Haupt. Pencil. Verso: 670A.

Head of *Pierre-François Darerès de La Tour*, after the terracotta bust by Guillaume Coustou, in the Louvre. See fig. 96. Cf. No. 1116.

BIBLIOGRAPHY: Rewald, *Carnets*: C IV, p. XII verso (not reproduced). Berthold, cat. No. 195 (reproduced).

COLLECTIONS: Cézanne *fils*, Paris. M. Renou, Paris. Poyet, Lyons. M. Renou, Paris. Sam Salz, New York. Mrs. Enid A. Haupt, New York.

670A. SEATED BATHER
Pencil. Inaccessible reverse side of No. 670. (Not reproduced.)

BIBLIOGRAPHY: Rewald, *Carnets*: C IV, p. XII "croquis d'un baigneur assis, vu de face" (not reproduced).

671. AFTER A FLORENTINE BUST: *Beatrice of Aragon*, 1884–87
$8\frac{3}{16} \times 5\frac{3}{16}$ inches—20,8 × 13,1. Page IX from the sketchbook BS I. Pencil. Verso: blank page.

Head seen slightly from below. After a plaster cast from the Florentine bust of *Beatrice of Aragon*, generally attributed to Francesco Laurana. Formerly this cast was in the Musée de Sculpture Comparée of the Trocadéro. See fig. 97. Cézanne had crossed out the face but these strokes have been lightened.

BIBLIOGRAPHY: Venturi No. 1333. Berthold, cat. No. 93 (reproduced Abb. 106). Basel catalog, No. 121 (reproduced).

COLLECTIONS: Cézanne *fils*, Paris. Paul Guillaume, Paris. W. Feuz, Bern. Kunstmuseum, Basel.

672. AFTER GERMAIN PILON: *The Three Graces*, and a head, 1883–86
$7\frac{3}{16} \times 4\frac{9}{16}$ inches—18,2 × 11,6 cm. Page 24 verso from the first sketchbook Mrs. Enid A. Haupt. Pencil. Verso: No. 672A.

Two sketches of only mediocre interest.—(a) Funeral urn, held up by the three marble figures, part of Pilon's *Monu-*

ment for the Heart of King Henri II, now in the Louvre. See fig. 84. Cf. Nos. 585, 1113.—(b) Unfinished head of a man seen full face.

BIBLIOGRAPHY: Rewald, *Carnets*: C I, p. 24 verso (not reproduced). Berthold, cat. No. 146 (reproduced).

COLLECTIONS: Cézanne *fils*, Paris. M. Renou, Paris. Poyet, Lyons. M. Renou, Paris. Sam Salz, New York. Mrs. Enid A. Haupt, New York.

672A. SCISSORS
Pencil. Inaccessible reverse side of No. 672. (Not reproduced.)

BIBLIOGRAPHY: Rewald, *Carnets*: C I, p. 24 "croquis de ciseaux" (not reproduced).

673. AFTER DELACROIX: A BACK, 1883–86
$8\frac{1}{4} \times 4\frac{13}{16}$ inches—20,9 × 12,2 cm. Page XLI from the sketchbook BS II. Pencil. Verso: No. 1138.

FIG. 97. Florentine bust: *Beatrice of Aragon* (died 1508), daughter of King Ferdinand I of Naples. This work is generally attributed to the Dalmatian artist Francesco Laurana (about 1425–1502), architect, sculptor, and medalist. Our photograph was taken from a plaster cast in the Victoria and Albert Museum, London. The cast after which Cézanne drew, formerly in the Trocadero, has been lost. The original marble, according to Berthold, is in the John D. Rockefeller collection, New York; height: 45 cm. *Catalogue général du Musée de Sculpture comparée du Trocadéro* III, 1928, No. I 204.

(Photograph: R. W. Ratcliffe)

FIG. 98. Eugène Delacroix (1799–1863): detail from *L'Entrée des Croisés à Constantinople* (or *Prise de Constantinople par les Croisés*), canvas dated 1840 and signed, in the Louvre. There is a replica with variations in the Collection Moreau. Oil on canvas, 4,10 m. × 4,98 m. Robaut No. 734. Musée National du Louvre, *Catalogue des Peintures* I, 1924, No. 213. There is a drawing by Delacroix (Robaut 735) representing this same detail, of which a wood engraving was printed in *Le Magasin Pittoresque*, 1841. The drawing was also reproduced in photolithography by Arosa and in facsimile by Robaut. The sketch by Cézanne seems to have been done after the painting.
(Photograph: R. W. Ratcliffe)

Study after the woman leaning over her dead daughter in the lower right corner of Eugène Delacroix's painting *The Crusaders entering Constantinople*, in the Louvre. See fig. 98.

BIBLIOGRAPHY: Venturi No. 1376. Basel catalog, No. 125 (reproduced).

COLLECTIONS: Cézanne *fils*, Paris. Paul Guillaume, Paris. W. Feuz, Bern. Kunstmuseum, Basel.

674. AFTER SIGNORELLI: STUDY OF LEGS, 1884–86
$7\frac{5}{8} \times 4\frac{5}{8}$ inches—19,4 × 11,8 cm. Page LII verso from the sketchbook CP I. Pencil. Verso: blank page.

A man's legs, after a drawing by Luca Signorelli in the Cabinet des Dessins of the Louvre: *Two nude men conversing* See fig. 23. For other studies by Cézanne after this drawing, see Nos. 183, 184.

BIBLIOGRAPHY: Venturi, No. 1281. Th. Reff, in *AB*, June 1960, p. 148, note 40.

COLLECTIONS: Cézanne *fils*, Paris. Paul Guillaume, Paris. A. Chappuis, Tresserve. Léo Marchutz, Aix-en-Provence.

675. AFTER SIGNORELLI: BUTTOCKS AND LEGS, 1883–86
$7\frac{5}{8} \times 4\frac{5}{8}$ inches—19,4 × 11,8 cm. Page LIII verso from the sketchbook CP I. Pencil, light watercolor stains; Verso: No. 360.

After the drawing *The Living* (or *A Demon*) *carrying the Dead* by Luca Signorelli in the Cabinet des Dessins of the Louvre. See fig. 22. Other copies of the same subject: Nos. 182, 488. An exceptionally fine drawing notwithstanding its rather special nature.

BIBLIOGRAPHY: Venturi No. 1282: "Jambes: étude d'après nature pour les Nos. 390, 393, 394."

COLLECTIONS: Cézanne *fils*, Paris. Paul Guillaume. Paris. A. Chappuis, Tresserve.

676. AFTER C.-J. VERNET: WOMAN BATHER SEEN FROM THE BACK, 1884–87
$7\frac{3}{16} \times 4\frac{9}{16}$ inches—18,2 × 11,6 cm. Page 17 from the first sketchbook Mrs. Enid A. Haupt. Pencil. Verso: No. 761.

Standing woman bather drying herself; after Claude-Joseph Vernet's painting *Les Baigneuses* in the Louvre. See fig. 99.

BIBLIOGRAPHY: Rewald, *Carnets:* C I, p. 17 (not reproduced). Berthold, cat. No. 236; original source identified (reproduced Abb. 34). *Selearte*, No. 52, July-Aug. 1961 (reproduced fig. 11).

COLLECTIONS: Cézanne *fils*, Paris. M. Renou, Paris. Poyet, Lyons. M. Renou, Paris. Sam Salz, New York. Mrs. Enid A. Haupt.

FIG. 99. Claude-Joseph Vernet (1714–89): detail from the painting *Les Baigneuses* in the Louvre. Canvas, 98 cm. × 1,62 cm. Musée National du Louvre, *Catalogue des Peintures* I, 1924, No. 921.
(Photograph: Giraudon)

FIG. 100. Peter Paul Rubens (1577–1640): *Mercury*, detail from the painting *La Reine reçoit des offres de paix*, in the Medici series in the Louvre. Musée National du Louvre, *Catalogue des Peintures* III, 1922, No. 1202. *(Photograph: Giraudon)*

677. AFTER RUBENS: MERCURY, 1884–87

$8\frac{1}{2} \times 5$ inches—21,6 × 12,7 cm. Page XLI verso from the second sketchbook Mrs. Enid A. Haupt. Pencil. Verso: blank page.

After the figure of Mercury in Rubens' painting *Marie de' Médicis receives the Olive Branch of Peace*, in the Louvre. See fig. 100.

BIBLIOGRAPHY: Rewald, *Carnets:* C IV, p. XLI verso (reproduced pl. 137). Berthold, cat. No. 226 (reproduced Abb. 126).

COLLECTIONS: Cézanne *fils*, Paris. M. Renou, Paris. Poyet, Lyons. M. Renou, Paris. Sam Salz, New York. Mrs. Enid A. Haupt.

678. AFTER MICHELANGELO: A SLAVE, 1884–87

$8\frac{1}{8} \times 4\frac{15}{16}$ inches—20,7 × 12,5 cm. Page XIII from the sketchbook BS III. Pencil. Verso: blank page.

After Michelangelo's marble known as *The Dying Slave*, in the Louvre. See fig. 54. Cf. Nos. 375, 473, 1208.

BIBLIOGRAPHY: Venturi No. 1415. Berthold, cat. No. 64 (reproduced Abb. 122). J. Rewald, Cézanne au Louvre, *AA*, 1935, p. 284 (reproduced).

COLLECTIONS: Cézanne *fils*, Paris. Paul Guillaume, Paris. W. Feuz, Bern. R. von Hirsch, Basel.

679. AFTER MICHELANGELO: A SLAVE, 1885–88

$17\frac{5}{8} \times 11\frac{5}{8}$ inches—44,7 × 29,5 cm. Pencil. Verso: blank page.

After Michelangelo's *Slave* in the Louvre. We know three other copies: Nos. 303, 589, 590, but this is the only one also showing the column that formerly stood behind the statue in the Michelangelo room. See Berthold, Abb. 88: "the Michelangelo room in 1906"; also fig. 42.

BIBLIOGRAPHY: Venturi No. 1443. Berthold, cat. No. 58 (reproduced Abb. 86). Waldemar George, *Le Dessin français*, Paris, 1929 (reproduced pl. 85). M. Denis, in *AA*, 1924, vol. 2 (reproduced p. 38).

EXHIBITIONS: San Francisco, 1937, No. 59 (reproduced). Chicago and New York, 1952, No. 34 (reproduced). Belvedere, Vienna, 1961, No. 91. Aix-en-Provence, 1961, No. 45, Phillips Collection, Washington, D.C., Chicago, Boston, 1971, No. 76 (reproduced).

COLLECTIONS: Bernheim-Jeune, Paris. Thanhauser, Lucerne. Paul Lamb, Cleveland. Curt Valentin, New York. John S. Newberry, Grosse Pointe, Michigan. Detroit Institute of Arts.

680. AFTER A. DEL POLLAIUOLO: *Charles VIII*, 1884–87

$8\frac{1}{8} \times 5\frac{3}{16}$ inches—20,7 × 13,1 cm. Page XXVIII from the sketchbook BS I. Pencil. Verso: blank page.

After a bust of *Charles VIII*, King of France, attributed to Antonio del Pollaiuolo; plaster cast formerly (from 1882 or perhaps 1883) in the Musée de Sculpture Comparée of the Trocadéro. See fig. 101.

BIBLIOGRAPHY: Venturi No. 1354. Berthold, cat. No. 89, text p. 52, original source identified (reproduced Abb.

FIG. 101. Attributed to Antonio del Pollaiuolo (1429–98): *King Charles VIII*, terra-cotta bust in the National Museum (Bargello), Florence. An unsuccessful search was made in 1959 for the plaster cast drawn by Cézanne; however, our photograph is of this cast, which was on exhibition in the Trocadero from 1882 on. *Catalogue général du Musée de Sculpture comparée du Trocadéro* III, 1928, No. I 162.

FIG. 102. François Rude (1784–1855): *Jeune Pêcheur napolitain*, 1833. The original marble from which Cézanne drew is in the Louvre; height: 82 cm. The boy is playing with a tortoise. For technical reasons our photograph was taken from a plaster cast in the Palais de Chaillot, Paris. Musée National du Louvre, *Catalogue des Sculptures* II, 1922, No. 1486. In emulation of his master Rude, Jean-Baptiste Carpeaux (1827–75) also did a sculpture of a young Neapolitan fisherman (1857) kneeling on the ground, holding a shell attentively to his ear, while his face lights up with a smile. The work of Carpeaux, less classicist in style, was subsequently more widely reproduced than that of Rude, for which it is sometimes mistaken. *(Photograph: R. W. Ratcliffe)*

FIG. 103. Attributed to Jean Goujon (1510–67): *Diane d'Anet*, marble in the Louvre. Musée National du Louvre, *Catalogue des Sculptures* I, 1922, No. 392.

(Photograph: Archives photographiques, Paris)

117). Basel catalog, No. 155 (reproduced). R. Cogniat, Paris, 1967 (reproduced p. 11); "tête de femme."

COLLECTIONS: Cézanne *fils*, Paris. Paul Guillaume, Paris. W. Feuz, Basel. Kunstmuseum, Basel.

681. AFTER RUDE: *Neapolitan Fisherboy*, 1884–87

$5\frac{3}{16} \times 8\frac{1}{4}$ inches—13,1 × 20,9 cm. Page XIV from the sketchbook BS I. Pencil. Verso: blank page.

Nude boy sitting on the ground playing with a tortoise. After François Rude's marble *The Neapolitan Fisherboy*, in the Louvre. See fig. 102.

BIBLIOGRAPHY: Venturi No. 1338. Berthold, cat. No. 169 (reproduced Abb. 119). Basel catalog, No. 143 (reproduced).

COLLECTIONS: Cézanne *fils*, Paris. Paul Guillaume, Paris. W. Feuz, Bern. Kunstmuseum, Basel.

682. AFTER JEAN GOUJON: *Diana of Anet*, 1884–87

$5\frac{3}{16} \times 8\frac{5}{8}$ inches—13,1 × 21,8 cm. Page XVII verso from the sketchbook BS I. Pencil. Verso: No. 943.

Roughly-drawn sketch of the figure of Diana on the monument attributed to Jean Goujon and called *The Diana of Anet*: this marble is now in the Louvre. See fig. 103. The goddess seems to be half reclining on a stag's back.

BIBLIOGRAPHY: Venturi No. 1342. Berthold, cat. No. 143 (reproduced Abb. 118).

EXHIBITIONS: Zurich, 1956, No. 193. Munich, 1956, No. 147.

COLLECTIONS: Cézanne *fils*, Paris. Paul Guillaume, Paris. W. Feuz, Bern. Carl Roesch, Diessenhofen.

683. AFTER THE ANTIQUE: *Hermes fixing his winged sandal*, 1884–87

$8\frac{1}{2} \times 5$ inches—21,6 × 12,7 cm. Page XXVI from the second sketchbook Mrs. Enid A. Haupt. Pencil. Verso: blank page.

After the antique marble *Hermes fixing his winged sandal*, also known as *Cincinnatus*, or *Jason*, in the Louvre. See fig. 104.

BIBLIOGRAPHY: Rewald, *Carnets*: C IV, p. XXVI (reproduced pl. 128). Berthold, cat. No. 38 (reproduced Abb. 125); the author reproduces (Abb. 26 and 27) two statues copied by Cézanne and indicates the figures of bathers influenced by these models.

COLLECTIONS: Cézanne *fils*, Paris. M. Renou, Paris. Poyet, Lyons. M. Renou, Paris. Sam Salz, New York. Mrs. Enid A. Haupt, New York.

684. TWO BATHERS, HANDWRITTEN NOTATIONS, 1884–87

$6 \times 9\frac{5}{16}$ inches—15,2 × 23,7 cm. Page LIIII verso of the Album, Paul Mellon Collection. This is the last page, facing the back endpaper. Pen and pencil. Verso: blank page.

FIG. 104. *Hermès attachant ses talonnières*, also known as *Jason*, or *Cincinnatus*, antique marble replica in the Louvre of a sculpture of the School of Lysippus. Musée National du Louvre, *Catalogue sommaire des Marbres antiques*, 1922, No. 83. Since the original is not lighted on this side, we reproduce a plaster cast.　　　　*(Photograph: Skulpturhalle, Basel)*

(a) Left: pen drawing of two bathers, one seated, the other standing.—Above: an address, *Léon Robert au Bas-Samois (Seine et Marne) par Fontainebleau.*—On the right half of the page there are several handwritten notations and the last lines of an unfinished poem that starts on the page opposite. For these texts, see the Album, 1966.

BIBLIOGRAPHY: Venturi, Vol. I, under No. 1315 (not reproduced). *Album*, 1966 (reproduced).

COLLECTIONS: Cézanne *fils*, Paris. Paul Guillaume, Paris. A. Chappuis, Tresserve. Mr. and Mrs. Paul Mellon, Upperville, Va.

685. AFTER THE ANTIQUE: *African Fisherman*, 1884–87

$8\frac{7}{16} \times 5\frac{3}{16}$ inches—21,4 × 13,1 cm. Page VI from the sketchbook BS I. Pencil. Verso: No. 1223.

Study after the antique marble *The African Fisherman* (or *The Old Fisherman*), in the Louvre. See fig. 105.

BIBLIOGRAPHY: Venturi No. 1329. Berthold, cat. No. 40 (reproduced Abb. 121). Basel catalog, No. 122 (reproduced).

COLLECTIONS: Cézanne *fils*, Paris. Paul Guillaume, Paris. W. Feuz, Bern. Kunstmuseum, Basel.

686. SKETCH OF A HEAD, 1885–89

$8\frac{1}{4} \times 4\frac{13}{16}$ inches—21 × 12,2 cm. Page XLIV verso from the sketchbook BS II. Pencil. Verso: No. 1204.

Unfinished study of a head, from the antique marble *Young Satyr and Satyresque* in the Louvre. See fig. 106. Cf. No. 687.

BIBLIOGRAPHY: Basel catalog, No. 145 (reproduced).

COLLECTIONS: Cézanne *fils*, Paris. Paul Guillaume, Paris. W. Feuz, Bern. Kunstmuseum, Basel.

687. AFTER THE ANTIQUE: *Young Satyr and Satyresque*, 1886–89

$8\frac{1}{16} \times 4\frac{1}{8}$ inches—20,5 × 10,4 cm. Page XLIII verso from the sketchbook BS II. Pencil. Verso: No. 1027.

Figure of an adolescent from the antique marble *Young Satyr and Satyresque*, in the Louvre. See fig. 106.

BIBLIOGRAPHY: Venturi No. 1381. Berthold, cat. No. 33 (reproduced). Basel catalog, No. 144 (reproduced).

COLLECTIONS: Cézanne *fils*, Paris. Paul Guillaume, Paris. W. Feuz, Bern. Kunstmuseum, Basel.

FIG. 105. *African Fisherman* (or *The Old Fisherman*), antique replica of a Hellenistic original dating from the second century B.C. Black marble veined with gray; the belt in yellow marble. It is much restored, the head and arms being modern. In the Louvre. Musée National du Louvre, *Catalogue sommaire des Marbres antiques*, 1922, No. 1354.

(Photograph: R. W. Ratcliffe)

FIG. 106. *Young Satyr and Satyresque*, antique replica of a Hellenistic marble; in the Louvre. Musée National du Louvre, *Catalogue sommaire des Marbres antiques*, 1922, No. 318. We reproduce a photograph taken about 1872.

(Photograph: Giraudon)

688. AFTER THE ANTIQUE: YOUNG SATYR, 1886–89

$18\frac{1}{2} \times 11\frac{13}{16}$ inches—47×30 cm. Pencil. Verso: blank page.

After the antique marble *Young Satyr and Satyresque* in the Louvre. See fig. 106. A fine, balanced drawing.

BIBLIOGRAPHY: Venturi No. 1439. Berthold, cat. No. 34 (reproduced). J. Rewald, Thesis, Paris 1936 (reproduced fig. 66). Idem, *Cézanne au Louvre*, *AA*, 1935, mentioned p. 288.

COLLECTIONS: H. von Simolin, Berlin. Baronin von Simolin, Schloss Seeseiten, Starnberg.

689. AFTER PUGET: ATLAS, 1886–89

$7\frac{3}{16} \times 4\frac{9}{16}$ inches—$18,2 \times 11,6$ cm. Page 15 from the first sketchbook Mrs. Enid A. Haupt. Pencil. Verso: No. 955.

This sketch, probably done from a plaster cast, shows one of the atlantes (the one on the right) of the entrance to the Toulon town hall. These atlantes are attributed to Pierre Puget; see fig. 57. The head, supported by the figure's bent arm, holds up the cornice, which is indicated by Cézanne. Cf. No. 391.

BIBLIOGRAPHY: Rewald, *Carnets*: C I, p. 15 (reproduced pl. 131). Idem, *Cézanne*, New York, 1952 (reproduced p. 152). Berthold, cat. No. 128 (reproduced Abb. 134).

COLLECTIONS: Cézanne *fils*, Paris. M. Renou, Paris. Poyet, Lyons. M. Renou, Paris. Sam Salz, New York. Mrs. Enid A. Haupt, New York.

689A. AFTER PUGET: ATLAS

Inaccessible page L verso from the second sketchbook Mrs. Enid A. Haupt. (Not reproduced.) Pencil. Verso: No. 689.

BIBLIOGRAPHY: Rewald, *Carnets*: C IV, p. L verso "croquis d'après une Cariatide attribuée à Puget (voir Carnet I, page 15) et annotation: 'Hermann-Paul, 135, rue du Ranelagh', suivie de comptes" (not reproduced). Berthold, cat. No. 130 (not reproduced).

690. FIGURE LYING DOWN READING, 1886–89

$10\frac{11}{16} \times 8\frac{5}{16}$ inches—$27,2 \times 21,1$ cm. Page LX from the sketchbook CP IV. Pencil, blue and brown watercolor stains. Verso: No. 1169.

This page must be seen as a unity: unfinished drawing of a figure lying on his back outdoors, with a round hat on his stomach. The right elbow touches the ground, the face is hidden by a newspaper and the legs by a blanket. The upper edge of the newspaper is indicated. Cf. the subjects of Nos. 178, 626, 663, 855.

BIBLIOGRAPHY: Venturi, Vol. I, under No. 1316 "esquisse très vague d'un paysan" (not reproduced).

COLLECTIONS: Cézanne *fils*, Paris. Paul Guillaume, Paris. A. Chappuis, Tresserve.

691. MAN SEEN FROM THE BACK, 1886–89

$8\frac{5}{16} \times 10\frac{11}{16}$ inches—$21,1 \times 27,2$ cm. Page XLIV from the sketchbook CP IV. Pencil. Verso: unfinished landscape with lake and mountain in violet, green, gray, and rose watercolor; paginated XLIII.

Studies of a man in a round hat, standing with his back turned.—(a) Top left: contour of the shoulders.—(b) Top right: head and shoulders seen in right lost profile.—(c) Lower left: hat and sketch.—(d) Lower right: man seen from the back down to the knees.

BIBLIOGRAPHY: Venturi, Vol. I, under No. 1316 (not reproduced).

COLLECTIONS: Cézanne *fils*, Paris. Paul Guillaume, Paris. A. Chappuis, Tresserve.

692. PAGE OF STUDIES, 1873–75

$9\frac{7}{16} \times 12\frac{5}{8}$ inches—24×32 cm. Pencil, restored tears, diagonal fold. Verso: a lithograph by Y. Lalaisse, two heads of a horse.

Eight subjects.—(a) Head of Mme Cézanne with background of hatching.—(b) A spoon lying on a plate, with its cast shadow.—(c) Above: light sketch of the young Paul's head.—(d) Same subject, in left three-quarter view.—(e) Lower left: head of Mme Cézanne in left three-quarter view (paper torn below).—(f) Head of the young Paul in left lost profile.—(g) Head and shoulders of the boy, his head in right lost profile; a more developed drawing with background indications.—(h) Right: grandfather clock, the hands standing at ten after seven.

BIBLIOGRAPHY: Venturi No. 1222. A. van Buren, Mme Cézanne's Fashions and the dates of her Portraits, *The Art Quarterly*, Vol. XXIX, No. 2, 1966, p. 120.

EXHIBITIONS: Cézanne, Aquarelle & Zeichnungen, Galerie A. Flechtheim, Berlin, 1937, No. 45. Seit Cézanne in Paris, Galerie A. Flechtheim, Berlin, Christmas 1929, No. 31. Paul Cassirer, London, 1939, No. 1.

COLLECTIONS: Egon Zerner, Berlin. Sale, Egon Zerner, Berlin, Dec. 15-16, 1924, No. 212 (reproduced pl. 70). A. Flechtheim, Berlin. Unknown collection. Ashmolean Museum, Oxford.

693. CHILD LYING ASLEEP, circa 1874

$8\frac{9}{16} \times 5$ inches—21,7 × 12,6 cm. Page XXII of the sketchbook Leigh Block. Pencil on blue-gray paper. Verso: No. 300.

Head, seen in foreshortening, of a child asleep in bed, his shoulder in the foreground.

BIBLIOGRAPHY: Rewald, *Carnets*: C V, p. XXII (not reproduced).

COLLECTIONS: Cézanne *fils*, Paris. M. Renou, Paris. Poyet, Lyons. M. Renou, Paris. Sam Salz, New York. Mr. and Mrs. Leigh Block, Chicago.

694. SKETCH OF A DOOR, HEAD OF THE YOUNG PAUL, circa 1876

$4\frac{7}{8} \times 8\frac{9}{16}$ inches—12,4 × 21,7 cm. Page XXIIII verso of the sketchbook A.I.C. Pencil, stains. Verso: No. 408.

(a) Left: light sketch of the door and window of a house; indications of foliage.—(b) Head of the young Paul, placed diagonally on the page.

BIBLIOGRAPHY: Rewald, *Carnets*: C II, p. XXIIII verso (not reproduced). Schniewind, text p. 30 (reproduced). Andersen, *Sk.* (not reproduced).

COLLECTIONS: Cézanne *fils*, Paris. M. Renou, Paris. Poyet, Lyons. M. Renou, Paris. Sam Salz, New York. Art Institute, Chicago.

695. UNFINISHED SKETCHES OF TWO HEADS, circa 1876

$8\frac{9}{16} \times 4\frac{7}{8}$ inches—21,7 × 12,4 cm. Page XL verso of the sketchbook A.I.C. Pencil, stains. Verso: No. 819.

(a) Head of the artist's little son, Paul.—(b) Upside down at the opposite end of the page: unfinished sketch of a woman's head.

BIBLIOGRAPHY: Rewald, *Carnets*: C II, p. XL verso (not reproduced). Schniewind, text p. 32 (reproduced). Andersen, *Sk.* (not reproduced).

COLLECTIONS: Cézanne *fils*, Paris. M. Renou, Paris. Poyet, Lyons. M. Renou, Paris. Sam Salz, New York. Art Institute, Chicago.

696. PAGE OF STUDIES, INCLUDING ONE OF MME CÉZANNE, 1873–76

$10\frac{7}{16} \times 7\frac{7}{8}$ inches—26,5 × 20 cm. Pencil, on a page removed from a book or fascicle marked Vol. II 79. Verso: an engraving after the painting *Environs d'Etretat* by Jean-Marie-Auguste Jugelet (1805–1875).

(a) Head of Mme Cézanne of particular feminine charm; cf. No. 692.—(b) At right angles: study of a draped garment, the back of a dress with two buttons at the waist; fine rendering of the folds.

BIBLIOGRAPHY: Neumeyer, 1958, No. 35 (reproduced).

EXHIBITION: Fine Arts Association, New York, 1952, No. 6 (reproduced).

COLLECTIONS: Cassirer, Berlin. O. T. Falk, Oxford. Matthiesen Gallery, London. Knoedler & Co., New York. Mrs. E. F. Hutton, New York. Sale, Sotheby's, London, Nov. 24-25, 1964, No. 129 (reproduced). Laing Galleries.

697. PAGE OF STUDIES, circa 1876

$8\frac{11}{16} \times 9\frac{1}{16}$ inches—22 × 23 cm. Pencil on gray-brown laid paper. Verso: No. 697a.

(a) Left: study of drapery, the sleeve and collar of a little jacket.—(b) Top right: head of Mme Cézanne.—(c) Lower right: head of the artist's son, the cheek left white on the left.

BIBLIOGRAPHY: Venturi No. 1472.

COLLECTION: Kenneth Clark, London.

697A. PAGE OF STUDIES

Pencil on gray-brown laid paper. Verso of No. 697. (Not reproduced.)

Venturi writes: "d'autres études d'après la femme et le fils de l'artiste."

BIBLIOGRAPHY: Venturi, Vol. I, above mention under No. 1472; not reproduced.

698. TWO STUDIES OF THE ARTIST'S SON: top, circa 1876; bottom, circa 1878

$8\frac{9}{16} \times 4\frac{7}{8}$ inches—21,7 × 12,4 cm. Page XLV of the sketchbook A.I.C. Pencil. Verso: No. 346.

(a) Top: head of the artist's son. Although the sketch is little developed, the eyes are expressive.—(b) Below: unfinished sketch of the son's head in a bell-shaped hat with its brim turned down. See the text of No. 707; cf. No. 334 (b).

BIBLIOGRAPHY: Rewald, *Carnets*: C II, p. XLV (not reproduced). Schniewind, text p. 33 (reproduced). Andersen, *Sk.* (not reproduced).

COLLECTIONS: Cézanne *fils*, Paris. M. Renou, Paris. Poyet, Lyons. M. Renou, Paris. Sam Salz, New York. Art Institute, Chicago.

699. HEAD OF A BOY, AND A CHILD'S DRAWINGS, circa 1876

$9 \times 13\frac{3}{4}$ inches—22,8 × 35 cm. Pencil (and pen), three corners damaged, holes restored, paper torn at edges, vertical fold on the right, stains. Verso: No. 162.

(a) By the artist: pencil sketch of his son's head, seen full face.—(b) Upside down: a child's drawings. Scene with a camel, figures (Rebecca and Eliezer), a fountain, and a tree; to the right, the three Fates (Clotho, Lachesis, Atropos), houses, figure, helmet, etc.

BIBLIOGRAPHY: Venturi, Vol. I, p. 352, Oeuvres Inédites (not reproduced). Basel catalog, No. 96 (reproduced).

COLLECTIONS: Cézanne *fils*, Paris. W. Feuz, Bern. Kunstmuseum, Basel.

700. TWO STUDIES OF THE SON'S HEAD, circa 1876

$4\frac{7}{8} \times 8\frac{9}{16}$ inches—12,4 × 21,7 cm. Page XLIII of the sketchbook A.I.C. Pencil, stains. Verso: No. 706.

(a) The artist's son, his head tilted to the right; the shoulder is indicated by the top part of a full sleeve.—(b) The head only. On both drawings the dark parts are stumped in places.

BIBLIOGRAPHY: Rewald, *Carnets:* C II, p. XLIII (reproduced pl. 25). Schniewind, text p. 33 (reproduced). Andersen, *Sk.* (not reproduced).

COLLECTIONS: Cézanne *fils*, Paris. M. Renou, Paris. Poyet, Lyons. M. Renou, Paris. Sam Salz, New York. Art Institute, Chicago.

701. HEAD OF A CHILD ASLEEP: THE ARTIST'S SON, circa 1877

$6\frac{5}{16} \times 9\frac{1}{4}$ inches—16 × 23,5 cm. Pencil on beige laid paper. Verso: No. 887.

The artist's son in bed with only his head emerging from the sheets. Fine drawing, expressing both fatherly tenderness and a keen interest in the oval form of the volume.

BIBLIOGRAPHY: Venturi No. 1244. *The World of Cézanne* (reproduced p. 118).

EXHIBITIONS: The Art Institute of Chicago and the Metropolitan Museum, New York, 1952, No. 41 (reproduced).

COLLECTION: Kenneth Clark, London.

701bis. HEAD OF THE ARTIST'S SON, AND KETTLE, circa 1877

$7\frac{7}{8} \times 9\frac{7}{16}$ inches—20 × 24 cm. Pencil on beige paper. Verso: No. 398.

(a) Head of the artist's son.—(b) Top left: kettle on a little spirit-stove, strong cast shadow.—(c) Upside down: portrait of Victor Chocquet showing through in reverse from the other side of the page.

BIBLIOGRAPHY: Venturi, Vol. I, as verso of No. 1240 (mentioned, not reproduced).

EXHIBITION: Belvedere, Vienna, 1961, described as verso of No. 104 (mentioned but not reproduced in the catalog).

COLLECTIONS: Kenneth Clark, London. Benjamin Sonnenberg, New York.

701ter. HEAD OF THE ARTIST'S SON, 1876–77

$8\frac{3}{4} \times 5\frac{1}{2}$ inches—22,2 × 14 cm. Pencil on laid paper. Verso: No. 489bis.

Unfinished sketch; expressive stroke on the right indicating the eyebrow.

BIBLIOGRAPHY: Venturi, Vol. I, p. 349, Oeuvres Inédites (not reproduced).

COLLECTIONS: Kenneth Clark, London. Private collection, England.

702. HEAD OF THE ARTIST'S SON, WOMAN BATHER, 1877–78

$6 \times 4\frac{1}{8}$ inches—15,3 × 10,4 cm. Pencil on laid paper. Verso: No. 319.

(a) Head of the artist's son, drawn in light strokes; the eyes are eloquent.—(b) Lower left: figure, cut off by the edge of the page.—(c) Lower right: detail of an undetermined object, also cut off by the edge.

BIBLIOGRAPHY: Venturi, Vol. I, not mentioned as verso of No. 1228. Catalog of the exhibition in the Belvedere, Vienna, 1961, described as verso of No. 84.

COLLECTION: Albertina, Vienna (Inv. 24086).

703. TWO STUDIES OF THE SON'S HEAD, 1877–78

$4\frac{7}{8} \times 8\frac{9}{16}$ inches—12,4 × 21,7 cm. Page XLVIII verso of the sketchbook A.I.C. Pencil. Verso: No. 842.

(a) Left: head of the boy seen in left three-quarter view; amused expression.—(b) To the right and at right angles: sketch of the head, with parts of the cheeks and chin left white. There is a certain finesse in the expression of the eyes and drawing of the mouth.—Beside the drawing: the name *paul* in a child's handwriting.

BIBLIOGRAPHY: Rewald, *Carnets:* C II, p. XLVIII verso (reproduced pl. 24). Schniewind, text p. 33 (reproduced). Andersen, *Sk.* (not reproduced).

COLLECTIONS: Cézanne *fils*, Paris. M. Renou, Paris. Poyet, Lyons. M. Renou, Paris. Sam Salz, New York. Art Institute, Chicago.

704. TWO PORTRAITS OF THE ARTIST'S SON, 1877–78

$8\frac{9}{16} \times 4\frac{7}{8}$ inches—21,7 × 12,4 cm. Page XXXIX verso of the sketchbook A.I.C. Pencil, stains. Verso: No. 407.

(a) Top: head of the artist's son, the light falling from the right.—(b) Below: the head, with the light coming from the left; this drawing is more developed and in a different spirit.

BIBLIOGRAPHY: Rewald, *Carnets:* C II, p. XXXIX verso (reproduced pl. 20). Schniewind, text p. 32 (reproduced). Th. Rousseau Jr., *Paul Cézanne*, Paris, 1953 (reproduced pl. 33). Idem, Amsterdam, 1954 (reproduced pl. 33). Yvon Taillandier, *Paul Cézanne*, Paris, New York, Munich, 1961 and 1965 ((b) reproduced p. 92). Andersen, *Sk.* (not reproduced).

COLLECTIONS: Cézanne *fils*, Paris. M. Renou, Paris. Poyet, Lyons. M. Renou, Paris. Sam Salz, New York. Art Institute, Chicago.

705. Head of a boy, and landscape, 1877–78

$4\frac{7}{8} \times 8\frac{9}{16}$ inches—12,4 × 21,7 cm. Page XVI verso of the sketchbook A.I.C. Pencil, stains. Verso: sketch of a head; the drawing is defaced to such an extent by scribbles that it is unrecognizable (not classified, but reproduced by Schniewind, pl. XVI).

(a) Left: head of the son, very youthful.—(b) Delicate but magnificent sketch showing a view of L'Estaque, almost similar to No. 783. The son's face, drawn by himself, intrudes between (a) and (b).

BIBLIOGRAPHY: Rewald, *Carnets:* C II, p. XVI verso (not reproduced). Schniewind, text p. 28 (reproduced). Andersen, *Sk.* (not reproduced).

COLLECTIONS: Cézanne *fils*, Paris. M. Renou, Paris. Poyet, Lyons. M. Renou, Paris. Sam Salz, New York. Art Institute, Chicago.

706. Two studies of the son's head, 1877–78

$4\frac{7}{8} \times 8\frac{9}{16}$ inches—12,4 × 21,7 cm. Page XLIII verso of the sketchbook A.I.C. Pencil. Verso: No. 700.

(a) Right: head of the artist's son rather curiously delineated by an oval, a fixed expression on the face. Two strokes on the forehead indicate volume.—(b) Left, at right angles: sketch of the son's head leaning on his forearm.

BIBLIOGRAPHY: Rewald, *Carnets:* C II, p. XLIII verso (reproduced pl. 27). Schniewind, text p. 33 (reproduced). Meyer Schapiro, *Cézanne*, New York, 1952 (reproduced p. 27). Andersen, *Sk.* (not reproduced).

COLLECTIONS: Cézanne *fils*, Paris. M. Renou, Paris. Poyet, Lyons. M. Renou, Paris. Sam Salz, New York. Art Institute, Chicago.

707. Two sketches of the artist's son, circa 1878

$8\frac{9}{16} \times 4\frac{7}{8}$ inches—21,7 × 12,4 cm. Page XLIV verso of the sketchbook A.I.C. Pencil. Verso: No. 712.

(a) Top: head of the young Paul in a round hat with turned-up brim; possibly the same bell-shaped hat as seen in No. 698 (b), study figuring immediately after the present one in the sketchbook, at the bottom of the opposite page.—(b) Below: same subject, but in more detail; the clothing is indicated around the shoulders.

BIBLIOGRAPHY: Rewald, *Carnets:* C II, p. XLIV verso (not reproduced). Schniewind, text p. 33 (reproduced). Andersen, *Sk.* (not reproduced).

COLLECTIONS: Cézanne *fils*, Paris. M. Renou, Paris. Poyet, Lyons. M. Renou, Paris. Sam Salz, New York. Art Institute, Chicago.

708. Head of the artist's son, circa 1878

$8\frac{9}{16} \times 4\frac{7}{8}$ inches—21,7 × 12,4 cm. Page XLVI of the sketchbook A.I.C. Pencil. Verso: No. 290.

(a) Head of the young Paul, drawn with a soft pencil.—(b) Below: unfinished sketch done with a different pencil, possibly a study of drapery (looking at the page lengthwise).—Numerals by an alien hand; pieces of saw-edged stamp paper adhering to the page.

BIBLIOGRAPHY: Rewald, *Carnets:* C II, p. XLVI (not reproduced). Schniewind, text p. 33 (reproduced). Andersen, *Sk.* (not reproduced).

COLLECTIONS: Cézanne *fils*, Paris. M. Renou, Paris. Poyet, Lyons. M. Renou, Paris. Sam Salz, New York. Art Institute, Chicago.

709. Portrait of the artist's son, circa 1878

$8\frac{9}{16} \times 4\frac{7}{8}$ inches—21,7 × 12,4 cm. Page XLI verso of the sketchbook A.I.C. Pencil, stains. Verso: No. 714.

Head of the young Paul, indications of a collar and garment with a characteristic round button. Lively study, if rather summary.

BIBLIOGRAPHY: Rewald, *Carnets:* C II, p. XLII (reproduced pl. 19); he states in error that p. XLI is missing and that p. XLII figures twice, the present drawing being classified by him as XLII recto; this anomaly has perhaps been rectified since. Schniewind, text p. 32 (reproduced). Andersen, *Sk.* (not reproduced).

COLLECTIONS: Cézanne *fils*, Paris. M. Renou, Paris. Poyet, Lyons. M. Renou, Paris. Sam Salz, New York. Art Institute, Chicago.

710. The young Paul, asleep, 1878–80

$14 \times 19\frac{3}{8}$ inches—35,6 × 49,2 cm. Pencil. Verso: a watercolored pencil sketch of foliage.

Three sketches of the head of the child lying asleep on his right cheek. These studies are unfinished; behind the one on the right the headboard of the bed is indicated.

BIBLIOGRAPHY: Venturi No. 1471.

COLLECTION: Kenneth Clark, London.

711. Head of Mme Cézanne, head of a woman asleep, 1878–80

$9\frac{7}{8} \times 12\frac{5}{8}$ inches—25 × 32 cm. Pencil on gray paper, heavy fold marks. Verso: No. 728.

(a) Left: head, on a pillow, of Mme Cézanne asleep, the lower part of the face hidden by a blanket. Sketch drawn in fine close strokes, stressing the contours.—(b) At right angles: smaller sketch of a head lying flat on a pillow, the crown to the right. Below: two lines forming an arc, probably part of a bedstead; cf. Nos. 336, 710.

BIBLIOGRAPHY: Venturi, Vol. I, p. 348, Oeuvres Inédites (not reproduced); Venturi must have referred to this drawing (of which he had no photograph) forgetting that he had already cited it as the verso of No. 1477. Catalog of the exhibition, Aix-en-Provence, 1961, mentioned under No. 43.

COLLECTIONS: Ambroise Vollard, Paris. Kenneth Clark, London.

712. Head of a boy, sketch of a woman, circa 1878

$4\frac{7}{8} \times 8\frac{9}{16}$ inches—12,4 × 21,7 cm. Page XLIV of the sketchbook A.I.C. Pencil and pen. Verso: No. 707.

(a) On the left (page lengthwise, with the binding to the right): pen drawing of the artist's son. His head, leaning to the right, is resting on his forearm or an upholstered chair back.—(b) Page upside down: small, bust-length pencil sketch of a woman.

BIBLIOGRAPHY: Rewald, *Carnets:* C II, p. XLIV (reproduced pl. 29). Schniewind, text p. 33 (reproduced). Andersen, *Sk.* (not reproduced).

COLLECTIONS: Cézanne *fils*, Paris. M. Renou, Paris. Poyet, Lyons. M. Renou, Paris. Sam Salz, New York. Art Institute, Chicago.

713. Studies, and portraits of the artist's son, circa 1878

12¹³⁄₁₆ × 11¹³⁄₁₆ inches—32,5 × 30 cm. Pencil, ink stain. Verso: No. 722.

(a) Top left: young bather with outstretched arms, in a summarily indicated landscape. The sketch is framed with strokes and annotated by the words: *tel, fait*. See Note 25. —(b) Below the bather: water glass ornamented with molded thumbprint design.—(c) Lower center: head of the artist's son, detailed drawing annotated by the word *tel* and a cross. See Note 25.—(d) Top right and at right angles: portrait of the son with his shadow in the background, also annotated by *tel* and a cross. See Note 25.—(e) Silhouette in contours of a seated woman, drawn after a figure ornamenting a clock; cf. No. 458.

BIBLIOGRAPHY: Venturi No. 1242 reproduces the detail (c), taken from the line engraving in Vollard's book. Vollard, 1914 ((c) reproduced p. 37). Meier-Graefe, *Cézanne und sein Kreis*, Munich, 1922 ((c) reproduced p. 26, from Vollard). *AA*, 1920, p. 287 ((c) reproduced from Vollard). Frantisek Rachlik, *Cézanne*, Prague, 1948 ((c) reproduced from Vollard, pl. 3).

EXHIBITIONS: Kunsthalle, Basel, 1936, No. 124. San Francisco, 1937, No. 61 (reproduced). Belvedere, Vienna, 1961, No. 90.

COLLECTIONS: Ambroise Vollard, Paris. Albertina, Vienna (Inv. 24088).

714. Portrait of the artist's son, rocks at Bibémus, circa 1878

8⁹⁄₁₆ × 4⁷⁄₈ inches—21,7 × 12,4 cm. Page XLI of the sketchbook A.I.C. Pencil, stains, trial dabs of watercolor. Verso: No. 709.

(a) Head and one shoulder of the artist's son, a lock of hair falling down over his forehead.—(b) Adjoining, but upside down: small landscape with trees and rocks, drawn in Bibémus quarry; cf. No. 1184 and the paintings Venturi Nos. 767, 778. The dabs of color near the binding indicate that a watercolored page was removed before the sketchbook was paginated.

BIBLIOGRAPHY: Rewald, *Carnets*: C II, p. XLII (reproduced pl. 18). By error he states that p. XLI is missing and that p. XLII figures twice. This anomaly has perhaps been rectified since. Schniewind, text p. 32 (reproduced). Andersen, *Sk.* (not reproduced).

COLLECTIONS: Cézanne *fils*, Paris. M. Renou, Paris. Poyet, Lyons. M. Renou, Paris. Sam Salz, New York. Art Institute, Chicago.

715. Page of studies, circa 1879

9⁷⁄₁₆ × 12³⁄₁₆ inches—24 × 31 cm. Pencil. Verso: No. 731.

(a) Head of the artist's son, with a shadow to the left of the nose.—(b) Below: detailed drawing after an engraving by Marcantonio Raimondi, *Caryatids*; cf. No. 481.—(c) Study of drapery: garment thrown over the back of a chair.

BIBLIOGRAPHY: Venturi No. 1475, described as verso (reproduced). Berthold, cat. Nos. 261, 263 (reproduced).

EXHIBITION: Phillips Collection, Washington, D.C., Chicago, Boston, 1971, No. 68B (reproduced).

COLLECTIONS: Kenneth Clark, London. Eger, Paris. Rousso, Paris. The Lazarus and Rosalie Phillips Family Collection, Montreal.

716. Portrait of Mme Cézanne, 1876–79

8⁹⁄₁₆ × 4⁷⁄₈ inches—21,7 × 12,4 cm. Page XLIX verso of the sketchbook A.I.C. Pencil. Verso: No. 825.

Half-length sketch of Mme Cézanne, her head against one hand; the head is rather big in proportion to the rest. Cf. Nos. 828, 846.—Top right: written by the young son, "*a madame cezanne.*"

BIBLIOGRAPHY: Rewald, *Carnets*: C II, p. XLIX verso (reproduced pl. 6). Schniewind, text p. 34 (reproduced). Andersen, *Sk.* (reproduced fig. 26).

COLLECTIONS: Cézanne *fils*, Paris. M. Renou, Paris. Poyet, Lyons. M. Renou, Paris. Sam Salz, New York. Art Institute, Chicago.

717. Mme Cézanne, milk can, 1877–80

9¹⁄₁₆ × 5⁷⁄₈ inches—23 × 15 cm. Pencil on gray-brown laid paper. Verso: ?

(a) Portrait of Mme Cézanne: her head and neck, with indications of bodice. There is a peaceful, gentle expression in the eyes. This sketch is earlier than the milk can.—(b) At right angles: a milk can in the shape of a truncated cone, with a metal handle, standing upside down; cast shadow. The same milk can figures in the still lifes Venturi Nos. 337, 338, 340, 356, 357.

BIBLIOGRAPHY: Venturi No. 1481. F. Novotny, *Cézanne*, Phaidon, Vienna, Paris, London, 1937 and 1961 (reproduced fig. 121).

COLLECTION: Kenneth Clark, London.

718. Head of Mme Cézanne, 1877–80

5⁵⁄₁₆ × 3¹⁵⁄₁₆ inches—13,5 × 10 cm. Pencil on laid paper. Verso: blank page.

The head is bent over to the right, leaning against a cushion. Small sketch cut out of a page of studies.

BIBLIOGRAPHY: Venturi No. 1246.

COLLECTIONS: W. Feuz, Bern. Present owner unknown.

719. Mme Cézanne and another sketch, 1877–80

8⁹⁄₁₆ × 4⁷⁄₈ inches—21,7 × 12,4 cm. Page L verso of the sketchbook A.I.C. Pencil. Verso: handwriting exercises by the son.

(a) Top: head and shoulders of Mme Cézanne; the collar is fastened by the ribbon bow under her chin.—(b) Center: sketch of a young man, standing with one foot in front of the other, his hands in his pockets. This figure calls to mind certain children in paintings by the Le Nain brothers.—(c) Below: unfinished sketch of Mme Cézanne's head; study for Venturi No. 291.—Below (a), the son has written "*madame cèzanne*" (*sic*).

BIBLIOGRAPHY: Rewald, *Carnets*: C II, p. L verso (not reproduced). Schniewind, text p. 34 (reproduced). Andersen, *Sk.* (reproduced fig. 27). A. van Buren, Mme Cézanne's Fashions and the dates of her Portraits, *The Art Quarterly*, Vol. XXIX, No. 2, 1966, p. 115; in Note 20, the author indicates the relation between (c) and Venturi No. 291, while doubting that the model was Mme Cézanne. *The World of Cézanne* (reproduced p. 104).

COLLECTIONS: Cézanne *fils,* Paris. M. Renou, Paris. Poyet, Lyons. M. Renou, Paris. Sam Salz, New York. Art Institute, Chicago.

720. PAGE OF STUDIES, INCLUDING HEADS OF MME CÉZANNE AND LOUIS-AUGUSTE CÉZANNE, 1878–81

$8\frac{9}{16} \times 4\frac{7}{8}$ inches—21,7 × 12,4 cm. Page XLI verso from the sketchbook CP II. Pencil, two round stains. Verso: No. 536.

(a) Top: head of Mme Cézanne, her eyes looking to the right of the viewer.—(b) Below, upside down: head of the artist's father, Louis-Auguste Cézanne. The banker, formerly a hat-manufacturer, is wearing a peaked cap and gives the impression of a man totally occupied in reading; cf. No. 411.

BIBLIOGRAPHY: Venturi, Vol. I, under No. 1293 (not reproduced).

EXHIBITIONS: Nice, Aix-en-Provence, Grenoble, 1953, No. 33; title given: "Le père et le fils de l'artiste."

COLLECTIONS: Cézanne *fils,* Paris. Paul Guillaume, Paris. A. Chappuis, Tresserve. Private collection, Paris. Fogg Art Museum, Cambridge, Mass. (Inv. 1962.24. Bequest Marion H. Phinney).

721. STUDIES: HEADS AND COPIES, 1878–80

$9\frac{5}{8} \times 12$ inches—24,5 × 30,5 cm. Pencil. Verso: No. 458.

(a) Top left: profile of the artist's son, unfinished study.—(b) Center: profile of the son, his expression sulky.—(c) Lower right: head of the son, left white on the right side.—(d) Head of Mme Cézanne, her eyelids lowered; annotated *tel.* See Note 25.—(e) Top: head of a figure ornamenting a clock, and shadow; cf. No. 821.—(f) Left: woman leaning over; copy of a detail.—(g) Head and breast of a naiad by Rubens. See fig. 53. Cf. No. 455.

COLLECTIONS: Kenneth Clark, London. E. Katzenellenbogen, Santa Monica, Calif.

722. STUDIES, INCLUDING A HEAD AND A SMALL CASSEROLE, 1878–80

$11\frac{13}{16} \times 12\frac{13}{16}$ inches—30 × 32,5 cm. Pencil, traces of glue at the top corners. Verso: No. 713.

(a) Top left: head and shoulders of a boy, no doubt the artist's son.—(b) Top, to the right: unfinished study of a woman's head.—(c) Right: small covered casserole standing on a spirit stove.—(d) Lower left: unfinished study of a head.—(e) Below, near the center: head of Mme Cézanne, her eyelids lowered; unfinished sketch.—(f) Lower down: a pair of scissors.—(g) Lower right corner, at right angles: nape of a neck with chignon and ear, seen in right profile.—(h) Halfway up the page: unfinished study of a head.

BIBLIOGRAPHY: Described in the catalog of the Cézanne exhibition at the Belvedere, Vienna, 1961, No. 90, as being on the reverse side of our No. 713.

COLLECTION: Albertina, Vienna (Inv. 24088 verso).

723. STUDIES OF HEADS, circa 1878

$8\frac{9}{16} \times 5$ inches—21,7 × 12,6 cm. Page IX of the sketchbook Leigh Block. Pencil. Verso: No. 766.

(a) Top: head of the artist's son, in a cap. The round eye and indefinable lack of balance in this study combine to render it unpleasing.—(b) Below: right profile of Mme Cézanne's head, leaning forward; the portrait is interrupted by the edge of the page at the level of the nostrils.—(c) Above: rough study of the same subject.

BIBLIOGRAPHY: Rewald, *Carnets:* C V, p. IX (not reproduced).

COLLECTIONS: Cézanne *fils,* Paris. M. Renou, Paris. Poyet, Lyons. M. Renou, Paris. Sam Salz, New York. Mr. and Mrs. Leigh Block, Chicago.

724. HEAD OF A BOY, circa 1878

$8\frac{9}{16} \times 4\frac{7}{8}$ inches—21,7 × 12,4 cm. Page XIII of the sketchbook A.I.C. Pencil, stains. Verso: No. 811.

Rewald and Schniewind take this to be a portrait of the artist's son, which seems probable.—In the lower part of the page the child has drawn a few vague pencil strokes; there is also an unfinished sketch of a little round flower, (perhaps a scabiosa) by Cézanne.

BIBLIOGRAPHY: Rewald, *Carnets:* C II, p. XIII (not reproduced). Schniewind, text p. 28 (reproduced). Andersen, *Sk.* (not reproduced).

COLLECTIONS: Cézanne *fils,* Paris. M. Renou, Paris. Poyet, Lyons. M. Renou, Paris. Sam Salz, New York. Art Institute, Chicago.

725. THREE HEADS, SLEEVE OF A GARMENT, circa 1879

$9\frac{7}{8} \times 12\frac{13}{16}$ inches—25 × 32,5 cm. Pencil, two corners damaged. Verso: No. 726.

(a) Top left: head of the artist's son lying down on his right side and looking straight at the viewer.—(b) Top right: young Paul, in a hat.—(c) Lower left: sleeve of a garment, from elbow to wrist.—(d) Head tilted forward, with the back of an upholstered chair behind the shoulder.

BIBLIOGRAPHY: Venturi, Vol. I, p. 352, Oeuvres Inédites (not reproduced). Basel catalog, No. 92 (reproduced). Douglas Cooper, in *Master Drawings,* Vol. 1, No. 4, 1963, p. 56.

COLLECTIONS: Cézanne *fils,* Paris. W. Feuz, Bern. Kunstmuseum, Basel.

726. BOY'S HEAD, AND COPY AFTER PAREJA, circa 1879

$12\frac{13}{16} \times 9\frac{7}{8}$ inches—32,5 × 25 cm. Pencil, left corners damaged. Verso: No. 725.

(a) top left; (b) top right; (c) right center; (d) lower right: head of a boy, probably the artist's son at the age of about seven.—(e) Lower left and at right angles: incomplete copy, in same dimensions, of the engraving in Charles Blanc, *Ecole Espagnole,* 1869, of Juan de Pareja's painting *The Calling of Saint Matthew.* See fig. 107. Cf. No. 244. The copy is a little earlier than the portraits of the boy.

BIBLIOGRAPHY: Venturi, Vol. I, p. 352, Oeuvres Inédites (not reproduced). Berthold, cat. No. 311 ((e) reproduced). Basel catalog, No. 90 (reproduced). Douglas Cooper, in *Master Drawings,* Vol. 1, No. 4, 1963, p. 56. Longstreet, 1964 (reproduced).

EXHIBITIONS: The Hague, 1956, No. 104. Zurich, 1956, No. 159.

COLLECTIONS: Cézanne *fils,* Paris. W. Feuz, Bern. Kunstmuseum, Basel.

FIG. 107. Wood engraving after Juan de Pareja (1606–70) reproduced in Charles Blanc, *Ecole espagnole* (1869). Subject: *The Calling of Saint Matthew*. Below the engraving, at left: E. Bocourt D; at right: A. Delangle. As told by the Gospel according to Saint Matthew, 9:9: "And as Jesus passed forth from thence, He saw a man, named Matthew, sitting at the receipt of custom: and saith unto him, Follow me. And he arose, and followed Him." The original painting is in Madrid: see Don Pedro de Madrazo, *Catalogue des tableaux du Musée du Prado*, first French edition, Madrid, 1913, No. 1401, p. 207.
(Photograph: Chappuis)

727. STUDIES OF HEADS, EAR, circa 1879

$4\frac{7}{8} \times 8\frac{5}{8}$ inches—12,4 × 21,8 cm. Page XXX from the sketchbook CP II. Pencil on ocher paper. Verso: faint counterproof of the drawing on the preceding page, XXIX verso.

Child asleep in bed. Cf. No. 862 (a).—(a) Top left: the head seen in left lost profile, leaning to the right; the ear is in the center of the oval.—(b) Repetition of the ear in the same position.—(c) Lower right: top part of a head.

BIBLIOGRAPHY: Venturi, Vol. I, under No. 1290 (not reproduced).

COLLECTIONS: Cézanne *fils*, Paris. Paul Guillaume, Paris. A. Chappuis, Tresserve.

728. PAGE OF STUDIES, INCLUDING MME CÉZANNE, 1879–80

$12\frac{5}{8} \times 9\frac{7}{8}$ inches—32 × 25 cm. Pencil. Verso: No. 711.

(a) Mme Cézanne sewing; study for the painting Venturi No. 291. A very fine drawing.—(b) Lower left: repetition, but larger, of Mme Cézanne's head.—(c) Lower right and at right angles: rapid unfinished sketch of a couple, in the style of the "scenes of love and violence." The woman, leaning against a cushion, has her arm bent in the same way as Rubens' Bellona. See fig. 9.

BIBLIOGRAPHY: Venturi No. 1477.

EXHIBITIONS: Kunsthalle, Basel, 1936, No. 159. Belvedere, Vienna, 1961, No. 106. Aix-en-Provence, 1961, No. 43.

COLLECTIONS: Ambroise Vollard, Paris. Kenneth Clark, London.

729. MME CÉZANNE SEWING, circa 1880

$18\frac{7}{8} \times 12\frac{3}{8}$ inches—48 × 31,5 cm. Pencil on laid paper. Verso: blank page.

Mme Cézanne sitting on a chair, sewing. In the left background: a piece of furniture with a drawer and a few books lying on the top. The upright of a bed can be seen close to the head but further back; this same bed figures in some of the artist's watercolors. Cf. No. 398.

BIBLIOGRAPHY: Venturi No. 1466. Vollard, 1914 (reproduced as frontispiece). Meier-Graefe, *Cézanne und sein Kreis*, Munich, 1922 (reproduced p. 37).

EXHIBITIONS: Drawings from Ingres to Seurat, Boymans Museum, Rotterdam, 1933–34. Retrospective, Paris, 1939, No. 44. Paul Cassirer, London, 1939, No. 2.

COLLECTIONS: Ambroise Vollard, Paris. Meller, Munich. P. Cassirer, Berlin. H. von Simolin, Berlin. P. Cassirer, Amsterdam.

730. PORTRAIT OF THE ARTIST'S SON IN A ROUND HAT, 1879–80

$8\frac{9}{16} \times 5$ inches—21,7 × 12,6 cm. Page XLVI verso of the sketchbook Leigh Block. Pencil. Verso: No. 340.

It is the round hat worn by the boy, then about seven, that gives character to this drawing.

BIBLIOGRAPHY: Rewald, *Carnets*: C V, p. XLVI verso (reproduced pl. 28).

COLLECTIONS: Cézanne *fils*, Paris. M. Renou, Paris. Poyet, Lyons. M. Renou, Paris. Sam Salz, New York. Mr. and Mrs. Leigh Block, Chicago.

731. PAGE OF STUDIES, 1879–80

$9\frac{7}{16} \times 12\frac{3}{16}$ inches—24 × 31 cm. Pencil. Verso: No. 715.

Page upright, lower left: (a) Draped half-length figure of Christ in right three-quarter view, after engraving (in Charles Blanc, *Ecole Espagnole*) of Pedro de Moya's paint-

FIG. 108. After Pedro de Moya (born 1610): *Saint Theresa*, detail of the vignette reproducing this canvas in Charles Blanc, *Ecole espagnole* (1869). *(Photograph: Chappuis)*

FIG. 109. After Pedro de Moya (born 1610): engraving reproducing the painting *Joseph Sold by his Brothers* in Charles Blanc, *Ecole espagnole* (1869). *(Photograph: Chappuis)*

FIG. 110. After Tintoretto (1512–94): engraving reproducing the portrait of Maria Robusti, known as *Tintoretta*, in Charles Blanc, *Ecole vénitienne* (1868). *(Photograph: Chappuis)*

ing *Saint Theresa*. See fig. 108.—(b) Lower right: sketch after an engraving (in Charles Blanc, *Ecole Espagnole*) of Pedro de Moya's painting *Joseph Sold by his Brothers*. See fig. 109.—(c) Left: head of the artist's son, his look attentive.—Page lengthwise, top right: (d) Head of the son, looking calmly at the viewer.—(e) Lower right: head of the son, an impatient expression on his face; only the left ear breaks the oval contour of the head.—(f) Toward the center: head (in heavier strokes) after the engraving (in Charles Blanc, *Ecole Vénitienne*) of Tintoretto's portrait of

his daugher, *Tintoretta*. See fig. 110. The engraving is mediocre. The Venetian atmosphere achieved by Cézanne in copying this head is nearer to Titian than to Tintoretto, and it is masterly. The stroke separating the heads from the rest is not by Cézanne, nor the inscription and crosses. See Note 25.

BIBLIOGRAPHY: Venturi, Vol. I, No. 1475, described as recto (not reproduced). Berthold, cat. No. 336 (not reproduced). *Cézanne dessinateur*, *GBA*, Nov. 1965, p. 296 (reproduced fig. 9).

EXHIBITION: The Phillips Collection, Washington, D.C., Chicago, Boston, 1971, No. 68A (reproduced).

COLLECTIONS: Kenneth Clark, London. Eger, Paris. Rousso, Paris. The Lazarus and Rosalie Phillips Family Collection, Montreal.

732. HEAD OF THE ARTIST'S SON, 1879–80

$8\frac{9}{16} \times 4\frac{15}{16}$ inches—21,7 × 12,5 cm. Page X verso from the sketchbook CP II. Pencil. Verso: No. 622.

Head of the son, a candid expression on his face. To the left, the hatching around the cheek and chin indicates shadow, perspective, and gradations. The boy's temple is worth noting.

BIBLIOGRAPHY: Venturi, Vol. I, under No. 1284 (not reproduced). *Dessins*, 1938, No. 23 (reproduced). Neumeyer, 1958, No. 39 (reproduced).

EXHIBITION: Phillips Collection, Washington, D.C., Chicago, Boston, 1971, No. 69 (reproduced).

COLLECTIONS: Cézanne *fils*, Paris. Paul Guillaume, Paris. A. Chappuis, Tresserve. Private collection, Paris.

733. THE ARTIST'S SON ASLEEP, AND STUDY OF A HAT, circa 1880

$4\frac{7}{8} \times 8\frac{9}{16}$ inches—12,4 × 21,7 cm. Page XLVII verso of the sketchbook A.I.C. Pencil. Verso: No. 843.

(a) Right: head of the boy, his eyes closed. In spite of the direction of the hatching strokes, it seems to me that the head is lying flat on the nape of the neck.—(b) Left: study of a hat on a piece of furniture; the right side has not been drawn. (b) is on a larger scale than (a) yet the page is co-ordinated visually as a whole.

BIBLIOGRAPHY: Rewald, *Carnets*: C II, p. XLVII verso (not reproduced). Schniewind, text p. 33 (reproduced). Andersen, *Sk.* (not reproduced).

COLLECTIONS: Cézanne *fils*, Paris. M, Renou, Paris. Poyet, Lyons. M. Renou, Paris. Sam Salz, New York. Art Institute, Chicago.

734. HEAD OF THE ARTIST'S SON, circa 1880

$8\frac{5}{8} \times 5$ inches—21,8 × 12,6 cm. Back endpaper of the sketchbook CP II. Pencil, slight tears on the right, pen notations. Verso: the cloth cover of the sketchbook.

Head of the artist's son, bent forward and almost in profile, the eyelids half closed.—Notations, in ink: 30—*à* 3 *c.* —18 *sous*/3 *à* 4 *c.*—12.

BIBLIOGRAPHY: Venturi, Vol. I, under No. 1299 (not reproduced). *Dessins*, 1957, No. 34 (reproduced).

COLLECTIONS: Cézanne *fils*, Paris. Paul Guillaume, Paris. A. Chappuis, Tresserve.

735. HEAD OF A BOY ASLEEP, circa 1880

$10\frac{1}{16} \times 7\frac{13}{16}$ inches—25,5 × 19,8 cm. Pencil and wash on laid paper with the watermark: HALLINES (crowned with a fleur-de-lis), horizontal fold. Verso: No. 264.

Only the head is drawn, at the corner of a bed; a collar is indicated by horizontal strokes. The left edge of the page has been trimmed, the mat covering $\frac{3}{16}$ of an inch of the sketch on this side. I am by no means sure that this drawing represents the artist's son.

BIBLIOGRAPHY: Venturi, Vol. I, p. 352, Oeuvres Inédites "Portrait du fils de l'artiste" (not reproduced). Basel catalog No. 100, dated circa 1882 (reproduced). Douglas Cooper, in *Master Drawings*, Vol. 1, No. 4, 1963, p. 56.

COLLECTIONS: Cézanne *fils*, Paris. W. Feuz, Bern. Kunstmuseum, Basel.

736. HEAD OF MME CÉZANNE, circa 1880

$6\frac{3}{4} \times 4\frac{3}{4}$ inches—17,2 × 12 cm. Pencil on laid paper. Verso: blank page.

Mme Cézanne seen in left three-quarter view. There is a resemblance between this drawing and the painting Venturi No. 229. Cf. our Nos. 520 (i), 718.

BIBLIOGRAPHY: Venturi, Vol. I, p. 350, Oeuvres Inédites (not reproduced).

EXHIBITIONS: Influences in French Drawing, East Hampton, New York, 1952, No. 27. New York, Nov. 1952, No. 6 (reproduced). Aix-en-Provence, 1956, No. 89. The Hague, 1956, No. 118 (reproduced). Zurich, 1956, No. 73 (reproduced). Munich, 1956, No. 137 (reproduced). Los Angeles, No. 14 (reproduced). Wildenstein Gallery, New York, 1956, No. 65 (reproduced). Kunstverein, Hamburg, 1963, No. 28.

COLLECTIONS: Ambroise Vollard, Paris. J. Rewald, New York. Sale, Sotheby's, London, July 7, 1960, No. 15 (reproduced). H. Berggruen, Paris.

737. VIEW OF THE FARM AT THE JAS DE BOUFFAN, early 1874

$6\frac{5}{16} \times 9\frac{7}{8}$ inches—16 × 25 cm. Pencil, handwriting in ink. Verso: No. 738.

Unfinished sketch showing the farm buildings of the Jas de Bouffan, partly hidden by a tree; cf. Nos. 618, 880, 916. Rough draft of a letter to a Pontoise collector; see *Correspondance*, letter XXIX.

BIBLIOGRAPHY: *Correspondance* (reproduced fig. 16).

COLLECTIONS: Cézanne *fils*, Paris. Galerie Zak, Paris. Present owner unknown.

738. LANDSCAPE AT AUVERS-SUR-OISE, towards 1874

$6\frac{5}{16} \times 9\frac{7}{8}$ inches—16 × 25 cm. Pencil, small stains. Verso: No. 737.

Study for the painting Venturi No. 135. A wide road leads from the foreground toward the right background; lower down on the left there is a thatched cottage, and beyond the trees a ridge of hills. A kind of rustic intimacy predominates in this work.

BIBLIOGRAPHY: *Correspondance* (reproduced fig. 15).

COLLECTIONS: Cézanne *fils*, Paris. Galerie Zak, Paris. Present owner unknown.

739. TREES IN A PARK, towards 1874

$9\frac{5}{16} \times 6\frac{15}{16}$ inches—23,6 × 17,7 cm. Page from the sketchbook 18 × 24. Soft pencil on brown paper, top right corner restored. Verso: rough draft of a letter (1885); see *Correspondance*, fig. 28.

In the foreground of this landscape, which has a distinctive style evoking that of Venturi No. 148, we see the border of the bend of a road, above a trench. Three pine trees rise vertically in the middle ground, and to the right there is a clump of gnarled trunks with numerous spreading branches, counterbalanced to the left by a slender pine. Lower down, at right center, the roof of a small building is indicated. The slope opposite forms a light diagonal with a road going up to the left. A rather indistinct wooded area stretches out in the background beyond the road, the treetops standing out against the sky.

BIBLIOGRAPHY: F. Novotny, *Cézanne*, Phaidon, 1937, No. 120 (reproduced). J. Rewald, Eine unbekannte Episode aus dem Leben Cézannes, *Neue Zürcher Zeitung*, Feb. 6, 1938 (reproduced). Neumeyer, 1958, No. 74 (reproduced).

EXHIBITIONS: Kunsthalle, Basel, 1936, No. 105. Belvedere, Vienna, 1961, No. 89; dated 1877–80.

COLLECTION: Albertina, Vienna (Inv. No. 24080).

739bis. LANDSCAPE, circa 1874

$10\frac{1}{16} \times 7\frac{1}{2}$ inches (sight)—25,5 × 19 cm. Pencil. Verso: blank page.

Study assigning a plane to each of the different elements composing the landscape: trees on the right, crown of a tree on the left, farm on a hill.

COLLECTIONS: Kenneth Clark, London. M. and Mme Albert Skira, Geneva. Jean-Michel Skira, Geneva.

740. LANDSCAPE WITH TREES, circa 1874

$4\frac{7}{8} \times 8\frac{9}{16}$ inches—12,4 × 21,7 cm. Page VII of the sketchbook A.I.C. Pencil, stains. Verso: No. 618.

Although this sketch is sparely drawn, and the subject seen from a certain distance, its unity is clear. There seems to be a stream flowing across the foreground.

BIBLIOGRAPHY: Rewald, *Carnets*: C II, p. VII (reproduced pl. 42). Schniewind, text p. 26 (reproduced). Andersen, *Sk.* (not reproduced).

COLLECTIONS: Cézanne *fils*, Paris. M. Renou, Paris. Poyet, Lyons. M. Renou, Paris. Sam Salz, New York. Art Institute, Chicago.

741. LANDSCAPE WITH HOUSES AND TREES, circa 1874

$7\frac{1}{4} \times 8\frac{7}{8}$ inches—18,4 × 22,4 cm. Pencil on laid paper with watermark: fragment of a volute, cut off by the lower left edge of the paper; splotches and stains. Verso: No. 320.

Study of a wide landscape with houses and trees. In the right foreground a few leafy branches thrust diagonally into the composition; the houses on the left are drawn in perspective, a range of hills extends across the background. Probably a view of Auvers-sur-Oise. Cf. Venturi No. 150.

BIBLIOGRAPHY: Venturi, Vol. I, p. 351, Oeuvres Inédites (not reproduced). Basel catalog, No. 85 (reproduced).

COLLECTIONS: Cézanne *fils*, Paris. W. Feuz, Bern. Kunstmuseum, Basel.

742. SUNSET, circa 1873

$8\frac{1}{2} \times 13$ inches—21,6 × 33 cm. Pastel. Verso: blank page.

Landscape with roofs in the foreground, and further back a few isolated trees in front of a river.

BIBLIOGRAPHY: Venturi, Vol. I, p. 347, Oeuvres Inédites, "Coll. Gachet. Paysage avec maisons" (not reproduced.)

COLLECTIONS: Dr. Gachet, Auvers. Paul Gachet, Auvers (Inv. PG 28). Jacques O'Hana, London. Maurice Harris, London.

742A. THE QUARRY, circa 1873

$10\frac{5}{8} \times 18\frac{1}{8}$ inches—27 × 46 cm. Pencil and pastel on gray-blue laid paper. Watermark: P.L. Verso: blank page. (Not reproduced.)

Sketch of an abandoned quarry near Dr. Gachet's house at Auvers-sur-Oise.

BIBLIOGRAPHY: Venturi, Vol. I, p. 347, Oeuvres Inédites, "Paysage avec collines" (not reproduced.)

COLLECTIONS: Dr. Gachet, Auvers. Paul Gachet, Auvers. Present owner unknown.

743. TREES AND A WALL AT THE JAS DE BOUFFAN, circa 1874

$4\frac{7}{8} \times 8\frac{9}{16}$ inches—12,4 × 21,7 cm. Page III of the sketchbook A.I.C. Pencil, stains. Verso: blank page.

Part of the garden surrounding the Jas, seen from a higher level. Two large tree branches form a V in the foreground. Top: scribbles by a child.

BIBLIOGRAPHY: Rewald, Carnets: C II, p. III (not reproduced). Schniewind, text p. 26 (reproduced). Andersen, Sk. (reproduced fig. 20B).

COLLECTIONS: Cézanne fils, Paris. M. Renou, Paris. Poyet, Lyons. M. Renou, Paris. Sam Salz, New York. Art Institute, Chicago.

744. STUDY OF A TREE, 1875–78

$17\frac{7}{8} \times 11$ inches—45,5 × 28 cm. Pencil on laid paper. Verso: a watercolor of trees.

In the upper part of this large page there is a lightly sketched cluster of tree trunks in the form of a fan, their branches spreading out in coils; cf. No. 792.

COLLECTIONS: Sale, Sotheby's, London, Dec. 1, 1965, No. 114 (the verso reproduced). Adolphe Stein, Paris. James Lord, New York. Mr. and Mrs. Warren Brandt, New York.

745. STUDY OF A TREE, 1875–78

$14\frac{3}{4} \times 11\frac{3}{4}$ inches—37,5 × 29,8 cm. Pencil. Reverse side inaccessible.

Tree in a garden. Its branches grow out in coils and then shoot up almost vertically. Other vegetation is seen in the background, beyond a horizontally fenced enclosure.

EXHIBITION: W. R. Valentiner Memorial Exhibition, Nov.–Jan. 1963–64, J. L. Hudson Gallery, Detroit, Michigan, cat. No. 3 (reproduced).

COLLECTIONS: W. R. Valentiner, Detroit. Present owner unknown.

746. STUDY OF TREES AND HEAD OF A BOY, 1875–78

Measurements not known. Pencil, a few stains; strip of paper glued along the lower edge. Verso: ?

(a) Study of trees; the crowns of the two trees on the left join with the foliage of another tree on the right.—(b) Below, at right angles: portrait of the artist's young son Paul.

COLLECTION: Present owner unknown.

747. GARDEN ENTRANCE, 1875–78

$8\frac{5}{8} \times 4\frac{7}{8}$ inches—21,8 × 12,4 cm. Page XXXIX from the sketchbook CP II. Pencil. Verso: No. 542.

Entrance in a garden wall topped with tiles. Further back there is a tree, a tall house, and to the right a curious building with a window; a receding line on the right indicates a stairway shaft. Cf. the watercolors Venturi Nos. 840, 842.

BIBLIOGRAPHY: Venturi, Vol. I, under No. 1292 (not reproduced).

COLLECTIONS: Cézanne fils, Paris. Paul Guillaume, Paris. A. Chappuis, Tresserve. Private collection, Paris. Private collection, New York.

748. GNARLED TREE, 1875–78

$17\frac{3}{4} \times 12\frac{3}{16}$ inches—45 × 31 cm. Pencil. Verso: blank page.

Large study that was not classified by Venturi in 1936. It represents a big tree, with a smaller one in the left background. Characteristic gnarl below the main fork of the big tree.

COLLECTIONS: Private collection, Paris. Bollag, Zurich. Bollag sale, Zurich, April 3, 1925, cat. No. 35, "Knorriger Baum" (not reproduced). Amélie Bollag, Zurich.

749. LANDSCAPE STUDY, 1875–78

$5 \times 8\frac{9}{16}$ inches—12,6 × 21,7 cm. Page XLII verso of the sketchbook Leigh Block. Pencil, page soiled by smudging. Verso: No. 341.

The foreground consists of a grassy slope leading down to the right, balanced in the middle ground by an inclined plane slanting in the opposite direction; a path leads between the two. A tree trunk and the horizon line are indicated near the top of the page.

BIBLIOGRAPHY: Rewald, Carnets: C V, p. XLII verso (not reproduced).

COLLECTIONS: Cézanne fils, Paris. M. Renou, Paris. Poyet, Lyons. M. Renou, Paris. Sam Salz, New York. Mr. and Mrs. Leigh Block, Chicago.

750. LANDSCAPE SKETCH, 1875–78

$8\frac{9}{16} \times 5$ inches—21,7 × 12,6 cm. Page XXXIX verso of the sketchbook Leigh Block. Pencil. Verso: No. 1077.

A number of trees in leaf on a slope leading down to the left, where a rectangular block is seen low down beside a little path. All over the page the strokes are lightly drawn.

BIBLIOGRAPHY: Rewald, Carnets: C V, p. XXXIX verso (not reproduced).

COLLECTIONS: Cézanne fils, Paris. M. Renou, Paris. Poyet, Lyons. M. Renou, Paris. Sam Salz, New York. Mr. and Mrs. Leigh Block, Chicago.

751. LANDSCAPE SKETCH, 1875–78

$8\frac{9}{16} \times 5$ inches—21,7 × 12,6 cm. Page XI verso of the sketchbook Leigh Block. Pencil. Verso: No. 752.

Sketch done in rapid hatching indicating shadow and light, almost without contours. A bright, massive volume soaring up like a tower represents a sheer wall of rock in Bibémus quarry, surrounded by vegetation. On the right, a sapling.

BIBLIOGRAPHY: Rewald, *Carnets*: C V, p. XI verso (not reproduced).

COLLECTIONS: Cézanne *fils*, Paris. M. Renou, Paris. Poyet, Lyons. M. Renou, Paris. Sam Salz, New York. Mr. and Mrs. Leigh Block, Chicago.

752. LANDSCAPE SKETCH, 1875–78

$8\frac{9}{16} \times 5$ inches—21,7 × 12,6 cm. Page XI of the sketchbook Leigh Block. Pencil. Verso: No. 751.

The rapidly sketched foreground of this landscape leads down to the right; a few boulders are strewn on a stretch of land sloping to the left. Leafy trees in the background.

BIBLIOGRAPHY: Rewald, *Carnets*: C V, p. XI (not reproduced).

COLLECTIONS: Cézanne *fils*, Paris. M. Renou, Paris. Poyet, Lyons. M. Renou, Paris. Sam Salz, New York. Mr. and Mrs. Leigh Block, Chicago.

753. IN BIBÉMUS QUARRY, 1875–78

$5 \times 8\frac{9}{16}$ inches—12,6 × 21,7 cm. Page XLIII of the sketchbook Leigh Block. Pencil. Verso: No. 844.

A corner of Bibémus quarry: the same motif as No. 754. The site is curiously shaped, owing to the extraction of blocks of stone. A shadow (top left) indicates an almost rectangular cavity where a section of the rock has been quarried. The shadow on the right represents an overhanging inclined plane.

BIBLIOGRAPHY: Rewald, *Carnets*: C V, p. XLIII (not reproduced).

COLLECTIONS: Cézanne *fils,* Paris. M. Renou, Paris. Poyet, Lyons. M. Renou, Paris. Sam Salz, New York. Mr. and Mrs. Leigh Block.

754. IN BIBÉMUS QUARRY, STUDY, 1875–78

$8\frac{9}{16} \times 5$ inches—21,7 × 12,6 cm. Page VIII verso of the sketchbook Leigh Block. Pencil. Verso: No. 339.

The same motif as No. 753.

BIBLIOGRAPHY: Rewald, *Carnets*: C V, p. VIII verso (not reproduced).

COLLECTIONS: Cézanne *fils,* Paris. M. Renou, Paris. Poyet, Lyons. M. Renou, Paris. Sam Salz, New York. Mr. and Mrs. Leigh Block.

755. HOUSE WITH TREES, 1876–79

$4\frac{7}{8} \times 8\frac{9}{16}$ inches—12,4 × 21,7 cm. Page V of the sketchbook A.I.C. Pencil, stains. Verso: No. 790.

Rich zones of sunlight intermingle with the trees, both in the garden of the foreground and in the more distant view seen on the right. Cf. the same subject No. 811 and the left part of the canvas Venturi No. 407. The impressionist quality of this drawing has been stressed; it may be added that clearly defined structural research is also evident.

BIBLIOGRAPHY: Rewald, *Carnets*: C II, p. V (reproduced pl. 65). Schniewind, text p. 26 (reproduced). J. Rewald, Cézanne: Landschaften, *Kleine Enzyklopädie der Kunst*, Hazan, Paris, 1958 (reproduced). Andersen, *Sk.* (reproduced fig. 23B). *The World of Cézanne* (reproduced p. 94). F. Mathey, Les Impressionnistes, Paris, 1959, and New York, 1961 (reproduced p. 219).

COLLECTIONS: Cézanne *fils*, Paris. M. Renou, Paris. Poyet, Lyons. M. Renou, Paris. Sam Salz, New York. Art Institute, Chicago.

756. LANDSCAPE WITH CHURCH, 1876–79

$4\frac{5}{8} \times 7\frac{5}{8}$ inches—11,8 × 19,4 cm. Page XIV verso from the sketchbook CP I. Pencil. Verso: No. 1175.

Unfinished sketch of a landscape and the silhouette of a church (or other building) with a small dome, lantern, and turret.

BIBLIOGRAPHY: Venturi, Vol. I, under No. 1270 (not reproduced).

COLLECTIONS: Cézanne *fils*, Paris. Paul Guillaume, Paris. A. Chappuis, Tresserve.

757. LANDSCAPE, 1876–79

$8\frac{11}{16} \times 11\frac{13}{16}$ inches—22 × 30 cm. Pencil, small violet ink stain lower right. Verso: No. 477.

Landscape without houses or figures. There are trees on the left, several boulders in the foreground, and further back the bend of a river in the flat of a valley.

BIBLIOGRAPHY: Venturi, Vol. I, verso of No. 1583 (not reproduced). Basel catalog, No. 88 (reproduced).

COLLECTIONS: Cézanne *fils*, Paris. W. Feuz, Bern. Kunstmuseum, Basel.

758. LANDSCAPE WITH TREES, 1876–79

$8\frac{3}{8} \times 5\frac{1}{8}$ inches—21,3 × 12,9 cm. Page from a sketchbook. Pencil, rectangular stamp. Verso: No. 151.

Rather confused landscape, showing a kind of oval clearing surrounded by vegetation.

COLLECTIONS: Camille Pissarro, Paris. Pissarro sale, Dec. 3, 1928, as verso of No. 62. Cabinet des Dessins of the Louvre.

759. ROCKY WOODED LANDSCAPE, 1876–79

$5 \times 8\frac{9}{16}$ inches—12,6 × 21,7 cm. Page IIII verso of the sketchbook Leigh Block. Pencil, small stains, smudging. Verso: No. 414.

Walls of sheer rock are revealed by irregularities in the terrain, with bushes and trees in the background. View of Bibémus quarry, near Aix.

BIBLIOGRAPHY: Rewald, *Carnets*: C V, p. IIII verso (not reproduced).

COLLECTIONS: Cézanne *fils*, Paris. M. Renou, Paris. Poyet, Lyons. M. Renou, Paris. Sam Salz, New York. Mr. and Mrs. Leigh Block, Chicago.

760. TREES AND A HOUSE, 1876–79

$5 \times 8\frac{9}{16}$ inches—12,6 × 21,7 cm. Page XLIV verso of the sketchbook Leigh Block. Pencil. Verso: No. 653.

An open space stretching back, broken by some trees and

a flower bed; a few bushes in receding perspective and a house on the right. Fine sketch full of sunlight.

BIBLIOGRAPHY: Rewald, *Carnets*: C V, p. XLIV verso (not reproduced).

COLLECTIONS: Cézanne *fils*, Paris. M. Renou, Paris. Poyet, Lyons. M. Renou, Paris. Sam Salz, New York. Mr. and Mrs. Leigh Block, Chicago.

761. LANDSCAPE WITH A DONKEY, 1876–79

$4\frac{9}{16} \times 7\frac{3}{16}$ inches—11,6 × 18,2 cm. Page 17 verso from the first sketchbook Mrs. Enid A. Haupt. Pencil. Verso: No. 676.

This drawing is related to the painting Venturi No. 108 *The Thieves and the Donkey*, the date of which is generally accepted as around 1870. The canvas represents a scene from Lucius Apuleius' romance *The Metamorphoses*, written in Latin in the second century and known also, though nobody knows why, as *The Golden Ass*. The title given to Cézanne's painting, *The Thieves and the Donkey*, is taken from a fable by La Fontaine (Book I, No. XIII) of which every Frenchman knows the lines:

Arrive un troisième larron
Qui saisit maître Aliboron . . .

We have no reason to believe that Cézanne intended to illustrate this fable.—The painting shows a group of men near a rock jutting out over the sea, carrying heavy loot of some kind towards a donkey. A man is sitting smoking a pipe at the foot of the rock, while another is at work near a tree on the right. Which particular scene from Apuleius' story can this picture represent? In the narrative, which Cézanne read in the Latin text (J. Gasquet, 1926, p. 134), a certain Lucius tells how he was changed by magic into a donkey and recounts the donkey life he led up till his miraculous release and return to human form. As a donkey, Lucius was loaded with burdens and received all kinds of treatment at the hands of succeeding owners. Cézanne was probably illustrating Chapter 25 of Book IV, where certain brigands load the animal with booty hauled out of a cave. Apuleius' romance creates a world rich in color that may well have incited Cézanne to paint this episode within the framework of his own imagination. The touch of irony mentioned by Venturi was already there in the story. But a personal reason also impelled the artist to represent this stoic donkey in the center of the picture: I think that a sense of something shared between them linked the artist to the animal. For Lucius, having become a donkey, retains his human conscience and intelligence, and his cultured spirit renders him far superior to the men whose affronts he has to suffer. In the same way Cézanne felt himself superior to the critics whose lack of understanding led them to trample his painting underfoot. Added to this, from his early youth a chance assonance had ordained Cézanne twin to the donkey: In speaking of the Cézanne family, it was always easy to pronounce the name "*ces ânes*" (these donkeys): also, before becoming a banker the artist's father ran a hat business on the Cours Mirabeau with the help of two partners, Martin and Coupin. The name Martin is commonly given in France to donkeys: there is a proverbial saying, "There are several donkeys called Martin." And by a play on words, which no doubt originated over a glass or two of absinthe, the inhabitants of Aix described the three hatters by saying: "Martin, Coupin, and Cézanne make eighteen animals" (*Martin, copain, et seize ânes*—Martin, his pal, and

FIG. 111.
Paul Cézanne:
pen sketch.

sixteen donkeys). The painter had heard this joke as a child, and his schoolmates no doubt seldom failed to stress the second half of Paul's surname. At that time he happened to spell it "CEZANE" himself. Through the efforts of Marcel Provence, the Chemin des Lauves studio in Aix now has a book, a souvenir of the artist's boyhood, discovered in the house of his sister Marie. See Note 55. The drawing reproduced here as fig. 111 appears on the title page, with the name "Cezane" written in pencil. It is the first self-portrait by the painter known to us. In a letter to Zola dated January 17, 1859, he signed with the Latinized name *Paulus Cezasinus*, after using the vocative Cezasine in the text (*Correspondance*, letter VIII). Gasquet's evidence differs slightly (1926, p. 116): "Lately someone else, wanting to illustrate a poem dedicated to the eminent hermit (read: a defamatory pamphlet) scribbled a donkey's head beneath the noble rhymes . . . ." But let us come back to the drawing. It shows the landscape and donkey, without the brigands, in a less anecdotal spirit than that of the painting. The sea stretches out on the left under a cloudy sky, and in front of the sea stands one solitary rock. To its right rises the profile of a cliff, which itself has been left white and is partly hidden by a tree in the right foreground. Cf. No. 274 (f) and (g), fragment showing two brigands and the donkey. The page embodying this fragment dates from 1869–70, which means that the sketches are in direct rapport with the painting, whereas our No. 761 would have been drawn in the sketchbook seven or eight years later. Judging from the treatment and style, I see no other possibility, although I realize that others will not accept this undisciplined return to an earlier theme.

The following are other works in which donkeys figure: Nos. 531, 532; Venturi Nos. 239, 249. And finally, a note by Gasquet (1926, p. 26): "At his brother-in-law's I saw one of his first canvases, a little donkey, drawn naïvely and with adorable clumsiness, gentle and gray but with a vague pantheism floating around it."

BIBLIOGRAPHY: Rewald, *Carnets*: C I, p. 17 verso (reproduced pl. 43).

COLLECTIONS: Cézanne *fils*, Paris. M. Renou, Paris. Poyet, Lyons. M. Renou, Paris. Sam Salz, New York. Mrs. Enid A. Haupt, New York.

762. LANDSCAPE WITH TREES, 1876–79

$5\frac{1}{8} \times 8\frac{1}{16}$ inches—13 × 20,5 cm. Pencil. Verso: a child's scribbles.

A tree in the center with a luxurious crown of foliage, and a vista to the right with two trees in the distance. This impetuous sketch contains details that are difficult to interpret.

COLLECTIONS: Cézanne *fils*, Paris. Galerie L. G. Baugin, Paris. Maurice Laffaille, Neuilly-sur-Seine. Dina Vierny, Paris.

763. THE POOL AT THE JAS DE BOUFFAN, 1877–80

$5 \times 8\frac{9}{16}$ inches—12,7 × 21,7 cm. Page XXXVI verso from the second sketchbook Mrs. Enid A. Haupt. Pencil. Verso: No. 1134.

Composition stressing vertical, horizontal, and diagonal lines. From center to far right of the middleground, seen in perspective, there is an iron enclosure with upright posts: the grille that surrounded the pool at the Jas de Bouffan. Cf. Venturi Nos. 648, 166, and our Nos. 672, 891.

BIBLIOGRAPHY: Rewald, *Carnets:* C IV, p. XXXVI verso (reproduced pl. 57). Yvon Taillandier, *Paul Cézanne,* Paris, New York, Munich, 1961 and 1965 (reproduced p. 24).

COLLECTIONS: Cézanne *fils,* Paris. M. Renou, Paris. Poyet, Lyons. M. Renou, Paris. Sam Salz, New York. Mrs. Enid A. Haupt, New York.

764. VIEW OF A HOUSE ON A HILL, 1877–80

$5 \times 8\frac{9}{16}$ inches—12,6 × 21,7 cm. Page XXVII of the sketchbook Leigh Block. Pencil on gray paper. Verso: No. 663.

Landscape sketch, mainly in contours. To the right of the house, a distant view and the foliage of a tree. A little valley runs across between the foreground and the house.

BIBLIOGRAPHY: Rewald, *Carnets:* C V, p. XXVII (not reproduced).

COLLECTIONS: Cézanne *fils,* Paris. M. Renou, Paris. Poyet, Lyons. M. Renou, Paris. Sam Salz, New York. Mr. and Mrs. Leigh Block, Chicago.

765. PANORAMIC LANDSCAPE SPREADING OVER TWO PAGES, 1877–80

$4\frac{9}{16} \times 14\frac{5}{16}$ inches—11,6 × 36,4 cm. Pages 7 verso and 8 from the first sketchbook Mrs. Enid A. Haupt. Pencil. Verso: Nos. 262 and 806.

Provençal landscape. Rewald thinks it must be a view of L'Estaque, but Reff questions this site and refers to the painting Venturi No. 302.

BIBLIOGRAPHY: Rewald, *Carnets:* C I, pp. 7 verso and 8 (reproduced pls. 60 and 61). Th. Reff, *Cézanne's Drawings 1875–85, BurlM,* May 1959, p. 172 (reproduced fig. 24).

COLLECTIONS: Cézanne *fils,* Paris. M. Renou, Paris. Poyet, Lyons. M. Renou, Paris. Sam Salz, New York. Mrs. Enid A. Haupt, New York.

766. HOUSE AND TREES, 1877–80

$8\frac{9}{16} \times 5$ inches—21,7 × 12,6 cm. Page IX verso of the sketchbook Leigh Block. Pencil. Verso: No. 723.

Right: corner of a house with three windows, one above the other, and two small chimneys on the roof; to the left a cluster of trees and bushes, shaded by hatching. This hatching calls to mind eighteenth-century red chalk drawings. Although the trees are further back, their tops

appear to be in a line with the roof; this is because the view is not from ground level, but from an upper window.

BIBLIOGRAPHY: Rewald, *Carnets:* C V, p. IX verso (reproduced pl. 51).

COLLECTIONS: Cézanne *fils,* Paris. M. Renou, Paris. Poyet, Lyons. M. Renou, Paris. Sam Salz, New York. Mrs. Enid A. Haupt, New York.

767. LANDSCAPE WITH PIGEON TOWER, 1877–80

$4\frac{7}{8} \times 8\frac{5}{8}$ inches—12,4 × 21,8 cm. Page XXXI from the sketchbook CP II. Pencil on gray paper. Verso: No. 661.

Landscape showing a *pigeonnier* and a farmhouse surrounded by a wall, in a simple but expressive setting; cf. the painting of Bellevue, Venturi No. 654. That site, however, is unidentifiable in our drawing.

BIBLIOGRAPHY: Venturi, Vol. I, under 1290 (not reproduced).

COLLECTIONS: Cézanne *fils,* Paris. Paul Guillaume, Paris. A. Chappuis, Tresserve.

768. LANDSCAPE NEAR AIX-EN-PROVENCE, 1877–80

$6 \times 18\frac{5}{8}$ inches—15,2 × 47,4 cm. Pages III verso and IIII of the Album, Paul Mellon Collection. Pencil drawing spreading over two pages. Verso of the first page: No. 866; of the second: blank page.

Panoramic sketch of the environs of Aix, the background summarily drawn. A photograph of the motif published by Rewald allows us to identify a gazometer figuring in the center of the left page. The houses shown by Cézanne no longer exist.

BIBLIOGRAPHY: Venturi No. 1302. J. Rewald and Léo Marchutz, *Cézanne et la Provence, Le Point,* Aug. 1936 (reproduced pp. 12 & 13 with a photograph of the motif). F. Novotny, *Cézanne und das Ende der wissenschaftlichen Perspektive,* Vienna, 1938, p. 201, No. 65 (not reproduced). *Album,* 1966 (reproduced with a photograph of the motif).

COLLECTIONS: Cézanne *fils,* Paris. Paul Guillaume, Paris. A. Chappuis, Tresserve. Mr. and Mrs. Paul Mellon, Upperville, Va.

769. LANDSCAPE, WITH SEA AND MOUNTAINS, 1877–80

$4\frac{7}{8} \times 4$ inches—12,4 × 10,1 cm. Page XII of the sketchbook A.I.C. Pencil. Verso: No. 492. The outer half of the page has been cut off.

Landscape drawn in little strokes: a house with the sea behind and mountains in the background. The curving rhythm of the two summits seems characteristic.

BIBLIOGRAPHY: Rewald, *Carnets:* C II, p. XII (not reproduced). Schniewind, text p. 28 (reproduced). Andersen, *Sk.* (not reproduced).

COLLECTIONS: Cézanne *fils,* Paris. M. Renou, Paris. Poyet, Lyons. M. Renou, Paris. Sam Salz, New York. Art Institute, Chicago.

770. MOUNTAIN LANDSCAPE, 1877–80

$8\frac{9}{16} \times 5$ inches—21,7 × 12,6 cm. Page II of the sketchbook Leigh Block. Pencil. Verso: No. 299.

Unfinished sketch of a mountain landscape with three cows in the foreground and two pine trunks.

BIBLIOGRAPHY: Rewald, *Carnets:* C V, p. II (not reproduced).

COLLECTIONS: Cézanne *fils*, Paris. M. Renou, Paris. Poyet, Lyons. M. Renou, Paris. Sam Salz, New York. Mr. and Mrs. Leigh Block, Chicago.

771 · STUDY OF A TREE, BATHER, 1875–80

$8\frac{9}{16} \times 4\frac{7}{8}$ inches—21,7 × 12,4 cm. Page XXV verso of the sketchbook A.I.C. Pencil, stains. Verso: No. 883.

Page lengthwise: (a) Incomplete sketch of a bather with his right arm outstretched.—Page upright (b): Near to the bather: rapid study of a shoulder and arm, partly covered by foliage.—(c) Study of a tree with a dense crown of leaves, the ground indicated by a few strokes.

BIBLIOGRAPHY: Rewald, *Carnets*: C II, p. XXV verso (not reproduced). Schniewind, text p. 30 (reproduced). Andersen, *Sk.* (not reproduced). Th. Reff, Bather (not reproduced).

COLLECTIONS: Cézanne *fils*, Paris. M. Renou, Paris. Poyet, Lyons. M. Renou, Paris. Sam Salz, New York. Art Institute, Chicago.

772 · LANDSCAPE WITH TREES, 1877–80

$4\frac{7}{8} \times 8\frac{9}{16}$ inches—12,4 × 21,7 cm. Page XX verso of the sketchbook A.I.C. Pencil, stains. Verso: No. 570.

Left, an old willow tree, and in the middleground, the wall of an enclosure; cf. No. 883.

BIBLIOGRAPHY: Rewald, *Carnets*: C II, p. XX verso (reproduced pl. 54). Schniewind, text p. 29 (reproduced). Andersen, *Sk.* (not reproduced). Yvon Taillandier, *Paul Cézanne*, Paris, New York, Munich, 1961 and 1965 (reproduced p. 28).

COLLECTIONS: Cézanne *fils*, Paris. M. Renou, Paris. Poyet, Lyons. M. Renou, Paris. Sam Salz, New York. Art Institute, Chicago.

773 · IN THE GARDEN, circa 1880

$5\frac{5}{8} \times 7\frac{3}{4}$ inches—14,3 × 19,6 cm. Pencil on laid paper, fold on the right, upper part of the page cut off. Verso: No. 222.

In the foreground, a cluster of geranium stalks growing like trees, with a little mound at the roots. Further away, a garden path bending round a patch of grass with a tree trunk and some bushes.

BIBLIOGRAPHY: Venturi, Vol. I, p. 352, Oeuvres Inédites (not reproduced). Basel catalog, No. 102 (reproduced).

COLLECTIONS: Cézanne *fils*, Paris. W. Feuz, Bern. Kunstmuseum, Basel.

774 · LANDSCAPE WITH BARE TREES, PORTRAIT OF MME CÉZANNE, 1880–85

$8\frac{9}{16} \times 5$ inches—21,7 × 12,6 cm. Page XXXVII of the sketchbook Leigh Block. Pencil. Verso: No. 335.

(a) Landscape with two trees, and behind them successive horizontal planes leading back to a group of houses dominated by a mountain. Rewald is of the opinion that this drawing was done at the Jas de Bouffan.—(b) At right angles: head and shoulders of Mme Cézanne, the head bent forward; she is wearing a striped waist with a festooned collar; cf. Venturi Nos. 228, 229.

BIBLIOGRAPHY: Rewald, *Carnets*: C V, p. XXXVII (reproduced pl. 50). F. Erpel, *Paul Cézanne*, Berlin, 1960 (reproduced p. 41).

775 · STUDY OF BRANCHES, circa 1880

$4\frac{5}{16} \times 9\frac{1}{4}$ inches—11 × 23,5 cm. Page cut to the dimensions of the drawing verso. Pencil on grayish laid paper. Verso: No. 214.

Almost straight branch rising to the right; the treatment of shadow and light are noteworthy. On the left a vertical branch sends out a long slender shoot to the right. A tree and vegetation can be seen in the background, and close by, a curved bough.

COLLECTIONS: Pierre Loeb, Paris. J. Rewald, New York. E. V. Thaw, New York. M. Feilchenfeldt, Zurich.

776 · LANDSCAPE WITH A LITTLE BRIDGE, circa 1808

$8\frac{5}{8} \times 4\frac{7}{8}$ inches—21,8 × 12,4 cm. Page XXXVIII verso from the sketchbook CP II. Pencil. Verso: No. 840.

Compositional study for a landscape: stone arch of a little bridge in front of a clump of trees: further back, a wall with apertures and a house behind it.

BIBLIOGRAPHY: Venturi, Vol. I, under No. 1290 (not reproduced). *Correspondance* (reproduced fig. 42). *Dessins*, 1938, No. 39 (reproduced). J. Rewald, Cézanne Landschaften, *Kleine Enzyklopädie der Kunst*, Hazan, Paris, 1958 (reproduced).

EXHIBITION: Kunsthalle, Basel, 1936, No. 162.

COLLECTIONS: Cézanne *fils*, Paris. Paul Guillaume, Paris. A. Chappuis, Tresserve. Private collection, Paris. Private collection, New York.

777 · LANDSCAPE, WITH A MAN FISHING, circa 1880

$11\frac{1}{4} \times 17\frac{7}{8}$ inches—28,5 × 45,3 cm. Pencil on beige paper. Verso: blank page.

Sitting at the edge of a calm stretch of water, a man is seen fishing with a rod. Above him a huge branch crosses the whole page, and in the center is a patch of open sky. Magnificent drawing.

BIBLIOGRAPHY: Venturi No. 1243.

COLLECTION: Kenneth Clark, London.

778 · LANDSCAPE, circa 1880

$8\frac{1}{4} \times 10\frac{3}{4}$ inches—21 × 27,3 cm. Page XLV from the sketchbook CP IV. Pencil. Verso: unfinished watercolor portrait of Mme Cézanne.

Extensive landscape showing the banks of a river (or a quarry) in a plain, and a long, sloping hill on the left.

BIBLIOGRAPHY: Venturi, Vol. I, under No. 1316 (not reproduced): "Bords d'une rivière. Coupe un peu à la Daubigny. Voir No. 1002." *Dessins*, 1938, No. 42 (reproduced).

EXHIBITIONS: Rétrospective, Paris, 1939, No. 29. Lyons, 1939, No. 64.

COLLECTIONS: Cézanne *fils*, Paris. Paul Guillaume, Paris. A. Chappuis, Tresserve.

779 · LANDSCAPE IN THE VAL HARMÉ, circa 1880

$5 \times 8\frac{9}{16}$ inches—12,6 × 21,7 cm. Page XII of the sketchbook Leigh Block. Pencil. Verso: No. 644.

Landscape without houses, comprising successive planes leading down to a gully on the right, with a poplar tree. Cf. the paintings of the Val Harmé, Venturi No. 315, etc.

BIBLIOGRAPHY: Rewald, *Carnets*: C V, p. XII (reproduced pl. 40).

COLLECTIONS: Cézanne *fils*, Paris. M. Renou, Paris. Poyet, Lyons. M. Renou, Paris. Sam Salz, New York. Mr. and Mrs. Leigh Block, Chicago.

780. VIEW OF THE VAL HARMÉ, circa 1880

$5 \times 8\frac{9}{16}$ inches—12,6 × 21,7 cm. Page XLV verso of the sketchbook Leigh Block. Pencil. Verso: No. 934.

Study for the painting of the Val Harmé, in vicinity of Auvers-sur-Oise, Venturi No. 315. A river flows across the foreground. Cf. No. 779.

BIBLIOGRAPHY: Rewald, *Carnets*: C V, p. XLV verso (reproduced pl. 41). Th. Reff, *Cézanne's Drawings 1875–85*, *BurlM*, May 1959, p. 171 (reproduced fig. 18). Yvon Taillandier, *Paul Cézanne*, 1965 (reproduced p. 44).

COLLECTIONS: Cézanne *fils*, Paris. M. Renou, Paris. Poyet, Lyons. M. Renou, Paris. Sam Salz, New York. Mr. and Mrs. Leigh Block, Chicago.

781. STUDY OF TREES AND FOLIAGE, 1879–80

$8\frac{9}{16} \times 4\frac{7}{8}$ inches—21,7 × 12,4 cm. Page XVIII of the sketchbook A.I.C. Pencil, stains. Verso: No. 384.

Rapid but precise study of a mass of high trees; on the right a few poplars and the corner of a house, showing roof and window. The vegetation in this drawing is outlined in winding contours that curve at the pencil's will. Shadows are indicated by vigorous hatching.

BIBLIOGRAPHY: Rewald, *Carnets*: C II, p. XVIII (not reproduced). Schniewind, text p. 29 (reproduced). Andersen, *Sk.* (not reproduced).

COLLECTIONS: Cézanne *fils*, Paris. M. Renou, Paris. Poyet, Lyons. M. Renou, Paris. Sam Salz, New York. Art Institute, Chicago.

782. TREE AND STUDIES, 1879–80

$5 \times 8\frac{9}{16}$ inches—12,6 × 21,7 cm. Page XL of the sketchbook Leigh Block. Pencil. Verso: No. 919.

Page lengthwise: (a) Study of foliage.—(b) Right: seated woman, recalling (although the evidence is not conclusive) the figure ornamenting a clock in Nos. 457, 459, seen from a different angle. Page upright (with the bush at the bottom).—(c) Unfinished sketch of an object of which part appears to unroll in cylindrical form (a form that today seems surrealist).

BIBLIOGRAPHY: Rewald, *Carnets*: C V, p. XL (not reproduced).

COLLECTIONS: Cézanne *fils*, Paris. M. Renou, Paris. Poyet, Lyons. M. Renou, Paris. Sam Salz, New York. Mr. and Mrs. Leigh Block, Chicago.

783. HOUSES IN L'ESTAQUE, THE HILLS OF MARSEILLE-VEYRE AND THE ISLE OF MAIRE, 1879–80

$4\frac{7}{8} \times 8\frac{9}{16}$ inches—12,4 × 21,7 cm. Page XIII verso of the sketchbook A.I.C. Pencil, stains. Verso: No. 811.

Landscape corresponding to the painting Venturi No. 408 and watercolor Venturi No. 915. A drawing full of charm in which trees, houses, and sea are indicated by a multitude of patches and strokes that make the whiteness of the paper vibrate. Cf. the same landscape, No. 705.

BIBLIOGRAPHY: Rewald, *Carnets*: C II, p. XIIII verso (reproduced pl. 62). Schniewind, text p. 28 (reproduced). Andersen, *Sk.* (not reproduced).

COLLECTIONS: Cézanne *fils*, Paris. M. Renou, Paris. Poyet, Lyons. M. Renou, Paris. Sam Salz, New York. Art Institute, Chicago.

784. LANDSCAPE AT L'ESTAQUE, 1879–80

$4\frac{7}{8} \times 8\frac{9}{16}$ inches—12,4 × 21,7 cm. Page XV verso of the sketchbook A.I.C. Pencil, stains. Verso: a child's drawing.

Rising in a diagonal to the right: a group of houses with trees, summarily indicated. On the far shore of an expanse of sea, a long chain of hills spreads across the whole page. Cf. Venturi Nos. 407, 408, 915.

BIBLIOGRAPHY: Rewald, *Carnets*: C II, p. XV verso (reproduced pl. 63). Schniewind, text p. 28 (reproduced). Andersen, *Sk.* (not reproduced).

COLLECTIONS: Cézanne *fils*, Paris. M. Renou, Paris. Poyet, Lyons. M. Renou, Paris. Sam Salz, New York. Art Institute, Chicago.

785. VIEW OF L'ESTAQUE, 1879–80

$9\frac{1}{16} \times 11\frac{13}{16}$ inches—23 × 30 cm. Pencil. Verso: blank page.

Between the branches of a tree a horizontal stroke indicates the far shore of the bay with its low hills. In the lower right corner three houses are sketchily drawn, the walls seen as rectangles, the roofs forming diamond shapes.

COLLECTIONS: Mouradian & Vallotton, Paris. Private collection, Paris. Present owner unknown.

786. LANDSCAPE AT MÉDAN, 1879–80

$11 \times 6\frac{11}{16}$ inches—28 × 17 cm. Pencil. Verso: No. 646.

The ordonnance of this drawing becomes clear in comparing it with the *View of Médan*, Venturi No. 439. Cf. our No. 787.

COLLECTIONS: Cézanne *fils*, Paris. W. Walter, Paris. Private collection, Holland. Mr. and Mrs. Leigh Block, Chicago.

787. LANDSCAPE AT MÉDAN, 1879–80

$10\frac{3}{8} \times 11\frac{13}{16}$ inches—26,4 × 30 cm. Pencil on gray laid paper with the watermark: E D & Cie. Verso: blank page.

Study for the canvas Venturi No. 325: *Le Château de Médan*; several details of the drawing figure also in the painting. Cf. the watercolor Venturi No. 847 and our No. 786.

BIBLIOGRAPHY: Venturi No. 1588. Basel catalog, No. 87 (reproduced). *Werkzeitung Geigy*, Basel, 1966, Vol. 24 (reproduced p. 20).

EXHIBITIONS: Meisterzeichnungen französischer Künstler, Kunsthalle, Basel, 1935, No. 202. The Hague, 1956, No. 109. Zurich, 1956, No. 166.

COLLECTIONS: Cézanne *fils*, Paris. W. Feuz, Bern. Kunst-museum, Basel.

788. LANDSCAPE WITH A ROW OF TREES, 1879–82

$10\frac{1}{4} \times 13$ inches—26×33 cm. Pencil on laid paper, watercolor stain top right, fold lower left, paper soiled. Verso: blank page.

Large study in which the vertical lines of the trees contrast with horizontals indicating the ground planes.

COLLECTIONS: Mouradian & Vallotton, Paris. Private collection, Paris. Present owner unknown.

789. LANDSCAPE, FIGURES AFTER GOYA, circa 1882

$9\frac{7}{8} \times 11\frac{13}{16}$ inches—25×30 cm. Pencil. Verso: No. 611.

(a) Lightly-drawn sketch showing the curve of a road with telegraph poles and trees along the right side, and a house in the left background. R. W. Ratcliffe considers it to be a study for the canvas Venturi No. 401, painted in L'Estaque; the subject is not exactly the same, but the component parts are similarly placed.—(b) Upside down: a woman with outstretched arms looking upward, with another woman close behind her.—(c) Man kneeling in prayer. The two sketches (b) and (c) are drawn from Goya's etching *One can't watch it*, in the series *The Disasters of War*. See fig. 112.

BIBLIOGRAPHY: Venturi, Vol. I, as verso of No. 1237 (mentioned but not described).

COLLECTIONS: De Majovsky, Budapest. Museum of Fine Arts, Budapest.

FIG. 112. Francisco de Goya y Lucientes (1746–1828): etching (detail) from the series *Los Entragos de la Guerra*, bearing the legend "*No se puede mirar. . . .*"

(*Photograph: Bibliothèque Nationale, Paris*)

790. HOUSES AND VIADUCT AT L'ESTAQUE, 1879–82

$4\frac{7}{8} \times 8\frac{9}{16}$ inches—$12,4 \times 21,7$ cm. Page V verso of the sketchbook A.I.C. Pencil, stains. Verso: No. 755.

Group of houses close to a railroad at L'Estaque; a particularly detailed study, done from nature. The same motif is seen in the canvas Venturi No. 402.

BIBLIOGRAPHY: Rewald, *Carnets*: C II, p. V verso (reproduced pl. 67). Schniewind, text p. 26 (reproduced). Andersen, *Sk.* (reproduced fig. 24A).

COLLECTIONS: Cézanne *fils*, Paris. M. Renou, Paris. Poyet, Lyons. M. Renou, Paris. Sam Salz, New York. Art Institute, Chicago.

791. LANDSCAPE, AND WOMEN BATHERS, 1879–82

$4\frac{7}{8} \times 8\frac{9}{16}$ inches—$12,6 \times 21,7$ cm. Page III verso of the sketchbook Leigh Block. Pencil. Verso: No. 331.

(a) Left: landscape (separated from (b) by a stroke) with a house seen across a field or pond. The turning movement leading from the right foreground toward the house is noteworthy.—(b) At right angles: three women bathers surrounded by vegetation; cf. No. 314.

BIBLIOGRAPHY: Rewald, *Carnets*: C V, p. III verso (reproduced pl. 104). H. Perruchot, *La Vie de Cézanne*, Paris, 1958 ((b) reproduced as endpaper). Idem, *Cézanne*, New York, 1961.

COLLECTIONS: Cézanne *fils*, Paris. M. Renou, Paris. Poyet, Lyons. M. Renou, Paris. Sam Salz, New York. Mr. and Mrs. Leigh Block, Chicago.

792. IN A FOREST, 1880–83

$17\frac{3}{4} \times 11$ inches—45×28 cm. Pencil on laid paper. Verso: blank page.

The finest part of the drawing is in the center: the eye is naturally drawn toward a clearing seen through a kind of vault formed by branches in the foreground. To the left, a curiously gnarled tree trunk.

EXHIBITION: Galerie A. Flechtheim, Berlin, 1927, No. 48.

COLLECTIONS: Hugo Perls, Berlin. O. Wertheimer, Paris. Matthew H. Futter, New York.

793. TREE WITH FOLIAGE, 1880–83

$7\frac{5}{8} \times 4\frac{5}{8}$ inches—$19,4 \times 11,8$ cm. Page XVII from the sketchbook CP I. Pencil. Verso: No. 452.

Venturi saw this drawing as lengthwise on the page and showing the pool of the Jas de Bouffan. It seems to me that it was drawn upright on the page, since in this way the lines of hatching follow their customary direction. Unfinished sketch, which nevertheless forms a definite little composition.

BIBLIOGRAPHY: Venturi, Vol. I, under No. 1273 (not reproduced).

COLLECTIONS: Cézanne *fils*, Paris. Paul Guillaume, Paris. A. Chappuis, Tresserve. Private collection, Paris. H. Purrmann, Montagnola. Dr. R. Purrmann, Starnberg.

794. LANDSCAPE, 1880–83

$4\frac{15}{16} \times 8\frac{9}{16}$ inches—$12,5 \times 21,7$ cm. Page IX from the sketchbook CP II. Pencil. Verso: No. 630.

Unfinished Provençal landscape. In the right foreground there is a mass of vegetation, left white. The various elements in this drawing combine to create an impressive balance.

BIBLIOGRAPHY: Venturi, Vol. I, under No. 1284 "Paysage semblable aux nos. 304, 974" (not reproduced).

COLLECTIONS: Cézanne *fils*, Paris. Paul Guillaume, Paris. A. Chappuis, Tresserve. Private collection, Paris.

795. THE BANKS OF A RIVER, 1880–83

$8\frac{5}{16} \times 10\frac{11}{16}$ inches—$21,1 \times 27,2$ cm. Page VII from the sketchbook CP IV. Pencil, several rust spots. Verso: No. 1219.

Very lightly sketched river landscape with trees; indications of a house on the right. Cf. the watercolor Venturi No. 1002.

BIBLIOGRAPHY: Venturi, Vol. I, under No. 1315 (not reproduced).

COLLECTIONS: Cézanne *fils*, Paris. Paul Guillaume, Paris. A. Chappuis, Tresserve. Private collection, Paris.

796. LANDSCAPE WITH TREES AND A FARMHOUSE, 1880–83

$9\frac{7}{8} \times 11\frac{13}{16}$ inches—25 × 30 cm. Pencil on laid paper. Verso: blank page.

Landscape suggestive of the environs of the Jas de Bouffan; traces of curved line in the sky; large hatching on the left. The general effect is one of somewhat cold perfection.

EXHIBITIONS: Zurich, 1956, No. 215. Munich, 1956, No. 144.

COLLECTIONS: Jos. Hessel, Paris. Hessel sale, Paris, March 30, 1938, No. 1 (reproduced). Carl Roesch, Diessenhofen.

797. TREE, HEAD, STUDY OF DRAPERY, 1880–83

$5 \times 8\frac{9}{16}$ inches—12,6 × 21,7 cm. Page XLI of the sketchbook Leigh Block. Pencil. Verso: No. 347.

(a) Left: tree in the form of a V, its foliage lightly indicated.—(b) Right: study of drapery, apparently next to the wooden frame of an unmade bed.—(c) At right angles: rough sketch of a woman's head.

BIBLIOGRAPHY: Rewald, *Carnets:* C V, p. XLI (not reproduced).

COLLECTIONS: Cézanne *fils*, Paris. M. Renou, Paris. Poyet, Lyons. M. Renou, Paris. Sam Salz, New York. Mr. and Mrs. Leigh Block, Chicago.

798. HILLS, WITH HOUSES AND TREES, 1880–83

$12\frac{5}{16} \times 18\frac{5}{8}$ inches—31,3 × 47,3 cm. Pencil on laid paper with the watermark MICHALLET, the letter H formed by two juxtaposed I's. Verso: No. 823.

Terraced planes all over the page. The style of this drawing seems a little labored; a first lightly drawn, detailed layout has been heightened by more vigorous strokes.

BIBLIOGRAPHY: Venturi, Vol. I, as verso of No. 1590 (not reproduced). Basel catalog, No. 86, dated 1870–74 (reproduced). Th. Reff, *BurlM*, Aug. 1963, p. 376, dated circa 1880. Douglas Cooper, in *Master Drawings*, Vol. I, No. 4, 1963, p. 56, dated 1879–80, or 1879–82.

COLLECTIONS: Cézanne *fils*, Paris. W. Feuz, Bern. Kunstmuseum, Basel.

798bis. LANDSCAPE IN THE ILE-DE-FRANCE, 1879–83

$8\frac{3}{8} \times 12\frac{5}{8}$ inches—21,2 × 32 cm. Pencil. Verso: blank page.

A few houses drawn in contours and seen from above, with a castle on the left and a roughly sketched landscape beyond the roofs. Some of the strokes are hesitant (cf. No. 776), but the whole reveals the unity of vision peculiar to Cézanne. The lack of hatching suggests that the drawing remains unfinished. Léo Marchutz is of the opinion that

the painter was in front of an autumn landscape and that the rounded strokes in the center represent vividly colored bushes. The sloping fields on the right are typical of the Pontoise region and are also to be seen in Pissarro's paintings, in which a nearby hill often shuts out the horizon. Cf. No. 780.

EXHIBITIONS: The Hague, 1956, No. 106. Zurich, 1956, No. 161. Munich, 1956, No. 122 (dated circa 1875).

COLLECTIONS: Hans Purrmann, Montagnola. Dr. Robert Purrmann, Starnberg.

799. RIVER BANK WITH BRIDGE AND BARGES, 1880–83

$18\frac{1}{8} \times 22\frac{1}{4}$ inches—46 × 56,5 cm. Pencil. Verso: the watercolor Venturi No. 918.

A barge is seen in foreshortening, moored in the foreground; the vertical of its mast strengthens the composition. Retouches to the pillars of the bridge. Cf. the watercolors Venturi Nos. 830 and 831: *The Quays of the Seine.*

COLLECTIONS: Bernheim-Jeune, Paris. Lord Ivor Spencer Churchill, London, Knoedler & Co., New York. Present owner unknown.

800. LANDSCAPE IN THE ARC VALLEY, 1879–82

$4\frac{7}{8} \times 8\frac{5}{8}$ inches—12,4 × 21,8 cm. Page XXXIV from the sketchbook CP II. Pencil. Verso: No. 662.

Left foreground: the gable and ridge, consisting of two rows of rounded tiles, of a little house; a cloud in the sky. Cf. Venturi Nos. 908, 909.

BIBLIOGRAPHY: Venturi, Vol. I, under No. 1290 (not reproduced). *Dessins*, 1957, No. 35 (reproduced).

COLLECTIONS: Cézanne *fils*, Paris. Paul Guillaume, Paris. A. Chappuis, Tresserve.

801. VIEW OVER PARIS, 1879–82

$5 \times 8\frac{9}{16}$ inches—12,6 × 21,7 cm. Page XXX verso of the sketchbook Leigh Block. Pencil on greenish paper. Verso: blank page.

View showing the twin spires of Sainte-Clotilde and the dome of the Invalides. Th. Reff had the idea of consulting a plan of Paris to find the direction indicated by the relative positions of the spires and dome. A direct line leads to the rue de Rivoli near the rue d'Alger and continues on toward Montmartre. Reff's supposition was that Cézanne had done the drawing from one of the windows of Victor Chocquet's apartment at No. 198 rue de Rivoli (see Bibliography). John Rewald replied that this was not possible since from Chocquet's windows on the rue de Rivoli the spires were to the right of the dome; this is confirmed by a photograph as well as by a painting by Renoir and another by Monet. The roofs in the foreground and the distance of the general view much lower down indicate that the drawing was done from a place high up in Montmartre. The trapezoidal shape halfway up the page represents the Seine, with Solferino bridge and a tree.

BIBLIOGRAPHY: Rewald, *Carnets:* C V, page XXX verso (reproduced pl. 44). Th. Reff, *Cézanne's Drawings 1875–85*, *BurlM*, May 1959, p. 171, dated 1875–80 (reproduced fig. 14). John Rewald, *Chocquet and Cézanne*, *GBA*, July-Aug. 1969, note 33.

COLLECTIONS: Cézanne *fils*, Paris. M. Renou, Paris. Poyet, Lyons. M. Renou, Paris. Sam Salz, New York. Mr. and Mrs. Leigh Block, Chicago.

802. A HOUSE, 1879–82

$8\frac{9}{16} \times 5$ inches—21,7 × 12,6 cm. Page VII of the sketchbook Leigh Block. Pencil. Verso: No. 531.

A small house standing back from the street behind a wall with a gateway; on the right, the corner of a much higher house. The drawing stresses the surfaces, as in No. 803.

BIBLIOGRAPHY: Rewald, *Carnets:* C V, p. VII (reproduced pl. 48). Th. Reff, *Cézanne's Drawings 1875–85, BurlM,* May 1959, p. 176 (not reproduced).

COLLECTIONS: Cézanne *fils,* Paris. M. Renou, Paris. Poyet, Lyons. M. Renou, Paris. Sam Salz, New York. Mr. and Mrs. Leigh Block, Chicago.

803. GROUP OF HOUSES, 1879–82

$8\frac{9}{16} \times 5$ inches—21,7 × 12,6 cm. Page VI of the sketchbook Leigh Block. Pencil. Verso: No. 532.

Rewald believes that this drawing represents houses in Paris, which seems highly probable. Stress is laid on the surfaces, even down to the curious detail of the gas lamp fixed to the house on the left: it stands out yet forms part of the façade, together with the shutter that it screens.

BIBLIOGRAPHY: Rewald, *Carnets:* C V, p. VI (reproduced pl. 49). A. Neumeyer, 1958, No. 68 (reproduced). Th. Reff, *Cézanne's Drawings 1875–85, BurlM,* May 1959, p. 175 (not reproduced).

COLLECTIONS: Cézanne *fils,* Paris. M. Renou, Paris. Poyet, Lyons. M. Renou, Paris. Sam Salz, New York. Mr. and Mrs. Leigh Block, Chicago.

804. VIEW OVER THE ROOF TOPS, circa 1881

$5 \times 8\frac{9}{16}$ inches—12,6 × 21,7 cm. Page XXIV verso of the sketchbook Leigh Block. Pencil on gray paper. Verso: blank page.

Unfinished sketch looking out over the roofs, no doubt in Paris. The view presents certain analogies to that of No. 805.

BIBLIOGRAPHY: Rewald, *Carnets:* C V, p. XXIV verso (not reproduced).

COLLECTIONS: Cézanne *fils,* Paris. M. Renou, Paris. Poyet, Lyons. M. Renou, Paris. Sam Salz, New York. Mr. and Mrs. Leigh Block, Chicago.

805. TOWERS, AND NOTATIONS, 1880–82

$4\frac{9}{16} \times 7\frac{3}{16}$ inches—11,6 × 18,2 cm. Endpaper of the first sketchbook Mrs. Enid A. Haupt. Pencil. Verso: front cover.

Sketch of some houses in Paris, with the towers of Saint-Sulpice and Saint-Germain-des-Prés; cf. No. 804.— Notations: *Vermillon/blanc/ocre jaune/laque fine/terre verte/ rouge saturne.* Label gummed to the page: *Papeterie Maison Michallet, Pluchet Succr.* 11 *and* 12 *rue du Pont Neuf/Paris.* Price marked: 1,50.

BIBLIOGRAPHY: Rewald, *Carnets:* C I, "verso de la couverture" (not reproduced). Th. Reff, *Cézanne's Drawings 1875–85, BurlM,* May 1959, p. 174 (reproduced fig. 25).

COLLECTIONS: Cézanne *fils,* Paris. M. Renou, Paris. Poyet, Lyons. M. Renou, Paris. Sam Salz, New York. Mrs. Enid A. Haupt, New York.

806. TOWERS, VIEW OVER THE ROOF TOPS, 1880–82

$4\frac{9}{16} \times 7\frac{3}{16}$ inches—11,6 × 18,2 cm. Page 8 verso from the first sketchbook Mrs. Enid A. Haupt. Pencil. Verso: No. 765.

The towers of Notre-Dame-des-Champs and, further back, those of Saint-Sulpice, seen across the roof tops of Paris. Cézanne did this drawing between 1880 and 1882 from his studio on the seventh floor of No. 32 rue de l'Ouest. Cf. the canvas Venturi No. 175 (small part on the left) painted from the same spot.

BIBLIOGRAPHY: Rewald, *Carnets:* C I, p. 8 verso (reproduced pl. 45). Th. Reff, *Cézanne's Drawings 1875–85, BurlM,* May 1959, p. 170 (reproduced fig. 13).

COLLECTIONS: Cézanne *fils,* Paris. M. Renou, Paris. Poyet, Lyons. M. Renou, Paris. Sam Salz, New York. Mrs. Enid A. Haupt, New York.

807. VIEW OF THE PANTHEON, 1880–82

$8\frac{9}{16} \times 4\frac{7}{8}$ inches—21,7 × 12,5 cm. Page III verso from the sketchbook CP II. Pencil. Verso: No. 267.

The dome of the Pantheon in Paris, seen across the roof tops. An object, unrelated but difficult to define, is sketched in the foreground, on a larger scale than the Pantheon. Th. Reff is of the opinion that this drawing was done from the window of Cézanne's studio, 32 rue de l'Ouest, Paris VI: from here the Pantheon is seen from this angle. Cf. Nos. 581, 801.

BIBLIOGRAPHY: Venturi, Vol. I, under No. 1282 (not reproduced). *Dessins,* 1957, No. 15 (reproduced). Th. Reff, *Cézanne's Drawings 1875–85, BurlM,* May 1959, p. 175 (reproduced fig. 27).

COLLECTIONS: Cézanne *fils,* Paris. Paul Guillaume, Paris. A. Chappuis, Tresserve. Private collection, Paris.

808. STUDY OF HOUSES, 1879–82

$6 \times 9\frac{5}{16}$ inches—15,2 × 23,7 cm. Page V of the Album, Paul Mellon Collection. Pencil. Verso: blank page.

Rough sketch indicating some rounded tiles, projections, doors, a chimney, and, to the left, part of a hill. This does not add up to much, yet it suggests a delightful country setting, realistic yet unreal.

BIBLIOGRAPHY: Venturi, Vol. I, under No. 1302 (not reproduced). *Album,* 1966 (reproduced).

COLLECTIONS: Cézanne *fils,* Paris. Paul Guillaume, Paris. A. Chappuis, Tresserve. Mr. and Mrs. Paul Mellon, Upperville, Va.

809. THE COAST NEAR L'ESTAQUE, 1881–84

$4\frac{7}{8} \times 8\frac{9}{16}$ inches—12,4 × 21,7 cm. Page X verso of the sketchbook A.I.C. Pencil, stains. Verso: No. 900.

Study for the painting Venturi No. 404. A deep ravine in the foreground; further back, a stretch of sea and two rocky islands. A small house is seen in silhouette against the sea. On the first island: the Château d'If.

BIBLIOGRAPHY: Rewald, *Carnets:* C II, p. X verso (not reproduced). Schniewind, text p. 27 (reproduced). Andersen, *Sk.* (not reproduced).

COLLECTIONS: Cézanne *fils,* Paris. M. Renou, Paris. Poyet, Lyons. M. Renou, Paris. Sam Salz, New York. Art Institute, Chicago.

810. ROCKY COAST NEAR L'ESTAQUE, 1881–84

$4\frac{7}{8} \times 8\frac{9}{16}$ inches—$12,4 \times 21,7$ cm. Page XVII verso of the sketchbook A.I.C. Pencil, stains. Verso: No. 383.

Vast landscape, somewhat similar to No. 809 but drawn from a spot further to the left; cf. Venturi No. 404. The house beyond the ravine and the tower of the Château d'If can be seen.

BIBLIOGRAPHY: Rewald, *Carnets:* C II, p. XVII verso (reproduced pl. 66). Schniewind, text p. 29 (reproduced). Andersen, *Sk.* (not reproduced).

COLLECTIONS: Cézanne *fils*, Paris. M. Renou, Paris. Poyet, Lyons. M. Renou, Paris. Sam Salz, New York. Art Institute, Chicago.

811. LANDSCAPE, AND MAN ON ALL FOURS; man, circa 1877; landscape, 1881–84

$4\frac{7}{8} \times 17\frac{1}{8}$ inches—$12,4 \times 43,4$ cm. Pages XIII verso and XIIII of the sketchbook A.I.C. Pencil, stains on both pages. On the reverse side of XIII verso: No. 724; of XIIII: No. 783.

(a) Vast seascape spreading across two pages of the sketchbook; cf. the same subject in our No. 755 and the painting Venturi No. 407.—(b) Right: man on all fours, sketch anterior to (a) and which should be related to the more or less erotic scenes of violence; cf. Nos. 126, 197, 254, 289.—House and hat scribbled by the son.

BIBLIOGRAPHY: Rewald, *Carnets:* C II, pp. XIII verso (not reproduced) and XIIII (reproduced pl. 64). Schniewind, text p. 28 (reproduced). Th. Reff, Cézanne's Drawings 1875–85, *BurlM*, May 1959, p. 170 (reproduced fig. 16). Andersen, *Sk.* (reproduced fig. 28).

COLLECTIONS: Cézanne *fils*, Paris. M. Renou, Paris. Poyet, Lyons. M. Renou, Paris. Sam Salz, New York. Art Institute, Chicago.

812. VIEW OF L'ESTAQUE, 1881–84

$11 \times 13\frac{3}{4}$ inches—28×35 cm. Pencil, dark stains lower right. Verso: unknown.

Solidly composed study, with an expanse of sea in the background; a wall on the right is shaped like the segment of an arc. Nearly all the details figure in the center of the painting Venturi No. 399.

BIBLIOGRAPHY: *Vie, Art et Cité*, Geneva, Dec. 1939 (reproduced).

EXHIBITIONS: Rétrospective Paul Cézanne, Paris, 1939, No. 30. Lyons, 1939, No. 77.

COLLECTION: John Wyeth, New York.

813. HOUSES AT L'ESTAQUE, 1881–84

$11\frac{7}{16} \times 9\frac{7}{16}$ inches—29×24 cm. Pencil on beige laid paper. Verso: blank page.

View of the sea seen across several roofs, chimneys, and trees, with the opposite shore in the distance. This same view figures in the right half of the canvas Venturi No. 405, though the perspective is different.

BIBLIOGRAPHY: Venturi, Vol. I, p. 348, Oeuvres Inédites (not reproduced). *Vie, Art et Cité*, Geneva, Dec. 1939 (reproduced). J. Rewald, Cézanne-Landschaften, *Kleine Enzyklopaedie der Kunst*, Hazan, Paris, 1958 (reproduced).

COLLECTIONS: Kenneth Clark, London. Henry Moore. Graham Sutherland.

814. VIEW OF L'ESTAQUE, 1881–84

Pencil on laid paper. Verso: blank page.

View over the houses of L'Estaque, with a tower and smokestack rising up in front of the sea; cf. the watercolor Venturi No. 916, painted from a different angle. A few trees are indicated in the foreground. Cf. also our Nos. 815, 816.

COLLECTIONS: Barlein. Hein. Viguier. Sale, Paris, 1931. Pietro Feroldi, Brescia.

815. VIEW OF L'ESTAQUE, 1881–84

$11\frac{13}{16} \times 8\frac{11}{16}$ inches—30×22 cm. Black crayon and charcoal. Verso: blank page.

The houses of L'Estaque seen from a higher level with the sea behind; cf. Nos. 814, 816, and Venturi Nos. 406, 916.

BIBLIOGRAPHY: Venturi, No. 1631; the word "Aquarelle" could lead to confusion and should read "Aquarelle No. 916."

EXHIBITION: Orangerie, Paris, 1936, No. 147; dated 1876–78.

COLLECTIONS: Cézanne *fils*, Paris. Present owner unknown.

816. VIEW OF L'ESTAQUE, 1882–85

$17\frac{5}{16} \times 10\frac{1}{4}$ inches—44×26 cm. Pencil. Verso: a watercolor, branch of a rosebush.

The houses of L'Estaque seen from a higher level with the sea behind; cf. Nos. 814, 815, and Venturi Nos. 406, 916. Vollard has signed his name on the left margin, and in the left lower corner is written (upside down): "*PH* 135 *Vollard.*"

COLLECTIONS: Ambroise Vollard, Paris. L. Lichtenhan, Basel. Private collection, Basel.

817. LANDSCAPE, 1882–86

$19\frac{1}{4} \times 13$ inches—49×33 cm. Pencil, little strokes of watercolor. Verso: blank page.

A few rustic roofs and an extensive plain seen from a wooded hill higher up. The twist of the tree trunk in the foreground counterbalances the bend of the tree on the right and brings the whole page into equilibrium.

EXHIBITION: Quatre Chemins, Paris, 1936.

COLLECTIONS: Cézanne *fils*, Paris. W. Walter, Paris. Present owner unknown.

818. HEAD OF MME CÉZANNE, 1880–81

$4\frac{7}{8} \times 8\frac{9}{16}$ inches—$12,4 \times 21,7$ cm. Page VI verso of the sketchbook A.I.C. Pencil, stains. Verso: No. 280.

Head of Mme Cézanne.

BIBLIOGRAPHY: Rewald, *Carnets:* C II, p. VI verso (not reproduced). Schniewind, text p. 26 (reproduced). Andersen, *Sk.* (not reproduced).

COLLECTIONS: Cézanne *fils*, Paris. M. Renou, Paris. Poyet, Lyons. M. Renou, Paris. Sam Salz, New York. Art Institute, Chicago.

819. HEAD OF A CHILD, circa 1880

$8\frac{9}{16} \times 4\frac{7}{8}$ inches—$21,7 \times 12,4$ cm. Page XL of the sketchbook A.I.C. Pencil, stains. Verso: No. 695.

Head of a child, probably the artist's son, seen in profile; the contour of the forehead is retouched.—Scribbles by the boy lower down on the page.

BIBLIOGRAPHY: Rewald, *Carnets:* C II, p. XL (not reproduced). Schniewind, text p. 32 (reproduced). Andersen, *Sk.* (not reproduced).

COLLECTIONS: Cézanne *fils*, Paris. M. Renou, Paris. Poyet, Lyons. M. Renou, Paris. Sam Salz, New York. Art Institute, Chicago.

820. THE ARTIST'S SON, 1880–81

$6\frac{3}{4} \times 6\frac{1}{2}$ inches—17,1 × 16,6 cm. Pencil, tear restored at lower edge. Verso: No. 245.

BIBLIOGRAPHY: Venturi, No. 1572. Basel catalog, No. 99 (reproduced).

EXHIBITIONS: The Hague, 1956, No. 114. Zurich, 1956, No. 174.

COLLECTIONS: Cézanne *fils*, Paris. W. Feuz, Bern. Kunstmuseum, Basel.

821. PAGE OF STUDIES, 1880–81

$11\frac{13}{16} \times 19\frac{11}{16}$ inches—30 × 50 cm. Pencil, fold across the page. Verso: No. 405.

(a) Top left: rough sketch of a head.—(b) Below and at right angles: unfinished head.—(c) Lower left corner: head of the artist's son, front face, with a cast shadow, encircled by a stroke, to the left of the nose.—(d) Top center: copy after a figure ornamenting a clock; cf. Nos. 457 (a), 459.—(e) Below: head of Mme Cézanne, her eyelids lowered.—(f) Above and a little to the right: sketch of a hand leaning against a cheek; cf. No. 875.—(g) Right: boy with his back turned, leaning on his right elbow; copy of a detail after Pedro de Moya. See No. 731 and fig. 109. —(h) Top right: head of Mme Cézanne, seen in profile.

BIBLIOGRAPHY: Venturi, Vol. I, as verso of No. 1474 (not reproduced). Berthold, cat. No. 328 (reproduced), and No. 289((g) reproduced). R. Longhi, Appunti, in *Paragone* No. 133, Jan. 1961 ((g) reproduced opposite p. 72).

COLLECTION: Kenneth Clark, London.

822. THE ARTIST'S SON ASLEEP, AND STUDY OF FOLIAGE, 1880–81

$4\frac{9}{16} \times 7\frac{3}{16}$ inches—11,6 × 18,2 cm. Page 11 from the first sketchbook Mrs. Enid A. Haupt. Pencil. Verso: No. 1097.

(a) Right: sketch of the artist's son asleep. The boy's hand is toward the viewer; above his head: a cushion shaded by hatching.—(b) Left: study of a small tree.

BIBLIOGRAPHY: Rewald, *Carnets:* C I, p. 11 (not reproduced).

COLLECTIONS: Cézanne *fils*, Paris. M. Renou, Paris. Poyet, Lyons. M. Renou, Paris. Sam Salz, New York. Mrs. Enid A. Haupt, New York.

823. PIECE OF FURNITURE MADE OF CHAIR RUNGS AND UPRIGHTS, AND PORTRAIT OF THE ARTIST'S SON, 1880–81

$12\frac{5}{16} \times 18\frac{5}{8}$ inches—31,3 × 47,3 cm. Pencil on laid paper with the watermark: MICHALLET, the letter H formed by two juxtaposed I's, stains obliterated. Verso: No. 798.

(a) Kind of stool consisting of rungs and uprights; on it there is a slightly curved wooden board and a book; a small shaded plank is seen behind one of the uprights. This stool, on which Cézanne used to lay his palette, is still to be seen in the painter's Aix-en-Provence studio.—(b) Right: head and shoulder of the artist's son standing out against the shaded back of an armchair. Study used for the painting Venturi No. 535.—(c) Above: small sketch of a head.

BIBLIOGRAPHY: Venturi No. 1590. Basel catalog, No. 101 (reproduced, but in reverse). W. V. Andersen, in *AB*, April 1963.

COLLECTIONS: Cézanne *fils*, Paris. W. Feuz, Bern. Kunstmuseum, Basel.

824. HEAD OF A CHILD, AND HAND, 1880–81

$4\frac{9}{16} \times 7\frac{3}{16}$ inches—11,6 × 18,2 cm. Page 9 from the first sketchbook Mrs. Enid A. Haupt. Pencil. Verso: No. 336.

(a) Left: head of a child, the mouth and contour of the cheek left blank.—(b) A right hand, palm forward, the fingers half closed and the thumb much in evidence.

BIBLIOGRAPHY: Rewald, *Carnets:* C I, p. 9 (not reproduced).

COLLECTIONS: Cézanne *fils*, Paris. M. Renou, Paris. Poyet, Lyons. M. Renou, Paris. Sam Salz, New York. Mrs. Enid A. Haupt, New York.

825. TWO SKETCHES OF THE SON'S HEAD, circa 1881

$4\frac{7}{8} \times 8\frac{9}{16}$ inches—12,4 × 21,7 cm. Page XLIX of the sketchbook A.I.C. Pencil. Verso: No. 716.

(a) Left: head of the artist's son; detailed drawing with fine depth of tones.—(b) Right: head of the boy, the right side left white.

BIBLIOGRAPHY: Rewald, *Carnets:* C II, p. XLIX (reproduced pl. 26). Schniewind, text p. 33 (reproduced). Andersen, *Sk.* (not reproduced).

COLLECTIONS: Cézanne *fils*, Paris. M. Renou, Paris. Poyet, Lyons. M. Renou, Paris. Sam Salz, New York. Art Institute, Chicago.

826. PORTRAIT OF A YOUNG WOMAN, circa 1881

$8\frac{9}{16} \times 5$ inches—21,7 × 12,6 cm. Page I verso of the sketchbook Leigh Block. Pencil. Verso: No. 510.

Head of a young woman, possibly Mme Cézanne. A firm, luminous drawing; the volume of the head, shaded on the left side by wide hatching strokes, is very fine. Cf. Venturi No. 533.

BIBLIOGRAPHY: Rewald, *Carnets:* C V, p. I verso (reproduced pl. 9). Anne van Buren, Mme Cézanne's Fashions and the dates of her Portraits, *The Art Quarterly*, Vol. XXIX, No. 2, 1966, p. 117; dated as later than 1878 and related to Venturi No. 369.

COLLECTIONS: Cézanne *fils*, Paris. M. Renou, Paris. Poyet, Lyons. M. Renou, Paris. Sam Salz, New York. Mr. and Mrs. Leigh Block, Chicago.

827. HEAD OF MME CÉZANNE, 1882–87

$6 \times 9\frac{5}{16}$ inches—15,2 × 23,7 cm. Page XII of the Album, Paul Mellon Collection. Pencil. Verso: No. 538.

This head is probably a study for the painting Venturi No. 521, but the drawing only goes down to the collar; the nose is pointed, the expression on the face tense. However, here as in other portraits, Mme Cézanne gives the impression of posing with great patience.

BIBLIOGRAPHY: Venturi, Vol. I, under No. 1304 (not reproduced). Anne van Buren, Mme Cézanne's Fashions and the dates of her Portraits, *The Art Quarterly*, Vol. XXIX, No. 2, 1966, p. 118, gives the date of Venturi No. 521 as 1886–88. She does not mention this drawing, but if her point of view is adopted, it should be dated 1886–88 on account of the cut of the collar. *Album*, 1966, dated 1878–82 (reproduced).

COLLECTIONS: Cézanne *fils*, Paris. Paul Guillaume, Paris. A. Chappuis, Tresserve. Mr. and Mrs. Paul Mellon, Upperville, Va.

828. MME CÉZANNE, HER HEAD LEANING ON HER HAND, 1881–82

$8\frac{9}{16} \times 5$ inches—21,7 × 12,6 cm. Page V verso of the sketchbook Leigh Block. Pencil. Verso: No. 314.

Head and shoulders of Mme Cézanne, her hand up to her cheek; cf. No. 716. Her gaze passes beside the viewer and expresses the model's resolute patience.

BIBLIOGRAPHY: Rewald, *Carnets*: C V, p. V verso (reproduced pl. 7). Y. Taillandier, *Paul Cézanne*, Paris, New York, Munich, 1961 and 1965 (reproduced p. 8).

COLLECTIONS: Cézanne *fils*, Paris. M. Renou, Paris. Poyet, Lyons. M. Renou, Paris. Sam Salz, New York. Mr. and Mrs. Leigh Block, Chicago.

829. ROUGH SKETCH OF A HEAD, AND NUMBERS, date uncertain

$7\frac{5}{8} \times 4\frac{5}{8}$ inches—19,4 × 11,8 cm. Page I verso from the sketchbook CP I. Pencil. Verso: No. 533.

Study of a head seen frontally, tilted to the left, drawn only down to the nostrils. A sum:

$$225 \ loyer$$
$$200$$
$$850$$
$$170$$
$$\overline{1445}$$

BIBLIOGRAPHY: Venturi, Vol. I, under No. 1266 (not reproduced).

COLLECTIONS: Cézanne *fils*, Paris. Paul Guillaume, Paris. A. Chappuis, Tresserve.

830. TWO HEADS, 1880–83

$4\frac{5}{8} \times 7\frac{5}{8}$ inches—11,8 × 19,4 cm. Page XIII verso from the sketchbook CP I. Pencil. Verso: blank page.

(a) Head of a woman, her hair elaborately dressed; drawn with a very light pencil.—(b) More detailed sketch of a woman's head, tilted to the left; the face expresses tenderness and suffering.

BIBLIOGRAPHY: Venturi, Vol. I, under No. 1270 (not reproduced).

COLLECTIONS: Cézanne *fils*, Paris. Paul Guillaume, Paris. A. Chappuis, Tresserve.

831. TWO SKETCHES OF THE ARTIST'S SON, circa 1882

$4\frac{7}{8} \times 8\frac{5}{8}$ inches—12,4 × 21,8 cm. Page XXXVI from the sketchbook CP II. Pencil. Verso: No. 484.

(a) Page upright: head of the son, a worried expression on his face. The shadows seem to indicate that the sketch was done by lamplight; the effect recalls the work of Goya. —(b) Page lengthwise: the boy's head, tilted back as though resting on a cushion. Drawn with a different pencil.

BIBLIOGRAPHY: Venturi, Vol. I, under No. 1290 (not reproduced).

COLLECTIONS: Cézanne *fils*, Paris. Paul Guillaume, Paris. A. Chappuis, Tresserve.

832. PAGE OF STUDIES: HEAD, 1882–83; WOMAN BATHER, circa 1880; Ceres, 1879

$8\frac{5}{8} \times 4\frac{7}{8}$ inches—21,8 × 12,4 cm. Page XXXV verso from the sketchbook CP II. Pencil. Verso: No. 886.

(a) Head of the artist's son, detailed drawing with notation on the right of the date 1877, when young Paul would have been only five. According to our date, which is close to that of Venturi, he would be ten to eleven years old.—(b) Upside down: woman bather walking toward the background.—(c) At right angles: head of a woman wearing an ancient headdress: copy after Rubens' figure of *Ceres* in the Hermitage Museum, Leningrad, of which

FIG. 113. After Peter Paul Rubens (1577–1640): engraving after the painting of *Ceres* (Hermitage, Leningrad) reproduced in *Le Magasin Pittoresque*, 1879, p. 137. (*Photograph: Chappuis*)

there was formerly a replica in Hamburg. Cézanne copied a reproduction printed in *Le Magasin Pittoresque* for 1879, p. 137. See fig. 113.

BIBLIOGRAPHY: Venturi, Vol. I, under No. 1290 (not reproduced). *Dessins,* 1938, No. 28 (reproduced). Berthold, cat. No. 319 (reproduced). Th. Reff, in *AB,* June 1960, p. 148, note 34.

COLLECTIONS: Cézanne *fils,* Paris. Paul Guillaume, Paris. A. Chappuis, Tresserve. Private collection, Paris.

833. BOOK ON A TABLE, HEAD OF A BOY, 1880–82
$4\frac{15}{16} \times 8\frac{9}{16}$ inches—12,5 × 21,7 cm. Page IV verso from the sketchbook CP II. Pencil. Verso: No. 838.

(a) Left: a book, and behind it a round ashtray, standing on a massive table (or some other piece of furniture) seen from slightly above; to the right, a corner and a receding line. Cf. No. 537 (a).—(b) Right: the face of the artist's son with a strong cast shadow to the right. His look, more piercing than usual, is directed straight at the viewer.

BIBLIOGRAPHY: Venturi, under No. 1282 (not reproduced). *Dessins,* 1938, No. 8 (reproduced).

COLLECTIONS: Cézanne *fils,* Paris. Paul Guillaume, Paris. A. Chappuis, Tresserve. Sale, Maître M. Rheims, Palais Galliera, Paris, March 23, 1965, No. 9. H. Berggruen, Paris.

834. HEAD OF THE ARTIST'S SON, TREES, 1882–86
$12\frac{3}{16} \times 9\frac{1}{16}$ inches—31 × 23 cm. Pencil on laid paper. Verso: No. 244.

(a) Head of the artist's son; first sketch on the page.—(b) Upside down: landscape with trees, their trunks vertical.

COLLECTION: Private collection, New York.

835. HEAD OF A YOUNG BATHER, AND NUMBERS, 1882–83
$8\frac{5}{8} \times 4\frac{7}{8}$ inches—21,8 × 12,4 cm. Page XLII verso from the sketchbook CP II. Pencil. Verso: No. 654.

Tilted head of a young bather, frequently identified as the artist's son. This sketch is no doubt a detail for the bather overleaf, No. 654 (a). The lower part of the page is covered with numbers (one subtraction seems to be incorrect).

BIBLIOGRAPHY: Venturi No. 1300.

EXHIBITION: Orangerie, Paris, 1936, No. 153, "Portrait du fils de l'artiste."

COLLECTIONS: Cézanne *fils,* Paris. Paul Guillaume, Paris. A. Chappuis, Tresserve. Sale, Maître M. Rheims, Palais Galliera, Paris, March 23, 1965, No. 15 (not reproduced). Private collection, Paris. Sale, Galerie Motte, Geneva, June 12, 1970, No. 33 (reproduced).

836. PORTRAIT OF THE ARTIST'S SON, circa 1883
$10\frac{7}{8} \times 9\frac{1}{16}$ inches—27,7 × 23 cm. Pencil on laid paper. Verso: blank page.

The artist's son, his head bent and his expression vivacious; collar and shoulder are indicated.

BIBLIOGRAPHY: A. Stix, *Von Ingres bis Cézanne,* Vienna, 1927, No. 32 (reproduced). *Correspondance* (reproduced

fig. 25). Rewald, *Paul Cézanne,* New York, 1948 (reproduced p. 99). Idem, Spring Books, London, 1959 and 1965 (reproduced p. 79). Neumeyer, 1958, No. 38 (reproduced).

EXHIBITIONS: Kunsthalle, Basel, 1936, No. 130. Albertina, 1950, No. 250. Belvedere, Vienna, 1961, No. 93 (reproduced).

COLLECTION: Albertina, Vienna (Inv. 24087).

837. PORTRAIT OF THE ARTIST'S SON, circa 1883
$8\frac{9}{16} \times 5$ inches—21,7 × 12,6 cm. Page XLIX verso of the sketchbook Leigh Block. Pencil. Verso: No. 342.

Under the chin, a round collar and four coat buttons. The sketch is placed slightly on a diagonal rising to the right. The boredom of posing is suggested in the boy's expression.

BIBLIOGRAPHY: Rewald, *Carnets:* C V, p. XLIX verso (reproduced pl. 21).

COLLECTIONS: Cézanne *fils,* Paris. M. Renou, Paris. Poyet, Lyons. M. Renou, Paris. Sam Salz, New York. Mr. and Mrs. Leigh Block, Chicago.

838. HEAD OF A BOY, circa 1884
$4\frac{15}{16} \times 8\frac{9}{16}$ inches—12,5 × 21,7 cm. Page IV from the sketchbook CP II. Pencil. Verso: No. 833.

The form of the face is brought into relief by hatching around the contour. The drawing seems especially clear and incisive, while remaining pictorial. A certain resemblance to the portrait of Louis Guillaume (No. 940) may be noted.

BIBLIOGRAPHY: Venturi, under No. 1282, "Tête de Cézanne fils âgé d'environ douze ans" (not reproduced).

COLLECTIONS: Cézanne *fils,* Paris. Paul Guillaume, Paris. A. Chappuis, Tresserve. Sale, Maître M. Rheims, Palais Galliera, Paris, March 23, 1965, No. 9 (not reproduced in catalog). H. Berggruen, Paris.

839. THE ARTIST'S SON ASLEEP, 1883–84
$7\frac{3}{16} \times 4\frac{9}{16}$ inches—18,2 × 11,6 cm. Page 3 from the first sketchbook Mrs. Enid A. Haupt. Pencil. Verso: No. 848.

(a) Top: head of a boy asleep, in foreshortening, and at left above, strokes indicating folds in the pillow.—(b) Below: left profile of the head of the boy asleep, seen in foreshortening from the chin up. The head is oval and the ear conspicuous; the cheek area is left blank, forming a rounded bulge. Cf. Nos. 842, 843.—Notation: *Lambert 17 rue de Loursine.*

BIBLIOGRAPHY: Rewald, *Carnets:* C I, p. 3 (reproduced pl. 23).

COLLECTIONS: Cézanne *fils,* Paris. M. Renou, Paris. Poyet, Lyons. M. Renou, Paris. Sam Salz, New York. Mrs. Enid A. Haupt, New York.

840. HEAD AND SHOULDERS OF MME CÉZANNE, ROUND FRUIT, 1884–85
$8\frac{5}{8} \times 4\frac{7}{8}$ inches—21,8 × 12,4 cm. Page XXXIII from the sketchbook CP II. Pencil. Verso: No. 776.

(a) Mme Cézanne, her eyelids lowered. A diagonal stroke cuts across the drawing below her chin, duplicated by another one lower down; these strokes no doubt indicate a newspaper.—(b) Below and at right angles: round fruit with cast shadow. This sketch seems to be earlier than the first.

BIBLIOGRAPHY: Venturi, Vol. I, under No. 1290, "Deux têtes, l'une est celle de Paul Cézanne *fils*, (not reproduced). *Dessins*, 1938, No. 24 "Tête de femme. Orange" (reproduced).

COLLECTIONS: Cézanne *fils*, Paris. Paul Guillaume, Paris. A. Chappuis, Tresserve. Private collection, Paris. Private collection, New York.

841. PAGE OF STUDIES, INCLUDING ONE OF MME CÉZANNE, 1882–85

$9\frac{5}{16} \times 6$ inches—23,7 × 15,2 cm. Page XXXIbis of the Album, Paul Mellon Collection. Pencil, traces of watercolor independent of the drawings. Verso: No. 530.

Pagination: This page, like No. 1082, is numbered XXXI; whoever did the paging made a mistake. The traces of watercolor lead to the supposition that the pagination was done later than the watercolor; this latter, removed from the sketchbook, would normally have been numbered XXXII.—(a) Top: head and shoulders of Mme Cézanne leaning against a pillow.—(b) Page lengthwise: head of a boy of whom only the nape of the neck and back of the head are drawn. The face remains unfinished, though the ear and neck are studied with attention. Cf. Nos. 865, 866, 869, 870.—(c) Sketch of a figure in movement; probably a study for a figure in the missing watercolor.

BIBLIOGRAPHY: Venturi, Vol. I, under No. 1309 (not reproduced). *Album*, 1966 (reproduced).

COLLECTIONS: Cézanne *fils*, Paris. Paul Guillaume, Paris. A. Chappuis, Tresserve. Mr. and Mrs. Paul Mellon, Upperville, Va.

842. TWO SKETCHES OF THE HEAD OF THE ARTIST'S SON, head at right, 1883–84; head at left, 1878–79

$4\frac{7}{8} \times 8\frac{9}{16}$ inches—12,4 × 21,7 cm. Page XLVIII of the sketchbook A.I.C. Pencil. Verso: No. 703.

(a) Right: head of the son lying asleep on his cheek; cf. Nos. 839, 843.—(b) Page upright: another head of the boy, a vivacious expression on his face.

BIBLIOGRAPHY: Rewald, *Carnets*: C II, p. XLVIII (reproduced pl. 17). Schniewind, text p. 33 (reproduced). Andersen, *Sk.* (not reproduced).

COLLECTIONS: Cézanne *fils*, Paris. M. Renou, Paris. Poyet, Lyons. M. Renou, Paris. Sam Salz, New York. Art Institute, Chicago.

843. THE ARTIST'S SON ASLEEP, 1883–84

$4\frac{7}{8} \times 8\frac{9}{16}$ inches—12,4 × 21,7 cm. Page XLVII of the sketchbook A.I.C. Soft pencil, ink stains from the page opposite. Verso: No. 733.

A collar and round button are shown near the chin; the head of the bed is indicated by hatching. Cf. No. 842.

BIBLIOGRAPHY: Rewald, *Carnets*: C II, p. XLVII (not reproduced). Schniewind, text p. 33 (reproduced). Andersen, *Sk.* (not reproduced).

COLLECTIONS: Cézanne *fils*, Paris. M. Renou, Paris. Poyet, Lyons. M. Renou, Paris. Sam Salz, New York. Art Institute, Chicago.

844. HEAD OF THE ARTIST'S SON, AND STILL LIFE, circa 1884

$5 \times 8\frac{9}{16}$ inches—12,6 × 21,7 cm. Page XLIII verso of the sketchbook Leigh Block. Pencil. Verso: No. 753.

(a) Portrait of the son; the graphic treatment is unusual, particularly of the forehead, mouth, and chin.—(b) Left: cup (similar to the one in No. 347), two glasses, and a bowl standing on a flat surface. Curious irregular delineation in the background, perhaps by another hand.

BIBLIOGRAPHY: Rewald, *Carnets*: C V, p. XLIII verso (reproduced pl. 22).

COLLECTIONS: Cézanne *fils*, Paris. M. Renou, Paris. Poyet, Lyons. M. Renou, Paris. Sam Salz, New York. Mr. and Mrs. Leigh Block, Chicago.

845. YOUNG MAN ASLEEP, circa 1884

$7\frac{5}{8} \times 4\frac{5}{8}$ inches—19,4 × 11,8 cm. Page IX from the sketchbook CP I. Pen drawing on paper yellowed with age. Verso: No. 1079.

The young man's head is resting on his closed fist, held against his cheek. The line of shadow running up the jacket to the ear and the shadow cast by the arm are curious.

BIBLIOGRAPHY: Venturi, Vol. I, under No. 1270 (not reproduced). *Dessins*, 1938 (reproduced on the title page).

COLLECTIONS: Cézanne *fils*, Paris. Paul Guillaume, Paris. A. Chappuis, Tresserve.

846. MME CÉZANNE, circa 1885

$12 \times 9\frac{1}{4}$ inches—30,5 × 23,5 cm. Pencil on laid paper. Verso: blank page.

Bust-length portrait of Mme Cézanne dozing, her cheek resting against her left hand, the forearm vertical.

BIBLIOGRAPHY: *Correspondance* (reproduced fig. 26).

COLLECTIONS: Galerie Zak, Paris. Present owner unknown.

847. HAND AND SHOULDER OF A BOY, circa 1885

$9\frac{1}{4} \times 6$ inches—23,5 × 15,2 cm. Page XXIII verso of the Album, Paul Mellon Collection. Pencil. Verso: No. 651.

Page upright: a boy engrossed in his studies. Cézanne has drawn his right hand, shoulder, and neck, with the back of a chair and indications of background. The hand is resting on a book and the tip of a pen is shown. Cf. No. 867.

BIBLIOGRAPHY: Venturi, Vol. I, under No. 1306 (not reproduced). *Album*, 1966 (reproduced).

COLLECTIONS: Cézanne *fils*, Paris. Paul Guillaume, Paris. A. Chappuis, Tresserve. Mr. and Mrs. Paul Mellon, Upperville, Va.

848. THE ARTIST'S SON ASLEEP, circa 1885

$4\frac{9}{16} \times 7\frac{3}{16}$ inches—11,6 × 18,2 cm. Page 3 verso from the first sketchbook Mrs. Enid A. Haupt. Pencil. Verso: No. 839.

The boy lying asleep in bed, his chin hidden by a blanket.

BIBLIOGRAPHY: Rewald, *Carnets:* C I, p. 3 verso (not reproduced).

COLLECTIONS: Cézanne *fils*, Paris. M. Renou, Paris. Poyet, Lyons. M. Renou, Paris. Sam Salz, New York. Mrs. Enid A. Haupt, New York.

849. THE ARTIST'S SON, FULL-LENGTH STUDY, circa 1885

$19\frac{1}{4} \times 12\frac{3}{16}$ inches—49 × 31 cm. Pencil on gray-brown laid paper. Verso: blank page.

Compared with the drawing following, No. 850, this one seems more classical in treatment. The left arm and hand seem anatomically natural; the line of the wainscot is unbroken. The expression on the face is more confident, but also emptier; the collar forms a roll on the right side of the neck.

BIBLIOGRAPHY: Venturi No. 1470.

EXHIBITIONS: Dessins d'Ingres à Seurat, Boymans Museum, Rotterdam, 1933–34, No. 7. Paul Cassirer, London, 1939, No. 5.

COLLECTIONS: Private collection, Berlin. Paul Cassirer, London. Present owner unknown.

850. THE ARTIST'S SON, FULL-LENGTH STUDY, circa 1885

$19\frac{1}{4} \times 12\frac{3}{16}$ inches—49 × 31 cm. Pencil. Verso: Venturi No. 868.

The wainscot appears to be higher on the right of the figure than on the left. The arm from the shoulder down as well as the leg with the foot stepping forward seem deformed. Several lines deviate from accepted classical perspective. Cf. No. 849.

BIBLIOGRAPHY: Venturi No. 1469. Rewald, *Cézanne et Zola*, Paris, 1936 (reproduced pl. 47). Coll. Génies et Réalités, Hachette, Paris, 1966, p. 19 (reproduced fig. 7).

EXHIBITIONS: Aix-en-Provence, 1956, No. 90. The Hague, 1956, No. 117. Zurich, 1956, No. 178 (reproduced). Belvedere, Vienna, 1961, No. 98. Phillips Collection, Washington, D.C., Chicago, Boston, 1971, No. 75 (reproduced).

COLLECTIONS: Cézanne *fils,* Paris. Richard S. Davis, Minneapolis. A. L. Hillman Family Foundation, New York.

851. PORTRAIT OF THE ARTIST'S SON, circa 1885

$8\frac{1}{2} \times 4\frac{7}{8}$ inches—21,5 × 12,4 cm. Page XXXVII verso from the sketchbook CP II. Pencil and black ink. Verso: No. 470.

The boy's head with indications of clothing, and emphasis on a round button. The light comes from the left and the shadows are stressed.

BIBLIOGRAPHY: Venturi, Vol. I, under No. 1291 (not reproduced). F. H. Lem, *Paul Cézanne,* Paris, 1969 (reproduced fig. 6).

EXHIBITION: Prague, 1956, No. 65.

COLLECTIONS: Cézanne *fils*, Paris. Paul Guillaume, Paris. A. Chappuis, Tresserve. Musée National de la Ville de Paris, Petit Palais (Inv. D. 3288).

852. A HEAD, circa 1885

$9\frac{5}{16} \times 5\frac{7}{8}$ inches—23,6 × 15 cm. Page XX, removed about 1923 from the Album now in the Paul Mellon Collection. Soft pencil, fold top right. Verso: No. 937.

Incomplete and seemingly unsuccessful study: head of a young man, and collar.

BIBLIOGRAPHY: Basel catalog, No. 91, date proposed 1876–80 (reproduced).

COLLECTIONS: Cézanne *fils*, Paris. W. Feuz, Bern. Kunstmuseum, Basel.

853. THE ARTIST'S SON, WRITING, circa 1885

$8\frac{7}{8} \times 12\frac{3}{16}$ inches—22,5 × 31 cm. Pencil on laid paper. Verso: blank page.

There is an inkpot in front of the boy, and a chair back behind him; cf. Nos. 847, 865, 867, 870.

BIBLIOGRAPHY: Venturi No. 1468.

COLLECTIONS: Cézanne *fils*, Paris. W. Feuz, Bern. Present owner unknown.

854. THE ARTIST'S SON ASLEEP, A HAND, 1884–86

$4\frac{9}{16} \times 7\frac{3}{16}$ inches—11,6 × 18,2 cm. Page 10 verso from the first sketchbook Mrs. Enid A. Haupt. Pencil. Verso: No. 858.

(a) Right: the boy's head, half hidden by a pillow, his mouth open; indication of clothing behind the ear.—(b) Left: study of the sleeper's right hand, the thumb and index finger emerging from a sleeve; cf. No. 824.

BIBLIOGRAPHY: Rewald, *Carnets:* C I, p. 10 verso (not reproduced).

COLLECTIONS: Cézanne *fils*, Paris. M. Renou, Paris. Poyet, Lyons. M. Renou, Paris. Sam Salz, New York. Mrs. Enid A. Haupt, New York.

855. SKETCH OF THE ARTIST'S SON ASLEEP ON A BED, 1885–86

$5 \times 8\frac{1}{2}$ inches—12,7 × 21,6 cm. Page XLV from the second sketchbook Mrs. Enid A. Haupt. Pencil. Verso: No. 420.

The boy seen in foreshortening lying on a bed, his head in the foreground and further back the shoe of a left foot; a few cushions on the right. Incomplete sketch, slightly baroque. Cf. Nos. 626 (b), 854, 856.

BIBLIOGRAPHY: Rewald, *Carnets:* C IV, p. XLV (not reproduced).

COLLECTIONS: Cézanne *fils*, Paris. M. Renou, Paris. Poyet, Lyons. M. Renou, Paris. Sam Salz, New York. Mrs. Enid A. Haupt, New York.

856. THE ARTIST'S SON ASLEEP, circa 1886

$5 \times 8\frac{1}{2}$ inches—12,7 × 21,6 cm. Page VI from the second sketchbook Mrs. Enid A. Haupt. Pencil. Verso: blank page.

Left: head of the boy lying asleep in bed, his mouth and chin hidden by a blanket. This drawing consists of ellipses, shadows indicated by hatching, and rubbings that imitate touches of watercolor.

BIBLIOGRAPHY: Rewald, *Carnets*: C IV, p. VI (not reproduced).

COLLECTIONS: Cézanne *fils*, Paris. M. Renou, Paris. Poyet, Lyons. M. Renou, Paris. Sam Salz, New York. Mrs. Enid A. Haupt, New York.

857. THE ARTIST'S SON ASLEEP, circa 1886

$4\frac{9}{16} \times 7\frac{3}{16}$ inches—11,6 × 18,2 cm. Page 2 verso from the first sketchbook Mrs. Enid A. Haupt. Pencil. Verso: No. 857A.

The hatching indicates that the page should be seen lengthwise. Drawing of the boy's head as he lies asleep, part of his forehead and cheek covered by draped folds.

BIBLIOGRAPHY: Rewald, *Carnets*: C I, p. 2 verso (not reproduced).

COLLECTIONS: Cézanne *fils*, Paris. M. Renou, Paris. Poyet, Lyons. M. Renou, Paris. Sam Salz, New York. Mrs. Enid A. Haupt, New York.

857A. SKETCH

Pencil. Inaccessible reverse side of No. 857 (not reproduced).

BIBLIOGRAPHY: Rewald, *Carnets*, C I, p. 2 "Croquis" (not reproduced).

858. THE ARTIST'S SON ASLEEP, circa 1886

$4\frac{9}{16} \times 7\frac{3}{16}$ inches—11,6 × 18,2 cm. Page 10 from the first sketchbook Mrs. Enid A. Haupt. Pencil. Verso: No. 854.

A roll formed by a blanket is vigorously drawn. One is at first tempted to see it as an arm, but I think it can only be the blanket.

BIBLIOGRAPHY: Rewald, *Carnets*: C I, p. 10 (not reproduced).

COLLECTIONS: Cézanne *fils*, Paris. M. Renou, Paris. Poyet, Lyons. M. Renou, Paris. Sam Salz, New York. Mrs. Enid A. Haupt, New York.

859. CUSHION ON AN ARMCHAIR, 1886–89

$6 \times 9\frac{5}{16}$ inches—15,2 × 23,7 cm. Page XVI verso of the Album, Paul Mellon Collection. Pencil. Verso: No. 954.

This drawing represents an indoor detail seen from above: the arm of a chair, its angle ornamented with a snail-shaped design, and a cushion placed upright, against the arm. The circular strokes probably indicate the same cushion, or perhaps another one. Venturi interpreted this grouping of unusual forms as a shell. Cf. No. 960.

BIBLIOGRAPHY: Venturi, Vol. I, under No. 1304 (not reproduced). *Album*, 1966 (reproduced).

COLLECTIONS: Cézanne *fils*, Paris. Paul Guillaume, Paris. A. Chappuis, Tresserve. Mr. and Mrs. Paul Mellon, Upperville, Va.

860. HEAD AND SHOULDERS OF THE ARTIST'S SON, 1886–87

$5\frac{3}{16} \times 5$ inches—13,2 × 12,7 cm. Page XLVII from the second sketchbook Mrs. Enid A. Haupt. Pencil, pencil rubbings, part of page cut off. Verso: No. 860A.

Vigorous drawing, but effaced and darkened by smudging. The volume of the bent head stands out in a surprising way. Cf. No. 869.

BIBLIOGRAPHY: Rewald, *Carnets*: C IV, p. XLVII "tête du fils de l'artiste—dessin très effacé" (not reproduced).

COLLECTIONS: Cézanne *fils*, Paris. M. Renou, Paris. Poyet, Lyons. M. Renou, Paris. Sam Salz, New York. Mrs. Enid A. Haupt, New York.

860A. SKETCH

Pencil, on the inaccessible reverse side of No. 860 (not reproduced).

BIBLIOGRAPHY: Rewald, *Carnets*: C IV, p. XLVII verso "croquis d'un col" (not reproduced).

861. HEAD OF A BOY, 1886–87

$7\frac{5}{8} \times 4\frac{5}{8}$ inches—19,4 × 11,8 cm. Page LI verso from the sketchbook CP I. Pencil. Verso: blank page.

Probably the artist's son. His eyelids are lowered, his collar is in shadow and there is also a little shadow under the nose; the top of the head, however, is luminous, which seems to indicate that the boy was drawn under a lamp.

BIBLIOGRAPHY: Venturi, Vol. I, under No. 1280 (not reproduced).

COLLECTIONS: Cézanne *fils*, Paris. Paul Guillaume, Paris. A. Chappuis, Tresserve. Private collection, Paris.

862. STUDY OF HEADS, 1886–87

$4\frac{7}{8} \times 8\frac{5}{8}$ inches—12,4 × 21,8 cm. Page XXIX verso from the sketchbook CP II. Pencil on pale blue paper. Verso: blank page.

(a) Left: head seen from the chin up, foreshortened and in right three-quarter view. The contour almost describes a circle. Study of a child asleep in bed, a stroke under the chin indicating the blanket; cf. No. 727.—(b) Above: the top part of the drawing repeated.—(c) Right: head of the artist's son, the collar of his coat forming a vault-shaped volume behind his neck. Drawn with a softer pencil.

BIBLIOGRAPHY: Venturi No. 1290, in error as page XXVIII verso.

COLLECTIONS: Cézanne *fils*, Paris. Paul Guillaume, Paris. A. Chappuis, Tresserve.

863. HEAD OF THE ARTIST'S SON, BATHER, 1886–87

$4\frac{3}{4} \times 7\frac{11}{16}$ inches—12 × 19,5 cm. Page from the sketchbook CP I. Pencil. Verso: a few touches of watercolor.

(a) Right: the boy's head is bent forward, the tip of his right index finger touching his cheek; broad area of light on the hair. The whole is much foreshortened.—(b) Left: seated bather, of the type *Bather going down into the Water*; cf. No. 524.

BIBLIOGRAPHY: Venturi, Vol. I, p. 349, Oeuvres Inédites (not reproduced).

COLLECTIONS: Kenneth Clark, London. Collin Clark, New York.

864. THE ARTIST'S SON, circa 1887

$6 \times 9\frac{5}{16}$ inches—15,2 × 23,7 cm. Page XVIII of the Album, Paul Mellon Collection. Pencil. Verso: No. 872.

The boy is leaning forward as though bent over his studies, a scarf around his neck; light on the hair. Cf. Nos. 861, 867.

BIBLIOGRAPHY: Venturi No. 1306. Venturi presents this page upright; the direction of the hatching suggests to me that it should be seen lengthwise. *Album* 1966 (reproduced).

COLLECTIONS: Cézanne *fils*, Paris. Paul Guillaume, Paris. A. Chappuis, Tresserve. Mr. and Mrs. Paul Mellon, Upperville, Va.

865. THE ARTIST'S SON READING, circa 1887

$6 \times 9\frac{5}{16}$ inches—15,2 × 23,7 cm. Page XXXII of the Album, Paul Mellon Collection. Pencil. Verso: No. 1146.

(a) The chin is not drawn; indications of a hand near the nose, and the back of a chair behind the boy's neck. The way the head stands out has been carefully observed.—(b) Left: light sketch of the right forearm supporting a head, position similar to that of the arm in No. 875.

BIBLIOGRAPHY: Venturi, Vol. I, under No. 1309 (not reproduced). *Album*, 1966 (reproduced).

COLLECTIONS: Cézanne *fils*, Paris. Paul Guillaume, Paris. A. Chappuis, Tresserve. Mr. and Mrs. Paul Mellon, Upperville, Va.

866. THE ARTIST'S SON LEANING ON HIS ELBOW, circa 1887

$6 \times 9\frac{5}{16}$ inches—15,2 × 23,7 cm. Page III of the Album, Paul Mellon Collection. Pencil. Verso: No. 768.

Figure of the boy drawn from the waist up, seated or reclining. In the center: an open book, seen in foreshortening. The hand supporting the head seems to me worthy of a Puget sculpture. Cf. Nos. 865, 875.

BIBLIOGRAPHY: Venturi, Vol. I, under No. 1301 (not reproduced). *Album*, 1966 (reproduced).

COLLECTIONS: Cézanne *fils*, Paris. Paul Guillaume, Paris. A. Chappuis, Tresserve. Mr. and Mrs. Paul Mellon, Upperville, Va.

867. THE ARTIST'S SON WRITING, circa 1887

$6 \times 9\frac{5}{16}$ inches—15,2 × 23,7 cm. Page XVII verso of the Album, Paul Mellon Collection. Pencil. Verso: No. 1073.

This powerful sketch shows the boy with a pen in his hand. The silhouette of the shoulders and head and the intense rendering of the pen nib are remarkable. Cf. Nos. 847, 853, 865, 870.

BIBLIOGRAPHY: Venturi No. 1305. F. Novotny, *Cézanne*, Phaidon, 1937, No. 118 (reproduced). *Album*, 1966 (reproduced).

COLLECTIONS: Cézanne *fils*, Paris. Paul Guillaume, Paris. A. Chappuis, Tresserve. Mr. and Mrs. Paul Mellon, Upperville, Va.

868. HEAD OF THE ARTIST'S SON, 1887

$4\frac{5}{8} \times 7\frac{5}{8}$ inches—11,8 × 19,4 cm. Page XXX from the sketchbook CP I. Pencil on ocher paper. Verso: No. 433.

The face is seen in foreshortening beneath the spherical volume of the crown. To the left a part of the boy's back is indicated, and lower down the lapel of his coat.

COLLECTIONS: Cézanne *fils*, Paris. Paul Guillaume, Paris. A. Chappuis, Tresserve.

869. HEAD OF THE ARTIST'S SON, 1888

$8\frac{1}{2} \times 5\frac{3}{8}$ inches—21,6 × 13,7 cm. Page 6 of the sketchbook ML. Pencil. Verso: No. 1040.

The boy is leaning forward, his face seen in foreshortening. The turning movement of the volumes is noteworthy. Cf. Nos. 865, 868.

BIBLIOGRAPHY: Rewald, *Carnets*: C III, p. 6 (not reproduced).

COLLECTIONS: Cézanne *fils*, Paris. M. Renou, Paris. Poyet, Lyons. M. Renou, Paris. Sam Salz, New York. Cabinet des Dessins au Musée du Louvre, Paris.

870. TWO HEADS, 1888

$9\frac{5}{16} \times 6$ inches—23,7 × 15,2 cm. Page IX of the Album, Paul Mellon Collection. Pencil. Verso: No. 1064.

(a) Top: head of a boy, his coat collar standing out from his neck.—(b) On a larger scale: head seen in right profile; the expression is attentive. Cf. No. 864.

BIBLIOGRAPHY: Venturi, Vol. I, under No. 1303 (not reproduced). *Album*, 1966 (reproduced).

COLLECTIONS: Cézanne *fils*, Paris. Paul Guillaume, Paris. A. Chappuis, Tresserve. Mr. and Mrs. Paul Mellon, Upperville, Va.

871. HEAD OF THE ARTIST'S SON, 1888–89

$9\frac{5}{16} \times 6$ inches—23,7 × 15,2 cm. Page XXI verso of the Album, Paul Mellon Collection. Pencil. Verso: No. 1014.

The head is leaning slightly forward supported by one hand near the lower lip, the expression meditative. Cézanne has often portrayed this gesture of meditation: see our Nos. 272, 608, 866, 875, and Venturi Nos. 679, 681, 684, 686, 688, 690, 701. The rendering of light is particularly sensitive in this sketch.

BIBLIOGRAPHY: Venturi, Vol. I, under No. 1306 (not reproduced). *Album*, 1966 (reproduced).

COLLECTIONS: Cézanne *fils*, Paris. Paul Guillaume, Paris. A. Chappuis, Tresserve. Mr. and Mrs. Paul Mellon, Upperville, Va.

872. HEAD OF A BOY, 1887–89

$6 \times 9\frac{5}{16}$ inches—15,2 × 23,7 cm. Page XVIII verso of the Album, Paul Mellon Collection. Pencil. Verso: No. 864.

(a) Left: unfinished sketch of a hand holding some object. —(b) Head of a young man; the right eye seems to be less open than the left one, giving a sidelong look. Cf. No. 660.

BIBLIOGRAPHY: Venturi, Vol. I, under No. 1306; described in error as right profile (not reproduced). *Album*, 1966 (reproduced).

COLLECTIONS: Cézanne *fils*, Paris. Paul Guillaume, Paris. A. Chappuis, Tresserve. Mr. and Mrs. Paul Mellon, Upperville, Va.

873. SKETCH OF THE ARTIST'S SON, circa 1889

$7\frac{5}{8} \times 4\frac{5}{8}$ inches—19,4 × 11,8 cm. Page XLIII verso from the sketchbook CP I. Pencil. Verso: No. 664.

The boy's chin touches one of his hands resting on a table; to the lower left there is an indication of the sleeve cuff of the other hand. This drawing seems confused at first, but graphic when seen from a certain distance.

BIBLIOGRAPHY: Venturi, Vol. I, under No. 1275; the word "verso" is omitted (not reproduced).

COLLECTIONS: Cézanne *fils*, Paris. Paul Guillaume, Paris. A. Chappuis, Tresserve. H. Berggruen, Paris.

874. HEAD OF THE ARTIST'S SON, circa 1889

$5\frac{1}{2} \times 5\frac{1}{8}$ inches—14 × 13 cm. Pencil, stains. Verso: blank page.

The unfinished state of this portrait leads me to suppose that the artist was interrupted while working on it. The volume is nevertheless remarkable.

COLLECTIONS: Mané-Katz, Jerusalem. Dr. Sauville, Paris.

875. HALF-LENGTH STUDY OF A FIGURE, HEAD ON HAND, circa 1889

$6 \times 9\frac{5}{16}$ inches—15,2 × 23,7 cm. Page XXXIII of the Album, Paul Mellon Collection. Pencil. Verso: No. 891.

The subject, in an open-necked shirt, is asleep, one elbow leaning on a table. The heavy shadow on the hair to the left, where the strokes are graven into the paper, is noteworthy. Is it the artist's son? Perhaps. On the other hand a comparison may be made with the canvas Venturi No. 701, *Young Italian Girl leaning on her Elbow*.

BIBLIOGRAPHY: Venturi, Vol. I, under No. 1309 (not reproduced). *Dessins*, 1938 (reproduced pl. 14). *Album*, 1966, dated 1890–94 (reproduced).

COLLECTIONS: Cézanne *fils*, Paris. Paul Guillaume, Paris. A. Chappuis, Tresserve. Mr. and Mrs. Paul Mellon, Upperville, Va.

876. PROVENÇAL LANDSCAPE, 1882–85

$5 \times 8\frac{9}{16}$ inches—12,6 × 21,7 cm. Page XXXV of the sketchbook Leigh Block. Pencil, page soiled by smudging. Verso: No. 903.

Landscape studied several times by Cézanne, no doubt with a view to a painting which has not come down to us. There is a little shelter in the foreground and a horizontal chain of low hills spreading across the background; a tree on the left. Cf. No. 877, and Venturi Nos. 920, 921.

BIBLIOGRAPHY: Rewald, *Carnets:* C V, p. XXXV (not reproduced).

COLLECTIONS: Cézanne *fils*, Paris. M. Renou, Paris. Poyet, Lyons. M. Renou, Paris. Sam Salz, New York. Mr. and Mrs. Leigh Block, Chicago.

877. PROVENÇAL LANDSCAPE, 1882–85

$4\frac{7}{8} \times 8\frac{5}{8}$ inches—12,4 × 21,8 cm. Page XXXVIII verso from the sketchbook CP II. Pencil. Verso: No. 307.

The watercolors Venturi Nos. 920 and 921 show the same view and help in interpreting this drawing. The landscape is seen from a flat roof, the little shelter on the left covering a stairway leading up to it. The ridge of a very low roof stretching out to the right of the shelter is seen in the drawing as a narrow horizontal rectangle, and a stroke lower in the foreground indicates the edge of the terrace. Behind: an expanse of fields, with a kind of pylon (not a chimney) on the left and a tree on the right. It seems to me that the main zone of interest in this composition is the right background.

BIBLIOGRAPHY: Venturi, Vol. I, under No. 1292 (not reproduced).

COLLECTIONS: Cézanne *fils*, Paris. Paul Guillaume, Paris. A. Chappuis, Tresserve.

878. TREES AND ROOF, 1882–83

$12\frac{13}{16} \times 13\frac{9}{16}$ inches—32,6 × 34,5 cm. Pencil. Verso: No. 909.

A fine study, though a little confused and probably unfinished. On the left there are some trees on a knoll sloping steeply to the right. A forked tree rises up straight to the top of the page, and a wide roof in diminishing perspective can be seen behind a wall.

BIBLIOGRAPHY: Venturi No. 1496. H. R. Hoetink, *Franse Tekeningen uit de 19e Eeuw*, Rotterdam, 1968, No. 15, dated 1879–80 (reproduced).

EXHIBITIONS: Amsterdam, 1946, No. 3. The Hague, 1956, No. 116. Zurich, 1956, No. 177. Munich, 1956, No. 134. Hamburg, 1963, No. 29 (reproduced).

COLLECTIONS: J. Koenigs, Haarlem. Boymans-van Beuningen Museum, Rotterdam (Inv. F II 26).

879. SKETCH OF A TERRACED LANDSCAPE, 1883–85

$5 \times 8\frac{1}{2}$ inches—12,7 × 21,6 cm. Page IX from the second sketchbook Mrs. Enid A. Haupt. Pencil. Verso: No. 879A.

Some trees on the left mark the foreground, while the middle distance consists of a slope spreading across to the right; the wooden crest of a hill establishes the horizon. Parallel and spiral strokes in the sky.

BIBLIOGRAPHY: Rewald, *Carnets:* C IV, p. IX "croquis d'un paysage" (not reproduced).

COLLECTIONS: Cézanne *fils*, Paris. M. Renou, Paris. Poyet, Lyons. M. Renou, Paris. Sam Salz, New York. Mrs. Enid A. Haupt, New York.

879A. SKETCH OF A CLUMP OF BUSHES

Pencil. Inaccessible reverse side of No. 879 (not reproduced).

BIBLIOGRAPHY: Rewald, *Carnets:* C IV, p. IX verso "croquis d'un groupe d'arbustes" (not reproduced).

879bis. HOUSE SURROUNDED BY TREES, 1881–84

$12\frac{3}{8} \times 19$ inches—31,5 × 48,3 cm. Pencil with a few touches of watercolor. Verso: No. 972bis.

Landscape in northern France: a wall and a few rustic buildings, seen at the end of a summarily indicated winding path. The view opening out to the houses is bordered with vegetation; tree trunks on the left.

COLLECTIONS: Alfred Flechtheim, Berlin. Bernheim-Jeune, Paris. Art Institute of Chicago (Inv. 65.14), gift of Tiffany and Margaret Blake.

880. THE FARMHOUSE OF THE JAS DE BOUFFAN, 1883–85

$8\frac{1}{16} \times 18\frac{11}{16}$ inches—20,5 × 47,5 cm. Pencil. Verso: blank page.

The subject of this very fine drawing resembles that of the paintings Venturi Nos. 461-464. Cf. also our No. 608.

BIBLIOGRAPHY: Venturi No. 1507. Meier-Graefe, *Cézanne und seine Ahnen*, Marées-Gesellschaft, Munich, 1921, No. 13 (reproduced). *Dessins*, 1957, No. 28 (reproduced). F. Novotny, *Cézanne und das Ende der wissenshaftlichen Perspektive*, Vienna, 1938, p. 200, No. 60 (not reproduced).

EXHIBITIONS: Meisterzeichnungen französischer Künstler, Kunsthalle, Basel, 1935, No. 187. Kunsthalle, Basel, 1936, No. 133. Zurich, 1956, No. 214. Munich, 1956, No. 136. Europäische Meisterwerke aus Schweizer Sammlungen, Munich, 1969, No. 28 (reproduced Abb. 26).

COLLECTIONS: Ambroise Vollard, Paris. A. Hahnloser, Winterthur. H. Hahnloser, Bern.

881. EXTENSIVE LANDSCAPE WITH A HOUSE, 1883–85

Measurements not known. Pencil. Verso: blank page.

The landscape, unfortunately not finished, spreads out on all sides of a house seen from the top of a hill; further away, indications of a few clusters of trees and irregular tracts of land. Very faint lines suggest distant mountains.

COLLECTIONS: Galerie Bénézit, Paris. John Wyeth, New York. Weyhe Gallery, New York. Present owner unknown.

882. LANDSCAPE WITH ROOFS, HOUSES, AND A NARROW ROAD, circa 1885

Measurements not known. Pencil. Verso: blank page.

Narrow road leading down to the left flanked by houses consisting of right angles and diagonal lines; a field with trees in the background. View characteristic of the region around Paris.

BIBLIOGRAPHY: Venturi No. 1247.

EXHIBITIONS: Galerie Flechtheim, Cézanne Aquarelle und Zeichnungen, Berlin, 1927, No. 43 (reproduced). Idem, Seit Cézanne in Paris, 1929, No. 28.

COLLECTIONS: Egon Zerner, Berlin. Egon Zerner sale, Berlin, Dec. 15-16, 1924 (reproduced pl. 70). Alfred Flechtheim, Berlin. Galerie Thannhauser, Berlin. Present owner unknown.

883. TREES, circa 1885

$8\frac{9}{16} \times 4\frac{7}{8}$ inches—21,7 × 12,4 cm. Page XXV of the sketchbook A.I.C. Pencil, stains. Verso: No. 771.

A large tree on the left, with a younger trunk to the right and some shrubs. Cf. No. 772, and also No. 915, which shows the same motif in winter.

BIBLIOGRAPHY: Rewald, *Carnets:* C II, p. XXV (repro-

duced pl. 56). Schniewind, text p. 30 (reproduced). Andersen, *Sk.* (reproduced fig. 21).

COLLECTIONS: Cézanne *fils*, Paris. M. Renou, Paris. Poyet, Lyons. M. Renou, Paris. Sam Salz, New York. Art Institute, Chicago.

884. STUDY OF FOLIAGE, circa 1884

$5 \times 8\frac{9}{16}$ inches—12,6 × 21,7 cm. Page XXXVI verso of the sketchbook Leigh Block. Pencil. Verso: No. 349.

Study of a dense thicket with different kinds of foliage, lit with sunshine; a distant horizontal plane is indicated on the right.

BIBLIOGRAPHY: Rewald, *Carnets:* C V, p. XXXVI verso (not reproduced).

COLLECTIONS: Cézanne *fils*, Paris. M. Renou, Paris. Poyet, Lyons. M. Renou, Paris. Sam Salz, New York. Mr. and Mrs. Leigh Block, Chicago.

885. THE POOL OF THE JAS DE BOUFFAN, 1883–86

$7\frac{5}{8} \times 4\frac{5}{8}$ inches—19,4 × 11,8 cm. Page XII verso from the sketchbook CP I. Pencil. Verso: very small unfinished sketch of a head in a cocked hat (not classified).

Two tree trunks in the foreground to right and left of a patch of meadow, and further back the double-curved stone slab of an outdoor basin, against the wall of the pool; the wall is surmounted by an iron paling. Reflections can be seen mirrored in the water. Study for the painting Venturi No. 648. Cf. our No. 763.

BIBLIOGRAPHY: Venturi, Vol. I, under No. 1270 (not reproduced). *Dessins*, 1957, No. 37 (reproduced).

COLLECTIONS: Cézanne *fils*, Paris. Paul Guillaume, Paris. A. Chappuis, Tresserve.

886. LANDSCAPE WITH TREES AND HOUSES, 1883–86

$4\frac{7}{8} \times 8\frac{5}{8}$ inches—12,4 × 21,8 cm. Page XXXV from the sketchbook CP II. Pencil. Verso: No. 832.

Left: a vertical indicating the corner of a house, the wall left white; a few bushes indicated by hatching. A fir tree rises straight up, with another rising similarly behind it; a twisted, forked branch is seen in silhouette. This is a winter landscape. For the branch, cf. Venturi No. 661. To the right there are some houses, and the landscape stretches back through an empty space.

BIBLIOGRAPHY: Venturi, Vol. I, under No. 1290 (not reproduced). *Dessins*, 1938, No. 17 (reproduced).

COLLECTIONS: Cézanne *fils*, Paris. Paul Guillaume, Paris. A. Chappuis, Tresserve. Private collection, Paris.

887. WOODED LANDSCAPE, 1882–85

$6\frac{5}{16} \times 9\frac{1}{4}$ inches—16 × 23,5 cm. Pencil on beige laid paper, creased and stained. Verso: No. 701.

An area stretching diagonally toward the right fills the middle distance, while the foreground on the left is on a higher level. The treetops spread out in fan shape. Though lacking in precision, this drawing impresses by an appearance of gravity.

BIBLIOGRAPHY: Venturi, Vol. I, No. 1244 verso "étude d'arbres" (not reproduced).

COLLECTION: Kenneth Clark, London.

888. STUDY OF CLOUDS, 1884–87

$4\frac{7}{8} \times 8\frac{5}{8}$ inches—12,4 × 21,8 cm. Page XLVII verso from the sketchbook CP II. Pencil. Verso: No. 308.

A subject that is rare in Cézanne's drawings, although fairly dense clouds sometimes figure in his oils (the sky is heavily clouded in certain landscapes and paintings of *Bathers*). Cf. Venturi Nos. 313, 315, 324, 580.

BIBLIOGRAPHY: Venturi, Vol. I, under No. 1296 (not reproduced).

COLLECTIONS: Cézanne *fils*, Paris. Paul Guillaume, Paris. A. Chappuis, Tresserve.

889. HOUSE IN A PARK, 1883–86

$6 \times 9\frac{5}{16}$ inches—15,2 × 23,7 cm. Page XLIX of the Album, Paul Mellon Collection. Pencil. Verso: No. 599.

Landscape rapidly sketched with vigorous strokes, much of the paper left white. A house with a window near the roof is seen surrounded by vegetation, with receding driveways to the left and right. In the foreground, the edge of a pool and to its right a decorative statue seen from the back, perhaps Neptune holding a trident. Cf. Nos. 1146, 1152.

BIBLIOGRAPHY: Venturi, Vol. I, under No. 1313 "maison au milieu des arbres. Un homme assis donne une sérénade" (not reproduced). *Album*, 1966, dated circa 1890 (reproduced).

COLLECTIONS: Cézanne *fils*, Paris. Paul Guillaume, Paris. A. Chappuis, Tresserve. Mr. and Mrs. Paul Mellon, Upperville, Va.

890. TREES AND SHRUBS, 1883–87

$9\frac{5}{16} \times 6$ inches—23,7 × 15,2 cm. Page LIII verso of the Album, Paul Mellon Collection. Pencil. Verso: a very small sketch of a basket (not classified).

Part of a garden with little paths leading through plots of grass. Further back the view is cut off by a clump of shrubs and trees. Neumeyer senses Pissarro's influence here in the rendering of the bushes but sees the placing of the trees as pure Cézanne. The motif is certainly impressionist, though the style of the drawing goes beyond that trend.

BIBLIOGRAPHY: Venturi, Vol. I, under No. 1315 (not reproduced). *Dessins*, 1938 (reproduced pl. 31). Neumeyer, 1958 (reproduced pl. 73). *Album*, 1966 (reproduced; the little sketch p. LIII also).

COLLECTIONS: Cézanne *fils*, Paris. Paul Guillaume, Paris. A. Chappuis, Tresserve. Mr. and Mrs. Paul Mellon, Upperville, Va.

891. NEAR THE POOL AT THE JAS DE BOUFFAN, 1883–87

$6 \times 9\frac{5}{16}$ inches—15,2 × 23,7 cm. Page XXXIII verso of the Album, Paul Mellon Collection. Pencil. Verso: No. 875.

At the lower edge of the page the border of a path can be seen, with trees and foliage on the farther side, and halfway up, an iron paling similar to the one surrounding the pool at the Jas de Bouffan. Cf. Nos. 763, 885, and Venturi Nos. 166, 648.

BIBLIOGRAPHY: Venturi, Vol. I, under No. 1309 (not reproduced). *Album*, 1966 (reproduced).

COLLECTIONS: Cézanne *fils*, Paris. Paul Guillaume, Paris. A. Chappuis, Tresserve. Mr. and Mrs. Paul Mellon, Upperville, Va.

892. STUDY OF A PINE TREE, 1882–85

$9\frac{5}{16} \times 6$ inches—23,7 × 15,2 cm. Page XXII verso of the Album, Paul Mellon Collection. Pencil. Verso: No. 923.

Study of the trunk and some branches of a pine tree, with a wall in the background. Cf. the branches in the paintings Venturi Nos. 454, 455, the watercolor Venturi No. 914, and our drawings Nos. 739, 893.

BIBLIOGRAPHY: Venturi, Vol. I, under No. 1306, the word "verso" omitted (not reproduced). *Album*, 1966 (reproduced).

COLLECTIONS: Cézanne *fils*, Paris. Paul Guillaume, Paris. A. Chappuis, Tresserve. Mr. and Mrs. Paul Mellon, Upperville, Va.

893. BRANCH OF A PINE TREE, circa 1885

$12\frac{3}{16} \times 18\frac{7}{8}$ inches—31 × 48 cm. Right margin trimmed. Pencil, traces of horizontal folds. Verso: blank page.

Detailed study of a pine tree branch spreading out horizontally with its clusters of twigs and needles; it resembles the branch on the left of the paintings Venturi Nos. 454, 455, and in the watercolor No. 914. Cf. our drawings Nos. 739, 892. On the lower part of the page there are some numbers written in pencil, perhaps by another hand.

BIBLIOGRAPHY: See Cézanne and a Pine Tree, by Ellen H. Johnson, bulletin of Allen Memorial Art Museum, Vol. XXI, No. 1, 1963, page 11. This drawing, however, is not mentioned.

COLLECTIONS: Mouradian & Vallotton, Paris. Kelekian, Paris. Unknown collection. Norman Schlenoff, New York.

894. LANDSCAPE OF HILLS, WITH A HOUSE, 1882–85

$4\frac{7}{8} \times 7\frac{13}{16}$ inches—12,4 × 19,8 cm. Page XXVI from the sketchbook BS III. Pencil, stain lower left. Verso: the handwritten notation "*rue Flétrier* 19   *Raphaël Ferry   Mme Louis Ferry.*"

Landscape near Aix-en-Provence; the Mont du Cengle can be recognized on the right. Cf. the painting Venturi No. 423 and our No. 895.

BIBLIOGRAPHY: Venturi No. 1432. F. Novotny, *Cézanne und das Ende der wissenschaftlichen Perspektive*, Vienna, 1938, p. 201, No. 67 (not reproduced). Basel catalog, No. 119 (reproduced). R. Cogniat, Paris, 1967 (reproduced p. 9).

COLLECTIONS: Cézanne *fils*, Paris. Paul Guillaume, Paris. W. Feuz, Bern. Kunstmuseum, Basel.

895. LANDSCAPE, WITH MONT SAINTE-VICTOIRE, 1883–85

$12\frac{1}{4} \times 18\frac{1}{2}$ inches—31,1 × 47 cm. Pencil. Verso: the watercolor Venturi No. 1021.

Study resembling the painting Venturi No. 423, the characteristic house with its chimney on the right; cf. No. 894.

This view can be seen when walking along the path between the Jas de Bouffan and Bellevue. The stroke in this drawing is a little hesitant; the silhouette of the mountain is indicated by three successive contours.—The numbers lower right correspond to a calculation of proportions for the size of a canvas: 16 cm. are added to the dimension 47×31 cm. (which is that of our drawing), giving 63×47 cm. (a canvas "12 *paysage*" measures 61×46 cm., i.e., $24 \times 18\frac{1}{8}$ inches).

COLLECTIONS: E. Blot, Paris. Eugène Blot sale, Paris, June 2, 1933, verso of No. 3 (not reproduced). Daber, Paris. E. M. Remarque, Ascona. E. Thaw, New York.

896. PINE TREE AND MONT SAINTE-VICTOIRE, 1883–86

$12\frac{3}{16} \times 18\frac{15}{16}$ inches—$31 \times 48,2$ cm. Pencil, small oil stains. Verso: No. 986.

Study for the painting Venturi No. 452: a pine tree rising up against the sky and the mountain in the left background, with the Mont du Cengle and viaduct on the right. The viewpoint is rather lower than that of Venturi No. 452, but from the same direction. Cf. No. 897.

BIBLIOGRAPHY: Venturi, Vol. I, mentioned as verso of No. 1461 (not reproduced). H. R. Hoetink, *Franse Tekeningen uit de 19e Eeuw*, Rotterdam, 1968, No. 16 verso, dated 1885–87 (reproduced).

COLLECTIONS: Bernheim-Jeune, Paris. P. Cassirer. F. Koenigs, Haarlem. Boymans-van Beuningen Museum, Rotterdam (Inv. F II 27 verso).

897. MONT SAINTE-VICTOIRE, 1883–86

$14\frac{3}{8} \times 19\frac{1}{16}$ inches—$36,5 \times 48,5$ cm. Pencil. Verso: blank page.

Trees on the left, mountain; viaduct lower right. This drawing should not be confused with the watercolor of the same subject, Venturi No. 1565. Cf. our No. 896.

BIBLIOGRAPHY: Venturi, No. 1502. Meier-Graefe, *Cézanne und seine Ahnen*, Marées-Gesellschaft, Munich, 1921, No. 11 (reproduced).

EXHIBITIONS: Zurich, 1956, No. 213. Munich, 1956, No. 135. Europäische Meisterwerke aus Schweizer Sammlungen, Munich, 1969, No. 29 (reproduced Abb. 27).

COLLECTIONS: Ambroise Vollard, Paris. A. Hahnloser, Winterthur. H. Hahnloser, Bern.

898. LANDSCAPE WITH HOUSES AND MOUNTAINS, 1883–86

$11\frac{13}{16} \times 15\frac{3}{4}$ inches—30×40 cm. Pencil. Verso: blank page.

Although this drawing has a classical aspect, the stroke is so light as to be almost ethereal. The houses in the foreground are indicated by straight lines. Venturi recognized Mont Sainte-Victoire without hesitation but apparently did not identify the site.

BIBLIOGRAPHY: Venturi No. 1504.

COLLECTIONS: Galerie Bollag, Zurich. Bollag sale, Zurich, April 3, 1925, cat. No. 37 (reproduced pl. 17). Max G. Bollag, Zurich.

899. VIEW ACROSS TO THE HEIGHTS OF THE SAINTE-BAUME, 1883–86

$11\frac{7}{16} \times 16\frac{15}{16}$ inches—29×43 cm. Pencil, smudging. Verso: blank page.

Lines and planes forming a panorama with one single house and two mountain ranges. The heights of Sainte-Baume establish the horizon.

BIBLIOGRAPHY: Venturi No. 1506.

EXHIBITION: De Cézanne à Picasso, Musée de l'Athénée, Geneva, 1967, No. 51 (reproduced).

COLLECTIONS. Galerie Bollag, Zurich. Bollag sale, Zurich, April 3, 1925, cat. No. 36 (reproduced pl. 17). Suzanne Bollag, Zurich. Galerie Bénador, Geneva.

900. THE HOUSE OF BELLEVUE, circa 1885

$4\frac{7}{8} \times 8\frac{9}{16}$ inches—$12,4 \times 21,7$ cm. Page X of the sketchbook A.I.C. Pencil, stains. Verso: No. 809.

Trees and buildings at Bellevue near Aix, where the artist's brother-in-law, Maxime Conil, lived from 1885. Cf. Venturi Nos. 651, 652, and the earlier No. 412; also our No. 901.

BIBLIOGRAPHY: Rewald, *Carnets:* C II, p. X (reproduced pl. 59). Schniewind, text p. 27 (reproduced). Andersen, *Sk.* (not reproduced).

COLLECTIONS: Cézanne *fils*, Paris. M. Renou, Paris. Poyet, Lyons. M. Renou, Paris. Sam Salz, New York. Art Institute, Chicago.

901. THE HOUSE OF BELLEVUE, circa 1885

$4\frac{7}{8} \times 8\frac{9}{16}$ inches—$12,4 \times 21,7$ cm. Page XXXII verso of the sketchbook A.I.C. Pencil, stains. Verso: No. 647.

The house is seen in the right background; cf. No. 900. See Venturi Nos. 651, 652, and the earlier No. 412; also our No. 124.

BIBLIOGRAPHY: Rewald, *Carnets:* C II, p. XXXII verso (reproduced pl. 58). Schniewind, text p. 31 (reproduced). Andersen, *Sk.* (not reproduced).

COLLECTIONS: Cézanne *fils*, Paris. M. Renou, Paris. Poyet, Lyons. M. Renou, Paris. Sam Salz, New York. Art Institute, Chicago.

902. VIEW OF GARDANNE, 1885–86

$8\frac{1}{4} \times 12$ inches—$21 \times 30,5$ cm. Pencil on laid paper with a watermark. Verso: the watercolor Venturi No. 912.

Preliminary sketch in which the artist studied and resolved the construction and general rhythm of his oil painting, Venturi No. 430. Vollard's signature and the number 129 have been added in the sky.

BIBLIOGRAPHY: Venturi No. 1505. Catalog, Museum of Modern Art, New York, 1934 (reproduced pl. 13A). F. Novotny, *Cézanne und das Ende der wissenschaftlichen Perspektive*, Vienna, 1938, p. 205, No. 102 (not reproduced).

COLLECTIONS: Ambroise Vollard, Paris. Museum of Modern Art, New York, Lillie P. Bliss Collection.

903. LANDSCAPE AT L'ESTAQUE, circa 1885

$5 \times 8\frac{9}{16}$ inches—$12,6 \times 21,7$ cm. Page XXXV verso of the sketchbook Leigh Block. Pencil. Verso: No. 876.

A tree on the left, a rock on the right, the space between opening out to the sea, with horizontal planes representing a landing stage. The ordonnance of the drawing can be clearly interpreted by referring to the painting Venturi No. 57, which shows the same site. The two trees at the upper right form a characteristic little Cézanne motif.

BIBLIOGRAPHY: Rewald, *Carnets:* C V, p. XXXV verso (reproduced pl. 47). R. W. Ratcliffe, p. 399, note 118.

COLLECTIONS: Cézanne *fils*, Paris. M. Renou, Paris. Poyet, Lyons. M. Renou, Paris. Sam Salz, New York. Mr. and Mrs. Leigh Block, Chicago.

904. LANDSCAPE, circa 1886

$10\frac{1}{2} \times 13$ inches—$26,7 \times 33$ cm. Pencil on laid paper. Verso: watercolor landscape with big trees (not classified by Venturi).

Preparatory drawing for the canvas Venturi No. 473, *Environs du Jas de Bouffan*. Rather symmetrical landscape, the successive planes of a hill rising in the background. In the right foreground a large tree trunk; branches in leaf are sketched against the sky, one of them forming an arabesque.

COLLECTION: Present owner unknown.

905. THE ARC VALLEY, 1885–87

$5 \times 8\frac{9}{16}$ inches—$12,6 \times 21,7$ cm. Page XXII verso of the sketchbook Leigh Block. Pencil on blue-gray paper. Verso: No. 412.

Rapidly sketched landscape showing Mont Sainte-Victoire on the left, Mont du Cengle on the right, and a pine tree in the center; the arches of the viaduct are indicated below the Mont du Cengle. All of this corresponds to the painting Venturi No. 453, and also to the watercolor Venturi No. 913, which, however, is considered anterior to our drawing. The pencil technique is in rapport with the somber tone of the paper, which attenuates the contrasts.

BIBLIOGRAPHY: Rewald, *Carnets:* C V, p. XXII verso (reproduced pl. 46). Franz Erpel, *Paul Cézanne*, Welt der Kunst series, Berlin, 1960 (reproduced p. 23).

COLLECTIONS: Cézanne *fils*, Paris. M. Renou, Paris. Poyet, Lyons. M. Renou, Paris. Sam Salz, New York. Mr. and Mrs. Leigh Block, Chicago.

906. STUDY FOR THE PAINTING KNOWN AS *L'Arbre tordu*, 1885–88

$9\frac{1}{16} \times 12\frac{3}{8}$ inches—23×31 cm. Pencil on laid paper, stains on the right half of the page. Verso: blank page.

Drawing establishing the components of the painting Venturi No. 420 but in a different perspective. At the lower right there is an enclosure wall, its top butting horizontally into the composition. The sketch shows a section with an opening forming a recess which breaks the wall surface; in the canvas this is replaced by a kind of crevice. Above there are a few houses, and a tree trunk comes into the drawing at the corner, its upper part forming a curve;

to the left a pine tree rises up straight, its branches bending down toward the center, and between the two trees there is a sapling. The stroke indicating the ground at the foot of the tree on the left is exactly repeated in the painting.

COLLECTIONS: Mouradian & Vallotton, Paris. Kelekian, Paris. Unknown collection. Norman Schlenoff, New York.

907. LANDSCAPE, 1884–87

$4\frac{7}{8} \times 8\frac{5}{8}$ inches—$12,4 \times 21,8$ cm. Page XLVI from the sketchbook CP II. Pencil and watercolor. Verso: No. 1083.

Unfinished pencil sketch with a few touches of watercolor. There is a cone-shaped bush in the center and several tree trunks behind a wall.

BIBLIOGRAPHY: Venturi, Vol. I, under No. 1295 (not reproduced).

COLLECTIONS: Cézanne *fils*, Paris. Paul Guillaume, Paris. A. Chappuis Tresserve.

908. WALL AND BRANCH, 1884–87

Measurements not known. Pencil, numerous stains caused by a liquid. Verso: ?

A garden wall crosses the page horizontally; a branch in leaf, stretching out from the right toward the left, forms a vault, under which there is a young tree.

EXHIBITION: Quatre Chemins, Paris, 1936.

COLLECTIONS: John Wyeth, New York. Weyhe Gallery, New York. Present owner unknown.

909. TWO TREES, 1885–87

$12\frac{13}{16} \times 13\frac{9}{16}$ inches—$32,6 \times 34,5$ cm. Pencil. Verso: No. 878.

To the right two almost vertical tree trunks, one slightly hidden by the other, the graceful canopy of their leaves stretching across the upper part of the page.

BIBLIOGRAPHY: Venturi No. 1245. H. R. Hoetink, *Franse Tekeningen uit de 19e Eeuw*, Rotterdam, 1968, verso of No. 15 (reproduced).

COLLECTIONS: J. Koenigs, Haarlem. Boymans-van Beuningen Museum, Rotterdam (Inv. F II 26).

909bis. TREE TRUNKS, 1885–87

$4\frac{5}{8} \times 7\frac{3}{4}$ inches—$11,8 \times 19,7$ cm. Page from the sketchbook CP I. Pencil. Verso: No. 466bis.

Group of tree trunks with indications of foliage.

COLLECTIONS: Cézanne *fils*, Paris. Private collection, Paris. Dr. W. Raeber, Basel. Private collection, Basel.

910. MASS OF TREES, 1885–87

$11\frac{7}{16} \times 15\frac{3}{4}$ inches—29×40 cm. Pencil on laid paper, traces of folds. Verso: ?

Unfinished study: wide flat area planted with three receding rows of trees. A stroke on the right establishes a horizon—perhaps a stretch of water.

EXHIBITIONS: Kunsthalle, Basel, 1936, No. 121. Quatre Chemins, Paris, 1936.

COLLECTIONS: W. Walter, Paris. Present owner unknown.

911. APPLE TREE, 1885–87

$12\frac{3}{16} \times 18\frac{7}{8}$ inches—31 × 48 cm. Pencil on gray-brown paper. Verso: blank page.

Detailed study of branch formations and the distribution of foliage. In the background: a horizontal line.

BIBLIOGRAPHY: Venturi, Vol. I, p. 348, Oeuvres Inédites (not reproduced).

COLLECTIONS: Frau Marg. Oppenheim, Berlin. Sale, Oppenheim Collection, Böhler's, Munich, May 18-20, 1936, No. 1231 (not reproduced). Kenneth Clark, London. Present owner unknown.

912. HOUSE IN THE TREES, 1886–89

$12\frac{3}{16} \times 18\frac{7}{8}$ inches—31 × 48 cm. Pencil on grayish-yellow paper. Verso: a watercolor.

Provençal house, seen from a lower level. In the foreground there are some bushes, left white by the artist, in front of a slope shaded by hatching. In the background, masses of vegetation.

BIBLIOGRAPHY: Venturi, Vol. I, p. 348, Oeuvres Inédites; the author indicates the Jas de Bouffan, but there seems little possibility of identifying the site. (Not reproduced.)

COLLECTION: Kenneth Clark, London.

913. TREES, 1884–87

$12\frac{3}{16} \times 19\frac{1}{16}$ inches—31 × 48,5 cm. Pencil on laid paper. Watermark: shield with caduceus accompanied by two initials. Verso: blank page.

Study of a large tree and its branches against a lightly indicated forest background.

BIBLIOGRAPHY: *Verzeichnis der Handzeichnungen, Pastelle und Aquarelle*, Von der Heydt Museum, Wuppertal, 1965, No. 34 (reproduced).

COLLECTIONS: E. von der Heydt, Von der Heydt Museum, Wuppertal (Inv. KK 1965–115).

914. STUDY OF TREES, 1884–87

$11\frac{13}{16} \times 18\frac{1}{8}$ inches—30 × 46 cm. Pencil on laid paper Verso: blank page.

On the right, the trunk of a tree with several of its heavy boughs spreading out in a fan shape and two other branches stretching over to the left. More vegetation in the background, interspersed with areas of light.

BIBLIOGRAPHY: Rewald, Paris, 1939 (reproduced fig. 75). Rewald, London, 1959 and 1965 (reproduced fig. 74). Neumeyer, 1958, No. 81 (reproduced).

EXHIBITIONS: Rétrospective du Centenaire, Paris, 1939, No. 51. Nineteenth Century French Drawings, California Palace of The Legion of Honor, San Francisco, 1947, No. 3. St. Louis Collections, City Art Museum, St. Louis, 1948, No. 61. Fine Art Associates, New York, 1952, No. 8 (reproduced). Phillips Collection, Washington, D.C., Chicago, Boston, 1971, No. 74 (reproduced).

COLLECTIONS: Reid & Lefevre, London. Mrs. Langton Douglas, New York. Mr. and Mrs. Perry T. Rathbone, Cambridge, Mass.

915. LANDSCAPE WITH TREES, 1885–87

$4\frac{7}{8} \times 8\frac{9}{16}$ inches—12,4 × 21,7 cm. Page XXXI verso of the sketchbook A.I.C. Pencil, stains. Verso: No. 344.

Several houses perched on a ridge, profiled against the horizon; a fall or winter landscape. This drawing has a curious quality on account of the hatching in parallel lines. Cf. No. 883, where the trees are in leaf.

BIBLIOGRAPHY: Rewald, *Carnets*: C II, p. XXXI verso (reproduced pl. 55). Schniewind, text p. 31 (reproduced). Andersen, *Sk.* (not reproduced). Neumeyer 1958, No. 72 (reproduced). Rewald, *Cézanne: Landschaften*, Kleine Enzyklopädie der Kunst, Paris, 1958 (reproduced). Yvon Taillandier, *Paul Cézanne*, Paris, New York, Munich, 1961 and 1965 (reproduced p. 25). F. Mathey, *Les Impressionistes*, Paris 1959 and New York 1961 (reproduced p. 123).

COLLECTIONS: Cézanne *fils*, Paris. M. Renou, Paris. Poyet, Lyons. M. Renou, Paris. Sam Salz, New York. Art Institute, Chicago.

916. AVENUE OF THE JAS DE BOUFFAN, 1884–87

$12\frac{1}{16} \times 18\frac{13}{16}$ inches—30,7 × 47,8 cm. Pencil. Watermark: JV. Verso: blank page.

Four almost vertical accents formed by an avenue of large trees leading to a group of houses in the right background. A rhythmic drawing with fan-shaped winter branches in the upper part of the page. Its relation to the painting Venturi No. 476, which shows the same trees from another viewpoint, is evident.

BIBLIOGRAPHY: Venturi No. 1495, and photograph of the motif: No. 1593. J. Rewald and L. Marchutz, Cézanne et la Provence, *Le Point*, Colmar, Aug. 1939 (reproduced p. 6, with the motif). F. Novotny, *Cézanne und das Ende der wissenschaftlichen Perspektive*, Vienna, 1938, p. 200, No. 53 (not reproduced). H. R. Hoetink, *Franse Tekeningen uit de 19e Eeuw*, Rotterdam, 1968, No. 35, dated 1885–87 (reproduced).

EXHIBITIONS: Galerie A. Flechtheim, Berlin, 1927, No. 58. Idem, Christmas 1929, No. 30. Boymans Museum, Rotterdam 1933–34, No. 9. Amsterdam, 1946, No. 15 (reproduced). Phillips Collection, Washington, D.C., Chicago, Boston, 1971, No. 73 (reproduced).

COLLECTIONS: F. Koenigs, Haarlem. Boymans-van Beuningen Museum, Rotterdam (Inv. F II 221).

917. LANDSCAPE, 1884–87

$13\frac{3}{4} \times 21\frac{1}{4}$ inches—35 × 54 cm. Pencil on grayish-yellow paper. Verso: blank page.

The main emphasis is on two trees in the center, their trunks rising parallel toward the right. In the foreground there is an open area divided by a trench winding its way back like a turning road, with a few bushes (rocks, according to Venturi) on the left. The ridge establishing a broken horizon is drawn in double, sometimes triple, strokes.

BIBLIOGRAPHY: Venturi, Vol. I, p. 348, Oeuvres Inédites (not reproduced).

COLLECTIONS: Kenneth Clark, London. British Museum, London.

918. TREES AND ENCLOSURE WALL, 1885–88

$16\frac{15}{16} \times 11\frac{7}{16}$ inches—43 × 29 cm. Pencil. Verso: blank page.

Two parts of an enclosure wall, with entrance space between them, and a building; the wall on the left is further back than the section on the right. The drawing is completed by several tree trunks and mases of foliage.

BIBLIOGRAPHY: Venturi No. 1500; by error: "au verso, paysage avec des arbres" (our No. 1160 having been framed as though on the reverse side of No. 918).

COLLECTIONS: Bernheim-Jeune, Paris. Thannhauser, Lucerne. Dudensing, New York. Knoedler & Co., New York. Sale, Klipstein & Kornfeld, Bern, June 5-6, 1959, No. 97 (reproduced pl. 40; pl. 31 is mistakenly indicated). James Lord, New York. Dina Vierny, Paris.

919. TWO TREES, 1886–89

$8\frac{9}{16} \times 5$ inches—21,7 × 12,6 cm. Page XL verso of the sketchbook Leigh Block. Pencil. Verso: No. 782.

The trunks form a V which fills up the whole page. Behind them, seen from above, a few bushes and some other trees. The sky can be pictured through the branches.

BIBLIOGRAPHY: Rewald, *Carnets:* C V, p. XL verso (reproduced pl. 52). Yvon Taillandier, *Paul Cézanne*, Paris, New York, Munich, 1961 and 1965 (reproduced p. 35).

COLLECTIONS: Cézanne *fils*, Paris. M. Renou, Paris. Poyet, Lyons. M. Renou, Paris. Sam Salz, New York. Mr. and Mrs. Leigh Block, Chicago.

920. STUDY OF TREES, 1886–88

$19 \times 12\frac{1}{2}$ inches—48,2 × 31,7 cm. Pencil. Verso: No. 933.

Study of pine trees. On the right a rather big trunk rises up, one branch stretching out to the right, another higher up to the left; this creates a rhythm which is accentuated by the tangle of trunks and branches in the background. Multiple contours almost everywhere.

COLLECTIONS: V. Bloch, London. John Wyeth, New York. Weyhe Gallery, New York. Meier Bernstein, Brooklyn, N.Y. Mr. and Mrs. Henry Pearlman, New York.

921. TREE AND ROOF, 1886–89

$10\frac{1}{2} \times 7$ inches—26,7 × 17,8 cm. Pencil on laid paper. Verso: blank page.

Unfinished study of a double-trunked tree with a few little leafy branches in front of a roof with rounded tiles, and further back a chimney in front of the gable of a larger house. There is musical rhythm in the lines of this sketch.

COLLECTION: Lady Olga Montagu, London.

922. BARE TREES, circa 1887

$8\frac{3}{16} \times 5\frac{3}{16}$ inches—20,8 × 13,1 cm. Page XXXI from the sketchbook BS I. Pencil. Verso: blank page.

A cluster of large trees in an entanglement of bare branches. The structures are indicated with a rather rigid sobriety and without depth, the main accent being on the diagonals.

BIBLIOGRAPHY: Venturi No. 1357. Basel catalog, No. 117 (reproduced).

EXHIBITION: Kunstverein, Hamburg, 1963, No. 30 (reproduced).

COLLECTIONS: Cézanne *fils*, Paris. Paul Guillaume, Paris. W. Feuz, Bern. Kunstmuseum, Basel.

923. BRANCH IN FLOWER, 1886–89

$9\frac{5}{16} \times 6$ inches—23,7 × 15,2 cm. Page XXII of the Album, Paul Mellon Collection. Pencil. Verso: No. 892.

Small branch with leaves and a flower; cf. Venturi No. 1137. Though the sketch is unfinished, the detail noted is admirable.

BIBLIOGRAPHY: Venturi, Vol. I, under No. 1306 (not reproduced). *Album,* 1966 (reproduced).

COLLECTIONS: Cézanne *fils*, Paris. Paul Guillaume, Paris. A. Chappuis, Tresserve. Mr. and Mrs. Paul Mellon, Upperville, Va.

924. STUDY OF A TREE, 1885–87

$15\frac{3}{16} \times 19\frac{5}{8}$ inches—38,7 × 49,8 cm. Pencil. Verso: the watercolor Venturi No. 1561.

A tree trunk, with gnarls below its crown of branches, fills the left part only of this large page.

COLLECTIONS: Vicomte B. d'Heudecourt. Sale, Sotheby's, London, May 9, 1929, No. 165 verso. Paul J. Sachs, Cambridge, Mass. Henry P. McIlhenny. Fogg Art Museum, Cambridge, Mass.

925. POPLAR TREE, STUDY, 1886–89

$8\frac{1}{8} \times 4\frac{15}{16}$ inches—20,7 × 12,5 cm. Page XXIII from the sketchbook BS III. Pencil. Verso: No. 974.

Study of a poplar standing some distance back; the light parts are made to stand out by hatching. The foot of the tree is hidden by smaller trees and the left side by a vertical trunk.

BIBLIOGRAPHY: Venturi No. 1429.

COLLECTIONS: Cézanne *fils*, Paris. Paul Guillaume, Paris. W. Feuz, Bern. R. von Hirsch, Basel.

926. STUDY OF A TREE, 1886–89

$7\frac{15}{16} \times 4\frac{7}{8}$ inches—20,2 × 12,3 cm. Page XIX from the sketchbook BS III. Pencil, brown stains upper right. Verso: No. 928.

Tree in full leaf, probably a birch. There is a delicate play of light in its branches, and the grouped hatching resembles brush strokes.

BIBLIOGRAPHY: Venturi No. 1421. Basel catalog, No. 171 (reproduced).

COLLECTIONS: Cézanne *fils*, Paris. Paul Guillaume, Paris. W. Feuz, Bern. Kunstmuseum, Basel.

927. STUDY OF TREES, 1886–89

$18\frac{3}{16} \times 11\frac{13}{16}$ inches (sight)—46,3 × 30 cm. Pencil. Reverse side inaccessible.

A pine tree, twisting to the right half way up, its crown spreading out against the sky. Lower left: the harmonious fork of another tree.

EXHIBITIONS: De Géricault à Matisse, Petit Palais, Paris, 1959, No. 146.

COLLECTION: Max Huggler, Sent (Grisons).

928. ROCKS AND TREES, 1886–89

$4\frac{7}{8} \times 7\frac{15}{16}$ inches—12,3 × 20,2 cm. Page XIX verso from the sketchbook BS III. Pencil, stains lower left. Verso: No. 926.

A group of rocks, trees, and bushes, rapidly noted in a few strokes.

BIBLIOGRAPHY: Venturi No. 1422. Basel catalog, No. 118 (reproduced).

COLLECTIONS: Cézanne *fils*, Paris. Paul Guillaume, Paris. W. Feuz, Bern. Kunstmuseum, Basel.

929. TREES, 1886–89

$11\frac{1}{4} \times 7\frac{1}{16}$ inches—28,5 × 18 cm. Pencil on laid paper. Verso: blank page.

Pine trees on a rock; I fancy that on the left side the rock goes steeply downwards. Other trees growing in the background. Fine study, probably done in Bibémus quarry.

COLLECTION: Robert Rey, Geneva.

930. STUDY OF TREES, 1886–89

$14\frac{9}{16} \times 18\frac{7}{8}$ inches—37 × 48 cm. Pencil on laid paper. Verso: ?

Vigorous study of curving trunks and branches, possibly pine trees in the vicinity of Château Noir; the whole forms a composition.

BIBLIOGRAPHY: Venturi No. 1497.

EXHIBITION: Paul Cassirer, Berlin, Nov.-Dec. 1921, No. 60.

COLLECTIONS: Frau Marg. Oppenheim, Berlin. Sale, Oppenheim Collection, Böhler's, Munich, May 18-20, 1936, No. 1230 (not reproduced). Present owner unknown.

931. LITTLE HOUSE SURROUNDED BY TREES, 1886–89

$12\frac{3}{16} \times 18\frac{1}{2}$ inches—31 × 47 cm. Pencil. Verso: blank page.

The drawing has been much worked on, though incomplete in places. A well can be seen to the right. A curious, rather symmetrical study, its beauty enhanced by a kind of intimacy with nature.

BIBLIOGRAPHY: Venturi No. 1571, "Forêt." Meier-Graefe, *Cézanne und seine Ahnen*, Marées-Gesellschaft, Munich, 1921, No. 9 (reproduced).

EXHIBITION: Galerie A. Flechtheim, Berlin, 1927, No. 57.

COLLECTIONS: Galerie Georg Caspari, Munich. Present owner unknown.

932. BARE BRANCHES, 1887–90

$16\frac{15}{16} \times 11\frac{13}{16}$ inches—43 × 30 cm. Pencil on laid paper, two small stains. Verso: No. 464.

Several bare branches rise and spread out in front of a background lightly indicated by hatching and two horizontal planes. A detailed and superbly rhythmical study.

BIBLIOGRAPHY: F. Novotny, Cézanne als Zeichner, *Wiener Jahrbuch* 1950 (reproduced fig. 116). Reprinted in *Ueber das Elementare in der Kunstgeschichte und andere Aufsätze*, Rosenbaum, Vienna, 1968 (reproduced fig. 45).

COLLECTION: Weyhe Gallery, New York. Present owner unknown.

933. TREES, circa 1891

$19 \times 12\frac{1}{2}$ inches—48,2 × 31,7 cm. Pencil on laid paper. Verso: No. 920.

Study of tree trunks and bare branches. Light but dense hatching within the contours.

BIBLIOGRAPHY: *Vie, Art et Cité*, Geneva, number dated Dec. 1939 (reproduced).

COLLECTIONS: V. Bloch, London. John Wyeth, New York. Weyhe Gallery, New York. Meier Bernstein, Brooklyn, N.Y. Mr. and Mrs. Henry Pearlman, New York.

934. STUDY OF BRANCHES, circa 1891

$8\frac{9}{16} \times 5$ inches—21,7 × 12,6 cm. Page XLV of the sketchbook Leigh Block. Pencil. Verso: No. 780.

Unfinished but precise study of a forked branch, some of its twigs in leaf.

BIBLIOGRAPHY: Rewald, *Carnets*: C V, p. XLV (reproduced pl. 53).

COLLECTIONS: Cézanne *fils*, Paris. M. Renou, Paris. Poyet, Lyons. M. Renou, Paris. Sam Salz, New York. Mr. and Mrs. Leigh Block, Chicago.

935. CARNIVAL SCENE, 1885–88

$4\frac{3}{4} \times 7\frac{1}{2}$ inches—12 × 19 cm. Page from the sketchbook CP I. Pencil. Verso: blank page.

This carnival scene is in rapport with the other studies which are thought to have preceded the painting *Mardi Gras*, Venturi No. 552. Cf. Nos. 666 (b), 936, 937.

BIBLIOGRAPHY: Venturi No. 1487. *Le Dessin français au XIXe siècle*, Mermod, Lausanne, 1948 (reproduced p. 103). Basel catalog, mentioned under No. 124; the opening on the left of this drawing is described erroneously as a French window, whereas it is actually an open window with a pot of flowers standing on the sill. Yvon Taillandier, *Paul Cézanne*, 1965 (reproduced p. 69).

COLLECTIONS: Cézanne *fils*, Paris. W. Feuz, Bern. R. von Hirsch, Basel.

936. CARNIVAL SCENE, 1885–88

$6 \times 9\frac{5}{16}$ inches—15,2 × 23,7 cm. Page XIX verso of the Album, Paul Mellon Collection. Pencil. Verso: No. 948.

For the subject of *Carnival*, cf. No. 937. The present sketch shows Harlequin on the left, impetuously clasping a woman. A figure in a cocked hat is seated behind a round table; on the right there is another couple. In the sketchbook this page was opposite p. XX (No. 937), which treats the same subject. Cf. Nos. 666 (b), 935, 937.

BIBLIOGRAPHY: Venturi, Vol. I, under No. 1306 (not reproduced). *Dessins*, 1938 (reproduced pl. 4). *Album*, 1966 (reproduced).

COLLECTIONS: Cézanne *fils*, Paris. Paul Guillaume, Paris. A. Chappuis, Tresserve. Mr. and Mrs. Paul Mellon, Upperville, Va.

937. CARNIVAL SCENE, STUDY, 1885–88

$5\frac{7}{8} \times 9\frac{5}{16}$ inches—15 × 23,6 cm. Page XX from the Album, Paul Mellon Collection, removed around 1923 by Cézanne *fils* for Georges Rivière; see Bibliography. Pencil, fold upper right. Verso: No. 852.

Lively scene comprising four figures. On the left, Harlequin is clasping a woman; his mask has fallen to the ground. Right: a man sitting on the floor, bending over to the right, his leg in the foreground, his hat in the right corner. Above him: a man in a cocked hat, bearded and masked, sitting behind a table. Cf. No. 936, which is a first study of the same subject, and also Nos. 435, 666 (b), 935.

BIBLIOGRAPHY: Venturi No. 1488. Basel catalog, No. 124 (reproduced). G. Rivière, *Le Maître Paul Cézanne*, Paris, 1923 (reproduced p. 1). *Dessins*, 1957, No. 19 (reproduced). *Album*, 1966 (reproduced in the text under p. XIX verso).

COLLECTIONS: Cézanne *fils*, Paris. W. Feuz, Bern. Kunstmuseum, Basel.

938. STUDIES FOR *Mardi Gras*, circa 1888

$9\frac{5}{8} \times 12\frac{1}{16}$ inches—24,5 × 30,7 cm. Pencil on laid paper, the shadows washed with white. Watermark: PL BAS. Verso: watercolor of a Provençal landscape.

Studies of the artist's son in Harlequin costume. Cf. the paintings Venturi Nos. 552-555, the watercolor No. 1079, and our Nos. 939, 941.

BIBLIOGRAPHY: Venturi No. 1473. Th. Duret, *Histoire des Peintres Impressionnistes*, Paris, 1906 (reproduced in sanguine opposite p. 166). *GBA*, 1907, I, p. 259 (reproduced). *Kunst und Künstler*, 1908 (reproduced p. 424). Vollard, 1914 (reproduced p. 148). Meier-Graefe, Munich, 1913 (reproduced p. 27). Idem, *Cézanne und sein Kreis*, Munich, 1922 (reproduced p. 210). Atzouji Seisho, 1921 (reproduced pl. 20). Kurt Pfister, 1927 (reproduced p. 104). Vergnet-Ruiz, La collection Personnaz, *Bulletin des Musées de France*, 1937 (reproduced p. 98).

COLLECTIONS: Personnaz, Bayonne. Cabinet des Dessins of the Louvre (RF 28802).

939. STUDIES FOR *Mardi Gras*, circa 1888

$9\frac{7}{8} \times 7\frac{1}{16}$ inches—25 × 18 cm. Pencil. Verso: blank page.

Studies for the canvas, *Mardi Gras*, Venturi No. 552. Cf. our No. 938.—(a) Left: portrait of the artist's son in Harlequin costume, with an accentuated vertical strip in the background hatching.—(b) Right: study of the eyes and nose of the same model, seen more nearly front face.

BIBLIOGRAPHY: Venturi No. 1622. Neumeyer, 1958, No. 41 (reproduced). Yvon Taillandier, *Paul Cézanne*, 1965 (reproduced p. 58).

EXHIBITION: Kunsthalle, Basel, 1936, No. 168.

COLLECTION: R. von Hirsch, Basel.

940. LOUIS GUILLAUME IN PIERROT COSTUME, circa 1888

$12\frac{3}{8} \times 9\frac{9}{16}$ inches—31,4 × 24,3 cm. Pencil on white laid paper, browned by a fixative. Verso: a few numbers.

Head and shoulder portrait of Louis Guillaume, a friend of Cézanne's son, dressed in Pierrot costume. The expression on his face, which is seen in right three-quarter view, is meditative and his look passes just beside the viewer. Study for the canvas Venturi No. 552, known as *Mardi Gras*.

BIBLIOGRAPHY: Venturi No. 1573. Basel catalog, No. 154 (reproduced). *Le Dessin français au XIXe siècle*, Mermod, Lausanne, 1948 (reproduced p. 102). *Dessins*, 1957, No. 18 (reproduced). Longstreet, 1964 (reproduced). Yvon Taillandier, *Paul Cézanne*, 1965 (reproduced p. 68).

EXHIBITIONS: Meisterzeichnungen französischer Künstler, Kunsthalle, Basel, 1935, No. 193. The Hague, 1956, No. 121. Zurich, 1956, No. 182.

COLLECTIONS: Cézanne *fils*, Paris. W. Feuz, Bern. Kunstmuseum, Basel, gift of the Freiwilliger Museumsverein Basel Society.

941. HARLEQUIN, circa 1888

$18\frac{5}{8} \times 12\frac{3}{16}$ inches—47,3 × 30,9 cm. Pencil on white wove paper. Verso: blank page.

Drawn from a lay figure dressed in Harlequin costume seen down to the knees, standing, in three-quarter view. Study for the figure in the canvas, *Mardi Gras*, Venturi No. 552, and for the paintings representing Harlequin alone, Venturi Nos. 553, 554, 555, 1079. Cf. our No. 944.

BIBLIOGRAPHY: Venturi No. 1486. Meier-Graefe, *Cézanne und sein Kreis*, Munich, 1922 (reproduced pl. 76). Göran Schildt, *Cézanne's Personligkeit* (reproduced fig. 10). *Dessins*, 1957, No. 16 (reproduced). Neumeyer, 1958, No. 23 (reproduced). Tietze, *Drawings*, No. 150 (reproduced). F. Mathey, Les Impressionnistes, Paris, 1959, New York, 1961 (reproduced p. 142). Y. Taillandier, *Paul Cézanne*, Paris, New York, Munich, 1961 and 1965 (reproduced p. 65). Longstreet, 1964 (reproduced). Collection Génies et Réalités, *Cézanne*, Paris, 1966 (reproduced p. 236, fig. 162). R. Cogniat, Paris, 1967 (reproduced p. 10).

EXHIBITIONS: Thannhauser, Berlin, 1927, No. 36. Meisterzeichnungen, etc., Kunsthalle, Basel, 1935, No. 109. Kunsthalle, Basel, 1936, No. 137. Centenaire, Galerie P. Rosenberg, Paris, 1939, hors catalogue. Lyons, 1939, No. 70. Modern Drawings, Museum of Modern Art, New York, 1944 (reproduced p. 26). Masterpieces etc., Philadelphia, 1950–51, No. 102 (reproduced). Art Institute, Chicago, and Metropolitan Museum, New York, 1952, No. 72 (reproduced). De David à Toulouse-Lautrec, Orangerie, Paris, 1955, No. 56. Phillips Collection, Washington, D.C., Chicago, Boston, 1971, No. 80 (reproduced).

COLLECTIONS: Cézanne *fils*, Paris. W. Halvorsen, Oslo. Thannhauser, Lucerne. Rosengart, Lucerne. Justin K. Thannhauser, New York. Art Institute, Chicago, Margaret Day Blake Collection.

942. SKETCH OF A HEAD, 1885–88

$8\frac{1}{4} \times 5\frac{3}{16}$ inches—21 × 13,1 cm. Page VIII from the sketchbook BS I. Pencil. Verso: blank page.

It is difficult to decide whether the drawings in the upper and lower parts of this unfinished page form one subject, or whether there are two sketches, begun and then rejected. Top: round cap surmounted by a circular button. Below: face in left three-quarter view with a broad, flattened nose; indication of lips. The center part of the face is crossed out with broad strokes. It is probably a copy.

BIBLIOGRAPHY: Venturi No. 1332.

COLLECTIONS: Cézanne *fils*, Paris. Paul Guillaume, Paris. W. Feuz, Bern. Hammer Galleries, New York. American Society for Technion Israel, New York.

FIG. 114. Jean-Antoine Houdon (1741–1828), bust of the philosopher *Denis Diderot* (1713–84), terra cotta in the Louvre. Legacy Walferdin 1880. RF 348. The bust being placed in a corner, it was not possible to photograph it in profile.   *(Photograph: Archives photographiques)*

943. J.-A. HOUDON : *Diderot,* circa 1888

$8\frac{5}{8} \times 5\frac{3}{16}$ inches—21,8 × 13,1 cm. Page XVII from the sketchbook BS I. Pencil. Verso: blank page.

Unfinished head seen in almost right profile, the left part not drawn. The eye is round, the look keen, the mouth denotes a talkative man. After the bust of Diderot by J.-A. Houdon, terracotta in the Louvre since 1880. See fig. 114.

BIBLIOGRAPHY: Venturi No. 1341, Berthold, cat. No. 324 (reproduced).

EXHIBITION: De David à Cézanne, La Vieille Fontaine, Lausanne, 1953, No. 107 (cited by error in the catalog as Venturi No. 1328).

COLLECTIONS: Cézanne *fils*, Paris. Paul Guillaume, Paris. W. Feuz, Bern. Carl Roesch, Diessenhofen.

944. HARLEQUIN, about 1888

$7\frac{3}{16} \times 4\frac{9}{16}$ inches—18,2 × 11,6 cm. Page 18 verso from the first sketchbook Mrs. Enid A. Haupt. Pencil heightened with bister wash. Verso: No. 592.

It seems to be the artist's son who posed, as in Nos. 938 and 939, whereas No. 941 was drawn from a lay figure. This page, heightened with bister wash, is curiously suggestive of eighteenth-century works. It is a study for the canvas, *Mardi Gras,* Venturi No. 552.

BIBLIOGRAPHY: Rewald, *Carnets:* C I, p. 18 verso (reproduced pl. 35). Meyer Schapiro, New York, 1952 (reproduced pl. 19). Th. Rousseau Jr., Paris, 1953 (reproduced pl. 39). Idem, Amsterdam, 1954 (reproduced pl. 39).

EXHIBITION: Cézanne Watercolors, Columbia University (Knoedler & Co.), New York, 1963, No. 23 (reproduced).

COLLECTIONS: Cézanne *fils*, Paris. M. Renou, Paris. Poyet, Lyons. M. Renou, Paris. Sam Salz, New York. Mrs. Enid A. Haupt, New York.

945. SPECTATORS, 1886–89 (see Note 56)

$5 \times 8\frac{1}{16}$ inches—12,6 × 20,4 cm. Unnumbered page removed from the sketchbook BS III in 1923 to be reproduced by Georges Rivière. Pencil, restored tear, brown stain upper left. Verso: No. 1217.

Four figures in a row on the page, seen from the back or in profile, dressed in the style of the period: a standing couple in the center, the woman holding an open umbrella, the man with his right arm raised, pointing with his index finger; this expressive gesture is characteristic of Cézanne. A seated man on the right and another on the left in the near foreground, in front of a leafy tree.

BIBLIOGRAPHY: Venturi, No. 1229. Basel catalog, No. 136 (reproduced). G. Rivière, Le Maître Paul Cézanne, Paris, 1923 (reproduced p. 55).

COLLECTIONS: Cézanne *fils*, Paris. W. Feuz, Bern. Kunstmuseum, Basel.

946. STUDY OF BATHERS, 1886–89

$8\frac{15}{16} \times 11\frac{5}{8}$ inches—22,7 × 29,5 cm. Pencil on gray paper, accidental abrasion, fold. Verso: blank page.

Three studies: (a) Bather seen front view with his hands on his hips; indication of foliage, hatching. The pose is one frequently used by Cézanne in his bather groups; for typical version of a *Bather with hands on hips* see Venturi No. 548 and our Nos. 351 (f), 625 (d), 947.—(b) Stylized outline of a bather sitting down drying under his arm.—(c) Upper right: bust-length figure; cf. the bather in No. 431.—(d) Rapid study of an unrecognizable object, to the right of (a) and separated from it by a line; cf. a similar rough sketch, No. 552.

BIBLIOGRAPHY: Venturi No. 1252. Basel catalog, No. 139 (reproduced). B. Dorival, Paris, 1948 (reproduced pl. XVI and (b) alone reproduced, in reverse, p. 101). *Dessins,* 1957, No. 26 ((a) reproduced).

EXHIBITIONS: The Hague, 1956, No. 119. Zurich, 1956, No. 180.

COLLECTIONS: Cézanne *fils,* Paris. W. Feuz, Bern. Kunstmuseum, Basel.

947. STANDING BATHER, IN FRONT OF MONT SAINTE-VICTOIRE, 1883–86

$8\frac{9}{16} \times 5$ inches—21,7 × 12,6 cm. Page XXVIII of the sketchbook Leigh Block. Pencil on yellowish paper. Verso: a rough sketch in watercolor.

Standing bather seen front view with his hands on his hips, before a summarily indicated landscape consisting of three successive planes, the most distant being the summit of Mont Sainte-Victoire. This drawing seems to be a compositional study; the treatment is characteristic of the pencil drawings on toned paper. On the left a tree trunk is seen in a field, and a dense screen of vegetation spreads out behind the torso of the bather. Cf. Nos. 625 (c), 946. Of many similar bather figures, the one in the painting Venturi No. 548, in my opinion, resembles this one most closely, although there is no mountain in the background; see also the lithograph Venturi No. 1157.

BIBLIOGRAPHY: Rewald, *Carnets:* C V, p. XXVIII (reproduced pl. 105).

COLLECTIONS: Cézanne *fils,* Paris. M. Renou, Paris. Poyet, Lyons. M. Renou, Paris. Sam Salz, New York. Mr. and Mrs. Leigh Block, Chicago.

948. HEAD OF A YOUNG MAN IN LOST PROFILE, circa 1885

$9\frac{5}{16} \times 6$ inches—23,7 × 15,2 cm. Page XIX of the Album, Paul Mellon Collection. Pencil. Verso: No. 946.

Head of a young man, seen in left lost profile: study of the nape of the neck, showing the volume of the head and neckline. It has a rather barren aspect. Venturi suggests that it portrays the artist's son, but the son's neck was shorter.

BIBLIOGRAPHY: Venturi, Vol. I, under No. 1306 (not reproduced). *Album,* 1966 (reproduced).

COLLECTIONS: Cézanne *fils,* Paris. Paul Guillaume, Paris. A. Chappuis, Tresserve. Mr. and Mrs. Paul Mellon, Upperville, Va.

949. STANDING BATHER, 1885–88

$17\frac{3}{4} \times 9\frac{1}{16}$ inches—45 × 23 cm. Pencil on laid paper. Verso: blank page.

The pose corresponds to that of the figure in Cézanne's sketches done after a drawing by Luca Signorelli, see Nos. 438, 998. Cf. also Nos. 428, 429. Similar bathers are seen in the paintings Venturi Nos. 580, 581.—A fine drawing, although there is an indefinable stiffness in the attitude of the head.

BIBLIOGRAPHY: *Correspondance* (reproduced fig. 19).

EXHIBITIONS: Galerie Flechtheim, Berlin, 1927, No. 56. Galerie Flechtheim, Berlin, 1929, No. 35. Orangerie, Paris, 1936, No. 161. San Francisco, 1937, No. 67. Wildenstein, London, 1939, No. 86.

COLLECTIONS: Silberberg, Breslau. Pfannstiel, Paris. A. Chappuis, Tresserve. Rogers, Paris (confiscated by the occupying forces in 1943).

950. AFTER CH.-A. COYSEVOX: *crouching Venus,* 1885–88

$18\frac{1}{2} \times 11\frac{13}{16}$ inches—47 × 30 cm. Pencil on laid paper. Verso: blank page.

After the marble figure (height $7\frac{1}{4}$ inches) by Charles-Antoine Coysevox in the Louvre. See fig. 69. Cf. No. 493.

BIBLIOGRAPHY: Venturi No. 1441. Berthold, cat. No. 147 (reproduced). Identification of the model.

COLLECTIONS: A. Vollard, Paris. Norton F. Simon, Los Angeles. Sale, Parke-Bernet, New York, May 5, 1971, No. 26 (reproduced). Mrs. Kasser, New York.

951. DERBY HAT AND GARMENT, 1884–87

$5 \times 8\frac{1}{2}$ inches—12,7 × 21,6 cm. Page XXXVIII verso from the second sketchbook Mrs. Enid A. Haupt. Pencil. Verso: No. 437.

This drawing is remarkable for its simplicity; the stroke is vigorous, almost impatient.

BIBLIOGRAPHY: Rewald, *Carnets:* C IV, p. XXXVIII verso (reproduced pl. 77).

COLLECTIONS: Cézanne *fils,* Paris. M. Renou, Paris. Poyet, Lyons. M. Renou, Paris. Sam Salz, New York. Mrs. Enid A. Haupt, New York.

952. PAGE OF STUDIES, WATER JUG AND HEAD OF A WOMAN, 1885–87

$8\frac{9}{16} \times 4\frac{7}{8}$ inches—21,8 × 12,4 cm. Page XLV verso from the sketchbook CP II. Pencil. Verso: No. 520.

(a) Top: still life of which the principal object is a water jug (the same as the one seen in Nos. 541, 542, and Venturi No. 1151).—(b) Below, at right angles: a woman's head, tilted forward; cf. No. 485 (b).

BIBLIOGRAPHY: Venturi, Vol. I, under No. 1295 (not reproduced).

COLLECTIONS: Cézanne *fils,* Paris. Paul Guillaume, Paris. A. Chappuis, Tresserve.

953. BELLOWS IN FRONT OF A FIREPLACE, 1887–92

$9\frac{5}{16} \times 6$ inches—23,7 × 15,2 cm. Page XV verso of the Album, Paul Mellon Collection. Pencil. Verso: No. 1069.

Bellows hanging on a peg, no doubt near a fireplace. On the right: the head of an andiron supporting a large log, inside a chimney frame. No. 954 is related to this study. Cf. No. 544; for the log, No. 545.

BIBLIOGRAPHY: Venturi, Vol. I, under No. 1304 (not reproduced); description incorrect. *Album,* 1966 (reproduced).

COLLECTIONS: Cézanne *fils,* Paris. Paul Guillaume, Paris. A. Chappuis, Tresserve. Mr. and Mrs. Paul Mellon, Upperville, Va.

954. TONGS AND HANDLE OF ANOTHER HEARTH IMPLEMENT, 1887–92

$9\frac{5}{16} \times 6$ inches—23,7 × 15,2 cm. Page XVI of the Album, Paul Mellon Collection. Pencil. Verso: No. 859.

Cf. the painting Venturi No. 621, which shows the tongs and round hook and, on the right, the little handle also seen in the drawing.

BIBLIOGRAPHY: Venturi, Vol. I, under No. 1304 (not reproduced). *Dessins,* 1938, No. 37 (reproduced). *Album,* 1966 (reproduced).

COLLECTIONS: Cézanne *fils,* Paris. Paul Guillaume, Paris. A. Chappuis, Tresserve. Mr. and Mrs. Paul Mellon, Upperville, Va.

955. KEROSENE LAMP, 1884–87

$7\frac{3}{16} \times 4\frac{9}{16}$ inches—18,2 × 11,6 cm. Page 15 verso from the first sketchbook Mrs. Enid A. Haupt. Pencil. Verso: No. 689.

This is no doubt the family lamp, under which Cézanne drew many of his sketches. Cf. Nos. 343, 956.

BIBLIOGRAPHY: Rewald, *Carnets:* C I, p. 15 verso (reproduced pl. 69).

COLLECTIONS: Cézanne *fils,* Paris. M. Renou, Paris. Poyet, Lyons. M. Renou, Paris. Sam Salz, New York. Mrs. Enid A. Haupt, New York.

956. KEROSENE LAMP, 1886–89

$18\frac{5}{16} \times 12\frac{3}{8}$ inches—46,5 × 31,5 cm. Pencil on white drawing paper, slightly soiled, traces of folds. Verso: a watercolor, *The Clearing*.

The base of this quite ordinary lamp, with its florid ornamentation, is typical of mass-production industrial taste of the second half of the nineteenth century. For the subject, cf. Nos. 343, 955.

COLLECTION: Claude Blancpain, Fribourg.

957. STILL LIFE "Pain sans mie," 1887–90

$12 \times 19\frac{1}{2}$ inches—30,5 × 49,7 cm. Pencil. Verso: blank page.

The carafe, little bottle, and ewer are standing in front of a cardboard box bearing the inscription PAIN SANS MIE (crumbless bread) and *Paris*. In the left background there is a decorative design on the wall.

BIBLIOGRAPHY: Venturi No. 1493.

EXHIBITION: Phillips Collection, Washington, D.C., Chicago, Boston, 1971, No. 78 (reproduced).

COLLECTIONS: Cézanne *fils*, Paris. Kenneth Clark, London.

958. AFTER CHARDIN: STILL LIFE WITH PITCHER, 1887–91

$4\frac{13}{16} \times 8\frac{3}{16}$ inches—12,2 × 20,8 cm. Page XLVI verso from the sketchbook BS II. Pencil. Verso: No. 1128.

FIG. 115. Jean-Baptiste-Siméon Chardin (1699–1779): *La Raie* (detail on the right). In the Louvre since 1795, with the former Académie collections. Canvas, 1,14 m. × 1,46 m. Musée National du Louvre, *Catalogue des Peintures* I, 1924, No. 86.   *(Photograph: Giraudon)*

Detail from Chardin's painting *The Skate* in the Louvre. See fig. 115.

BIBLIOGRAPHY: Venturi No. 1385. Berthold, cat. No. 234 (reproduced Abb. 24). Basel catalog, No. 123 (reproduced). *Dessins*, 1957, No. 32 (reproduced). John McCoubrey, The Revival of Chardin in French Still Life Painting 1850–1870, *AB*, March 1964, p. 39 (reproduced). *Selearte*, No. 52, July-Aug. 1961 (reproduced fig. 13).

COLLECTIONS: Cézanne *fils*, Paris. Paul Guillaume, Paris. W. Feuz, Bern. Kunstmuseum, Basel.

959. UNMADE BED, circa 1887

$10\frac{5}{8} \times 8\frac{1}{4}$ inches—27 × 21 cm. Page LXV from the sketchbook CP IV. Pencil. Verso: No. 959A.

Detailed decorative drawing of an unusual subject: an unmade bed, seen in foreshortening, with eiderdown and blankets thrown back. The metal frame with two ornamental scrolls is seen from in front; further back there is a window.

BIBLIOGRAPHY: Venturi, Vol. I, under No. 1317 (not reproduced). *Dessins*, 1938, No. 41 (reproduced). Neumeyer, 1958, No. 51 (reproduced).

EXHIBITIONS: Wildenstein, London, 1939, No. 83. Nice, Aix-en-Provence, Grenoble, 1953, No. 42. The Curtis O. Baer Collection, Fogg Art Museum, Cambridge, Mass., 1958 (reproduced).

COLLECTIONS: Cézanne *fils*, Paris. Paul Guillaume, Paris. A. Chappuis, Tresserve. Sale, Gutekunst & Klipstein, Bern, Nov. 22, 1956, No. 60 (reproduced). Wertheimer, Paris. Curtis O. Baer, New Rochelle, N.Y.

959A. UNMADE BED, sketch

Pencil. Verso of No. 959. (Not reproduced.)

Subject similar to that of No. 959.

BIBLIOGRAPHY: Venturi, Vol. I, under No. 1317, page LXVI (not reproduced).

960. CUSHION ON AN ARMCHAIR, circa 1887

$11\frac{3}{16} \times 8\frac{7}{8}$ inches—30 × 22,5 cm. Pencil on laid paper. Verso: blank page.

Still life showing a pillow propped against the arm of a chair. This drawing, a study of light and volumes, is one of the kind sketched by Cézanne when confined to his room: chairs, unmade beds, washstands. Cf. Nos. 535, 542, 546, 859, 959.

COLLECTIONS: André Derain, Paris. Sale, Gutekunst & Klipstein, Bern, Nov. 22, 1956, cat. No. 61 (reproduced). Dr. Koerfer, Bolligen (Bern).

961. SEATED NUDE WOMAN, 1886–89

$4\frac{5}{8} \times 7\frac{1}{16}$ inches—11,8 × 18 cm. Page XXXIII verso from the sketchbook CP I. Pencil on ocher paper. Verso: blank page.

Woman in a pose which calls to mind the studies for *Bathsheba*.

BIBLIOGRAPHY: Venturi, Vol. I, under No. 1274 (not reproduced). *XXe siècle*, Paris, number dated March 1938 (reproduced).

COLLECTIONS: Cézanne *fils*, Paris. Paul Guillaume, Paris. A. Chappuis, Tresserve. Private collection, Paris.

962. BATHER STEPPING DOWN INTO THE WATER, 1886–89

$7\frac{5}{8} \times 4\frac{5}{8}$ inches—19,4 × 11,8 cm. Page XXXI from the sketchbook CP I. Pencil, heightened with ink, on light blue paper. Verso: blank page.

This pose is repeated in several paintings of bathers, for example Venturi No. 541. Berthold thinks that Cézanne drew his inspiration for the pose from an engraving after Alonso Cano reproduced in Charles Blanc's book: see our No. 524. Technique: the artist used several different pencils, and heightened the head and one hand with ink.

BIBLIOGRAPHY: Venturi No. 1274. Mappe der Marées-Gesellschaft, Munich, 1918, No. 52 (reproduced in color). Pfister, Potsdam, 1927 (reproduced p. 11).

EXHIBITION: Orangerie, Paris, 1936, No. 148.

COLLECTIONS: Cézanne *fils*, Paris. Paul Guillaume, Paris. A. Chappuis, Tresserve.

963. HEAD, WOMAN BATHER, HANDWRITTEN NOTATIONS, circa 1888

$5 \times 8\frac{1}{16}$ inches—12,6 × 20,5 cm. Page XXVIII from the sketchbook BS III. Pencil, smudging, stains. Verso: rough draft of a letter; see Basel catalog No. 165.

Two sketches, covered by handwritten notations.—(a) Woman's head, bent slightly forward.—(b) Woman bather walking away toward the right background.—(c) Handwritten notations:

Gravure	18 *fr.*	*Chevalet*
pain	7,75	
Chabod	4	
Fontainebleau	15	
frotteur	10	

Blanc 4/*Outremer* 3/*Cobalt* 2/*Ocre jaune* 4/*Vert véronèse* 5/*Terre verte* 5/*Garance foncée* 2/*Garance rose* 2 *petits*/*Vert Emeraude*/*Vermillon.*

BIBLIOGRAPHY: Venturi No. 1434. Basel catalog, No. 130 (reproduced).

COLLECTIONS: Cézanne *fils*, Paris. Paul Guillaume, Paris. W. Feuz, Bern. Kunstmuseum, Basel.

964. WOMAN BATHER, circa 1888

$5 \times 7\frac{5}{8}$ inches—12,6 × 19,4 cm. Page IV from the sketchbook BS III. Pencil, brown stain upper left. Verso: No. 1008.

Woman bather standing with her arm raised in an expressive gesture.

BIBLIOGRAPHY: Venturi No. 1404. Basel catalog, No. 131 (reproduced).

COLLECTIONS: Cézanne *fils*, Paris. Paul Guillaume, Paris. W. Feuz, Bern. Kunstmuseum, Basel.

965. THREE BATHERS, 1887–90

$5 \times 8\frac{1}{16}$ inches—12,6 × 20,5 cm. Page XXIX from the sketchbook BS III. Pencil heightened with a little watercolor, stain lower left, spatterings on the right. Verso: rough draft of a letter, see Basel catalog No. 166.

(a) Left: sketch of a tree trunk.—(b) Bather running toward the left (pencil heightened by small touches of violet watercolor). In a search for the appropriate posture, one leg is studied in several renderings.—(c) Bather in the water, bending to the right.—(d) Seated woman bather with her hands on the ground; touch of watercolor on the buttocks.—(e) Above: sketch of a head (date 1892–95); cf. No. 1066 (a).

BIBLIOGRAPHY: Venturi No. 1435. Basel catalog, No. 140 (reproduced). Longstreet, 1964 (reproduced).

COLLECTIONS: Cézanne *fils*, Paris. Paul Guillaume, Paris. W. Feuz, Bern. Kunstmuseum, Basel.

966. STUDY OF THE NAPE OF A NECK, 1887–90

$5\frac{3}{8} \times 8\frac{1}{2}$ inches—13,7 × 21,6 cm. Page 7 of the sketchbook ML. Pencil. Verso: No. 1022.

Unfinished sketch of a woman's neck; her hair showing beneath the headdress is less accentuated than the headband. The subject was first sketched in lightly, then worked over with vigorous strokes.

BIBLIOGRAPHY: Rewald, *Carnets*: C III, p. 7 "croquis d'après un nid d'oiseau?" (not reproduced).

COLLECTIONS: Cézanne *fils*, Paris. M. Renou, Paris. Poyet, Lyons. M. Renou, Paris. Sam Salz, New York. Cabinet des Dessins of the Louvre, Paris (RF 29933).

967. VENUS AND CUPIDS, 1887–90

$4\frac{5}{8} \times 7\frac{5}{8}$ inches—11,8 × 19,4 cm. Page XV verso from the sketchbook CP I. Pencil. Verso: No. 604.

A free study, reminiscent of Rubens. The pose of Venus is unusual, vaguely recalling the theme of Bathsheba (see Venturi No. 252), but the overall design seems to be linked to the theme of the *Temptation.*

BIBLIOGRAPHY: Venturi, Vol. I, under No. 1271 (not reproduced). *Dessins*, 1938, No. 6 (reproduced). On the subject: Th. Reff, Cézanne, Flaubert, St. Anthony and the Queen of Sheba, *AB*, June 1962, p. 113.

EXHIBITIONS: Orangerie, Paris, 1936, No. 146. Aix-en-Provence, 1961, No. 54.

COLLECTIONS: Cézanne *fils*, Paris. Paul Guillaume, Paris. A. Chappuis, Tresserve.

968. STANDING WOMAN DOING HER HAIR, 1887–90

$8\frac{1}{2} \times 5$ inches—21,6 × 12,7 cm. Page XXX verso from the second sketchbook Mrs. Enid A. Haupt. Pencil. Verso: No. 557.

Nude woman standing in front of a draped background with her hands behind her head. Drawing inspired by *Le Lever* of Eugène Delacroix; see fig. 60. The contours of the figure are multiplied to an extraordinary degree and the rotund volumes expressed by areas of light. Cf. No. 467.

BIBLIOGRAPHY: Rewald, *Carnets*: C IV, p. XXX verso (reproduced pl. 89). See J. Rewald, Sources d'inspiration de Cézanne, *AA*, May 1936, p. 191. Berthold (reproduced Abb. 51).

COLLECTIONS: Cézanne *fils*, Paris. M. Renou, Paris. Poyet, Lyons. M. Renou, Paris. Sam Salz, New York. Mrs. Enid A. Haupt, New York.

969. WOMEN BATHERS, 1887–90

$4\frac{3}{4} \times 7\frac{7}{8}$ inches—12×20 cm. Page from a sketchbook (probably BS III), paginated LI. Pen drawing retouched with pencil, oil stain on the right. Verso: ?

Six women bathers standing or sitting in a landscape. Compositional study with some resemblance to the painting Venturi No. 540. The ink strokes have been retouched in many places.

BIBLIOGRAPHY: Venturi No. 1489. Vollard, 1914 (reproduced p. 91).

EXHIBITIONS: Aquarelles et Baignades de Cézanne, Galerie Renou & Colle, Paris, 1935.

COLLECTIONS: Cézanne fils, Paris. Present owner unknown.

970. NUDE WOMAN RESTING, 1888–91

$5 \times 7\frac{7}{8}$ inches—$12,6 \times 19,9$ cm. Page VII from the sketchbook BS III. Pencil, stain on the right. Verso: blank page.

Probably a study for the subject of Bathsheba; cf. Nos. 1103, 1150. The drawing has been reinforced with a blacker pencil, also used for a second rendering of the left leg.

BIBLIOGRAPHY: Venturi No. 1408. Basel catalog, No. 178 (reproduced). Longstreet, 1964 (reproduced).

COLLECTIONS: Cézanne fils, Paris. Paul Guillaume, Paris. W. Feuz, Bern. Kunstmuseum, Basel.

971. TWO GROUPS OF WOMEN BATHERS, 1888–91

$5\frac{1}{8} \times 7\frac{7}{8}$ inches—13×20 cm. Probably a page from the sketchbook BS I. Pencil. Verso: blank page.

(a) Left: group of three women bathers, the seated figure in the middle.—(b) Right: two women bathers sitting on the ground; both seem to be looking into a mirror which one of them is holding. A tree in the background. These studies are related to both the painting Venturi No. 540 and the watercolor No. 1107. Similar subject with slight variations appear in drawings of different periods: cf. Nos. 371, 649, 650, 1104. A very fine drawing; the group on the right especially is of remarkable quality.

BIBLIOGRAPHY: Venturi No. 1259. Vollard, 1914 ((b) reproduced p. 31). Dessins, 1957, No. 39 (reproduced).

EXHIBITION: Aquarelles et Baignades de Cézanne, Galerie Renou & Colle, Paris, 1935.

COLLECTIONS: Cézanne fils, Paris. Huguette Berès, Paris. Present owner unknown.

972. SEATED WOMAN, circa 1890

$4\frac{1}{4} \times 2\frac{11}{16}$ inches—$10,9 \times 6,8$ cm. Page III of the sketchbook violet moiré. Pencil, a few ink stains. Verso: handwriting, numbers.

Seated nude woman with drapery hanging down from the shoulder, leaving her breast bare; a few strokes indicate the background. W. V. Andersen is of the opinion that the original source was an interior scene in oils; it might also have been a garden sculpture.

BIBLIOGRAPHY: Berthold, p. 159 (not reproduced). W. V. Andersen, Cézanne's Carnet violet moiré, BurlM, June 1965, p. 313 (reproduced fig. 43).

COLLECTIONS: Cézanne fils and petit-fils, Paris. Mlle Edmée Maus, Geneva.

972bis. AFTER PIGALLE: Mercury 1887–90

$19 \times 12\frac{3}{8}$ inches—$48,3 \times 31,5$ cm. Pencil. Verso: No. 879bis.

After the marble by Jean-Baptiste Pigalle in the Louvre, or from a plaster cast. See fig. 44.

EXHIBITION: Phillips Collection, Washington, D.C., Chicago, Boston, 1971, No. 79 (reproduced).

COLLECTIONS: Alfred Flechtheim, Berlin and Düsseldorf. Bernheim-Jeune, Paris. Art Institute of Chicago (Inv. 65.14), Margaret Day Blake Collection.

973. AFTER PIGALLE: Mercury, circa 1890

$14\frac{3}{4} \times 9\frac{7}{8}$ inches—$37,5 \times 25$ cm. Pencil. Verso: blank page.

After Jean-Baptiste Pigalle's Mercury Fastening His Heel Wings, small marble statue in the Louvre (but perhaps drawn from a plaster cast). See fig. 44; cf. No. 305. In our sketch the head seems particularly big.

BIBLIOGRAPHY: Venturi No. 1454. Berthold, cat. No. 156. AA, 1920 (reproduced p. 272). J. Gasquet, Cézanne, Paris, 1921 & 1926 (reproduced p. 164). A. Fontainas & L. Vauxcelles, Histoire Générale de l'Art, Paris, 1922 (reproduced p. 222). Meier-Graefe, Cézanne und sein Kreis, Munich, 1922 (reproduced pl. 143). Ikouma Arishima, Cézanne, Ars, 1926 (reproduced pl. 30).

EXHIBITIONS: Kunsthalle, Basel, 1936, No. 141. Rétrospective, Paris, 1939, No. 47. Galerie Beyeler, Basel, 1967, No. 5 (reproduced).

COLLECTIONS: Bernheim-Jeune, Paris. André Lhote, Paris. Joh. Hohl, Basel. Galerie Beyeler, Basel. M. Feilchenfeldt, Zurich.

974. AFTER PIGALLE: Mercury, circa 1890

$8\frac{1}{8} \times 4\frac{15}{16}$ inches—$20,7 \times 12,5$ cm. Page XXIV from the sketchbook BS III. Pencil. Verso: No. 925.

After the marble by Jean-Baptiste Pigalle in the Louvre (or after a plaster cast of this statuette). See fig. 44. Cf. Nos. 305, 972bis, 973, and 975.

BIBLIOGRAPHY: Venturi No. 1430. Berthold, cat. No. 154 (reproduced).

COLLECTIONS: Cézanne fils, Paris. Paul Guillaume, Paris. W. Feuz, Bern. R. von Hirsch, Basel.

975. AFTER PIGALLE: Mercury, circa 1890

$10\frac{3}{4} \times 8\frac{15}{16}$ inches—$27,3 \times 21,1$ cm. Page LXXX from the sketchbook CP IV. Pencil, oil stains. Verso: No. 1198.

After the marble statuette of Mercury by Jean-Baptiste Pigalle, in the Louvre. See fig. 44. Cf. Nos. 972bis, 973, 974.

BIBLIOGRAPHY: Venturi No. 1321. Berthold, cat. No. 155 (reproduced).

COLLECTIONS: Cézanne fils, Paris. Paul Guillaume, Paris. A. Chappuis, Tresserve. Private collection, Paris.

976. AFTER PUGET: Milo of Crotona, circa 1890

$25\frac{1}{8} \times 12\frac{3}{8}$ inches—$64 \times 31,5$ cm. Pencil on laid paper. Verso: blank page.

After the marble *Milo of Crotona* by Pierre Puget, in the Louvre. See fig. 30. Cf. No. 505. The construction of the mass and distribution of volumes have been carefully studied on this large page.

BIBLIOGRAPHY: Venturi No. 1446. Berthold, cat. No. 98 (reproduced). J. Gasquet, *Cézanne*, Paris, 1921 and 1926 (reproduced p. 190). Meier-Graefe, *Cézanne und sein Kreis*, Munich, 1922 (reproduced p. 142). Ch. Rey, *La Renaissance du sentiment classique*, Paris, 1931 (reproduced p. 84).

EXHIBITION: Phillips Collection, Washington, D.C., Chicago, Boston, 1971, No. 82 (reproduced).

COLLECTIONS: Galerie Thannhauser, Lucerne. Frederic W. Cone. Baltimore Museum of Art, Frederic W. Cone Bequest.

977. AFTER PUGET: *Milo of Crotona*, circa 1890

$7\frac{3}{16} \times 4\frac{9}{16}$ inches—18,2 × 11,6 cm. Page 22 verso from the first sketchbook Mrs. Enid A. Haupt. Pencil. Verso: No. 628.

After the marble *Milo of Crotona* by Pierre Puget, in the Louvre. See fig. 30. Cf. especially No. 1201.

BIBLIOGRAPHY: Rewald, *Carnets:* C I, p. 22 verso (not reproduced). Berthold, cat. No. 104 (reproduced Abb. 130).

COLLECTIONS: Cézanne *fils*, Paris. M. Renou, Paris. Poyet, Lyons. M. Renou, Paris. Sam Salz, New York. Mrs. Enid A. Haupt, New York.

978. AFTER PUGET: *Milo of Crotona*, circa 1890

$7\frac{3}{16} \times 4\frac{9}{16}$ inches—18,2 × 11,6 cm. Page 33 from the first sketchbook Mrs. Enid A. Haupt. Pencil. Verso: No. 1110.

After the marble *Milo of Crotona* by Pierre Puget, in the Louvre. See fig. 30. The athlete, attacked by the lion, is seen here in left lost profile, facing the background; the animal's foreleg is indicated. Style and rounded volumes.

BIBLIOGRAPHY: Rewald, *Carnets:* C I, p. 33 or 25 (not reproduced). Berthold, cat. No. 107 (reproduced Abb. 135).

COLLECTIONS: Cézanne *fils*, Paris. M. Renou, Paris. Poyet, Lyons. M. Renou, Paris. Sam Salz, New York. Mrs. Enid A. Haupt, New York.

979. AFTER GÉRICAULT: *Draft horses,* 1887–90

$7\frac{1}{16} \times 6\frac{11}{16}$ inches—18 × 17 cm. Pencil. Verso: blank page.

Two horses in harness moving away toward the background. After a drawing by Th. Géricault in the Cabinet des Dessins of the Louvre. See fig. 116. It is one of Cézanne's most faithful copies, Géricault's style corresponding to his own temperament.

EXHIBITION: Athenaeum Museum, Helsinki, 1954, No. 22. Exhibition of Contemporary Art in Finnish Collections, Helsinki, 1962, No. 33.

COLLECTIONS: Private collection, Switzerland. W. Raeber, Basel. Bertel Hintze, Helsinki.

980. *L'Ecorché*, INTERIOR WITH A CHAIR, 1887–90

$12\frac{1}{4} \times 18\frac{3}{4}$ inches—31,2 × 47,7 cm. Pencil on gray laid paper with the watermark: Saint Mars; edges of the paper torn, small yellow stains. Verso: blank page.

(a) Left: study after *L'Ecorché*, see fig. 36. The figure seems to be standing near the rounded corner of a table or chest of drawers.—(b) Right: study of an interior, with the back of a chair.

BIBLIOGRAPHY: Venturi No. 1586. Berthold, cat. No. 66 (reproduced). Basel catalog, No. 153 (reproduced). *The World of Cézanne* (reproduced p. 131).

COLLECTIONS: Cézanne *fils*, Paris. W. Feuz, Bern. Kunstmuseum, Basel.

980bis. AFTER THE *Cupid* ATTRIBUTED TO PUGET, 1875–78

Measurements not known. Pencil. Verso: blank page.

After the plaster cast of this Cupid, owned by Cézanne; the nose on the drawing has been defaced by the young Paul. It is not known when Cézanne acquired the cast. (See fig. 117.) All his other studies of Cupid were done a few years later than the present one, which may well have been drawn elsewhere and not in his own home (copies of this plaster cast were to be found in most of the art schools). In any case, there is no reason why he should have studied it systematically.—(b) Lower left, at right angles: head and arm of St. Anthony; cf. No. 445. Higher up: rough sketch of the head.—(c) Upper right: study, covered with scribbles, of *The Tempter*; cf. No. 445. To the right: indications of another sketch, an outstretched arm. On the other side of (a): sketch of the arm resting on the saint's shoulder.

BIBLIOGRAPHY: Venturi, Vol. I, p. 352, Oeuvres Inédites, "Coll. Pierre Loeb" (not reproduced). Berthold, cat. No. 141 (not reproduced).

COLLECTIONS: Pierre Loeb, Paris. Present owner unknown.

FIG. 116. Théodore Géricault (1791–1824): *Chevaux de trait* (detail), pencil drawing in the Cabinet des Dessins of the Louvre (Inv. 26 740). *(Photograph: Giraudon)*

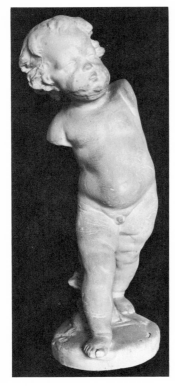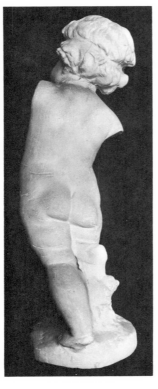

FIG. 117. Plaster cast of a *putto*, known as *l'Amour en plâtre*, which belonged to Cézanne, and is conserved in the atelier of the artist, Aix-en-Provence. It is believed to be after a sculpture by Pierre Puget, or by François du Quesnoy or his school.

981. AFTER THE *Cupid* ATTRIBUTED TO PUGET, 1879–82

$17\frac{15}{16} \times 11\frac{13}{16}$ inches—45,5 × 30 cm. Pencil. Verso: blank page.

After the plaster cast of Cupid, owned by Cézanne, seen here from the back. See fig. 117. A drawing with little detail, only the contour and a few shadows.

BIBLIOGRAPHY: Venturi, No. 1464. Berthold, cat. No. 135 (reproduced).

COLLECTIONS: A. Vollard, Paris. Arnold Seligmann, Paris.

982. AFTER THE *Cupid* ATTRIBUTED TO PUGET, 1879–82

$18\frac{1}{2} \times 15$ inches—47 × 38 cm. Pencil on laid paper. Verso: blank page.

After the plaster cast of Cupid owned by Cézanne, seen from the back. See fig. 117. A detailed drawing which shows the little round pedestal; background of hatching.

BIBLIOGRAPHY: Venturi No. 1465. Berthold, cat. No. 136 (reproduced). Longstreet, 1964 (reproduced). *The World of Cézanne* (reproduced p. 132).

EXHIBITIONS: Zurich, 1956, No. 187. Munich, 1956, No. 142.

COLLECTIONS: A. Vollard, Paris. Galerie Zak, Paris. Carl Roesch, Diessenhofen.

983. AFTER THE *Cupid* ATTRIBUTED TO PUGET, 1886–89

$17\frac{1}{2} \times 9\frac{1}{4}$ inches—44,5 × 23,5 cm. Pencil, red and green oil color stains on the upper part of the page. Verso: blank page.

After the plaster cast of Cupid owned by Cézanne, seen front view. See fig. 117.

BIBLIOGRAPHY: Venturi No. 1458. Berthold, cat. No. 138 (reproduced); error: the present drawing is reproduced under No. 142, but No. 142 should be No. 138. Kawakata Michiaki, *Cézanne*, Tokyo, Misuzu-shobô, 1957, p. 4.

EXHIBITIONS: Masterpieces of Occidental Art, National Museum of Tokyo, 1947. Cézanne and Renoir, Kamakura, Museum of Modern Art, 1951, No. 18 (reproduced). Watercolors and Drawings, Tokyo, National Museum of Modern Art, 1954. Masterpieces of Occidental Modern Art, Osaka, Daïmaru Gallery, 1959. Isetam, Tokyo, 1963, No. 10 (reproduced).

COLLECTIONS: Bernheim-Jeune, Paris. Homma Collection, Sakata. Private collection, Kyoto.

984. AFTER THE *Cupid* ATTRIBUTED TO PUGET, 1886–89

$11\frac{13}{16} \times 7\frac{15}{16}$ inches—30 × 20,2 cm. Pencil on ordinary paper, traces of folds, stains, edge of paper torn off on the left. Verso: blank page.

Unfinished sketch after the plaster cast owned by the artist and which is still to be seen in Cézanne's studio at Aix-en-Provence. See fig. 117. The figure is seen from the back. Around and even covering the drawing there are pencilled calculations in Cézanne's handwriting. Cf. No. 981.

BIBLIOGRAPHY: Berthold, cat. No. 137 (reproduced).

COLLECTIONS: Cézanne *fils*, Paris. W. Walter, Paris. A. Chappuis, Tresserve. Private collection, Paris.

985. AFTER THE *Cupid* ATTRIBUTED TO PUGET, 1886–89

$11\frac{5}{8} \times 9\frac{1}{16}$ inches—29,5 × 23 cm. Pencil on laid paper. Verso: hesitant strokes (according to Venturi) representing the Château Noir.

After the plaster cast of Cupid owned by Cézanne, seen front view. See fig. 117.

BIBLIOGRAPHY: Venturi No. 1463. Berthold, cat. No. 142 (reproduced); error: the present drawing is reproduced under No. 138; this No. 138 should be No. 142.

COLLECTION: Kunsthalle, Bremen (drawing lost during the 1939–45 war).

986. AFTER THE *Cupid* ATTRIBUTED TO PUGET, 1886–89

$19 \times 12\frac{3}{16}$ inches—48,2 × 31 cm. Pencil. Verso: No. 896.

After the plaster cast of Cupid owned by Cézanne. See fig. 117.

BIBLIOGRAPHY: Venturi No. 1461. Berthold, cat. No. 131 (reproduced). Maurice Denis, Le Dessin de Cézanne, *AA*, 1924, Vol. 2, pp. 37-38. H. R. Hoetink, *Franse Tekeningen uit de 19e Eeuw*, Rotterdam, 1968, No. 16 (reproduced).

EXHIBITIONS: Kunsthalle, Basel, 1936, No. 143. Rotterdam, 1933–34, No. 3. Musée Boymans de Rotterdam, Dessins du XVe au XIXe S., Bibliothèque Nationale, Paris, 1952, No. 142. Winterthur, 1955, No. 225. The Hague, 1956, No. 124 (reproduced). Zurich, 1956, No. 186 (reproduced). Munich, 1956, No. 141 (reproduced). Hamburg, Cézanne–Gauguin–Van Gogh–Seurat, 1963, No. 32 (reproduced).

COLLECTIONS: Bernheim-Jeune, Paris. F. Koenigs, Haarlem. Boymans-van Beuningen Museum, Rotterdam (Inv. F II 27).

987. AFTER THE *Cupid* ATTRIBUTED TO PUGET, 1886–89

$19\frac{1}{2} \times 11\frac{13}{16}$ inches—49,5 × 30 cm. Pencil on laid paper. Verso: blank page.

After the plaster cast of Cupid owned by Cézanne. See fig. 117. Magnificent drawing with an unidentifiable object in the background and hatching.

BIBLIOGRAPHY: Venturi No. 1459. Berthold, cat. No. 139 (reproduced). Longstreet, 1964 (reproduced).

EXHIBITIONS: Kunsthalle, Basel, 1936, No. 170. Lyons, 1939, No. 72. Art Institute, Chicago, and Metropolitan Museum, New York, 1952, No. 93.

COLLECTIONS: Thannhauser, Lucerne. Rosengart, Lucerne. Thannhauser, Paris. Dr. A. K. Solomon, Cambridge, Mass.

988. AFTER THE *Cupid* ATTRIBUTED TO PUGET, circa 1890

$19\frac{9}{16} \times 12\frac{9}{16}$ inches—49,7 × 31,9 cm. Pencil. Verso: blank page.

After the plaster cast of Cupid owned by Cézanne. The light falls from the left and the right leg remains white; from the shadows it would seem that the drawing was done by lamplight. A very fine drawing. See fig. 117.

BIBLIOGRAPHY: Venturi No. 1462. Berthold, cat. No. 134 (reproduced Abb. 11). J. Gasquet, Paris, 1921 and 1926 (reproduced pp. 192-3). *The British Museum Quarterly*, 1935, Vol. X, No. 1

COLLECTIONS: Reid & Lefevre, London. British Museum, London (Inv. 1935-4-13-2).

989. AFTER THE *Cupid* ATTRIBUTED TO PUGET, circa 1890

$18\frac{1}{8} \times 11$ inches—46 × 28 cm. Pencil on laid paper. Verso: blank page.

After the plaster cast of Cupid owned by Cézanne, seen in left profile. See fig. 117.

BIBLIOGRAPHY: Venturi No. 1460. Berthold, cat. No. 140 (reproduced); error: "A. Vollard" instead of "Art Vivant." *Art Vivant*, Paris, 1926 (reproduced p. 486).

COLLECTIONS: A. Vollard, Paris. Reber, Lugano. Th. Stoperan, Berlin. Sale, Graupe, Berlin, 1928. Wroclaw (Breslau) Museum.

990. AFTER THE *Cupid* ATTRIBUTED TO PUGET, circa 1890

$19\frac{1}{4} \times 12\frac{3}{4}$ inches—48,9 × 32,4 cm. Pencil on laid paper. Verso: blank page.

After the plaster cast of Cupid owned by Cézanne. See fig. 117.

BIBLIOGRAPHY: Venturi No. 1457. Berthold, cat. No. 133 (reproduced). Tristan Klingsor, Paris, 1923 (reproduced pl. 38). E. A. Jewell, New York, 1944, Wiesbaden and Berlin, 1954 (reproduced). Neumeyer, 1958, No. 19 (reproduced). R. Cogniat, *Le Siècle des Impressionnistes*, Paris, 1959 (reproduced p. 82). R. Cogniat, Paris, 1967 (reproduced p. 25). *The World of Cézanne* (reproduced p. 132).

EXHIBITIONS: Kunsthalle, Basel, 1936, No. 142. San Francisco, 1937, No. 66. Lyons, 1939, No. 71. Art Institute, Chicago, and Metropolitan Museum, New York, 1952, No. 92 (reproduced in the catalog). Phillips Collection, Boston, Chicago, Washington, D.C., 1971, No. 81 (reproduced).

COLLECTIONS: Cézanne *fils*, Paris. Bernheim-Jeune, Paris. Hugo Perls, Berlin. J. Seligmann, Paris (sale, Nov. 22, 1933). Lionello Venturi, Rome. Galerie Rosengart, Lucerne. Brooklyn Museum, New York.

991. AFTER F. BOUCHER: *Vulcan's Forge*, circa 1890

$8\frac{9}{16} \times 5$ inches—21,7 × 12,7 cm. Page XXXV verso from the second sketchbook Mrs. Enid A. Haupt. Pencil. Verso: No. 649.

Man seated seen in left three-quarter view, his face in right three-quarter view. Study after the figure of Vulcan in François Boucher's painting *Vulcan's Forge*, in the Louvre. See fig. 118.

BIBLIOGRAPHY: Rewald, *Carnets*: C IV, p. XXXV verso (reproduced pl. 127). Berthold, cat. No. 235 (reproduced); original source identified.

COLLECTIONS: Cézanne *fils*, Paris. M. Renou, Paris. Poyet, Lyons. M. Renou, Paris. Sam Salz, New York. Mrs. Enid A. Haupt, New York.

FIG. 118. François Boucher (1703–70): *La Forge de Vulcain*, painting in the Louvre. Musée National du Louvre, *Catalogue des Peintures* I, 1924, No. 46. Exhibited from 1870 on.

(Photograph: Alinari-Giraudon)

992. AFTER E. DELACROIX: *Daniel*, circa 1890

$4\frac{1}{4} \times 2\frac{11}{16}$ inches—10,9 × 6,8 cm. Page II recto of the sketchbook violet moiré. Pencil. Verso: No. 1122.

Seated male nude, from Eugène Delacroix's painting *Daniel in the Lions' Den*, in the Montpellier Museum. See fig. 119. The source was identified in 1967 by Léo Marchutz.

BIBLIOGRAPHY: Berthold, p. 159 (not reproduced). W. V. Andersen, Cézanne's Carnet violet moiré, *BurlM*, June 1965, p. 313 (reproduced fig. 42). On p. 317 the author

FIG. 119. Eugène Delacroix (1799–1863): *Daniel dans la fosse aux lions* (1849), canvas 74 cm. × 60 cm., in the Montpellier Museum (Robaut 1066). A lithograph was made by Jules Laurens after this work. It is possible that Cézanne drew from a second version of *Daniel* painted in 1853 (Robaut 1213), photographed by Goupil & Cie.

(Photograph: Archives photographiques, Paris)

writes: "Sketch of a seated nude female 'bather,' perhaps after a pictorial source, though the tight parallel relationship of forearms and lower legs, the straight alignment of the head and torso, the perpendicular contrast of upper arm to thigh, forearm to leg, is difficult to find in older or contemporaneous art; such parallel compositional constructions of a figure are in violation of Renaissance principles."

COLLECTIONS: Cézanne *fils*, Paris. Jean-Pierre Cézanne, Paris. Mlle Edmée Maus, Geneva.

993. AFTER THE ANTIQUE STATUE OF A ROMAN ORATOR, 1887–90
$8\frac{1}{4} \times 4\frac{7}{8}$ inches—21 × 12,3 cm. Page XLV from the sketchbook BS II. Pencil. Verso: blank page.

After the marble of a Roman nobleman symbolizing Mercury, protector of Eloquence, in the Louvre. This statue is known as *The Roman Orator*, or *Germanicus*. See fig. 88. Cf. Nos. 599, 1050.

BIBLIOGRAPHY: Venturi No. 1383. Berthold, cat. No. 31 (reproduced). Basel catalog, No. 146 (reproduced).

COLLECTIONS: Cézanne *fils*, Paris. Paul Guillaume, Paris. W. Feuz, Bern. Kunstmuseum, Basel.

994. AFTER MICHELANGELO: *The Resurrection*, 1887–90
$8\frac{1}{2} \times 5$ inches—21,6 × 12,7 cm. Page XXXI verso from the second sketchbook Mrs. Enid A. Haupt. Pencil. Verso: No. 998.

After Michelangelo's drawing *The Resurrection* in the Cabinet des Dessins of the Louvre. See fig. 19. Same subject: No. 172.

BIBLIOGRAPHY: Rewald, *Carnets:* C IV, p. XXXI verso (not reproduced). Berthold, cat. No. 253 (reproduced Abb. 133). Original source identified.

COLLECTIONS: Cézanne *fils*, Paris. M. Renou, Paris. Poyet, Lyons. M. Renou, Paris. Sam Salz, New York. Mrs. Enid A. Haupt, New York.

995. STANDING MAN (AFTER SIGNORELLI), SEATED BATHER, 1887–90
$8\frac{1}{2} \times 5$ inches—21,6 × 12,7 cm. Page XXXII from the second sketchbook Mrs. Enid A. Haupt. Pencil. Verso: a watercolor.

(a) Page upright, left: male nude, after a drawing by Luca Signorelli, *Two Women and Two Men*, in the Cabinet des Dessins of the Louvre. See fig. 120.—(b) Below and at right angles: seated bather.

BIBLIOGRAPHY: Rewald, *Carnets:* C IV, p. XXXII (reproduced pl. 114). Berthold, cat. No. 304 (reproduced).

COLLECTIONS: Cézanne *fils*, Paris. M. Renou, Paris. Poyet, Lyons. M. Renou, Paris. Sam Salz, New York. Mrs. Enid A. Haupt, New York.

996. AFTER SIGNORELLI: MAN WITH RAISED ARMS, 1887–90
$7\frac{3}{16} \times 4\frac{9}{16}$ inches—18,2 × 11,6 cm. Page 38 from the first sketchbook Mrs. Enid A. Haupt. Pencil. Verso: blank page.

Standing male nude drawn down to the thighs (model holding a cord), after a drawing by Luca Signorelli in the Cabinet des Dessins of the Louvre. See fig. 121. Cf. No. 997.

BIBLIOGRAPHY: Rewald, *Carnets:* C I, p. 38 (not reproduced). Berthold, cat. No. 280 (reproduced). Th. Reff, *AB*, June 1960, p. 148, note 23, indication of the source (identified in 1956 by R. W. Ratcliffe but not published).

COLLECTIONS: Cézanne *fils*, Paris. M. Renou, Paris. Poyet, Lyons. M. Renou, Paris. Sam Salz, New York. Mrs. Enid A. Haupt, New York.

997. AFTER SIGNORELLI: MAN WITH RAISED ARMS, 1887–90
$7\frac{3}{16} \times 4\frac{9}{16}$ inches—18,2 × 11,6 cm. Page 35 verso from the first sketchbook Mrs. Enid A. Haupt. Pencil. Verso: blank page.

Standing male nude (model holding a cord), after a drawing by Luca Signorelli in the Cabinet des Dessins of the Louvre. See fig. 121. Cf. No. 996.

BIBLIOGRAPHY: Rewald, *Carnets:* C I, p 35 verso (reproduced pl. 115). Berthold, cat. No. 279 (reproduced). Th. Reff, *AB*, June 1960, p. 148, note 23, indication of the source (identified in 1956 by R. W. Ratcliffe but not published). Neumeyer, 1958, No. 21 (reproduced).

COLLECTIONS: Cézanne *fils*, Paris. M. Renou, Paris. Poyet, Lyons. M. Renou, Paris. Sam Salz, New York. Mrs. Enid A. Haupt, New York.

998. AFTER SIGNORELLI: MAN WITH RAISED ARMS, 1887–90

$8\frac{1}{2} \times 5$ inches—21,6 × 12,7 cm. Page XXXI from the second sketchbook Mrs. Enid A. Haupt. Pencil. Verso: No. 994.

Standing male nude (model holding a cord), after a drawing by Luca Signorelli in the Cabinet des Dessins of the Louvre. See fig. 121. Cf. Nos. 996, 997.

BIBLIOGRAPHY: Rewald, *Carnets:* C IV, p. XXXI (not reproduced). Berthold, cat. No. 281 (reproduced Abb. 136). *Selearte,* No. 52, July-Aug. 1961 (reproduced fig. 12).

COLLECTIONS: Cézanne *fils*, Paris. M. Renou, Paris. Poyet, Lyons. M. Renou, Paris. Sam Salz, New York. Mrs. Enid A. Haupt, New York.

999. AFTER PUGET: *Hercules resting,* 1884–87

$18\frac{5}{8} \times 12\frac{5}{16}$ inches—47,3 × 31,3 cm. Pencil on laid paper, watermark: CF in a shield, with a caduceus. Verso: blank page.

After Pierre Puget's marble *Hercule au repos,* in the Louvre. See fig. 82. Large drawing of exceptional quality.

BIBLIOGRAPHY: Venturi No. 1438. Berthold, cat. No. 110 (reproduced Abb. 9). Meier-Graefe, *Cézanne und seine Ahnen,* Marées-Gesellschaft, Munich, 1921, No. 18 (reproduced). Kurt Pfister, Potsdam, 1927 (reproduced p. 15). H. R. Hoetink, *Franse Tekeningen uit de 19e Eeuw,* Rotterdam, 1968, No. 33 (reproduced).

EXHIBITIONS: P. Cassirer, Berlin, 1929, No. 9. Galerie A. Flechtheim, Berlin, 1929, No. 34. Boymans Museum, Rotterdam, 1934, No. 4. Maîtres français du XIXe S. et van Gogh, Kunsthalle, Bern, 1934. Kunsthalle, Basel, 1936, No. 169.

COLLECTIONS: J. W. Boehler, Lucerne. P. Cassirer, Berlin. F. Koenigs, Haarlem. Boymans-van Beuningen Museum, Rotterdam (Inv. F II 215).

1000. AFTER PUGET: *Hercules resting,* 1884–87

$18\frac{1}{2} \times 11\frac{13}{16}$ inches—47 × 30 cm. Pencil on laid paper. Verso: blank page.

After Pierre Puget's marble *Hercule au repos,* in the Louvre. See fig. 82. Cf. especially No. 999.

BIBLIOGRAPHY: Venturi No. 1437. Berthold, cat. No. 108 (reproduced Abb. 102). F. Novotny, *Paul Cézanne,* Phaidon, Vienna and Paris 1937 (reproduced pl. 124).

COLLECTIONS: A. Vollard, Paris. Galerie Zak, Paris. S. Meller, Budapest. Present owner unknown.

FIG. 120. Luca Signorelli (1440–1525): *Two women and two men,* black chalk drawing, 29,5 × 37 cm., in the Cabinet des Dessins of the Louvre (Inv. 1794).

FIG. 121. Lucas Signorelli (1440–1525): *Standing man* (model holding a cord), black chalk drawing in the Cabinet des Dessins of the Louvre. (Braun No. 140.)

1001. AFTER PUGET: *Hercules resting*, 1887–90

$19\frac{1}{4} \times 12\frac{3}{8}$ inches—49 × 31,5 cm. Pencil. Verso: blank page.

After Pierre Puget's marble *Hercule au repos* in the Louvre. See fig. 82.

BIBLIOGRAPHY: Venturi, Vol. I, p. 352, Oeuvres Inédites (not reproduced). Berthold, cat. No. 116 (reproduced). *Correspondance* (reproduced fig. 39).

COLLECTIONS: Pierre Loeb, Paris. Present owner unknown.

1002. AFTER PUGET: *Hercules resting*, 1887–90

$8\frac{3}{8} \times 4\frac{3}{4}$ inches—21,3 × 12,1 cm. Page II verso from the sketchbook BS II. Pencil. Verso: No. 1003.

Head seen in right three-quarter view from the back, after Pierre Puget's marble *Hercule au repos* in the Louvre. See fig. 141.

BIBLIOGRAPHY: Venturi No. 1360. Berthold, cat. No. 123 (reproduced). Basel catalog, No. 150 (reproduced).

COLLECTIONS: Cézanne *fils*, Paris. Paul Guillaume, Paris. W. Feuz, Bern. Kunstmuseum, Basel.

1003. AFTER PUGET: *Hercules resting*, 1887–90

$8\frac{3}{8} \times 4\frac{3}{4}$ inches—21,3 × 12,1 cm. Page II from the sketchbook BS II. Pencil. Verso: No. 1002.

After Pierre Puget's marble *Hercule au repos* in the Louvre. See fig. 82. Cf. especially No. 1004.

BIBLIOGRAPHY: Venturi No. 1359. Berthold, cat. No. 114 (reproduced Abb. 132). Basel catalog, No. 149 (reproduced).

COLLECTIONS: Cézanne *fils*, Paris. Paul Guillaume, Paris. W. Feuz, Bern. Kunstmuseum, Basel.

1004. AFTER PUGET: *Hercules resting*, 1887–90

$8\frac{1}{16} \times 4\frac{3}{4}$ inches—20,4 × 12,1 cm. Page XL from the sketchbook BS II. Pencil. Verso: sketch of a head, too insignificant to merit classification.

After Pierre Puget's *Hercule au repos* in the Louvre. See fig. 82. Cf. Nos. 1003, 1005.

BIBLIOGRAPHY: Venturi No. 1375. Berthold, cat. No. 115 (reproduced). Basel catalog, No. 148 (reproduced).

EXHIBITION: Belvedere, Vienna, 1961, No. 100.

COLLECTIONS: Cézanne *fils*, Paris. Paul Guillaume, Paris. W. Feuz, Bern. Kunstmuseum, Basel.

1005. AFTER PUGET: *Hercules resting*, 1887–90

$4\frac{3}{8} \times 5\frac{1}{8}$ inches—11,2 × 12,9 cm. Page II from the sketchbook BS I. Pencil. Verso: blank page.

Head and shoulder of *Hercule au repos*, marble by Pierre Puget in the Louvre; an unfinished sketch. Cf. Nos. 1002, 1003, 1004. See fig. 82.

BIBLIOGRAPHY: Venturi No. 1324. Berthold, cat. No. 112 (reproduced). Basel catalog, No. 147 (reproduced).

COLLECTIONS: Cézanne *fils*, Paris. Paul Guillaume, Paris. W. Feuz, Bern. Kunstmuseum, Basel.

1006. AFTER PUGET: *Hercules resting*, 1889–92

$7\frac{3}{16} \times 4\frac{9}{16}$ inches—18,2 × 11,6 cm. Page 28 verso from the first sketchbook Mrs. Enid A. Haupt. Pencil. Verso: blank page.

After Pierre Puget's marble *Hercule au repos* in the Louvre, seen from the thighs up. This is a closer view than usual of the statue.

BIBLIOGRAPHY: Rewald, *Carnets:* C I, p. 28 verso (reproduced pl. 130). Berthold, cat. No. 117 (reproduced Abb. 131).

COLLECTIONS: Cézanne *fils*, Paris. M. Renou, Paris. Poyet, Lyons. M. Renou, Paris. Sam Salz, New York. Mrs. Enid A. Haupt, New York.

1007. AFTER RUBENS: BELLONA, 1888–91

$8\frac{1}{2} \times 5$ inches—21,6 × 12,7 cm. Page XXXIX verso from the second sketchbook Mrs. Enid A. Haupt. Pencil. Verso: blank page.

After the allegorical figure of Bellona, goddess of War, in Rubens' painting *The Apotheosis of Henri IV*, in the Louvre. See fig. 9. Though unfinished, this sketch is more in harmony with Rubens' feeling than some others.

BIBLIOGRAPHY: Rewald, *Carnets:* C IV, p. XXXIX verso (reproduced pl. 140). Berthold, cat. No. 208 (reproduced).

COLLECTIONS: Cézanne *fils*, Paris. M. Renou, Paris. Poyet, Lyons. M. Renou, Paris. Sam Salz, New York. Mrs. Enid A. Haupt, New York.

1008. SKETCH OF A SEATED FIGURE, circa 1890

$5 \times 7\frac{5}{8}$ inches—12,6 × 19,4 cm. Page IV verso from the sketchbook BS III. Pencil, brown stain upper right, smudging. Verso: No. 964.

Unfinished sketch of a seated figure, turning around to the left.

BIBLIOGRAPHY: Basel catalog, No. 137 (reproduced).

COLLECTIONS: Cézanne *fils*, Paris. Paul Guillaume, Paris. W. Feuz, Bern. Kunstmuseum, Basel.

1009. FIGURE ORNAMENTING A CLOCK, 1888–91

$8\frac{1}{4} \times 4\frac{13}{16}$ inches—20,9 × 12,2 cm. Page XLII from the sketchbook BS II. Pencil. Verso: No. 588.

Woman seen front view, holding a rose up to her shoulder, her head slightly turned. After a figure ornamenting a clock. Cf. No. 1123.

BIBLIOGRAPHY: Venturi No. 1378. Basel catalog, No. 138 (reproduced).

COLLECTIONS: Cézanne *fils*, Paris. Paul Guillaume, Paris. W. Feuz, Bern. Kunstmuseum, Basel.

1010. UNFINISHED SKETCH, 1888–91

$7\frac{5}{8} \times 5\frac{7}{16}$ inches—19,4 × 11,8 cm. Page XLIIII from the sketchbook CP I. Pencil. Verso: No. 1062.

The top of a boy's head, perhaps seen by lamplight. Cf. Nos. 450, 666.

BIBLIOGRAPHY: Venturi, Vol. I, under No. 1275 (not reproduced).

COLLECTIONS: Cézanne *fils*, Paris. Paul Guillaume, Paris. A. Chappuis, Tresserve.

FIG. 122. Nicolas Poussin (1594–1665): *Bergers d'Arcadie,* painting in the Louvre (detail). Musée National du Louvre, *Catalogue des Peintures* I, 1924, No. 734. *(Photograph: Giraudon)*

1011. AFTER POUSSIN: ARCADIAN SHEPHERD, 1887–90

$8\frac{1}{4} \times 4\frac{13}{16}$ inches—20,9 × 12,2 cm. Page L verso from the sketchbook BS II. Pencil. Verso: No. 1140.

Young shepherd sitting with his elbow on his knee; his head is turned towards the viewer. After Nicolas Poussin's *Arcadian Shepherds* in the Louvre. See fig. 122.

BIBLIOGRAPHY: Venturi No. 1393. Berthold, cat. No. 232 (reproduced). Basel Catalog, No. 127 (reproduced). Th. Reff, Cézanne and Poussin, *The Journal of the Warburg and Courtauld Institutes,* Vol. XXIII, Nos. 1-2, 1960, p. 171; Cézanne et Poussin, *Art de France* III, 1963, p. 302. Idem, Copyists in the Louvre, *AB,* 1964, p. 555; the author says that Cézanne registered in 1864 to copy Poussin's painting.

COLLECTIONS: Cézanne *fils,* Paris. Paul Guillaume, Paris. W. Feuz, Bern. Kunstmuseum, Basel.

1012. AFTER POUSSIN: ARCADIAN SHEPHERDESS, 1887–90

$7\frac{15}{16} \times 4\frac{13}{16}$ inches—20,2 × 12,2 cm. Page XLVII verso from the sketchbook BS II. Pencil. Verso: No. 1052.

Bust-length sketch of a woman seen in left profile, in front of some trees. After the shepherdess in Nicolas Poussin's canvas *The Arcadian Shepherds* in the Louvre. See fig. 122.

BIBLIOGRAPHY: Venturi No. 1387. Berthold, cat. No. 233 (reproduced Abb. 15). Basel catalog, No. 128 (reproduced). *The World of Cézanne* (reproduced p. 80). Th. Reff, Copyists in the Louvre, *AB,* 1964, p. 555.

COLLECTIONS: Cézanne *fils,* Paris. Paul Guillaume, Paris. W. Feuz, Bern. Kunstmuseum, Basel.

1013. AFTER POUSSIN: *The Concert,* 1887–90

$8\frac{1}{4} \times 4\frac{13}{16}$ inches—20,9 × 12,2 cm. Page XLVIII from the sketchbook BS II. Pencil. Verso: No. 605.

Little nude boy with outstretched arms, seen front view. Behind him there is another boy, his head seen to the left of the first figure, his buttocks to the right. After a fragment (known as *Le Concert des Amours*) of Nicolas Poussin's painting *Venus and Mercury* in the Louvre. See fig. 123.

BIBLIOGRAPHY: Venturi No. 1388. Berthold, cat. No. 231 (reproduced). Basel catalog, No. 129 (reproduced). Rewald, Cézanne au Louvre, *L'Amour de l'Art,* 1935, p. 285 (reproduced).

COLLECTIONS: Cézanne *fils,* Paris. Paul Guillaume, Paris. W. Feuz, Bern. Kunstmuseum, Basel.

FIG. 123. Nicolas Poussin (1594–1665): *Concert des Amours,* detail from *Venus et Mercure,* a painting cut into several pieces, of which one is in the Louvre. The fragment, 57 cm. × 52 cm., is in oil on canvas. Musée National du Louvre, *Catalogue des Peintures* I, 1924, No. 733. *(Photograph: Giraudon)*

[233]

1014. WOMAN LEANING FORWARD, 1888–91

    $6 \times 9\frac{5}{16}$ inches—15,2 × 23,7 cm. Page XXI of the Album, Paul Mellon Collection. Pencil, accidental pencil rubbings, trace of a fold upper right. Verso: No. 871.

The head is bent forward and the face seen in foreshortening. On the right, the artist has noted the address of a model: Antonio Franchi Avenue du Maine 124.

BIBLIOGRAPHY: Venturi, Vol. I, under No. 1306 (not reproduced). *Album*, 1966 (reproduced).

COLLECTIONS: Cézanne *fils*, Paris. Paul Guillaume, Paris. A. Chappuis, Tresserve, Mr. and Mrs. Paul Mellon, Upperville, Va.

1015. WOMAN LEANING FORWARD, 1890–94

    $9\frac{5}{16} \times 6$ inches—23,7 × 15,2 cm. Page XIIII verso of the Album, Paul Mellon Collection. Pencil. Verso: No. 1016.

Light is reflected from the forehead and cheekbones, also from the hair, which is parted in the center. In the upper part of the drawing the wall forms a dark background, lightened with an eraser above the figure's ear. A colorful page. Cf. Nos. 1016 (b), 1069; see also Venturi Nos. 574, 576.

BIBLIOGRAPHY: Venturi, Vol. I, under No. 1304 (not reproduced). *Dessins*, 1938 (reproduced pl. 34). *Album*, 1966 (reproduced).

EXHIBITION: Aix-en-Provence, 1961, No. 53.

COLLECTIONS: Cézanne *fils*, Paris. Paul Guillaume, Paris. A. Chappuis, Tresserve. Mr. and Mrs. Paul Mellon, Upperville, Va.

1016. TWO HEADS OF WOMEN, 1890–94

    $9\frac{5}{16} \times 6$ inches—23,7 × 15,2 cm. Page XIIII of the Album, Paul Mellon Collection. Pencil. Verso: No. 1015.

(a) Top: woman's head, bent forward, indications of the shoulders. A lightly drawn, luminous compositional study, rather similar to No. 1069, which is related to the painting Venturi No. 228.—(b) Below, at right angles: head of a woman; it has a certain resemblance to Venturi No. 574, *Femme à la Cafetière*, and is another version of No. 1015.

BIBLIOGRAPHY: Venturi, Vol. I, under No. 1304 (not reproduced). *Album*, 1966 (reproduced).

COLLECTIONS: Cézanne *fils*, Paris. Paul Guillaume, Paris. A. Chappuis, Tresserve, Mr. and Mrs. Paul Mellon, Upperville, Va.

1017. AFTER N. G. VAN LEYDEN: *Barbara von Hottenheim*, circa 1890

    $8\frac{1}{2} \times 5\frac{3}{8}$ inches—21,6 × 13,7 cm. Page 29 of the sketchbook ML. Pencil. Verso: blank page.

Head in a double coif, seen in right three-quarter view; the eyelids are lowered. After a plaster cast of the bust of *Barbara von Hottenheim* (commonly called *Bärbele*) by Nicolaus Gerhaert van Leyden. See fig. 124. The original was formerly in the Strasbourg Chancellery and a plaster cast was exhibited in the Musée de Sculpture Comparée of the Trocadéro.

BIBLIOGRAPHY: Rewald, *Carnets:* C III, p. 29 (not reproduced). Berthold, cat. No. 295 (reproduced). Cézanne dessinateur, *GBA*, Nov. 1965, p. 303 (reproduced fig. 29).

FIG. 124. Nicolas-Gerhaert van Leyden (1430–73): *Barbara von Hottenheim* (commonly called Bärbele). Our photograph was taken from the plaster cast formerly in the Musée de Sculpture comparée du Trocadéro. The original (1464) decorated the Strasbourg Chancellerie and was later conserved in its Library (destroyed in 1870). A fragment—the head—was discovered in 1934. This admirable piece is today in the Staedel Institut, Frankfurt-on-Main. The cast indicates that the original bust stood beside a window frame.

(Photograph: Giraudon)

COLLECTIONS: Cézanne *fils*, Paris. M. Renou, Paris. Poyet, Lyons. M. Renou, Paris. Sam Salz, New York. Cabinet des Dessins of the Louvre, Paris (RF 29933).

1018. AFTER HOUDON: *Voltaire*, circa 1890

    $8\frac{1}{8} \times 5\frac{1}{4}$ inches—20,6 × 13 cm. Page XIX from the sketchbook BS I. Pencil. Verso: blank page.

Head of the writer and poet François-Marie Arouet Voltaire, seen front face. After the bronze bust by Jean-Antoine Houdon in the Louvre. See fig. 125.

BIBLIOGRAPHY: Venturi No. 1344. Berthold, cat. No. 201 (reproduced). Basel catalog, No. 186 (reproduced). Douglas Cooper, *Master Drawings*, Vol. 1, No. 4, 1963, p. 56. *The World of Cézanne* (reproduced p. 144). R. Cogniat, Cézanne, Flammarion, Paris, 1967 (reproduced p. 17).

COLLECTIONS: Cézanne *fils*, Paris. Paul Guillaume, Paris. W. Feuz, Bern. Kunstmuseum, Basel.

1019. AFTER THE ANTIQUE: *Caracalla*, circa 1890

    $8\frac{1}{2} \times 5\frac{3}{8}$ inches—21,6 × 13,7 cm. Page 1 of the sketchbook ML. Pencil. Verso: blank page.

After a bust of the Roman emperor *Caracalla*. See fig. 126. The attitude of the head has been captured by the artist, although the drawing remains unfinished.

BIBLIOGRAPHY: Rewald, *Carnets:* C III, p. 1 (not reproduced). Berthold, cat. No. 297 (reproduced). Th. Reff, *AB*, June 1960, p. 148, note 30.

COLLECTIONS: Cézanne *fils*, Paris. M. Renou, Paris. Poyet, Lyons. M. Renou, Paris. Sam Salz, New York. Cabinet des Dessins of the Louvre, Paris (RF 29933).

1020. SKETCH OF A FIGURE, circa 1890

$4\frac{15}{16} \times 8\frac{9}{16}$ inches—12,5 × 21,7 cm. Page V from the sketchbook CP II. Pencil. Verso: No. 482.

Seated figure drawn in light, staccato strokes. It is a kind of compositional study, the attitude recalling *The Cardplayers*.

BIBLIOGRAPHY: Venturi, Vol. I, under No. 1282 (not reproduced).

COLLECTIONS: Cézanne *fils*, Paris. Paul Guillaume, Paris. A. Chappuis, Tresserve. Private collection, Paris. Private collection, New York.

1021. FLOWER OUTDOORS, circa 1890

$8\frac{1}{16} \times 4\frac{15}{16}$ inches—20,4 × 12,5 cm. Page VIII from the sketchbook BS III. Pencil, edges of paper stained, fold lower right. Verso: watercolor drawing of two bathers, Venturi No. 1410.

FIG. 126. Bust of the Roman emperor Marcus Aurelius Antoninus *Caracalla* (188–217), plaster cast after the marble in the Louvre. Musée National du Louvre, *Catalogue sommaire des Marbres antiques*, 1922, No. 1106.

(Photograph: Skulpturhalle, Basel)

Zinnia, with its stalk and a few leaves; light, plain hatching on the face of the flower and indication of a background.

BIBLIOGRAPHY: Venturi No. 1409. Basel catalog, No. 170 (reproduced).

COLLECTIONS: Cézanne *fils*, Paris. Paul Guillaume, Paris. W. Feuz, Bern. Kunstmuseum, Basel.

1022. SKETCH OF A FLOWER, circa 1890

$8\frac{1}{2} \times 5\frac{3}{8}$ inches—21,6 × 13,7 cm. Page 7 verso of the sketchbook ML. Pencil. Verso: No. 966.

Although of no great significance, this unfinished study is interesting because it shows how Cézanne sketched in his drawings. He sometimes did the same thing for his paintings, using a fine brush and diluted blue color.

COLLECTIONS: Cézanne *fils*, Paris. M. Renou, Paris. Poyet, Lyons. M. Renou, Paris. Sam Salz, New York. Cabinet des Dessins of the Louvre, Paris (RF 29933).

1023. PEONIES, 1890–93

$9\frac{5}{16} \times 6$ inches—23,7 × 15,2 cm. Page XXX of the Album, Paul Mellon Collection. Pencil. Verso: No. 479.

A peony stalk with two flowers and a few leaves, placed vertically on the page. Spacious, decorative sketch. Cf. Nos. 648 and 1021.

BIBLIOGRAPHY: Venturi, Vol. I, under No. 1309 (not reproduced). *Album*, 1966 (reproduced).

FIG. 125. Jean-Antoine Houdon (1741–1828): bust of the writer François-Marie Arouet, *Voltaire* (1694–1778). The bronze, dated 1778 and signed, height 45 cm., is in the Louvre. Musée National du Louvre, *Catalogue des Sculptures* II, 1922, No. 1360. *(Photograph: R. W. Ratcliffe)*

FIG. 127. Peter Paul Rubens (1577–1640) and his School: *The Prophet Elijah*, painting in the Louvre (detail). Canvas, 4,71 m. × 4,13 m. Musée National du Louvre, *Catalogue des Peintures* III, 1922, No. 2076.

(Photograph: Archives photographiques, Paris)

COLLECTIONS: Cézanne *fils*, Paris. Paul Guillaume, Paris. A. Chappuis, Tresserve. Mr. and Mrs. Paul Mellon, Upperville, Va.

1024. AFTER RUBENS: AN ANGEL, 1892–95

$9\frac{5}{16}$ × 6 inches—23,7 × 15,2 cm. Page XXVI verso of the Album, Paul Mellon Collection. Pencil. Verso: No. 596.

Figure of the angel from the canvas in the Louvre: *The Prophet Elijah*, attributed to Rubens and his School. See fig. 127. The subject: Elijah, having fled into the wilderness, is miraculously fed. A passage from the first Book of Kings (19:5) describes the scene: " . . . then an angel touched him and said unto him 'Arise and eat.' And he looked, and, behold, there was a cake baken on the coals, and a cruse of water at his head." Both the powerful winged figure and the action appealed to Cézanne, and nothing could be more eloquent than the hand that accepts the food between the hands that give it.

BIBLIOGRAPHY: Venturi, No. 1309. Berthold, cat. No. 229 (reproduced). *Dessins*, 1957, No. 53 (reproduced). *Album*, 1966 (reproduced).

COLLECTIONS: Cézanne *fils*, Paris. Paul Guillaume, Paris. A. Chappuis, Tresserve. Mr. and Mrs. Paul Mellon, Upperville, Va.

1025. AFTER RUBENS: ALLEGORICAL FIGURE OF HYMEN, 1892–95

$11\frac{13}{16}$ × $9\frac{1}{16}$ inches—30 × 23 cm. Pencil on laid paper. Verso: blank page.

Allegorical nude winged figure carried aloft by a cloud: Hymen presenting the portrait of Marie de Médicis to Henri IV, detail from Rubens' painting in the Louvre. See fig. 128.

BIBLIOGRAPHY: Venturi No. 1444. Berthold, cat. No. 227 (reproduced Abb. 140). F. Novotny, *Paul Cézanne*, Phaidon, Vienna and Paris 1937 (reproduced No. 123).

COLLECTIONS: Kate Perls, Paris. Galerie Zak, Paris. H. Ganz, Zurich. W. Raeber, Basel.

1026. AFTER COYSEVOX: BUST OF *Charles Le Brun*, 1892–95

$8\frac{1}{2}$ × $4\frac{15}{16}$ inches—21,5 × 12,5 cm. Page XXXIV from the sketchbook BS II. Pencil. Verso: blank page.

Detailed study after the marble bust of *Charles Le Brun* by Charles-Antoine Coysevox, in the Louvre. See fig. 129. Cézanne's rendering of the enormous wig is more developed than usual, but it in no way detracts from the vigorous clarity of the drawing as a whole.

BIBLIOGRAPHY: Venturi No. 1369 (error: "au musée de Bâle"). Berthold, cat. No. 181 (reproduced Abb. 142). F. Novotny, *Paul Cézanne*, Phaidon, Vienna and Paris 1937, No. 25 (reproduced); error: "au musée de Bâle."

EXHIBITIONS: Meisterzeichnungen französischer Künstler, Kunsthalle, Basel, 1935, No. 185. Kunsthalle, Basel, 1936, No. 131.

COLLECTIONS: Cézanne *fils*, Paris. Paul Guillaume, Paris. W. Feuz, Bern. Adolf Busch, Riehen. Mrs. A. Busch, Brattleboro, Vermont.

1027. AFTER DESJARDINS: *Pierre Mignard*, 1892–95

$8\frac{1}{16}$ × $4\frac{7}{8}$ inches—20,5 × 12,4 cm. Page XLIII from the sketchbook BS II. Pencil. Verso: No. 687.

Head and shoulders of a male figure wearing a curled wig, seen front view. After the marble bust of the portraitist and painter of historical subjects *Pierre Mignard* by Martin van den Bogaert (known as Desjardins), in the Louvre. See fig. 130. Cf. Nos. 1028, 1216.

BIBLIOGRAPHY: Venturi No. 1380. Berthold, cat. No. 183 (reproduced Abb. 143). Basel catalog, No. 182 (repro-

FIG. 128. Peter Paul Rubens (1577–1640): *Henri IV reçoit le portrait de Marie de Médicis*, painting in the Medici series in the Louvre (detail). Musée National du Louvre, *Catalogue des Peintures* III, 1922, No. 2088. *(Photograph: Alinari-Giraudon)*

FIG. 129. Charles-Antoine Coysevox (1640–1720): bust of *Charles le Brun*, marble in the Louvre. Musée National du Louvre, *Catalogue des Sculptures* II, 1922, No. 1102.

(*Photograph: Giraudon*)

duced). Rewald, Cézanne au Louvre, *AA*, 1935, p. 286 (reproduced).

COLLECTIONS: Cézanne *fils*, Paris. Paul Guillaume, Paris. W. Feuz, Bern. Kunstmuseum, Basel.

1028. AFTER DESJARDINS: *Pierre Mignard*, 1892–95

$8\frac{1}{2} \times 5\frac{3}{8}$ inches—21,6 × 13,7 cm. Page 5 verso of the sketchbook ML. Pencil. Verso: No. 1139.

Unfinished sketch showing only the face and wig, after the marble bust of *Pierre Mignard* by Martin van den Bogaert (known as Desjardins), in the Louvre. See fig. 130. The model is seen front face and the right part of the drawing is left white. A vigorous work of extraordinary vivacity. Cf. Nos. 1027, 1216.

BIBLIOGRAPHY: Rewald, *Carnets*: C III, p. 5 verso (not reproduced). Berthold, cat. No. 184 (reproduced Abb. 144). F. Novotny, Die neuere Literatur zu Cézanne, *Bibliographie zur Kunstgeschichte des 19. Jahrhunderts* (Hilda Lietzmann), Munich, 1968 (reproduced fig. 1 next to Venturi No. 694, in which the attitude of the model is inspired by that of this drawing).

COLLECTIONS: Cézanne *fils*, Paris. M. Renou, Paris. Poyet, Lyons. M. Renou, Paris. Sam Salz, New York. Cabinet des Dessins of the Louvre, Paris (RF 29933).

1029. AFTER THE ANTIQUE: *Hermes*, 1892–95

$8\frac{1}{2} \times 5\frac{3}{8}$ inches—21,6 × 13,7 cm. Page 30 verso of the sketchbook ML. Pencil. Verso: No. 1132.

After the antique marble known as *The Richelieu Hermes* in the Louvre. The oval stroke delineating the head and the vigorous drawing of the legs are noteworthy. See fig. 131.

BIBLIOGRAPHY: Rewald, *Carnets*: C III, p. 30 verso (reproduced pl. 122). Berthold, cat. No. 39 (reproduced Abb. 150), with identification of the source.

COLLECTIONS: Cézanne *fils*, Paris. M. Renou, Paris. Poyet, Lyons. M. Renou, Paris. Sam Salz, New York. Cabinet des Dessins of the Louvre, Paris (RF 29933).

1030. AFTER COYSEVOX: BUST OF *Michel Le Tellier*, 1892–95

$8\frac{1}{2} \times 5\frac{3}{8}$ inches—21,6 × 13,7 cm. Page 31 verso of the sketchbook ML. Pencil. Verso: blank page.

The Chancellor *Michel Le Tellier*, by Charles-Antoine Coysevox. This bronze, formerly in the Louvre, was lost at sea in 1939. See fig. 132.—Above the head: a few strokes, difficult to interpret.

BIBLIOGRAPHY: Rewald, *Carnets*: C III, p. 31 verso (not reproduced). Berthold, cat. No. 180 (reproduced); model suggested: Le Tellier.

COLLECTIONS: Cézanne *fils*, Paris. M. Renou, Paris. Poyet, Lyons. M. Renou, Paris. Sam Salz, New York. Cabinet des Dessins of the Louvre, Paris (RF 29933).

FIG. 130. Martin van den Bogaert, known as Desjardins (1640–94): bust of the painter *Pierre Mignard*, called *le Romain* (1612–95). Marble in the Louvre; height 63 cm. Musée National du Louvre, *Catalogue des Sculptures* II, 1922, No. 1248.

(*Photograph: R. W. Ratcliffe*)

[237]

FIG. 131. *Hermes*, known as *Hermès Richelieu*, antique marble in the Louvre. Musée National du Louvre, *Catalogue sommaire des Marbres antiques*, 1922, No. 573.

(*Photograph: Archives photographiques, Paris*)

FIG. 132. Charles-Antoine Coysevox (1640–1720): bust of the Chancellor *Michel Le Tellier*, bronze formerly in the Louvre; lost at sea in 1939. Musée National du Louvre, *Catalogue des Sculptures* II, 1922, No. 1105. (*Photograph: Giraudon*)

FIG. 133. Augustin Pajou (1730–1809): *Madame Du Barry*, marble in the Louvre. Musée National du Louvre, *Catalogue des Sculptures* II, 1922, No. 1435. (*Photograph: Giraudon*)

1031. AFTER PAJOU: *Madame du Barry*, 1892–95

$7\frac{13}{16} \times 4\frac{9}{16}$ inches—18,2 × 11,6 cm. Page 1 verso from the first sketchbook Mrs. Enid A. Haupt. Pencil. Verso: No. 563.

After Augustin Pajou's marble bust of *Madame du Barry* in the Louvre. See fig. 133.

BIBLIOGRAPHY: Rewald, *Carnets*: C I, p. 1 verso (reproduced pl. 151). Berthold, cat. No. 200 (reproduced); identification of the model.

COLLECTIONS: Cézanne *fils*, Paris. M. Renou, Paris. Poyet, Lyons. M. Renou, Paris. Sam Salz, New York. Mrs. Enid A. Haupt, New York.

1032. AFTER TITIAN: HEAD OF A MAN, 1892–95

$8\frac{1}{2} \times 5\frac{3}{8}$ inches—21,6 × 13,7 cm. Page 2 of the sketchbook ML. Pencil. Verso: blank page.

After Titian's *Portrait of a Man* in the Louvre. See fig. 134. Although the drawing differs slightly from the model indicated, the general attitude and several details (for example the nose) suggest that the artist drew inspiration from this canvas, or from a reproduction of it.

BIBLIOGRAPHY: Rewald, *Carnets*: C III, p. 2 (reproduced pl. 31). Berthold, cat. No. 267 (reproduced). J. Bouchot-Saupique, *La Revue des Arts*, 1951, pp. 243 ff. (reproduced).

COLLECTIONS: Cézanne *fils*, Paris. M. Renou, Paris. Poyet, Lyons. M. Renou, Paris. Sam Salz, New York. Cabinet des Dessins of the Louvre, Paris (RF 29933).

1033. AFTER COYSEVOX: *Le Grand Condé*, 1892–95

$8\frac{3}{16} \times 4\frac{3}{4}$ inches—20,8 × 12,1 cm. Page VI from the sketchbook BS II. Pencil. Verso: blank page.

After Charles-Antoine Coysevox' bronze bust of Louis II of Bourbon, known as *Le Grand Condé*, in the Louvre. See fig. 135. Cf. Nos. 1034, 1035.

BIBLIOGRAPHY: Venturi No. 1365. Berthold, cat. No. 178 (reproduced). Basel catalog, No. 185 (reproduced). Douglas Cooper, in *Master Drawings*, Vol. 1, 1963, No. 4, p. 56.

COLLECTIONS: Cézanne *fils*, Paris. Paul Guillaume, Paris. W. Feuz, Bern. Kunstmuseum, Basel.

1034. AFTER COYSEVOX: *Le Grand Condé*, 1892–95

$7\frac{1}{2} \times 5\frac{1}{8}$ inches—19 × 13 cm. Page XXV from the sketchbook BS I. Soft pencil, two little spots of color. Verso: blank page.

FIG. 135. Charles Antoine Coysevox (1640–1720): bust of Louis II de Bourbon, prince de Condé, known as *Le Grand Condé* (1621–86). Bronze (1688), height 59 cm., in the Louvre. From the Palais Condé. Musée National du Louvre, *Catalogue des Sculptures* II, 1922, No. 1106. (*Photograph: R. W. Ratcliffe*)

FIG. 134. Titian (1489–1576): *Portrait of a Man,* painting in the Louvre. Musée National du Louvre, *Catalogue des Peintures* II, 1926, No. 1591. (*Photograph: Alinari-Giraudon*)

After Charles-Antoine Coysevox' bronze bust of *Le Grand Condé*, in the Louvre. See fig. 135. Part of the chin is left white and only a few curls of the voluminous wig are indicated.

BIBLIOGRAPHY: Venturi No. 1350. Berthold, cat. No. 179 (reproduced).

EXHIBITIONS: De David à Cézanne, La Vieille Fontaine, Lausanne, 1953, No. 108. Zurich, 1956, No. 192. Munich, 1956, No. 146.

COLLECTIONS: Cézanne *fils*, Paris. Paul Guillaume, Paris. W. Feuz, Bern. Carl Roesch, Diessenhofen.

1035. AFTER COYSEVOX: *Le Grand Condé*, 1894–97

$8\frac{1}{2} \times 5\frac{3}{8}$ inches—21,6 × 13,7 cm. Page 10 of the sketchbook ML. Pencil. Verso: No. 1108.

Drawing showing only the right half of the head of *Le Grand Condé*, bronze bust by Charles-Antoine Coysevox in the Louvre. See fig. 135. Cf. No. 1033.

BIBLIOGRAPHY: Rewald, *Carnets*: C III, p. 10 (not reproduced). Berthold, cat. No. 177 (reproduced). J. Bouchot-Saupique, *Revue des Arts*, 1951, pp. 243-4 (reproduced).

COLLECTIONS: Cézanne *fils*, Paris. M. Renou, Paris. Poyet, Lyons. M. Renou, Paris. Sam Salz, New York. Cabinet des Dessins of the Louvre, Paris (RF 29933).

FIG. 136. François Girardon (1628–1715): bust of the poet *Nicolas Boileau-Despréaux* (1636–1711). Marble in the Louvre, height 90 cm. Musée National du Louvre, *Catalogue des Sculptures* II, 1922, No. 1319.　　(*Photograph: R. W. Ratcliffe*)

1036. AFTER GIRARDON: *Boileau-Despréaux*, 1892–95

$10\frac{5}{8} \times 8\frac{5}{16}$ inches—27 × 21,1 cm. Page LXIX from the sketchbook CP IV. Pencil. Verso: No. 1196.

It was Gertrude Berthold who discovered the authentic source of this drawing: the marble bust of *Nicolas Boileau-Despréaux* by François Girardon, in the Louvre. See fig. 136. Cf. No. 1212.

BIBLIOGRAPHY: Venturi No. 1320, "d'après le buste du Régent par Coysevox, au musée d'Aix." Venturi mentions this drawing twice, but corrects the error. Berthold, cat. No. 186 (reproduced). *Dessins*, 1957, No. 51 (reproduced).

EXHIBITIONS: Lyons, 1939, No. 61. Wildenstein, London, 1939, No. 85.

COLLECTIONS: Cézanne *fils*, Paris. Paul Guillaume, Paris. A. Chappuis, Tresserve.

1037. AFTER MINO DA FIESOLE: *Rinaldo della Luna*, 1892–95

$11\frac{7}{16} \times 8\frac{1}{4}$ inches—29 × 21 cm. Pencil. Verso: blank page.

After a plaster cast of Mino da Fiesole's bust (1461) of *Rinaldo della Luna*, marble in the National Museum (Bargello), Florence. See fig. 137. Rewald suggested Lemoyne's bust of Louis XV as the original source. Novotny indicated Filippo Strozzi, while Berthold proposed Buirette de Belloy, by J.-J. Caffieri. Reff, while con-

testing this latter identification, offered no other solution. I think that the resemblance between the drawing and our fig. 137 removes all doubt. Cf. Nos. 1038, 1126; also No. 1039, which is No. 190 in the Basel catalog.

BIBLIOGRAPHY: *Correspondance* (reproduced fig. 35). Rewald, *Carnets*: see the text, C III, p. 11. Novotny, *Cézanne als Zeichner*, *Wiener Jahrbuch* 1950, note 4, p. 233 (reproduced pl. III. Berthold, cat. No. 294 (reproduced). Reff, in *AB*, June 1960, p. 148. F. Novotny, *Ueber das Elementare in der Kunstgeschichte und andere Aufsätze*, Vienna, 1968 (reproduced fig. 42).

COLLECTION: Kenneth Clark, London.

1038. AFTER MINO DA FIESOLE: *Rinaldo della Luna*, circa 1895

$8\frac{1}{2} \times 5\frac{3}{8}$ inches—21,6 × 13,7 cm. Page 11 verso of the sketchbook ML. Pencil. Verso: blank page.

The original marble (1461) by Mino da Fiesole is in the National Museum (Bargello), Florence. Cézanne did this drawing in the Musée de Sculpture Comparée of the Trocadéro after a plaster cast that has since been lost. See fig. 137.

FIG. 137. Mino da Fiesole (1431–84): bust of the count *Rinaldo della Luna*, marble (1461) in the National Museum (Bargello), Florence; height 25 cm. Inscription: RINALDO DELLA LUNA SUE ETATIS ANNO XXVII OPUS MINI N. E(tatis) MCCCCLXI. This inscription added later is probably correct. For the plaster cast drawn by Cézanne, see the *Catalogue général du Musée de Sculpture comparée du Trocadéro* III, 1928, No. I 166.　　(*Photograph: Giraudon*)

FIG. 138. *Aphrodite and Eros*, marble in the Louvre. Musée National du Louvre, *Catalogue sommaire des Marbres antiques*, 1922, No. 335. *(Photograph: Giraudon)*

BIBLIOGRAPHY: Rewald, *Carnets:* C III, p. 11 verso (reproduced pl. 152); model suggested: Louis XV, by Lemoyne. Berthold, cat. No. 199 (reproduced); model suggested: Buirette de Belloy, by J.-J. Caffieri. Th. Reff, in *AB*, June 1960, p. 147, indicates the bust of Rinaldo della Luna. J. Bouchot-Saupique, *Revue des Arts*, 1951, pp. 243-44 (reproduced).

COLLECTIONS: Cézanne *fils*, Paris. M. Renou, Paris. Poyet, Lyons. M. Renou, Paris. Sam Salz, New York. Cabinet des Dessins of the Louvre, Paris (RF 29933).

1039. AFTER MINO DA FIESOLE: *Rinaldo della Luna*, 1894–97

$8\frac{1}{16} \times 5\frac{1}{8}$ inches—20,5 × 12,9 cm. Page XXIV from the sketchbook BS I. Pencil. Verso: blank page.

After a plaster cast of Mino da Fiesole's bust of Count Rinaldo della Luna. The original marble is in the National Museum (Bargello), Florence. See fig. 137.

BIBLIOGRAPHY: Venturi No. 1349, "buste de Louis XV, de Lemoyne." Berthold, cat. No. 293 (reproduced); "bust of Buirette de Belloy, by J.-J. Caffieri." Basel catalog, No. 190 (reproduced); "Rinaldo della Luna." Th. Reff, *AB*, June 1960, p. 148; "Rinaldo della Luna." R. Cogniat, *Cézanne*, Flammarion, Paris, 1967 (reproduced p. 27).

COLLECTIONS: Cézanne *fils*, Paris. Paul Guillaume, Paris. W. Feuz, Bern. Kunstmuseum, Basel.

1040. BUST OF A MAN, circa 1895

$8\frac{1}{2} \times 5\frac{3}{8}$ inches—21,7 × 13,7 cm. Page 6 verso of the sketchbook ML. Pencil. Verso: No. 869.

Man with hair falling down in curls on either side of his face; the drawing seems to have been accentuated with a softer pencil. Perhaps after Christophe Veyrier's bust of the admiral *Jean de Gabaret*, in the Louvre since 1895. It has not been possible to check this identification proposed by Gertrude Berthold.

BIBLIOGRAPHY: Rewald, *Carnets:* C III, p. 6 verso (not reproduced); model suggested: "buste de Le Brun, par Coysevox." Berthold, cat. No. 187 (reproduced Abb. 141); model suggested: Admiral Gabaret.

COLLECTIONS: Cézanne *fils*, Paris. M. Renou, Paris. Poyet, Lyons. M. Renou, Paris. Sam Salz, New York. Cabinet des Dessins of the Louvre, Paris (RF 29933).

1041. AFTER THE ANTIQUE: *Aphrodite and Eros*, 1888–91

$8\frac{1}{2} \times 5$ inches—21,6 × 12,7 cm. Page XXXVII verso from the second sketchbook Mrs. Enid A. Haupt. Pencil. Verso: No. 650.

After the marble *Aphrodite and Eros*; cf. Nos. 1042 and 1043, which are drawn, however, from another replica of the same original.

BIBLIOGRAPHY: Rewald, *Carnets:* C IV, p. XXXVII verso (reproduced pl. 117). Berthold, cat. No. 24 (reproduced Abb. 124).

COLLECTIONS: Cézanne *fils*, Paris. M. Renou, Paris. Poyet, Lyons. M. Renou, Paris. Sam Salz, New York. Mrs. Enid A. Haupt, New York.

1042. AFTER THE ANTIQUE: *Aphrodite and Eros*, 1892–95

$8\frac{1}{2} \times 5$ inches—21,6 × 12,7 cm. Page XXIX from the second sketchbook Mrs. Enid A. Haupt. Pencil. Verso: a watercolor.

After the marble *Aphrodite and Eros* in the Louvre. See fig. 138.

BIBLIOGRAPHY: Rewald, *Carnets:* C IV, p. XXIX (reproduced pl. 116). Berthold, cat. No. 26 (reproduced).

COLLECTIONS: Cézanne *fils*, Paris. M. Renou, Paris. Poyet, Lyons. M. Renou, Paris. Sam Salz, New York. Mrs. Enid A. Haupt, New York.

1043. AFTER THE ANTIQUE: *Aphrodite and Eros*, 1892–95

$8\frac{1}{2} \times 5\frac{1}{4}$ inches—21,6 × 13,3 cm. Page 4 of the sketchbook ML. Pencil. Verso: blank page.

After the marble *Aphrodite and Eros* in the Louvre. See fig. 138.

BIBLIOGRAPHY: Rewald, *Carnets:* C III, p. 4 (not reproduced). Berthold, cat. No. 25 (reproduced Abb. 149). J. Bouchot-Saupique, *Revue des Arts*, 1951, p. 243 (reproduced); model indicated: the Capitoline Venus.

COLLECTIONS: Cézanne *fils*, Paris. M. Renou, Paris, Poyet, Lyons. M. Renou, Paris. Sam Salz, New York. Cabinet des Dessins of the Louvre (RF 29933).

1044. AFTER PIGALLE: *Love and Friendship*, circa 1895

$10\frac{11}{16} \times 8\frac{5}{16}$ inches—27,1 × 21,1 cm. Page XXVI from the sketchbook CP IV. Pencil. Verso: rough watercolor sketch of two round fruits.

After Jean-Baptiste Pigalle's marble *L'Amour et l'Amitié*, in the Louvre since 1879. The drawing shows only the upper half of the statue; beautiful movement of the arms. Five copies by Cézanne of this sculpture are known. Cf. Nos. 501, 1046. See fig. 73.

BIBLIOGRAPHY: Venturi No. 1316. Berthold, cat. No. 161 (reproduced Abb. 138).

COLLECTIONS: Cézanne *fils*, Paris. Paul Guillaume, Paris. A. Chappuis, Tresserve. Sale, Maître Maurice Rheims, Palais Galliera, Paris, March 23, 1965, cat. No. 14. Present owner unknown.

1045. AFTER PIGALLE: *Love and Friendship*, circa 1895

$8\frac{1}{2} \times 5$ inches—21,6 × 12,7 cm. Page XVI from the second sketchbook Mrs. Enid A. Haupt. Pencil. Verso: blank page.

After Jean-Baptiste Pigalle's marble *L'Amour et l'Amitié* in the Louvre. See fig. 73.

BIBLIOGRAPHY: Rewald, *Carnets:* C IV, p. XVI (reproduced pl. 126). Berthold, cat. No. 162 (reproduced).

COLLECTIONS: Cézanne *fils*, Paris. M. Renou, Paris. Poyet, Lyons. M. Renou, Paris. Sam Salz, New York. Mrs. Enid A. Haupt, New York.

1046. AFTER PIGALLE: *Love and Friendship*, circa 1895

$6\frac{11}{16} \times 5\frac{1}{8}$ inches—17 × 13 cm. Page XXXVIII from the sketchbook BS II. Pencil. Verso: blank page.

After Jean-Baptiste Pigalle's marble *L'Amour et l'Amitié* in the Louvre. See fig. 73. Cf. Nos. 501, 1044.

BIBLIOGRAPHY: Venturi No. 1373. Berthold, cat. No. 160 (reproduced). Longstreet, 1964 (reproduced).

EXHIBITIONS: De David à Cézanne, La Vieille Fontaine, Lausanne, 1953, No. 109. Zurich, 1956, No. 196. Munich, 1956, No. 148; title given, "Caritas, after Puget."

COLLECTIONS: Cézanne *fils*, Paris. Paul Guillaume, Paris. W. Feuz, Bern. Carl Roesch, Diessenhofen.

1047. AFTER PIGALLE: *Love and Friendship*, circa 1895

$8\frac{1}{2} \times 5\frac{3}{8}$ inches—21,6 × 13,7 cm. Page 8 verso of the sketchbook ML. Pencil. Verso: blank page.

After Jean-Baptiste Pigalle's marble *L'Amour et l'Amitié* in the Louvre. See fig. 73.

BIBLIOGRAPHY: Rewald, *Carnets:* C III, p. 8 verso (not reproduced). Berthold, cat. No. 158 (reproduced).

COLLECTIONS: Cézanne *fils*, Paris. M. Renou, Paris. Poyet, Lyons. M. Renou, Paris. Sam Salz, New York. Cabinet des Dessins of the Louvre, Paris (RF 29933).

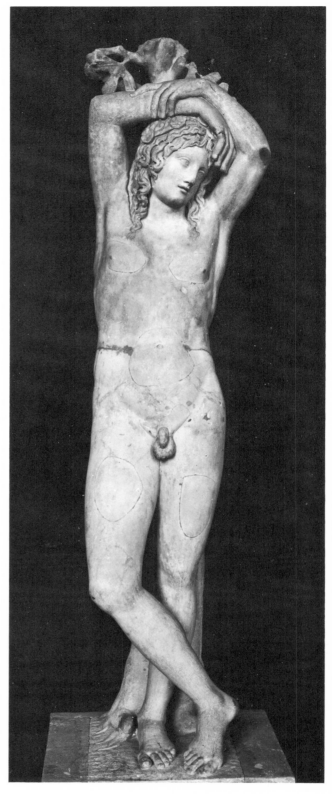

FIG. 139. *Genius of the Tomb*, Hellenistic marble in the Louvre. Musée national du Louvre, *Catalogue sommaire des Marbres antiques*, 1922, No. 435.   (*Photograph: Giraudon*)

1048. AFTER THE ANTIQUE: GENIUS OF THE TOMB, 1890–93

$8\frac{1}{2} \times 5\frac{3}{8}$ inches—21,6 × 13,7 cm. Page 27 of the sketchbook ML. Pencil. Verso: No. 1107.

After a *Génie Funéraire* (or genius presiding over a family sepulchre), antique marble in the Louvre. See fig. 139. It is characteristic of Cézanne to have chosen this statue of a figure with arms crossed above the head.

BIBLIOGRAPHY: Rewald, *Carnets*: C III, p. 27 (not reproduced). Berthold, cat. No. 45 (reproduced); "Genius of the Tomb."

COLLECTIONS: Cézanne *fils*, Paris. M. Renou, Paris. Poyet, Lyons. M. Renou, Paris. Sam Salz, New York. Cabinet des Dessins of the Louvre (RF 29933).

1049. AFTER THE ANTIQUE: *The Discophoros*, 1890–95
$7\frac{7}{8} \times 5\frac{3}{16}$ inches—19,9 × 13,1 cm. Page XXX from the sketchbook BS I. Pencil. Verso: blank page.

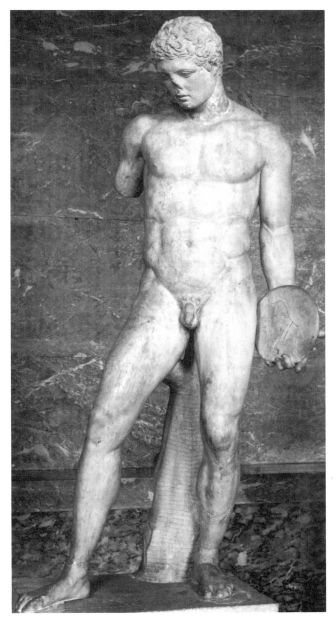

FIG. 140. *The Discophoros*, antique replica of a work attributed to Naucydes. Marble in the Louvre, height 1,83 m. Discovered at Colombaro on the Via Appia, Rome. The head was added from another antique statue; concerning other restorations, see Berthold, cat. No. 37. Musée National du Louvre, *Catalogue sommaire des Marbres antiques*, 1922, No. 89.
(Photograph: R. W. Ratcliffe)

After *The Discophoros*, antique marble in the Louvre. See fig. 140. Cézanne has indicated the join of a restoration to the right forearm.

BIBLIOGRAPHY: Venturi No. 1356. Berthold, cat. No. 37 (reproduced); model identified. Basel catalog No. 158 (reproduced).

COLLECTIONS: Cézanne *fils*, Paris. Paul Guillaume, Paris. W. Feuz, Bern. Kunstmuseum, Basel.

1050. AFTER THE ANTIQUE: *Roman orator*, 1892–95
$8\frac{1}{2} \times 5\frac{3}{8}$ inches—21,6 × 13,7 cm. Page 26 verso of the sketchbook ML. Pencil. Verso: blank page.

The antique marble known as *L'Orateur romain*, or *Germanicus*, in the Louvre, seen front view. See fig. 88. It represents a Roman nobleman personifying Mercury, Patron of Eloquence.

BIBLIOGRAPHY: Rewald, *Carnets*: C III, p. 26 verso (not reproduced). Berthold, cat. No. 32 (reproduced Abb. 151).

COLLECTIONS: Cézanne *fils*, Paris. M. Renou, Paris. Poyet, Lyons. M. Renou, Paris. Sam Salz, New York. Cabinet des Dessins of the Louvre (RF 29933).

1051. AFTER THE ANTIQUE: *Ares*, KNOWN AS *The Borghese Mars*, 1892–95
$7\frac{1}{16} \times 4\frac{3}{44}$ inches—18 × 12 cm. Page from a sketchbook. Pencil. Verso: No. 561.

After the marble *Ares*, known as *The Borghese Mars*, in the Louvre. See fig. 85. The sketch communicates a fine sense of rhythm.

BIBLIOGRAPHY: Venturi, Vol. I, p. 349, Oeuvres Inédites (not reproduced). Berthold, cat. No. 4 (reproduced).

COLLECTION: Kenneth Clark, London.

1052. AFTER THE ANTIQUE: *The Borghese Mars*, 1892–95
$7\frac{15}{16} \times 4\frac{13}{16}$ inches—20,2 × 12,2 cm. Page XLVII from the sketchbook BS II. Pencil. Verso: No. 1012.

After the marble *Ares*, known as *The Borghese Mars*, in the Louvre. See fig. 85. Cf. Nos. 1051, 1055.

BIBLIOGRAPHY: Venturi No. 1386. Berthold, cat. No. 3 (reproduced). Basel catalog, No. 161 (reproduced).

COLLECTIONS: Cézanne *fils*, Paris. Paul Guillaume, Paris. W. Feuz, Bern. Kunstmuseum, Basel.

1053. AFTER THE ANTIQUE: *The Borghese Mars*, 1892–95
$8\frac{1}{2} \times 5\frac{3}{8}$ inches—21,6 × 13,7 cm. Page 20 verso of the sketchbook ML. Pencil. Verso: blank page.

After the marble *Ares*, known as *The Borghese Mars*, in the Louvre. See fig. 85.

BIBLIOGRAPHY: Rewald, *Carnets*: C III, p. 20 verso (reproduced pl. 121). Berthold, cat. No. 1 (reproduced).

COLLECTIONS: Cézanne *fils*, Paris. M. Renou, Paris. Poyet, Lyons. M. Renou, Paris. Sam Salz, New York. Cabinet des Dessins of the Louvre, Paris (RF 29933).

1054. AFTER THE ANTIQUE: *The Borghese Mars*, circa 1895

$8\frac{7}{16} \times 5\frac{3}{16}$ inches—21,4 × 13,1 cm. Page XXVII verso from the sketchbook BS I. Pencil. Verso: No. 1114.

Standing male nude seen from the back; after the marble *Ares*, known as *The Borghese Mars*, in the Louvre. See fig. 85.

BIBLIOGRAPHY: Venturi No. 1353. Berthold, cat. No. 9 (reproduced). Basel catalog, No. 160 (reproduced).

COLLECTIONS: Cézanne *fils*, Paris. Paul Guillaume, Paris. W. Feuz, Bern. Kunstmuseum, Basel.

1055. AFTER THE ANTIQUE: *The Borghese Mars*, circa 1895

$8\frac{1}{16} \times 4\frac{13}{16}$ inches—20,5 × 12,2 cm. Page III from the sketchbook BS II. Pencil. Verso: blank page.

After the marble *Ares*, known as *The Borghese Mars*, in the Louvre. See fig. 85.

BIBLIOGRAPHY: Venturi No. 1361. Berthold, cat. No. 2 (reproduced). Basel catalog, No. 162 (reproduced).

COLLECTIONS: Cézanne *fils*, Paris. Paul Guillaume, Paris. W. Feuz, Bern. Kunstmuseum, Basel.

1056. AFTER THE ANTIQUE: *The Borghese Mars*, 1894–97

$8\frac{1}{8} \times 4\frac{15}{16}$ inches—20,6 × 12,5 cm. Page XVI from the sketchbook BS I. Pencil. Verso: blank page.

After the marble *Ares*, known as *The Borghese Mars*, in the Louvre. See fig. 85.

BIBLIOGRAPHY: Venturi No. 1340. Berthold, cat. No. 5 (reproduced Abb. 20). Basel catalog, No. 163 (reproduced).

EXHIBITION: Meisterzeichnungen französischer Künstler, Kunsthalle, Basel, 1935, No. 199.

COLLECTIONS: Cézanne *fils*, Paris. Paul Guillaume, Paris. W. Feuz, Bern. Kunstmuseum, Basel.

1057. AFTER PUGET: *Hercules resting*, 1890–94

$8\frac{1}{2} \times 5$ inches—21,6 × 12,7 cm. Page XVIII from the second sketchbook Mrs. Enid A. Haupt. Pencil. Verso: blank page.

After Pierre Puget's marble *Hercule au repos* in the Louvre. See fig. 82. The figure is drawn down to the thighs; curious distortion of the cheek.

BIBLIOGRAPHY: Rewald, *Carnets*: C IV, p. XVIII (not reproduced). Berthold, cat. No. 113 (reproduced).

COLLECTIONS: Cézanne *fils*, Paris. M. Renou, Paris. Poyet, Lyons. M. Renou, Paris. Sam Salz, New York. Mrs. Enid A. Haupt, New York.

1058. AFTER PUGET: *Hercules resting*, 1890–94

$8\frac{1}{4} \times 7\frac{1}{16}$ inches—21 × 18 cm. Page from a sketchbook, probably p. LXXII from CP IV. Pencil, small stains, trial dabs of watercolor lower left. Verso: a small watercolor sketch and an attestation by Cézanne *fils* dated July 27, 1937.

After Pierre Puget's marble *Hercule au repos* in the Louvre. See fig. 82.

[244]

BIBLIOGRAPHY: Berthold, cat. No. 109 (reproduced). Rewald, *Paul Cézanne*, New York, 1948 (reproduced pl. 97). F. Novotny, *Wiener Jahrbuch* 1950 (reproduced pl. 117). Idem, *Ueber das Elementare in der Kunstgeschichte und andere Aufsätze*, Vienna, 1968 (reproduced fig. 49).

EXHIBITIONS: East Hampton, New York, 1952, Influences in French Painting, No. 28. Fine Arts Associates, New York, 1952, No. 7. Nice, Aix-en-Provence, Grenoble, 1953, No. 39. The Hague, 1956, No. 123 (reproduced). Zurich, 1956, No. 185 (reproduced). Munich, 1956, No. 140 (reproduced). Los Angeles, No. 16. Wildenstein Galleries, New York, 1959, No. 74 (reproduced).

COLLECTIONS: Paul Cézanne *fils*, Paris. Galerie Zak, Paris. Dr. George Richter, New York. Miss G. Richter, New York. Mr. and Mrs. John Rewald, New York. Sale, Sotheby's, London, July 7, 1960, cat. No. 17 (reproduced). Private collection, England. Mr. and Mrs. E. V. Thaw, Scarborough, New York.

1059. AFTER PUGET: *Hercules resting*, 1890–94

$8 \times 4\frac{13}{16}$ inches—20,3 × 12,2 cm. Page XXXIX from the sketchbook BS II. Pencil. Verso: blank page.

After Pierre Puget's marble *Hercule au repos* in the Louvre. The figure is seen from the back, turned slightly to the right. See fig. 141. Cf. Nos. 1060, 1196.

BIBLIOGRAPHY: Venturi No. 1374. Berthold, cat. No. 122 (reproduced). Basel catalog, No. 152 (reproduced).

COLLECTIONS: Cézanne *fils*, Paris. Paul Guillaume, Paris. W. Feuz, Bern. Kunstmuseum, Basel.

FIG. 141. Pierre Puget: *Hercule au repos*. See fig. 82.

(Photograph: R. W. Ratcliffe)

1060. After Puget: *Hercules resting*, 1894–97

$7\frac{13}{16} \times 4\frac{15}{16}$ inches—19,8 × 12,5 cm. Page XXI from the sketchbook BS III. Pencil. Verso: watercolor landscape sketch, Venturi No. 1421, Basel catalog No. 172.

After Pierre Puget's marble *Hercule au repos* in the Louvre. See fig. 141. Cf. No. 1059.

BIBLIOGRAPHY: Venturi No. 1425. Berthold, cat. No. 120 (reproduced). Basel catalog, No. 151 (reproduced).

COLLECTIONS: Cézanne *fils*, Paris. Paul Guillaume, Paris. W. Feuz, Bern. Kunstmuseum, Basel.

1061. Peasant with his arms crossed, 1890–94

$15 \times 11\frac{7}{16}$ inches—38 × 29 cm. Pencil, small stains, brown blemish across the paper above the face, $\frac{1}{4}$-inch strip of margin added to the upper edge. Verso: No. 463.

Half-length portrait of a peasant in a round hat, looking at the viewer; cf. the painting Venturi No. 565.

BIBLIOGRAPHY: Venturi No. 1587. Basel catalog No. 156 (reproduced). Neumeyer, 1958, No. 42 (reproduced). *Le Dessin français au XIXe siècle*, Mermod, Lausanne, 1948 (reproduced p. 99). Longstreet, 1964 (reproduced). R. Cogniat, *Cézanne*, Flammarion, Paris, 1967 (reproduced p. 35).

COLLECTIONS: Cézanne *fils*, Paris. W. Feuz, Bern. Kunstmuseum, Basel.

1062. After the antique: *Lucius Verus*, 1890–94

$7\frac{5}{8} \times 4\frac{5}{8}$ inches—19,4 × 11,8 cm. Page XLIIII verso from the sketchbook CP I. Pencil, traces of pencil rubbings over the whole page. Verso: No. 1010.

After a bust representing the Roman emperor *Lucius Verus*, seen in right three-quarter view, his face turned toward the viewer. The original marble is in the Louvre. See fig. 142. Cf. Nos. 1063, 1137.

BIBLIOGRAPHY: Venturi No. 1276. Berthold, cat. No. 53 (reproduced); error in the No. of the Louvre catalog.

EXHIBITION: Kunsthalle, Basel, 1936, No. 123.

COLLECTIONS: Cézanne *fils*, Paris. Paul Guillaume, Paris. A. Chappuis, Tresserve.

1063. After the antique: *Lucius Verus*, 1890–94

$8\frac{1}{2} \times 5\frac{3}{8}$ inches—21,6 × 13,7 cm. Page 28 verso of the sketchbook ML. Pencil. Verso: blank page.

After a marble bust of the Roman emperor *Lucius Verus*, in the Louvre. See fig. 142. The folds of a garment and a round fibula are indicated. A very fine drawing. Cf. Nos. 1062, 1137.

BIBLIOGRAPHY: Rewald, *Carnets*: C III, p. 28 verso (reproduced pl. 144); model suggested: Marcus Aurelius. Berthold, cat. No. 54 (reproduced Abb. 145); model indicated: Lucius Verus.

COLLECTIONS: Cézanne *fils*, Paris. M. Renou, Paris. Poyet, Lyons. M. Renou, Paris. Sam Salz, New York. Cabinet des Dessins of the Louvre, Paris (RF 29933).

1064. Portrait of Mme Cézanne, 1886–89

$9\frac{5}{16} \times 6$ inches—23,7 × 15,2 cm. Page IX verso of the Album, Paul Mellon Collection. Pencil. Verso: No. 870.

FIG. 142. Antique bust of the Roman emperor *Lucius Verus*, marble in the Louvre. Musée national du Louvre, *Catalogue sommaire des Marbres antiques*, 1922, No. 1131.

(Photograph: R. W. Ratcliffe)

Head of Mme Cézanne, seen front face. Cf. the oil portrait Venturi No. 523, with which the present drawing is often compared. One of Cézanne's most remarkable pencil sketches.

BIBLIOGRAPHY: Venturi No. 1304. *Dessins*, 1957, No. 14 (reproduced). H. Perruchot, *La Vie de Cézanne*, Hachette, Paris, 1958 (reproduced in reverse p. 277). A. van Buren, Mme Cézanne's Fashions and the dates of her Portraits, *The Art Quarterly*, Vol. XXIX, 1966, p. 115; date given, 1886–89. *Album*, 1966 (reproduced)

EXHIBITIONS: Orangerie, Paris, 1936, No. 156. Lyons, 1939, No. 65. Wildenstein Gallery, London, 1939, No. 87.

COLLECTIONS: Cézanne *fils*, Paris. Paul Guillaume, Paris. A. Chappuis, Tresserve. Mr. and Mrs. Paul Mellon, Upperville, Va.

1065. Portrait of Mme Cézanne, 1887–90

$19\frac{1}{16} \times 12\frac{11}{16}$ inches—48,5 × 32,2 cm. Pencil on laid paper. Verso: blank page.

Bust-length portrait of the artist's wife wearing a hat, sitting on a divan, her look directed straight at the viewer. The figure is slightly on a diagonal in the page. Shadow cast on the back of the divan. Cf. No. 1068.

BIBLIOGRAPHY: Venturi No. 1467. A. Neumeyer, 1958, No. 37 (reproduced). R. Cogniat, *Le Siècle des Impressionnistes*, Flammarion, Paris, 1959, p. 81 (reproduced). Longstreet, 1964 (reproduced). *Cézanne*, Coll. Génies et

Réalités, Hachette, Paris, 1966, p. 18 (reproduced). A. van Buren, Madame Cézanne's Fashions and the dates of her Portraits, *The Art Quarterly*, Vol XXXIX, 1966, p. 118; date given 1886–88. H. R. Hoetink, *Franse Tekeningen uit de 19e Eeuw*, Rotterdam, 1968, No. 34 (reproduced); date given, circa 1887. J. Leymarie, *Dessins de la période impressionniste*, Skira, Geneva, 1969 (reproduced p. 87).

EXHIBITIONS: Rotterdam, 1933–34, No. 6. Haarlem, 1935, No. 33. Meisterzeichnungen französischer Künstler, Kunsthalle, Basel, 1935, No. 179. Kunsthalle, Basel, 1936, No. 136. P. Cassirer, Amsterdam, 1938, No. 21. Stedelijk Museum, Amsterdam, 1946, No. 14. Les dessins français de Fouquet à Cézanne, Brussels, Rotterdam, and Paris, 1949–50, No. 206 (reproduced pl. 91). Dessins du XVe au XIXe siècle du Musée Boymans, Bibliothèque Nationale, Paris, 1952, No. 141. Art Institute of Chicago and Metropolitan Museum of Art, New York, 1952, No. 45 (reproduced). French Drawings, Chicago, 1955–56, No. 156 (reproduced pl. 40). Phillips Collection, Washington, D.C., Chicago, Boston, 1971, No. 77 (reproduced).

COLLECTIONS: A. Vollard, Paris. S. Meller, Budapest. Paul Cassirer, Amsterdam. F. Koenigs, Haarlem. Boymans-van Beuningen Museum, Rotterdam (Inv. F II 220).

1066. PORTRAIT OF MME CÉZANNE, 1887–90

$8\frac{1}{8} \times 4\frac{15}{16}$ inches—20,7 × 12,5 cm. Page X from the sketchbook BS III. Pencil, touch of brick-red watercolor (today almost obliterated). Verso: No. 526.

(a) Head and shoulders of Mme Cézanne; a precise, detailed drawing. From an artistic point of view the reddish dab is inexplicable. Cf. the rough sketch No. 965 (e).— (b) At right angles: sketch of a bather going down into the water; cf. Nos. 526, 1218.

BIBLIOGRAPHY: Venturi No. 1411. Rewald, *Cézanne et Zola*, Paris, 1936 (reproduced fig. 45).

COLLECTIONS: Cézanne *fils*, Paris. Paul Guillaume, Paris. W. Feuz, Bern. R. von Hirsch, Basel.

1067. PORTRAIT OF MME CÉZANNE, 1888–91

$5\frac{7}{8} \times 4\frac{3}{4}$ inches—15 × 12 cm. Pencil on light gray laid paper. Verso: blank page.

The upright of a chair is visible behind the sitter's neck. Cf. No. 821 (g).

BIBLIOGRAPHY: *Correspondance* (reproduced fig. 27). *Dessins*, 1957, No. 43 (reproduced). K. Leonhard, *Paul Cézanne*, Rowohlt, 1966 (reproduced p. 25).

EXHIBITIONS: Orangerie, Paris, 1936, No. 155. Lyons, 1939, No. 66. Wildenstein, London, 1939, No. 88. Rétrospective, Paris, 1939, No. 34.

COLLECTIONS: Cézanne *fils*, Paris. Paul Guillaume, Paris. A. Chappuis, Tresserve. W. S. Schiess, Basel.

1068. PORTRAIT OF MME CÉZANNE, 1888–91

$9\frac{5}{16} \times 6$ inches—23,7 × 15,2 cm. Page VII of the Album, Paul Mellon Collection. Pencil. Verso: blank page.

Head of Mme Cézanne seen front face, slightly inclined over the right shoulder. This study is fairly close to the painting Venturi No. 569, *Madame Cézanne in the Greenhouse*, though the drawing seems to have been done outdoors. Cf. also our Nos. 696 (a), 1064, 1065.

BIBLIOGRAPHY: Venturi No. 1303. Idem, in *L'Arte*, Sept. 1935 (reproduced fig. 18). *Dessins*, 1938 (reproduced pl. 32). Neumeyer, 1958, No. 36 (reproduced). A. van Buren, Mme Cézanne's Fashions and the dates of her Portraits, *The Art Quarterly*, Vol. XXIX, 1966, p. 115; date given for Venturi No. 569 and for our drawing, 1886–87. *Album*, 1966 (reproduced). Th. Reff, Album de Paul Cézanne, *BurlM*, Nov. 1967, Vol. CIX, p. 652; the author compares our drawing also to Venturi No. 525.

EXHIBITION: Orangerie, Paris, 1936, No. 160.

COLLECTIONS: Cézanne *fils*, Paris. Paul Guillaume, Paris. A. Chappuis, Tresserve. Mr. and Mrs. Paul Mellon, Upperville, Va.

1069. WOMAN LEANING FORWARD, 1890–94

$6 \times 9\frac{5}{16}$ inches—15,2 × 23,7 cm. Page XV of the Album, Paul Mellon Collection. Pencil, pencil rubbings over nearly the whole page. Verso: No. 953.

The face is seen in foreshortening and there is remarkable beauty in the volume of the head. Cf. Venturi No. 228. —The pencil rubbings do not correspond to the contours of No. 1015 (on the page opposite in the Album) but are formed by the stressed strokes of No. 953, *Bellows in front of a Fireplace*, which figures on the reverse side of the present page. From this I conclude that No. 953 is later than Nos. 1015 and 1069; however this provides no key to the respective dates of the two women leaning forward.

BIBLIOGRAPHY: Venturi, Vol. I, under No. 1304 (not reproduced). *Album*, 1966 (reproduced); dated 1890–94, with the note "La contre-épreuve rend probable (non pas certain) que notre croquis est antérieur au précédent" (the counterproof makes it probable, though not certain, that this sketch is earlier than the one preceding).

COLLECTIONS: Cézanne *fils*, Paris. Paul Guillaume, Paris. A. Chappuis, Tresserve. Mr. and Mrs. Paul Mellon, Upperville, Va.

1070. HEAD OF A WOMAN, AND NOTATIONS, 1893–96

$4\frac{1}{4} \times 2\frac{11}{16}$ inches—10,9 × 6,8 cm. Page VII of the sketchbook violet moiré. Pencil, Verso: No. 1172.

Head of a woman seen in left three-quarter view. The drawing is covered with handwritten notations: *Mme Colomb/rue Jean-Jacques/Rousseau 8/dernier dimanche/du mois pendant/l'hiver*. Upside down: *Samedi Dimanche Mardi Mercredi Vendredi*.

BIBLIOGRAPHY: Berthold, p. 159 (not reproduced). *Carnet violet moiré* (reproduced). W. V. Andersen, Cézanne's Carnet violet moiré, *BurlM*, June 1965, p. 313 (reproduced fig. 47).

COLLECTIONS: Cézanne *fils*, Paris. Jean-Pierre Cézanne, Paris. Mlle Edmée Maus, Geneva.

1071. TWO HEADS, 1890–96

$6 \times 9\frac{5}{16}$ inches—15,2 × 23,7 cm. Page XXIIII of the Album, Paul Mellon Collection. Pencil. Verso: blank page.

Two unfinished studies of heads, drawn on a larger scale than usual.—(a) Page upright, top: head of the artist's son in right profile, bent forward. The mouth and chin are summarily indicated and covered by the hatching of (b). —(b) Page lengthwise: shoulder and head of another model; a fine study done some time later than the first. Léo Marchutz takes it to be Mme Cézanne.

BIBLIOGRAPHY: Venturi, Vol. I, under No. 1306 (not reproduced). *Dessins*, 1938 (reproduced pl. 11). *Album*, 1966 (reproduced).

COLLECTIONS: Cézanne *fils*, Paris. Paul Guillaume, Paris. A. Chappuis, Tresserve. Mr. and Mrs. Paul Mellon, Upperville, Va.

1072. SEATED FIGURE AND NOTATIONS, 1893–96

$4\frac{1}{4} \times 2\frac{11}{16}$ inches—10,9 × 6,8 cm. Page IX verso of the sketchbook violet moiré. Pencil. Verso: No. 1174.

Small sketch partly covered by handwriting. A seated figure can be distinguished, elbow on knee and head on hand, in left three-quarter view. W. V. Andersen believes it to be the artist's son, whereas Gertrude Berthold takes it for a woman.

BIBLIOGRAPHY: Berthold, p. 159 (not reproduced). Carnet violet moiré (reproduced). W. V. Andersen, Cézanne's Carnet violet moiré, *BurlM*, June 1965, p. 313 (reproduced fig. 42).

COLLECTIONS: Cézanne *fils*, Paris. Jean-Pierre Cézanne, Paris. Mlle Edmée Maus, Geneva.

1073. MME CÉZANNE, HER HEAD LOWERED, 1893–96

$9\frac{5}{16} \times 6$ inches—23,7 × 15,2 cm. Page XVII of the Album, Paul Mellon Collection. Pencil. Verso: No. 867.

The expression is that of someone peacefully reading. The movement of the hair and forceful hatching are noteworthy.

BIBLIOGRAPHY: Venturi, Vol. I, under No. 1304 (not reproduced). *Dessins*, 1938 (reproduced pl. 36). *Album*, 1966 (reproduced).

COLLECTIONS: Cézanne *fils*, Paris. Paul Guillaume, Paris. A. Chappuis, Tresserve. Mr. and Mrs. Paul Mellon, Upperville, Va.

1074. DOG, LYING DOWN, 1893–96

$2\frac{11}{16} \times 4\frac{1}{4}$ inches—6,8 × 10,9 cm. Page IV verso of the sketchbook violet moiré. Pencil. Verso: handwritten notations and a scarcely visible unfinished sketch of a tree trunk.

Unfinished sketch of a dog, the head and paws not drawn. Above this there are two unintelligible forms and written across them an address: Delaherche rue Halévy boulevard Haussmann. According to W. V. Andersen (see bibliography), note 30, Auguste Delaherche lived at No. 1 rue Halévy from 1890 to 1897; his house carried the sign: *Grès artistique* [art earthenware] *fabrication rue Blomet* 153.

BIBLIOGRAPHY: Berthold, p. 159 (not reproduced). Carnet violet moiré (reproduced). W. V. Andersen, Cézanne's Carnet violet moiré. *BurlM*, June 1965, p. 313 (reproduced fig. 47).

COLLECTIONS: Cézanne *fils*, Paris. Jean-Pierre Cézanne, Paris. Mlle Edmée Maus, Geneva.

1075. PAGE OF STUDIES, MAINLY HORSES, 1891–94

$10\frac{1}{8} \times 8\frac{1}{4}$ inches—25,7 × 21 cm. Page LXXXIII from the sketchbook CP IV. Pencil. Verso: No. 1154.

(a) Top: man in a helmet standing with his back turned, apparently a Municipal Guard of Paris. To his right, a guard-stone.—(b) In foreshortening: the rump of a horse. —(c) Below: mane and ear of a horse and a more complete, though unfinished, study of a horse.

BIBLIOGRAPHY: Venturi, Vol. I, under No. 1322 (not reproduced).

COLLECTIONS: Cézanne *fils*, Paris. Paul Guillaume, Paris. A. Chappuis, Tresserve.

1076. STUDY OF DRAPERY, 1891–94

$18\frac{7}{8} \times 12\frac{3}{16}$ inches—48 × 31 cm. Pencil on laid paper, trace of a fold. Verso: blank page.

The inner and outer folds are indicated with precision; the volume merges with the white of the paper. A right angle indicates a protruding corner lower on the right. Cézanne used draperies in his portraits and still lifes, but the play of folds in itself attracted him in the same way as did the quasi-abstract rock formations he studied. Cf. Venturi Nos. 747, 1123, 1124 and our No. 131. The direction of the hatching does not help to indicate which is the top and which the bottom of the drawing; the question can be decided only by individual feeling.

COLLECTIONS: Mouradian & Vallotton, Paris. Private collection, Paris.

1077. STUDY OF DRAPERY, 1891–94

$8\frac{9}{16} \times 5$ inches—21,7 × 12,6 cm. Page XXXIX of the sketchbook Leigh Block. Pencil. Verso: No. 750.

Still life: a disorderly heap of sheets and blankets, with a wall in the background.

BIBLIOGRAPHY: Rewald, *Carnets*: C V, p. XXXIX (reproduced, upside down, pl. 76).

COLLECTIONS: Cézanne *fils*, Paris. M. Renou, Paris. Poyet, Lyons. M. Renou, Paris. Sam Salz, New York. Mr. and Mrs. Leigh Block, Chicago.

1078. APPLES ON A PLATE, 1891–94

$8\frac{11}{16} \times 10\frac{3}{4}$ inches—22 × 27,3 cm. Page XXVIII from the sketchbook CP IV. Pencil. Verso: an unfinished watercolor portrait of Mme Cézanne, paginated XXVII.

Still life: six round apples, two of them with a leaf still attached, on a round plate. The edge of the table is clearly indicated and the whole composition firmly established.

BIBLIOGRAPHY: Venturi, Vol. I, under No. 1316 (not reproduced). *Dessins*, 1938, No. 44 (reproduced). Neumeyer, 1958, No. 59 (reproduced). Coll. Génies et Réalités,

Cézanne, Hachette, Paris, 1966 (reproduced p. 205, fig. 145).

EXHIBITIONS: Orangerie, Paris, 1936, No. 166bis. San Francisco, 1937, No. 70 (reproduced).

COLLECTIONS: Cézanne *fils*, Paris. Paul Guillaume, Paris. A. Chappuis, Tresserve. Private collection, Paris.

1079. EARTHENWARE PITCHER, POT, WOMAN BATHER, 1891–94

$5\frac{7}{16} \times 7\frac{5}{8}$ inches—11,8 × 19,4 cm. Page IX verso from the sketchbook CP I. Pencil. Verso: No. 845.

(a) Left, upside down: two sketches of a woman bather.—(b) Pitcher and pot; for the pitcher, cf. No. 770 and Venturi Nos. 499, 500, 601, 609, 612, 622, 749; for the pot, cf. No. 629 and Venturi Nos. 349, 363.

BIBLIOGRAPHY: Venturi, Vol. I, under No. 1270 (not reproduced). *Dessins*, 1938, No. 25 ((b) reproduced).

EXHIBITIONS: Lyons, 1939, No. 67. Wildenstein Gallery, London, 1939, No. 89. Rétrospective, Paris, 1939, No. 36.

COLLECTIONS: Cézanne *fils*, Paris. Paul Guillaume, Paris. A. Chappuis, Tresserve.

1080. PITCHER AND SPIRIT-STOVE, 1891–94

$8\frac{1}{2} \times 5$ inches—21,6 × 12,7 cm. Page XLVIII verso from the second sketchbook Mrs. Enid A. Haupt. Pencil. Verso: No. 1080A.

Left: a bottle left white but seen in silhouette, in front of the pitcher. Right: near the edge of the table, a spirit-stove with T-shaped uprights and a straight handle. The pitcher and spirit-stove figure in many of Cézanne's paintings, watercolors, and drawings; see for example Venturi Nos. 499, 601, 609, 1541, and our Nos. 957, 1079.

BIBLIOGRAPHY: Rewald, *Carnets*: C IV, p. XLVIII verso (reproduced pl. 75). *Dessins*, 1957, No. 22 (reproduced).

COLLECTIONS: Cézanne *fils*, Paris. M. Renou, Paris. Poyet, Lyons. M. Renou, Paris. Sam Salz, New York. Mrs. Enid A. Haupt, New York.

1080A. HANDLE OF A JUG, AND A JAR

Inaccessible reverse side of No. 1080 (not reproduced).

BIBLIOGRAPHY: Rewald, *Carnets*: C IV, p. XLVIII (not reproduced) "croquis de l'anse d'un pot et d'une jarre provençale."

1081. STUDIES: HEAD, CUP, AND BREAD ROLL, 1891–94

$9\frac{5}{16} \times 6$ inches—23,7 × 15,2 cm. Page VIII of the Album, Paul Mellon Collection. Pencil. Verso: No. 343.

(a) Top: rough sketch of a round object.—(b) Unfinished sketch of a boy's head.—(c) Below: still life comprising a split bread roll and a cup, its handle in profile to the right. The drawings (a) and (c), like our No. 954, are studies for the painting Venturi No. 621.

BIBLIOGRAPHY: Venturi, Vol. I, under No. 1303 (not reproduced). *Album*, 1966 (reproduced). Th. Reff, Album de Paul Cézanne, *BurlM*, Nov. 1967, Vol. CIX, p. 652 "the sketch of a cup on p. 8 was not necessarily made in

preparation for the still life with apples (Venturi No. 621 . . ."

COLLECTIONS: Cézanne *fils*, Paris. Paul Guillaume, Paris. A. Chappuis, Tresserve. Mr. and Mrs. Paul Mellon, Upperville, Va.

1082. STUDY OF A THISTLE, 1893–96

$9\frac{5}{16} \times 6$ inches—23,7 × 15,2 cm. Page XXXI of the Album, Paul Mellon Collection. Pencil. Verso: No. 488.

Thistle bud with its stalk and tongue-shaped leaves, beautifully outlined. A powerfully effective portrayal of the thistle plant, which grows in the countryside around Aix-en-Provence.

BIBLIOGRAPHY: Venturi, Vol. I, under No. 1309 (not reproduced). *Dessins*, 1938 (reproduced pl. 27). *Album*, 1966 (reproduced).

COLLECTIONS: Cézanne *fils*, Paris. Paul Guillaume, Paris. A. Chappuis, Tresserve. Mr. and Mrs. Paul Mellon, Upperville, Va.

1083. PAGE OF STUDIES, INCLUDING A BATHER AND A MAN SMOKING, 1891–96

$4\frac{7}{8} \times 8\frac{5}{8}$ inches—12,4 × 21,8 cm. Page XLVI verso from the sketchbook CP II. Pencil. Verso: No. 907.

(a) Right: head, shoulders, and chest of a bather with outstretched arms, the pose rather similar to that of the figure in Venturi No. 549. The stroke is vigorous and free, reminiscent of Eugène Delacroix's drawings. The strokes on the left near the chin of (b) are part of (a).—(b) Left and at right angles: portrait of a bearded man seen in left three-quarter view with a pipe stem in his mouth; several renderings of the contours. To date the model has not been identified but there is a close resemblance between him and the peasants smoking or playing cards; cf. the man standing in Venturi No. 559, also Venturi No. 686.

BIBLIOGRAPHY: Venturi, under No. 1295; for (a) "étude de tête d'après le petit Paul." Th. Reff, *Bather* ((a) reproduced fig. 9). The author thinks that (a) represents the artist's son at the age of about thirteen, and recognizes him also in Venturi No. 549; he identifies (b) as a portrait of Emile Zola (note 18).

COLLECTIONS: Cézanne *fils*, Paris. Paul Guillaume, Paris. A. Chappuis, Tresserve.

1084. FULL-LENGTH SKETCH OF A DANCER, 1893–96

$18\frac{3}{4} \times 8\frac{3}{4}$ inches—47,6 × 22,2 cm. Pencil on laid paper. Verso: a watercolor not cited by Venturi.

Woman dancing, seen front view with her hand on her hip; a light garment covers her bust and floats around her thighs. Part of the drawing is cut off on the left, and lower down there is a fragment which seems to be a foot. For the subject, cf. Nos. 263, 271, 317, 481, 657.

COLLECTIONS: Knoedler & Co., New York. Present owner unknown.

1085. PORTRAIT OF A CHILD, 1896

$14\frac{13}{16} \times 11\frac{7}{8}$ inches—37,6 × 30,2 cm. Pencil. Verso: watercolor study of a tree.

Head of a boy in a round straw hat. It is generally accepted that Cézanne did several studies of this model at Talloires, in 1896.

BIBLIOGRAPHY: Venturi No. 1485. H. R. Hoetink, *Franse Tekeningen uit de 19e Eeuw*, Rotterdam, 1968, No. 20 (reproduced).

EXHIBITIONS: Kunsthalle, Basel, 1936, No. 172. Amsterdam, 1946, No. 6.

COLLECTIONS: P. Cassirer. F. Koenigs, Haarlem. Boymans-van Beuningen Museum, Rotterdam (Inv. F II 119).

1086. AFTER *L'Ecorché*, 1893–96

$12\frac{1}{4} \times 9\frac{1}{4}$ inches—31,1 × 23,5 cm. Pencil on laid paper, flyspecks. Verso: blank page.

After the plaster cast owned by the artist. See fig. 36.

BIBLIOGRAPHY: Venturi, No. 1453. Berthold, cat. No. 74 (reproduced).

EXHIBITIONS: The Hague, 1956, No. 122. Zurich, 1956, No. 183. Munich, 1956, No. 139.

COLLECTIONS: Galerie Bollag, Zurich. Sale, Bollag, Zurich, April 3, 1925, No. 39 (reproduced in the catalog pl. XV). Jon Nicolas Streep, New York.

1087. AFTER *L'Ecorché*, 1893–96

$10\frac{11}{16} \times 8\frac{5}{16}$ inches—27,2 × 21,1 cm. Page LXIV from the sketchbook CP IV. Pencil. Verso: an unfinished watercolor, paginated LXIII.

Sketch after the plaster cast owned by the artist. See fig. 36.

BIBLIOGRAPHY: Venturi, No. 1317. Berthold, cat. No. 72 (reproduced). *Dessins*, 1957, No. 49 (reproduced).

EXHIBITION: Aix-en-Provence, 1961, No. 58.

COLLECTIONS: Cézanne *fils*, Paris. Paul Guillaume, Paris. A. Chappuis, Tresserve.

1087bis. AFTER *L'Ecorché*, 1893–96

$10\frac{5}{8} \times 6\frac{7}{8}$ inches—27 × 17,5 cm. Pencil. Verso: No. 662bis.

After the plaster cast owned by the artist. See fig. 36. Michael Sadler was fond of evoking Chinese art at Paul Guillaume's when looking at Cézanne's work and probably had it in mind when he bought this drawing from the dealer, around 1933. Sir Michael, who was Master of University College, Oxford, insisted that the principal enemies of study were "distractions, interruptions, and noise." If we consider Cézanne from this angle: he had no need of distractions, he isolated himself in order to avoid interruptions, and not only isolated himself but sometimes even moved house to get away from noises which annoyed him. In his book, Ambroise Vollard mentions the painter's irritation at a dog barking and the anathema that Cézanne hurled at a vibrating elevator which he apostrophized as a "steam-hammer factory." (Vollard, 1914, pp. 94, 95. See also Rivière, 1923, p. 103.) The unfinished state of certain drawings leads me to believe that the thread of the artist's sensations had been snapped by noise or by somebody's approach.

EXHIBITIONS: Leicester Galleries, London, Selection of works from the collection of Sir Michael Sadler, Jan. 1944, No. 9. Royal Academy, London, 1963, No. 233.

COLLECTIONS: Cézanne *fils*, Paris. Paul Guillaume, Paris. Michael Sadler, Oxford. Leicester Galleries, London. Edward le Bas, R.A., London. Sale, Christie's, Geneva, Nov. 6, 1969, No. 154 (reproduced); error in the indication recto/verso. Dr. Armand Hammer, Los Angeles.

1088. AFTER *L'Ecorché*, 1893–96

$8\frac{1}{4} \times 5\frac{5}{16}$ inches—21 × 13,5 cm. Page from a sketchbook, probably Rewald, *Carnets*: C III. Pencil. Verso: blank page.

After the plaster cast owned by the artist. See fig. 36. The contour of the back, the different kinds of hatching, the shadow under the chin, and the contrast under the arm should be especially noticed. A fine drawing, expressing suffering.

BIBLIOGRAPHY: *Correspondance* (reproduced fig. 43). Berthold, cat. No. 77 (reproduced). Rewald/Jedlicka, *Briefe* (reproduced pl. 41).

COLLECTIONS: Cézanne *fils*, Paris. Private collection, Paris.

1089. AFTER *L'Ecorché*, 1893–96

$11 \times 7\frac{1}{16}$ inches—28 × 18 cm. Pencil. Verso: No. 509.

After the plaster cast owned by the artist. See fig. 36. This drawing is distinctive for its notably delicate stroke.

BIBLIOGRAPHY: Venturi, Vol. I, under No. 1453 (not reproduced). Berthold, cat. No. 73 (reproduced). See John Rewald, *Lettres de Camille Pissarro à son fils Lucien*, Paris, 1950, letter dated Dec. 4, 1895. We know that Degas' interest in Cézanne's drawings continued far beyond the early period mentioned by Pissarro in his letter.

COLLECTIONS: Edgar Degas, Paris. Edgar Degas sale, Paris, March 26-27, 1918. Léon Bollag, Zurich. Sale, Bollag, Zurich, April 3, 1925, No. 32 (not reproduced). Herr and Frau H. Goldschmidt, Zurich.

1090. SEATED MAN, 1893–96

$10\frac{3}{4} \times 8\frac{5}{16}$ inches—27,3 × 21,1 cm. Page LXXVII from the sketchbook CP IV. Pencil. Verso: three handwritten addresses: *Jean Antonucci 87 rue Mouffetard 87 Mancini 7 rue Fermat Corsi Rue Saint-Médard N.5*—Page LXXVIII.

Unfinished, lightly drawn sketch. The right forearm is held above the thigh in an expressive gesture, similar to that in the portrait of *Vallier*, Venturi No. 716. There is a certain kinship between this study and those done from antique marble statues.

BIBLIOGRAPHY: Venturi, Vol. I, under No. 1320 (not reproduced).

COLLECTIONS: Cézanne *fils*, Paris. Paul Guillaume, Paris. A. Chappuis, Tresserve.

1091. HAT, FLOWERS IN A BOTTLE, 1892–96

$14\frac{3}{16} \times 18\frac{7}{8}$ inches—36 × 48 cm. Pencil. Verso: the watercolor Venturi No. 1057, "*Sous-bois*."

(a) Round hat laid on a piece of furniture; cf. the hat of the *Card player* seen front view in Venturi No. 559.—(b)

Upside down, the lower part cut off by the edge of the paper: flowers (perhaps pansies) in the neck of a bottle.

COLLECTIONS: Cézanne *fils*, Paris. Paul Cassirer, Amsterdam.

1092. A CARD PLAYER, 1892–96

$19\frac{1}{4} \times 15\frac{3}{4}$ inches—49×40 cm. Pencil on laid paper, light stains, watermark: VIDALON. Verso: blank page.

Study of the card player on the right of the canvas Venturi No. 559. Cf. the watercolor Venturi No. 1085, a study of the same rustic figure; our drawing differs only in a few details.

BIBLIOGRAPHY: Vollard, 1914 (reproduced p. 47). Venturi, confusing it with the watercolor, did not include this drawing in his 1936 catalog. However in Vol. I, under No. 1086, he mentions Vollard's reproduction of the drawing. The photograph we show was taken thanks to Venturi on July 20, 1937. *The World's Masters*, The Studio, London, 1929 (reproduced pl. VI).

COLLECTIONS: Ambroise Vollard, Paris. Present owner unknown.

1093. A CARD PLAYER, 1892–96

21×17 inches—$53,3 \times 43,1$ cm. Pencil, traces of folds. Verso: blank page.

Study for *The Card Players*. Seated man holding some playing cards, his hands resting on the table. Judging by the style, this drawing could be one of the first of the series; it is not in strict relation to any of the oils.

BIBLIOGRAPHY: A. Vollard, *Paul Cézanne, His Life and Work*, Brentano's, London, 1924 (reproduced opposite p. 72). Kurt Badt, *Die Kunst Cézannes*, Munich, 1956 (reproduced fig. 15).

COLLECTIONS: Ambroise Vollard, Paris. Matthiesen, Ltd., London. P. Rosenberg, New York. Hanley Collection, Bradford, Penna. E. Thaw, New York. Norton F. Simon, Los Angeles.

1094. MAN SMOKING, 1892–96

$19\frac{3}{4} \times 12\frac{5}{8}$ inches—50×32 cm. (page); $10\frac{7}{16} \times 10\frac{5}{8}$ inches—$26,5 \times 27$ cm. (sight). Pencil on laid paper with watermark. Verso: blank page.

Study for *The Card Players;* see especially Venturi Nos. 556, 557, 558. The sketch shows the head of the player sitting on the right. For me this is one of the artist's finest drawings.

BIBLIOGRAPHY: Venturi No. 1483. Vollard, 1914 (reproduced p. 107). Meier-Graefe, *Cézanne und sein Kreis*, Munich, 1922 (reproduced p. 11). Frantisek Rachlik, *Cézanne*, Prague, 1948 (reproduced pl. 2). Coll. Koenigs, *Art et Style*, No. 23, 1952 (reproduced). Kurt Badt, *Die Kunst Cézannes*, Munich, 1956 (reproduced fig. 14). *Dessins*, 1957 (reproduced). L. Zahn, *Eine Geschichte der modernen Kunst*, Berlin, 1958, p. 21 (reproduced). F. Mathey, *Les Impressionnistes*, Paris, 1959 (reproduced p. 222), and *The Impressionists*, New York, 1961, p. 220 (reproduced). H. R. Hoetink, *Franse Tekeningen uit de 19e Eeuw*, Rotterdam, 1968, No. 36, dated 1891–92 (reproduced).

EXHIBITIONS: Boymans Museum, Rotterdam, 1934, No. 8.

Meisterzeichnungen französischer Künstler, Kunsthalle, Basel, 1935, No. 180. Kunsthalle, Basel, 1936, No. 140. Amsterdam, 1938, No. 24. Amsterdam, 1946, No. 16 (reproduced). Paris, Brussels, Rotterdam, 1949–50, No. 208. Bibliothèque Nationale, Paris, 1952, No. 143 (reproduced). The Hague, 1956, No. 125 (reproduced). Zurich, 1956, No. 188 (reproduced). Munich, 1956, No. 143 (reproduced). Paris, Amsterdam, 1964, No. 204 (reproduced).

COLLECTIONS: S. Meller, Munich. P. Cassirer. F. Koenigs, Haarlem. Boymans-van Beuningen Museum, Rotterdam (Inv. F II 225).

1095. PÈRE ALEXANDRE, 1892–96

$20 \times 12\frac{5}{8}$ inches—51×32 cm. (the whole page). Pencil on laid paper with the watermark: VIDALON. Verso: the watercolor Venturi No. 1088.

Study for *The Card Players*. The head of *père* Alexandre in his characteristic hat. Our drawing covers only part of the page. The watercolor on the reverse side shows the same figure in a more complete version.

BIBLIOGRAPHY: Venturi No. 1482. Vollard, 1914 (reproduced p. 146). Meier-Graefe, *Cézanne und sein Kreis*, Munich, 1922 (reproduced p. 38). Ikouma Arishima, *Cézanne*, Ars, 1926 (14th year Tai-Sho) (reproduced p. 3). Rewald, *Cézanne*, Spring Books, London, 1959 and 1965 (reproduced p. 102).

COLLECTIONS: Ambroise Vollard, Paris. A. Chappuis, Paris. P. Rosenberg, Paris.

1096. AFTER THE ANTIQUE: *Crouching Venus*, 1892–96

$8\frac{1}{2} \times 5\frac{3}{8}$ inches—$21,6 \times 13,7$ cm. Page 13 of the sketchbook ML. Verso: blank page.

After the marble known as *The Crouching Venus*, or *The Venus of Vienna*, in the Louvre. See fig. 143. The distinguishing quality of this sketch is the stubborn search for a fading contour. The strokes are often parallel, both indicating and amplifying the shadows. It is the only study showing the figure in left profile.

BIBLIOGRAPHY: Rewald, *Carnets*: C III, p. 13 (reproduced pl. 119). Berthold, cat. No. 20 (reproduced).

COLLECTIONS: Cézanne *fils*, Paris. M. Renou, Paris. Poyet, Lyons. M. Renou, Paris. Sam Salz, New York. Cabinet des Dessins of the Louvre, Paris (RF 29933).

1097. AFTER THE ANTIQUE: *Crouching Venus*, 1892–96

$7\frac{3}{16} \times 4\frac{9}{16}$ inches—$18,2 \times 11,6$ cm. Page 11 verso from the first sketchbook Mrs. Enid A. Haupt. Pencil. Verso: No. 822.

After the marble known as *The Crouching Venus*, also called *The Venus of Vienna*, in the Louvre. See fig. 144. The stroke is more compact than usual, the volume less ample.

BIBLIOGRAPHY: Rewald, *Carnets*: C I, p. 11 verso (reproduced pl. 118). Berthold, cat. No. 19 (reproduced Abb. 87); see also the text p. 49.

COLLECTIONS: Cézanne *fils*, Paris. M. Renou, Paris. Poyet, Lyons. M. Renou, Paris. Sam Salz, New York. Mrs. Enid A. Haupt, New York.

1098. AFTER THE ANTIQUE: *Crouching Venus*, 1894–97

$7\frac{5}{8} \times 4\frac{5}{8}$ inches—$19,4 \times 11,8$ cm. Page XLII from the sketchbook CP I. Pencil. Verso: No. 450.

FIG. 143. *Crouching Venus* or *Venus of Vienna*, antique marble in the Louvre, on exhibition since 1879. Musée National du Louvre, *Catalogue sommaire des Marbres antiques*, 1922, No. 2240. Our photograph was taken from a plaster cast.

(Photograph: Skulpturhalle, Basel)

After the marble known as *The Venus of Vienna*, in the Louvre. See fig. 144.

BIBLIOGRAPHY: Venturi No. 1275. Berthold, cat. No. 21 (reproduced Abb. 139). *Dessins*, 1938, No. 21 (reproduced).

EXHIBITION: Kunsthalle, Basel, 1936, No. 122.

COLLECTIONS: Cézanne *fils*, Paris. Paul Guillaume, Paris. A. Chappuis, Tresserve. Private collection, Paris.

1099. AFTER THE ANTIQUE: *Crouching Venus*, 1894–97

$8\frac{1}{4} \times 4\frac{13}{16}$ inches—21 × 12,2 cm. Page IX from the sketchbook BS II. Pencil. Verso: blank page.

After *The Crouching Venus*, antique statuette in the Louvre. The head and right arm, restored at one time, have since been removed. See fig. 145. Cf. No. 1100.

BIBLIOGRAPHY: Venturi No. 1367. Berthold, cat. No. 22 (reproduced). Basel catalog, No. 126 (reproduced). *Dessins*, 1957, No. 56 (reproduced).

EXHIBITIONS: The Hague, 1956, No. 128. Zurich, 1956, No. 194.

COLLECTIONS: Cézanne *fils*, Paris. Paul Guillaume, Paris. W. Feuz, Bern. Kunstmuseum, Basel.

1100. AFTER THE ANTIQUE: *Crouching Venus*, 1894–97

$8\frac{1}{2} \times 5\frac{1}{4}$ inches—21,6 × 13,3 cm. Page 3 of the sketchbook ML. Pencil. Verso: blank page.

Upper part of the marble *The Crouching Venus*. See fig. 145. In Cézanne's day the head and right arm of this statuette had been restored and are copied in his drawing. The parts added were later removed.

BIBLIOGRAPHY: Rewald, *Carnets*: C III, p. 3 (not reproduced). Berthold, cat. No. 23 (reproduced); original source identified.

COLLECTIONS: Cézanne *fils*, Paris. M. Renou, Paris. Poyet, Lyons. M. Renou, Paris. Sam Salz, New York. Cabinet des Dessins of the Louvre, Paris (RF 29933).

1101. WOMAN KNEELING, 1894–98

$10\frac{5}{8} \times 8\frac{3}{8}$ inches—27 × 21,2 cm. Front endpaper of the sketchbook CP IV. Pencil and touches of watercolor on ordinary paper glued to the inside of the cover of the sketchbook CP IV. Verso: the gray cloth cover.

(a) Center: kneeling woman seen in left profile. Pencil drawing heightened with touches of blue and brown watercolor; study for the serving woman in the watercolor *Bathsheba*, Venturi No. 884. Cf. also our Nos. 463, 464, 467 (a).—(b) Lower left: pencil sketch of the head (and bent arm?) of the figure in the middleground of Venturi No. 884. Cf. No. 1102.—(c) Handwritten notations: *Tulio Pietro Paulo/rue du Château 64/Sienne naturelle/Laque fine*. In the upper right corner there is a stamp indicating the sketchbook supplier: *Dépôt Bodmer/Barbizon (S.-&-M.)* and the price marked in ink: 4 f. 90. See Note 57.

BIBLIOGRAPHY: Venturi, Vol. I, under No. 1322 (not reproduced).

COLLECTIONS: Cézanne *fils*, Paris. Paul Guillaume, Paris. A. Chappuis, Tresserve.

FIG. 144. The same marble as fig. 143, also photographed from a plaster cast. *(Photograph: Skulpturhalle, Basel)*

FIG. 145. *Crouching Venus*, antique statuette in the Louvre. Musée National du Louvre, *Catalogue sommaire des Marbres antiques*, 1922, No. 5.　　　　(*Photograph: R. W. Ratcliffe*)

1102. PAGE OF STUDIES, INCLUDING BATHSHEBA AND A STANDING BATHER, 1894–98

$8\frac{5}{16} \times 11$ inches—21,1 × 28 cm. Page XLI from the sketchbook CP IV. Pencil and watercolor; trial daubs of watercolor. Verso: No. 1193.

(a) On a diagonal leading down to the right: study for *Bathsheba* (Venturi No. 253), subject known also by other titles: *Sommeil, La toilette de la courtisane, Le Réveil* (Venturi Nos. 883, 884, 886), representing a nude woman waited on by a servant. Cf. Nos. 463, 464, 1101, 1103.—(b) Standing bather with his arms raised, seen in left lost profile, drawn with brushstrokes of blue watercolor; cf. Venturi Nos. 585, 722.—(c) Upper right: two small sketches of a hat; cf. No. 778.—Lower right: rough sketch of the dome of a skull.

BIBLIOGRAPHY: Venturi, Vol. I, under No. 1316 (not reproduced).

COLLECTIONS: Cézanne *fils*, Paris. Paul Guillaume, Paris. A. Chappuis, Tresserve.

1103. STUDY FOR BATHSHEBA, 1894–98

$8\frac{1}{16} \times 5$ inches—20,5 × 12,6 cm. Page V verso from the sketchbook BS III. Pencil, stain at the top of the page, smudging. Verso: No. 1150

Study for the subject of *Bathsheba*; the servant kneeling is sketched in roughly on the right. Three successive renderings of the position of the legs. Cf. Nos. 463, 464, 970, 1150, and Venturi No. 252.

BIBLIOGRAPHY: Venturi No. 1406. Basel catalog, No. 179 (reproduced).

COLLECTIONS: Cézanne *fils*, Paris. Paul Guillaume, Paris. W. Feuz, Bern. Kunstmuseum, Basel.

1104. THREE WOMEN BATHERS, 1894–98

$5\frac{1}{8} \times 7\frac{1}{2}$ inches—13 × 19 cm. Page II from the sketchbook BS III. Pencil. Verso: No. 454.

(a) Left: a woman bather leaning back against a sloping tree, her left knee raised and her heel resting against the bark of the trunk.—(b) Two seated women bathers, one seen in left lost profile (two renderings of the thigh), the other turned toward the viewer. Cf. No. 971, in which the first of the two women is holding a mirror; also Venturi Nos. 540, 720, 1107.

BIBLIOGRAPHY: Venturi No. 1400. Longstreet, 1964 (reproduced).

EXHIBITIONS: De David à Cézanne, La Vieille Fontaine, Lausanne, 1953, No. 110. Zurich, 1956, No. 197. Munich, 1956, No. 149.

COLLECTIONS: Cézanne *fils*, Paris. Paul Guillaume, Paris. W. Feuz, Bern. Carl Roesch, Diessenhofen.

FIG. 146. Gian Lorenzo Bernini (1598–1680): bust of *Cardinal Richelieu* (Armand-Jean du Plessis, Duc de Richelieu, 1585–1642). This bust was done after a triple portrait of Richelieu by Philippe de Champaigne; an inscription on the back of the painting attributes the bust to Francesco Mocchi (or Mochi) (1580–1654), sculptor and medalist. The Louvre visitors' guide (*Les Sculptures, Moyen Age, Renaissance, Temps Modernes au Musée du Louvre*, published by the Musées Nationaux, 1957, p. 153) affirms that this bust was carved by Mochi, not by Bernini. I am tempted to add that the bust lacks the sculptural quality of inner plenitude that distinguished the works of Bernini. If it is by Mochi, he has produced a masterpiece of portraiture. Musée National du Louvre, *Catalogue des Sculptures* II, 1922, No. 1545.

(*Photograph: R. W. Ratcliffe*)

1105. AFTER BERNINI: *Cardinal Richelieu*, 1894–98

8$\frac{5}{16}$ × 4$\frac{7}{8}$ inches—21 × 12,3 cm. Page V from the sketchbook BS II. Pencil. Verso: blank page.

After the bust of *Cardinal Richelieu* by Gian Lorenzo Bernini, in the Louvre; marble attributed also to Francesco Mocchi. See fig. 146.

BIBLIOGRAPHY: Venturi No. 1364. Berthold, cat. No. 95 (reproduced Abb. 195). Basel catalog, No. 184 (reproduced). F. Novotny, *Paul Cézanne*, Phaidon, Vienna and Paris, 1937 (reproduced fig. 126). Yvon Taillandier, *Paul Cézanne*, Paris, New York, Munich, 1961 and 1965 (reproduced p. 7). Neumeyer, 1958, No. 44 (reproduced).

EXHIBITIONS: Meisterzeichnungen französischer Künstler, Kunsthalle, Basel, 1935, No. 194. Belvedere, Vienna, 1961, No. 103 (reproduced pl. 48).

COLLECTIONS: Cézanne *fils*, Paris. Paul Guillaume, Paris. W. Feuz, Bern. Kunstmuseum, Basel.

1106. AFTER A BUST OF A MAN, 1894–98

8$\frac{1}{4}$ × 5$\frac{1}{8}$ inches—20,9 × 13 cm. Page XV from the sketchbook BS I. Pencil. Verso: blank page.

The source of this drawing has not been definitively identified.

FIG. 147. *Satyr with Cymbals*, antique marble in the Louvre. Musée National du Louvre, *Catalogue sommaire des Marbres atinques*, 1922, No. 395.   (*Photograph: R. W. Ratcliffe*)

BIBLIOGRAPHY: Venturi No. 1339: "Tête d'après le buste de l'empereur Vespasien." Berthold, cat. No. 203 (reproduced): "probably after the bust of Alexandre Dumas, by Chapu." Basel catalog, No. 192 (reproduced); no identification of the model. Th. Reff, *AB*, June 1960, p. 148: "after Vespasian."

COLLECTIONS: Cézanne *fils*, Paris. Paul Guillaume, Paris. W. Feuz, Bern. Kunstmuseum, Basel.

1107. AFTER VAN CLEVE: *Loire and Loiret*, 1894–98

8$\frac{1}{2}$ × 5$\frac{3}{8}$ inches—21,6 × 13,7 cm. Page 27 verso of the sketchbook ML. Pencil. Verso: No. 1048.

Detail from a marble group: man with his back turned holding an oar, and a child in the foreground seen front view; indications of ornamental motifs. After Cornelius van Cleve's *Loire et Loiret* in the Tuileries Gardens, belonging to the Louvre. Cézanne may have drawn from a plaster cast.

BIBLIOGRAPHY: Rewald, *Carnets*: C III, p. 27 verso (not reproduced). Berthold, cat. No. 151 (reproduced Abb. 147). J. Bouchot-Saupique, *Revue des Arts*, 1951, pp. 243-4 (reproduced).

COLLECTIONS: Cézanne *fils*, Paris. M. Renou, Paris. Poyet, Lyons. M. Renou, Paris. Sam Salz, New York. Cabinet des Dessins of the Louvre, Paris (RF 29933).

1108. AFTER THE ANTIQUE: *Dancing satyr*, 1894–98

8$\frac{1}{2}$ × 5$\frac{3}{8}$ inches—21,6 × 13,7 cm. Page 10 verso of the sketchbook ML. Pencil. Verso: No. 1035.

After the marble *Satyre dansant* in the Louvre. See fig. 147. A very fine drawing all in curved strokes, done apparently with great rapidity. From a distance it recalls the drawings of Tintoretto.

BIBLIOGRAPHY: Rewald, *Carnets*: C III, p. 10 verso (reproduced pl. 123). Berthold, cat. No. 41 (reproduced Abb. 146).

COLLECTIONS: Cézanne *fils*, Paris. M. Renou, Paris. Poyet, Lyons. M. Renou, Paris. Sam Salz, New York. Cabinet des Dessins of the Louvre, Paris (RF 29933).

1109. AFTER HOUDON: *L'Ecorché*, 1892–95

18$\frac{3}{4}$ × 8$\frac{1}{4}$ inches—47,5 × 21 cm. Brown charcoal. Verso: blank page.

After a plaster cast of Jean-Antoine Houdon's work. See fig. 148. *L'Ecorché* is drawn from the back, down to the calves; a background is indicated by diagonal hatching. Cf. No. 1111 and also No. 1110.

BIBLIOGRAPHY: Venturi No. 1626. Berthold, cat. No. 168 (reproduced).

EXHIBITIONS: Galerie Flechtheim, Berlin, 1927, No. 39 (reproduced). Same gallery, Seit Cézanne in Paris, 1929, No. 27.

COLLECTIONS: A. Flechtheim, Berlin. Silberberg, Breslau. Paul Graupe, Berlin. Graupe sale, Berlin, March 25, 1935, cat. No. 31 (reproduced). Present owner unknown.

1110. AFTER HOUDON: *L'Ecorché*, 1894–98

7$\frac{3}{16}$ × 4$\frac{9}{16}$ inches—18,2 × 11,6 cm. Page 33 verso from the first sketchbook Mrs. Enid A. Haupt. Pencil. Verso: No. 978.

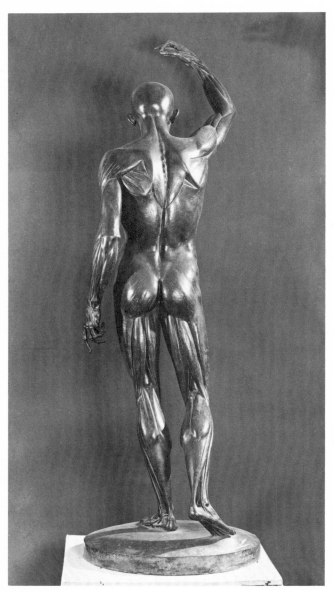

FIG. 148. Jean-Antoine Houdon (1741–1828): *Ecorché*, bronze in the Ecole des Beaux-Arts, Paris. Cézanne drew from a plaster cast of another version of this work, of which several exist. The drawing schools used plaster casts of varying dimensions.   *(Photograph: Giraudon)*

After a plaster cast of Jean-Antoine Houdon's *L'Ecorché*. See fig. 148. The figure is seen from the back.

BIBLIOGRAPHY: Rewald, *Carnets*: C I, p. 33 verso (reproduced pl. 133). Berthold, cat. No. 166 (reproduced).

COLLECTIONS: Cézanne *fils*, Paris. M. Renou, Paris. Poyet, Lyons. M. Renou, Paris. Sam Salz, New York. Mrs. Enid A. Haupt, New York.

1111. AFTER HOUDON: *L'Ecorché*, 1894–98

   $10\frac{13}{16} \times 8\frac{1}{4}$ inches—27,5 × 21 cm. Page from the sketchbook CP IV. Pencil. Verso: the watercolor Venturi No. 1115.

After a plaster cast of Jean-Antoine Houdon's *L'Ecorché*. See fig. 148.

BIBLIOGRAPHY: Venturi No. 1452. Berthold, cat. No. 167 (reproduced). J. Rewald, mention in *AA*, 1935, p. 288.

Idem, *Paul Cézanne*, New York, 1948 (reproduced fig. 95). Idem, *The Ordeal of Paul Cézanne*, London, 1950 (reproduced pl. 71). Idem, Spring Books, London, 1959 and 1965 (reproduced pl. 71). Ch. Slatkin & R. Schoolman, *Six Centuries of French Master Drawings in America*, New York, 1950 (reproduced pl. 107). A. Neumeyer, 1958, No. 25 (reproduced).

EXHIBITIONS: Masterpieces of 19th and 20th Century French Drawings, Detroit, 1941, No. 1. Modern Drawings, Museum of Modern Art, New York, 1944.

COLLECTIONS: G. Bernheim, Paris. Bernheim-Jeune, Paris. Montross Gallery, New York. Lillie P. Bliss Collection, Museum of Modern Art, New York (on loan from the Metropolitan Museum of Art).

1112. AFTER G. PILON: *The Three Graces*, 1894–98

   $8\frac{1}{2} \times 5$ inches—21,6 × 12,7 cm. Page V from the second sketchbook Mrs. Enid A. Haupt. Pencil. Verso: blank page.

Two of the three female figures known as *The Three Graces* on the monument for the heart of King Henri II, by Germain Pilon, in the Louvre. See fig. 84. Cf. Nos. 585, 1113.

BIBLIOGRAPHY: Rewald, *Carnets*: C IV, p. V (reproduced pl. 135). Berthold, cat. No. 144 (reproduced Abb. 123).

COLLECTIONS: Cézanne *fils*, Paris. M. Renou, Paris. Poyet, Lyons. M. Renou, Paris. Sam Salz, New York. Mrs. Enid A. Haupt, New York.

1113. AFTER G. PILON: *The Three Graces*, 1894–98

   $7\frac{15}{16} \times 5\frac{1}{8}$ inches—20,2 × 12,9 cm. Page XXVI from the sketchbook BS I. Pencil. Verso: blank page.

After Germain Pilon's *The Three Graces*, monument embodying three female figures standing back to back. See fig. 84.

BIBLIOGRAPHY: Venturi No. 1351. Berthold, cat. No. 145 and note 22 (reproduced). Basel catalog, No. 198 (reproduced).

COLLECTIONS: Cézanne *fils*, Paris. Paul Guillaume, Paris. W. Feuz, Bern. Kunstmuseum, Basel.

1114. AFTER TITIAN AND RUBENS: EVE PICKING THE APPLE, circa 1895

   $8\frac{7}{16} \times 5\frac{3}{8}$ inches—21,4 × 13,1 cm. Page XXVII from the sketchbook BS I. Pencil. Verso: No. 1054.

After a drawing attributed to Rubens in the Cabinet des Dessins of the Louvre, *Original Sin*, after Titian's canvas in the Prado Museum, Madrid. See fig. 149.

BIBLIOGRAPHY: Venturi No. 1352. Berthold, cat. No. 230 (reproduced). Basel catalog, No. 199 (reproduced). Th. Reff, *AB*, June 1960, p. 148; the author is the first to indicate the original model.

COLLECTIONS: Cézanne *fils*, Paris. Paul Guillaume, Paris. W. Feuz, Bern. Kunstmuseum, Basel.

1115. AFTER A STATUE, circa 1895

   $8\frac{1}{4} \times 5\frac{3}{16}$ inches—20,9 × 13,1 cm. Page XIII from the sketchbook BS I. Pencil. Verso: blank page.

Male nude with long hair in curls, seen front view; the

FIG. 149. Attributed to Peter Paul Rubens (1577–1640):
Original Sin, drawing after a canvas by Titian (1477–1576) in
the Prado Museum, Madrid. The drawing is in the Cabinet
des Dessins of the Louvre. Black chalk heightened with white
oil color and a few brush strokes in bister, on bluish paper;
height 25,9 cm. Lugt is of the opinion that this drawing is by
one of Rubens' helpers who accompanied him to Madrid.
Originally in the Jabach collection, it has been in the Louvre
since 1886. Fritz Lugt, *Inventaire général des Dessins du Musée du
Louvre et du Musée de Versailles, Ecole Flamande II*, Paris, 1948,
No. 1185. *(Photograph: R. W. Ratcliffe)*

head is covered by broad hatching strokes. Unfinished
sketch after an unidentified work.

BIBLIOGRAPHY: Venturi No. 1337. Berthold, cat. No. 44
(reproduced); the marble *Apollo*, known as *Bonus Eventus*,
in the Louvre is indicated as the probable original model.
Basel catalog, No. 157 (reproduced); *Apollo Bonus
Eventus* indicated as model. Th. Reff, *BurlM*, Aug. 1963,
p. 375, and Douglas Cooper, *Master Drawings*, Vol. 1,
No. 4, 1963, p. 56, both think that the drawing represents
some other work, unidentified.

COLLECTIONS Cézanne *fils*, Paris. Paul Guillaume, Paris.
W. Feuz, Bern. Kunstmuseum, Basel.

1116. AFTER G. COUSTOU: *Father de La Tour*, circa
1895

$7\frac{3}{16} \times 4\frac{9}{16}$ inches—18,2 × 11,6 cm. Page 42 from the
first sketchbook Mrs. Enid A. Haupt. Pencil. Verso:
1116A.

After the bust of *Pierre-François Dareрès de La Tour*, known
as Père de La Tour, Superior of the Oratory, terra cotta by
Guillaume Coustou in the Louvre. See fig. 150. Cf. No.
1117.

BIBLIOGRAPHY: Rewald, *Carnets:* C I, p. 42 (not reproduced). Berthold, cat. No. 194 (reproduced).

COLLECTIONS: Cézanne *fils*, Paris. M. Renou, Paris. Poyet,
Lyons. M. Renou, Paris. Sam Salz, New York. Mrs. Enid
A. Haupt, New York.

1116A. HEAD OF MME CÉZANNE

Inaccessible reverse side of No. 1116 (not reproduced).

BIBLIOGRAPHY: Rewald, *Carnets:* C I, p. 42 verso "tête de
Madame Cézanne" (not reproduced).

1117. AFTER G. COUSTOU: *Father de La Tour*, circa
1895

$7\frac{7}{8} \times 4\frac{13}{16}$ inches—20 × 12,2 cm. Page LI verso from
the sketchbook BS II. Pencil. Verso: No. 1207.

After the bust of *Pierre-François Dareрès de La Tour*, Superior
of the Oratory, terra cotta bust by Guillaume Coustou in
the Louvre. See fig. 150. Cf. No. 1116.

BIBLIOGRAPHY: Venturi No. 1395. Berthold, cat. No. 191
(reproduced). Basel catalog, No. 187 (reproduced).

COLLECTIONS: Cézanne *fils*, Paris. Paul Guillaume, Paris.
W. Feuz, Bern. Kunstmuseum, Basel.

1118. AFTER G. COUSTOU: *Father de La Tour*, circa
1895

$8\frac{1}{16} \times 5\frac{1}{8}$ inches—20,4 × 12,9 cm. Page III from the
sketchbook BS I. Pencil. Verso: blank page.

After the bust of *Pierre-François Dareрès de La Tour*, Superior
of the Oratory, terra cotta by Guillaume Coustou in the
Louvre. See fig. 150.

BIBLIOGRAPHY: Venturi No. 1326. Berthold, cat. No. 193
(reproduced). Basel catalog, No. 188 (reproduced).

EXHIBITION: Belvedere, Vienna, 1961, No. 102.

COLLECTIONS: Cézanne *fils*, Paris. Paul Guillaume, Paris.
W. Feuz, Bern. Kunstmuseum, Basel.

FIG. 150. The same bust as fig. 96, but seen in right profile.
(Photograph: R. W. Ratcliffe)

1119. After G. Coustou: *Father de La Tour*, circa 1895

$8\frac{1}{4} \times 5\frac{3}{16}$ inches—21 × 13,1 cm. Page VII from the sketchbook BS I. Pencil, small touch of green watercolor in the hair. Verso: blank page.

After the bust of *Pierre-François Darerès de La Tour*, Superior of the Oratory, terra cotta by Guillaume Coustou in the Louvre. See fig. 150.

BIBLIOGRAPHY: Venturi No. 1331. Berthold, cat. No. 192 (reproduced). Basel catalog, No. 189 (reproduced).

COLLECTIONS: Cézanne *fils*, Paris. Paul Guillaume, Paris. W. Feuz, Bern. Kunstmuseum, Basel.

1120. After G. Coustou: *Nicolas Coustou*, 1895–98

$8\frac{5}{8} \times 4\frac{7}{8}$ inches—21,8 × 12,4 cm. Page XXVII verso from the sketchbook CP II. Pencil on ocher paper. Verso: blank page.

After the terra cotta bust representing the sculptor *Nicolas Coustou*, by his brother Guillaume, in the Louvre. See fig. 151.—Note: this Guillaume Coustou (known as *le père*) had a son named Guillaume (known as *le fils*) who was also a sculptor.

BIBLIOGRAPHY: Venturi No. 1289. Berthold, cat. No. 196 (reproduced). J. Rewald, in *AA*, 1935, reproduces both drawing and model.

COLLECTIONS: Cézanne *fils*, Paris. Paul Guillaume, Paris. A. Chappuis, Tresserve.

1121. After the antique: standing man clothed in a draped chlamys, circa 1895

$9\frac{5}{16} \times 6$ inches—23,7 × 15,2 cm. Page XXXVI verso of the Album, Paul Mellon Collection. Pencil. Verso: blank page.

Unfinished sketch after an antique marble showing a bearded man, seen front view. A fine little sketch which captures the light on the marble and renders the Roman character.

BIBLIOGRAPHY: Venturi No. 1312. Berthold, cat. No. 48 (reproduced); the model is identified as the statue of *L. Aelius Caesar* (Musée du Louvre, cat. sommaire de 1922, No. 1157). Th. Reff, in *AB*, June 1960, p. 145, note 12, proposes as model: *Mercury*, marble in the Louvre; see Salomon Reinach, *Répertoire*, 1897, Vol. I, pp. 161 and 147. *Album*, 1966 (reproduced).

COLLECTIONS: Cézanne *fils*, Paris. Paul Guillaume, Paris. A. Chappuis, Tresserve. Mr. and Mrs. Paul Mellon, Upperville, Va.

1122. Seated figure and notations, circa 1895

$2\frac{11}{16} \times 4\frac{1}{4}$ inches—6,8 × 10,9 cm. Page II verso of the sketchbook violet moiré. Pencil. Verso: No. 992.

Beneath the handwritten notations there is a sketch, now practically undecipherable, representing a seated figure seen in left profile. The notations indicate the hours of departure and arrival of trains between Paris and Marseilles; Wayne V. Andersen specifies that these trains were in circulation from October 1, 1895, to May 1, 1896, proving that the sketch is of an earlier date. Andersen interprets the drawing as a woman sitting in a train compartment, and the back of a figure in front of her. All I

FIG. 151. Guillaume Coustou (1677–1746): bust of the artist's brother *Nicolas Coustou*, terra cotta in the Louvre; height 59 cm. Musée National du Louvre, *Catalogue des Sculptures* II, 1922, No. 1092.   (*Photograph: Giraudon*)

can see clearly in this sketch is a large hat, apparently a Panama, and the bench on which the figure is seated.

BIBLIOGRAPHY: *Carnet violet moiré* (reproduced). W. V. Andersen, Cézanne's Carnet violet moiré, *BurlM*, June 1965, p. 313 (reproduced fig. 49).

COLLECTIONS: Cézanne *fils*, Paris. Jean-Pierre Cézanne, Paris. Mlle Edmée Maus, Geneva.

1123. Study of a mantel clock, 1895–98

$9\frac{3}{8} \times 13\frac{9}{16}$ inches—23,9 × 34,5 cm. Pencil. Verso: blank page.

The figure of a woman seen front view, seated beside a clock dial. After an unidentified decorative clock. Cf. the same subject, No. 1009.

BIBLIOGRAPHY: Venturi, Vol. I, p. 352, Oeuvres Inédites (not reproduced). Berthold, cat. No. 332 (reproduced); in her text for cat. No. 331 (not reproduced), the author refers by error to this same drawing. Th. Reff, in *AB*, June 1960, p. 148 and note 34, refers to the original model as shown in Ernest Dumonthier, *Les Bronzes du Mobilier National, Pendules et Cartels*, Paris, 1911, pl. 19, No. 3. Basel catalog (reproduced in the text, fig. 52).

EXHIBITIONS: San Francisco, 1937, No. 57. The Hague, 1956, No. 110. Zurich, 1956, No. 167. Munich, 1956, No. 128.

COLLECTIONS: Pierre Loeb, Paris. Galerie Henriette Gomès, Paris. H. Vollmoeller, Zurich.

FIG. 152. Donatello (1386–1466): *Saint John the Baptist*, marble in the National Museum (Bargello), Florence. There was formerly a plaster cast in the Musée de Sculpture comparée du Trocadéro, *Catalogue I*, No. 140. See also the *Catalogue des Moulages des Musées Nationaux*, Paris, 1951, tome IV. C. 5039.   *(Photograph: Giraudon)*

1124. SELF-PORTRAIT, circa 1895

$9\frac{5}{16} \times 6$ inches—$23,7 \times 15,2$ cm. Page X of the Album, Paul Mellon Collection. Pencil. Verso: No. 1152.

The painter's head, in spite of the signs of age, expresses energy and profound serenity.

BIBLIOGRAPHY: Venturi, Vol. I, under No. 1304 (not reproduced). *Dessins*, 1938 (reproduced pl. 47). Idem, *Cézanne en Savoie (1896)*, *Revue de Savoie*, 1955–56, p. 111 (reproduced). *Album*, 1966 (reproduced).

EXHIBITION: Orangerie, Paris, 1936, No. 154.

COLLECTIONS: Cézanne *fils*, Paris. Paul Guillaume, Paris. A. Chappuis, Tresserve. Mr. and Mrs. Paul Mellon, Upperville, Va.

1125. SELF-PORTRAIT, 1897–1900

$12\frac{3}{16} \times 9\frac{7}{16}$ inches—31×24 cm. (sight). Pencil. Verso: a few touches of watercolor.

The portrait is placed on a diagonal, rising to the right. Remarkable simplification of forms.

BIBLIOGRAPHY: Venturi No. 1476 (reproduced from Vollard 1914). Vollard, 1914 (reproduced p. 119). Meier-Graefe, *Cézanne und sein Kreis*, Munich, 1922 (reproduced as frontispiece). The World's Masters, Cézanne, by A. Bertram, The Studio, London, 1929 (reproduced pl. I). *AA*, 1920 (reproduced p. 286). Rewald, *Cézanne et Zola*, Paris, 1936 (reproduced fig. 46). Idem, *The Ordeal of Paul Cézanne*, London, 1950 (reproduced). Idem, *Cézanne*, Spring Books, London, 1959 and 1965 (reproduced p. 122). Idem, *Briefe*, Diogenes Verlag, Zurich,

1962 (reproduced p. 177). Idem, *Paul Cézanne*, New York, 1968 (reproduced).

COLLECTIONS: Ambroise Vollard, Paris. Wertheimer, Paris. R. von Hirsch, Basel.

1126. AFTER DONATELLO: *St. John the Baptist*, 1895–98

$8\frac{1}{2} \times 5\frac{3}{8}$ inches—$21,6 \times 13,7$ cm. Page 12 verso of the sketchbook ML. Pencil. Verso: blank page.

After Donatello's marble bust of St. John the Baptist. An exceptionally calligraphic drawing, after a plaster cast. See fig. 152.

BIBLIOGRAPHY: Rewald, *Carnets:* C III, p. 12 verso (reproduced pl. 150). Berthold, cat. No. 92 (reproduced); model suggested: St. Jean-Baptiste, by Donatello. Th. Reff, *AB*, June 1960, p. 147; model suggested: bust of a Young Man by Desiderio da Settignano. Franz Erpel, *Paul Cézanne*, Berlin, 1960 (reproduced p. 29).

COLLECTIONS: Cézanne *fils*, Paris. M. Renou, Paris. Poyet, Lyons. M. Renou, Paris. Sam Salz, New York. Cabinet des Dessins of the Louvre, Paris (RF 29933).

1127. AFTER C. LEFÈBVRE: *Portrait of a Man*, 1895–98

$7\frac{3}{16} \times 4\frac{9}{16}$ inches—$18,2 \times 11,6$ cm. Page 29 from the first sketchbook Mrs. Enid A. Haupt. Pencil. Verso: blank page.

FIG. 153. Claude Lefèbvre (1632–75): *Portrait d'homme* (detail), painting dated 1667, in the Louvre. *Catalogue sommaire des Peintures exposées au Musée du Louvre*, by Louis Demonts and Lucien Huteau, Paris, 1923, Salle 530, XIV-S.   *(Photograph: Giraudon)*

After the *Portrait of a Man* by Claude Lefèbvre, in the Louvre. See fig. 153.

BIBLIOGRAPHY: Rewald, *Carnets:* C I, p. 29 (reproduced pl. 5). Berthold, cat. No. 296 (reproduced). *Cézanne dessinateur* (reproduced fig. 13); identification of the original model by Robert W. Ratcliffe. Th. Reff, *AB*, June 1960, p. 148, note 29.

COLLECTIONS: Cézanne *fils*, Paris. M. Renou, Paris. Poyet, Lyons. M. Renou, Paris. Sam Salz, New York. Mrs. Enid A. Haupt, New York.

1128. AFTER RUBENS: NAIAD, 1895–98

$8\frac{3}{16} \times 4\frac{13}{16}$ inches—20,8 × 12,2 cm. Page XLVI from the sketchbook BS II. Pencil. Verso: No. 958.

The head and hips are seen in left profile, the breast turned toward the viewer. After the central figure of the three naiads in Rubens' canvas *Marie de Médicis landing in the Port of Marseilles,* in the Louvre. See fig. 53. Cf. Nos. 369, 455.

BIBLIOGRAPHY: Venturi No. 1384. Berthold, cat. No. 216 (reproduced). Basel catalog, No. 202 (reproduced).

COLLECTIONS: Cézanne *fils*, Paris. Paul Guillaume, Paris. W. Feuz, Bern. Kunstmuseum, Basel.

1129. AFTER THE ANTIQUE: *Sleeping Hermaphrodite*, 1895–98

$9\frac{7}{16} \times 14\frac{3}{16}$ inches—24 × 36 cm. Pencil on laid paper. Verso: blank page.

After the marble *Sleeping Hermaphrodite* in the Louvre. See fig. 154. A particularly fine study. The drawing belonged to Edgar Degas who must have bought it from a dealer—perhaps Vollard—or at an auction sale after Cézanne's death. Degas called this *"acheter un petit article."* According to him it was not right for an artist to buy for large sums of money.

BIBLIOGRAPHY: Venturi No. 1456. Berthold, cat. No. 42 (reproduced).

COLLECTIONS: Edgar Degas, Paris. Catalog, Edgar Degas sale, Galerie Georges Petit, Paris, March 26 and 27, 1918. Galerie Bollag, Zurich. Sale, Bollag, Zurich, April 1925, cat. No. 33 (reproduced). Suzanne Bollag, Zurich.

1130. AFTER RUBENS: THE GENIUS OF HEALTH, 1895–98

$9\frac{5}{16} \times 6$ inches—23,7 × 15,2 cm. Page XXXV of the Album, Paul Mellon Collection. Pencil. Verso: No. 503.

Standing male figure draped in a loincloth, a serpent around his arm. Allegorical figure of the Genius of Health from Rubens' painting *The Birth of Louis XIII at Fontainebleau* in the Medici room of the Louvre. See fig. 155. Cf. Nos. 594, 595.

BIBLIOGRAPHY: Venturi No. 1310. Berthold, cat. No. 218 (reproduced); the allegorical figure is described as *Aesculapius. Album*, 1966 (reproduced).

COLLECTIONS: Cézanne *fils*, Paris. Paul Guillaume, Paris. A. Chappuis, Tresserve. Mr. and Mrs. Paul Mellon, Upperville, Va.

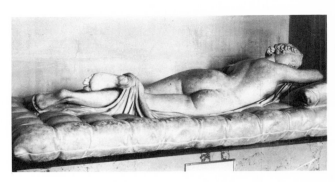

FIG. 154. *Sleeping Hermaphrodite*, antique replica of a Hellenistic marble, in the Louvre. Musée National du Louvre, *Catalogue sommaire des Marbres antiques*, 1922, No. 231.
(Photograph: R. W. Ratcliffe)

1131. AFTER PUGET: *Milo of Crotona*, 1895–98

$9\frac{5}{16} \times 6$ inches—23,6 × 15,2 cm. Page II verso of the Album, Paul Mellon Collection. Pencil, restored tears in the margin. Verso: rough draft of a letter to Octave Mirbeau (see *Album*, 1966).

After Pierre Puget's marble *Milo of Crotona* in the Louvre. See fig. 30. Cf. Nos. 506, 1200, 1201.

BIBLIOGRAPHY: Venturi No. 1301. Berthold, cat. No. 106 (reproduced). J. Rewald, *AA*, 1935, p. 285 (reproduced, together with the original model, for the first time). Idem, *Paul Cézanne*, New York, 1948 (reproduced pl. 93). Idem, *The Ordeal of Paul Cézanne*, London, 1950 (reproduced pl. 69). Idem, *Paul Cézanne*, Spring Books, London, 1959 and 1965 (reproduced pl. 69). *Album*, 1966 (reproduced).

COLLECTIONS: Cézanne *fils*, Paris. Paul Guillaume, Paris. A. Chappuis, Tresserve. Mr. and Mrs. Paul Mellon, Upperville, Va.

1132. AFTER P. PUGET: ATLAS, 1895–98

$8\frac{1}{2} \times 5\frac{3}{8}$ inches—21,6 × 13,7 cm. Page 30 of the sketchbook ML. Pencil. Verso: No. 1029.

Sketch of one of the *atlantes*, attributed to Pierre Puget, decorating the town hall in Toulon. See fig. 156. There were plaster casts of these figures in the Musée de Sculpture Comparée of the Trocadéro. Our sketch shows the figure on the left side of the door; cf. No. 689. Cézanne may well have drawn this in the Trocadéro after having seen the originals, as a passage from Joachim Gasquet's book on Cézanne (p. 191) would seem to confirm: "He [Puget] used the surrounding shadows in the same spirit as his contemporaries used dark under-painting. Go and look at the effect he achieved below the Caryatid balcony in Toulon."

BIBLIOGRAPHY: Rewald, *Carnets:* C III, p. 30 (not reproduced). Berthold, cat. No. 127 (reproduced Abb. 148). J. Bouchot-Saupique, *Revue des Arts*, 1951, pp. 243-44 (reproduced).

COLLECTIONS: Cézanne *fils*, Paris. M. Renou, Paris. Poyet, Lyons. M. Renou, Paris. Sam Salz, New York. Cabinet des Dessins of the Louvre, Paris (RF 29933).

1133. AFTER ONE OF THE *Foolish Virgins* OF STRASBOURG CATHEDRAL, 1895–98

$8\frac{1}{2} \times 5\frac{3}{8}$ inches—21,6 × 13,7 cm. Page 32 verso of the sketchbook ML. Pencil, light stains. Verso: blank page.

FIG. 155. Peter Paul Rubens (1577–1640): allegorical figure representing the *Genius of Health* (or *Aesculapius*), detail from the painting *La Naissance de Louis XIII à Fontainebleau*, in the Medici series in the Louvre. Musée National du Louvre, *Catalogue des Peintures* III, 1922, No. 2092.

(Photograph: Giraudon)

Head with a bandeau around the hair, tilted sideways in a movement characteristic of Gothic sculpture. After a plaster cast of the head of one of the *Vierges Folles*. See fig. 157.

BIBLIOGRAPHY: Rewald, *Carnets*: C III, p. 32 verso (not reproduced). Cézanne dessinateur (reproduced fig. 27).

COLLECTIONS: Cézanne *fils*, Paris. M. Renou, Paris. Poyet, Lyons. M. Renou, Paris. Sam Salz, New York. Cabinet des Dessins of the Louvre, Paris (RF 29933).

1134. SKETCHES OF WOMEN BATHERS AND A SWAN, 1895–1900

$5 \times 8\frac{9}{16}$ inches—12,7 × 21,7 cm. Page XXXVI from the second sketchbook Mrs. Enid A. Haupt. Pencil. Verso: No. 763.

(a) Left: study of a woman bather holding something in her hand.—(b) Right: similar figure drawn down to the hips; retouches added later. Both figures represent a type often portrayed by the artist; cf. for example No. 649.— (c) Upside down: sketch of a swan pecking at its breast feathers; cf. Nos. 479, 484, and Venturi No. 550.

BIBLIOGRAPHY: Rewald, *Carnets*: C IV, p. XXXVI (reproduced pl. 98).

COLLECTIONS: Cézanne *fils*, Paris. M. Renou, Paris. Poyet, Lyons. M. Renou, Paris. Sam Salz, New York. Mrs. Enid A. Haupt, New York.

FIG. 156. Pierre Puget (1620–94): *Atlas* on the left side of the entrance to the town hall in Toulon. Our photograph was taken from a plaster cast exhibited in the Musée des Monuments français. Cézanne drew from the cast that was in the Puget Room of the Louvre until 1886, then moved to the Musée de Sculpture comparée. *Catalogue général du Musée de Sculpture comparée du Trocadéro* III, 1928, No. C 164. Engravings of the two Atlantes were printed in *Le Magasin Pittoresque*, 1846, p. 160.   *(Photograph: Chappuis)*

FIG. 157. *Head of one of the Foolish Virgins*, plaster cast formerly in the Musée de Sculpture comparée du Trocadéro. It represents the first of the Foolish Virgins on the west façade of Strasbourg Cathedral, near the south door. *Catalogue du Musée de Sculpture comparée du Trocadéro*, 1926, France, Style gothique, No. D 156.3. *3 Têtes. Cinq vierges folles.* (Ancien cat. I 27–35.)　　　　　　　　(*Photograph: Giraudon*)

1135. BACK OF A CHAIR AND DECORATIVE DESIGN, 1896–99

$7\frac{15}{16} \times 4\frac{15}{16}$ inches—20,1 × 12,5 cm. Page XII from the sketchbook BS III. Pencil. Verso: blank page.

In the foreground, the back of a chair; cf. No. 546. Behind the chair there is a low piece of furniture with cambered arches and above a decorative design in an ornamental frame. The whole has great charm and resembles certain of the late watercolors.

BIBLIOGRAPHY: Venturi No. 1414. Basel catalog, No. 174 (reproduced).

EXHIBITIONS: The Hague, 1956, No. 133. Zurich, 1956, No. 202.

COLLECTIONS: Cézanne *fils*, Paris. Paul Guillaume, Paris. W. Feuz, Bern. Kunstmuseum, Basel.

1136. AFTER THE ANTIQUE: *Bust of the emperor Septimius Severus*, 1896–99

$8\frac{1}{4} \times 5\frac{3}{16}$ inches—21 × 13,1 cm. Page V from the sketchbook BS I. Pencil. Verso: blank page.

The left side of the chin has been left white. After a Roman bust of the emperor Lucius Septimius Severus (146-211), marble in the Louvre. See fig. 158. Cf. No. 1137, which however was drawn from another bust of Septimius Severus.

BIBLIOGRAPHY: Venturi No. 1362 (by error: this should read No. 1328, Venturi having confused the photographs of these two numbers). Berthold, cat. No. 50 (reproduced Abb. 22). Basel catalog, No. 181 (reproduced).

EXHIBITION: Meisterzeichnungen französischer Künstler, Kunsthalle, Basel, 1935, No. 197.

COLLECTIONS: Cézanne *fils*, Paris. Paul Guillaume, Paris. W. Feuz, Bern. Kunstmuseum, Basel.

1137. BUST OF A ROMAN EMPEROR, 1896–99

$7\frac{15}{16} \times 4\frac{7}{8}$ inches—20,1 × 12,4 cm. Page IV from the sketchbook BS II. Pencil. Verso: No. 1222.

After a marble bust representing a Roman emperor. One of Septimius Severus (fig. 158) and another of Lucius Verus (fig. 142) may be considered as possible models, though the question remains controversial. Cf. Nos. 1062, 1063, 1136.

BIBLIOGRAPHY: Venturi No. 1328: "d'après le buste de Marc Aurèle au Louvre," and by error: "pas de dessin au verso." Berthold, cat. No. 51 (reproduced): "bust of Septimius Severus." Basel catalog, No. 180 (reproduced). Cited by error in the catalog *De David à Cézanne*, La Vieille Fontaine, Lausanne, 1953, No. 107.

COLLECTIONS: Cézanne *fils*, Paris. Paul Guillaume, Paris. W. Feuz, Bern. Kunstmuseum, Basel.

FIG. 158. The Roman emperor *Lucius Septimius Severus* (146–211), marble in the Louvre. Musée National du Louvre, *Catalogue sommaire des Marbres antiques*, 1922, No. 1113 (corresponding to Berthold, cat. No. 51).

(*Photograph: R. W. Ratcliffe*)

1138. AFTER RUBENS: BELLONA, 1895–98

$8\frac{1}{4} \times 4\frac{13}{16}$ inches—20,9 × 12,2 cm. Page XLI verso from the sketchbook BS II. Pencil. Verso: No. 673.

After the allegorical figure of Bellona in Rubens' painting *The Apotheosis of Henri IV* in the Louvre. See fig. 9. Cf. No. 1140.

BIBLIOGRAPHY: Venturi, No. 1377. Berthold, cat. No. 211 (reproduced). Basel catalog, No. 200 (reproduced).

COLLECTIONS: Cézanne *fils*, Paris. Paul Guillaume, Paris. W. Feuz, Bern. Kunstmuseum, Basel.

1139. AFTER RUBENS: BELLONA, 1895–98

$8\frac{1}{2} \times 5\frac{3}{8}$ inches—21,6 × 13,7 cm. Page 5 of the sketchbook ML. Pencil. Verso: No. 1028.

After the allegorical figure of Bellona in Rubens' painting *The Apotheosis of Henri IV* in the Louvre. See fig. 9.

BIBLIOGRAPHY: Rewald, *Carnets*: C III, p. 5 (not reproduced). Berthold, cat. No. 209 (reproduced).

COLLECTIONS: Cézanne *fils*, Paris. M. Renou, Paris. Poyet, Lyons. M. Renou, Paris. Sam Salz, New York. Cabinet des Dessins of the Louvre, Paris (RF 29933).

1140. AFTER RUBENS: BELLONA, 1896–99

$8\frac{1}{4} \times 4\frac{13}{16}$ inches—20,9 × 12,2 cm. Page L from the sketchbook BS II. Pencil. Verso: No. 1011.

After the allegorical figure of Bellona in Rubens' painting *The Apotheosis of Henri IV* in the Louvre. See fig. 9. Cf. No. 1138.

BIBLIOGRAPHY: Venturi No. 1392. Berthold, cat. No. 212 (reproduced Abb. 5). Basel catalog, No. 201 (reproduced). *Dessins*, 1957, No. 47 (reproduced).

EXHIBITION: Kunstverein, Hamburg, 1963, No. 33 (reproduced).

COLLECTIONS: Cézanne *fils*, Paris. Paul Guillaume, Paris. W. Feuz, Bern. Kunstmuseum, Basel.

1141. PAGE OF STUDIES, INCLUDING A STRAW HAT, 1895–98

$6 \times 9\frac{5}{16}$ inches—15,2 × 23,7 cm. Page VI verso of the Album, Paul Mellon Collection. Pencil. Verso: No. 1177.

(a) Still life showing a straw hat on a table; to the left there is a flat object difficult to identify and a white pot indicated by its contour.—(b) At right angles: sketch of a seated woman, her head and shoulders twisted round to the left. —(c) Above (b): seated woman with her knees turned to the right.—(d) Light rough sketch of the upper part of (b).

BIBLIOGRAPHY: Venturi, Vol. I, under No. 1302 (not reproduced). *Dessins*, 1938 (reproduced pl. 12). *Album*, 1966 (reproduced).

COLLECTIONS: Cézanne *fils*, Paris. Paul Guillaume, Paris. A. Chappuis, Tresserve. Mr. and Mrs. Paul Mellon, Upperville, Va.

1142. STUDY OF TREES, 1889–92

$8\frac{1}{16} \times 5$ inches—20,5 × 12,6 cm. Page XIV from the sketchbook BS III. Pencil. Verso: No. 371.

On the right, a slightly curved tree trunk rises up to the left and disappears among the leaves. There is a vast patch of light on this almost vertical cluster of vegetation, its left side modeled and shaded. The far distance is seen through an opening between the trunk and the foliage. The setting calls to mind a scene with bathers.

BIBLIOGRAPHY: Venturi No. 1416.

COLLECTIONS: Cézanne *fils*, Paris. Paul Guillaume, Paris. W. Feuz, Bern. R. von Hirsch, Basel.

1143. THE MILL, 1889–92

$9\frac{5}{16} \times 6$ inches—23,6 × 15,2 cm. Page XXVII verso of the Album, Paul Mellon Collection. Pencil. Verso: blank page.

A construction built over a watercourse which is crossed by timberwork forming a gallery. A cluster of trees rises higher than the roof. Reflections in the water, which spreads out to the right in front of the vegetation, are indicated by hatching. This drawing probably represents a mill in the Ile-de-France.

BIBLIOGRAPHY: Venturi, Vol. I, under No. 1309 (not reproduced). *Dessins*, 1938, No. 29 (reproduced). *Album*, 1966 (reproduced).

COLLECTIONS: Cézanne *fils*, Paris. Paul Guillaume, Paris. A. Chappuis, Tresserve. Mr. and Mrs. Paul Mellon, Upperville, Va.

1144. ROOF AND WINDOW, 1889–92

$5 \times 8\frac{1}{8}$ inches—12,6 × 20,6 cm. Page XXII from the sketchbook BS III. Pencil, small stain top left. Verso: No. 475.

Upper part of a country cottage: its roof projects over an open-shuttered window, a chimney rises above the roof, and a gable is indicated on the left. The play of black and white is particularly graphic.

BIBLIOGRAPHY: Venturi No. 1427. Basel catalog, No. 169 (reproduced).

COLLECTIONS: Cézanne *fils*, Paris. Paul Guillaume, Paris. W. Feuz, Bern. Kunstmuseum, Basel.

1145. TREES AND A HOUSE, 1889–92

$18 \times 12\frac{3}{16}$ inches—44,7 × 31 cm. Pencil on laid paper. Verso: blank page.

View of a low house; the eye is attracted by a large window on ground level. Tree trunks with bare branches rise up on the left. A rectangular block is seen at the foot of the second tree.

BIBLIOGRAPHY: Neumeyer, 1958, No. 75 (reproduced); the author believes that this drawing represents the same site as No. 878.

EXHIBITIONS: The Hague, 1956, No. 120 (reproduced). Zurich, 1956, No. 181 (reproduced). Munich, 1956, No. 138 (reproduced). Belvedere, Vienna, 1961, No. 99. Aix-en-Provence, 1961, No. 44.

COLLECTIONS: Alfred Flechtheim, Berlin. Hans Purrmann, Montagnola.

1146. FAÇADE OF A HOUSE SURROUNDED BY VEGETATION, 1889–92

$9\frac{5}{16} \times 6$ inches—23,7 × 15,2 cm. Page XXXII verso of the Album, Paul Mellon Collection. Pencil. Verso: No. 865.

Sketch showing a French window and two other windows opening out onto a courtyard bordered by flowerbeds. The upper part of the house is hidden behind a mass of foliage. A shadow crosses the foreground of the court; to the left, a vase on a pedestal. At the bottom, the simple contours of two aloe leaves have been sketched in over the drawing. Cf. Nos. 889, 1143, and Venturi Nos. 627, 924.

BIBLIOGRAPHY: Venturi, Vol. I, under No. 1309 (not reproduced). *Album*, 1966 (reproduced).

COLLECTIONS: Cézanne *fils*, Paris. Paul Guillaume, Paris. A. Chappuis, Tresserve. Mr. and Mrs. Paul Mellon, Upperville, Va.

1147. SKETCH OF A HOUSE, 1889–92

$7\frac{3}{8} \times 5\frac{3}{8}$ inches—18,7 × 13,7 cm. Page XXXIII from the sketchbook CP IV, trimmed down by a bookbinder and inserted in a copy of Léo Larguier's book, *Cézanne, ou la lutte avec l'ange de la peinture* (Juillard, 1947). Pencil. Verso: No. 1187.

The page having been cut in two, there remains only a fragmentary and unfinished sketch of the side of a one-story house with a wide roof.

BIBLIOGRAPHY: Venturi, Vol. I, under No. 1316 (not reproduced).

COLLECTIONS: Cézanne *fils*, Paris. Paul Guillaume, Paris. A. Chappuis, Tresserve.

1148. PROVENÇAL LANDSCAPE, 1889–92

$4\frac{15}{16} \times 8$ inches—12,5 × 20,3 cm. Page XVI from the sketchbook BS III. Pencil. Verso: blank page.

Provençal landscape with houses half hidden among the trees. Though the drawing was composed with care, the details are difficult to interpret. It probably represents buildings adjacent to the Jas de Bouffan, seen from a higher level.

BIBLIOGRAPHY: Venturi No. 1418. Basel catalog, No. 168 (reproduced). *Dessins*, 1957, No. 33 (reproduced). *Werkzeitung Geigy*, Basel, 1966, Vol. 24 (reproduced p. 18).

EXHIBITIONS: The Hague, 1956, No. 134. Zurich, 1956, No. 203. Kunstverein, Hamburg, 1963, No. 31.

COLLECTIONS: Cézanne *fils*, Paris. Paul Guillaume, Paris. W. Feuz, Bern. Kunstmuseum, Basel.

1149. LANDSCAPE KNOWN AS *Le Moulin à plâtre* (The Plaster Mill), 1889–92

$9\frac{5}{16} \times 6$ inches—23,7 × 15,2 cm. Page I verso of the Album, Paul Mellon Collection. Pencil. Verso: a few handwritten notes.

The drawing is done in wide, lightly stressed strokes, producing a silvery effect; a group of buildings comprising rectangular or triangular wall surfaces and roofs, the whole forming a rhythm of horizontals, verticals, and diagonals. A large cloud of smoke is seen rising from the roof, and behind it a distant mountain.

produced). *Album*, 1966 (reproduced).

COLLECTIONS: Cézanne *fils*, Paris. Paul Guillaume, Paris. A. Chappuis, Tresserve. Mr. and Mrs. Paul Mellon, Upperville, Va.

1150. TREES, RECLINING WOMAN, 1889–92

$8\frac{1}{16} \times 5$ inches—20,5 × 12,6 cm. Page V from the sketchbook BS III. Pencil, stains lower left. Verso: No. 1103.

Two different subjects which together form an arabesque. —(a) Page upright: steep declivity seen in right profile, with rocks and rich vegetation.—(b) Page lengthwise: study of a nude woman, her head leaning against her hand; cf. Nos. 970, 1103.

BIBLIOGRAPHY: Venturi No. 1405. Basel catalog, No. 175 (reproduced).

COLLECTIONS: Cézanne *fils*, Paris. Paul Guillaume, Paris. W. Feuz, Bern. Kunstmuseum, Basel.

1151. TREES AND ROCKS AT BIBÉMUS, 1889–92

$12\frac{1}{2} \times 18\frac{3}{4}$ inches—31,7 × 47,6 cm. Pencil. Verso: the watercolor Venturi No. 1129.

Drawing in lightly traced strokes; the right part of the page has been left white. A corner of Bibémus quarry is shown: a hillock strewn with boulders framed by two rocks, the background blocked out by a sheer wall of stone with thick overhanging bushes. Venturi No. 1598 shows a similar motif. The drawing is of excellent quality despite its faintness.—To the right, a detail from the reverse side is seen in transparency.

COLLECTIONS: Ambroise Vollard, Paris. M. Feilchenfeldt, Zurich. Paul Rosenberg & Co., New York.

1152. LANDSCAPE SEEN FROM THE INSIDE OF A CAVE, 1889–92

$6 \times 9\frac{5}{16}$ inches—15,2 × 23,7 cm. Page X verso of the Album, Paul Mellon Collection. Pencil. Verso: No. 1124.

The walls of the cave join at the top, forming a vault. The observer looks down over a sunlit stretch of ground strewn with boulders to a background shaded by hatching. It is possible that this drawing represents a corner of Bibémus quarry and that the open area is a limited one, with a vertical plane at the back; in two watercolors of the same motif this feeling is even more pronounced.

BIBLIOGRAPHY: Venturi, Vol. I, under No. 1304 (not reproduced): "quelques traits vagues." *Dessins*, 1957 (reproduced pl. 55). *Album*, 1966 (reproduced).

COLLECTIONS: Cézanne *fils*, Paris. Paul Guillaume, Paris. A. Chappuis, Tresserve. Mr. and Mrs. Paul Mellon, Upperville, Va.

1153. STUDY OF TREES, 1889–92

$15 \times 11\frac{7}{16}$ inches—38 × 29 cm. Pencil, $\frac{1}{4}$ inch added to lower margin. Verso: No. 1061.

Unfinished study of a landscape with trees and rocks, difficult to interpret.

BIBLIOGRAPHY: Venturi, Vol. I, verso of No. 1587 (not reproduced). Basel catalog, No. 173 (reproduced).

COLLECTIONS: Cézanne *fils*, Paris. W. Feuz, Bern. Kunstmuseum, Basel.

1154. LANDSCAPE WITH BOULDERS AND TREES, 1890–94

$8\frac{1}{4} \times 10\frac{1}{8}$ inches—$21 \times 25,7$ cm. Page LXXXIII verso from the sketchbook CP IV. Pencil. Verso No. 1075 (recto only paginated).

This landscape is difficult to decipher clearly, but is situated by Venturi in Bibémus quarry. The curvilinear structure of the boulders would seem to indicate Fontainebleau Forest, but this question is of minor importance. The drawing shows trees growing out of rocks, with an open view leading back to the left. It has dynamic quality.

BIBLIOGRAPHY: Venturi, Vol. I, under No. 1322 (not reproduced); "Bibémus. Très près du No. 1050." *Dessins*, 1938, No. 45 (reproduced).

EXHIBITION: Phillips Collection, Washington, D.C., Chicago, Boston, 1971, No. 83 (reproduced).

COLLECTIONS: Cézanne *fils*, Paris. Paul Guillaume, Paris. A. Chappuis, Tresserve.

1154A. STEREOMETRIC SKETCH, NOTATIONS, AND NUMBERS, date uncertain.

$10\frac{11}{16} \times 8\frac{5}{16}$ inches—$27,1 \times 21,1$ cm. Interior of second board of the sketchbook CP IV, paginated LXXXIV. Venturi describes the first board in its place; see No. 1101. Pencil and blue crayon, blue and green dabs of watercolor. (Not reproduced).

(a) Small sketch of a leg.—(b) Stereometric sketch, probably a diagram study of a perspective projection.—(c) Notations: *Ocre jaune/902/343/Mme Chabod/Jaune brillant 4/ Outremer* 2. By another hand: No. 3, and a cross in blue crayon.

COLLECTIONS: Cézanne *fils*, Paris. Paul Guillaume, Paris. A. Chappuis, Tresserve.

1155. LANDSCAPE SKETCH, 1889–92

$4\frac{1}{4} \times 2\frac{11}{16}$ inches—$10,9 \times 6,8$ cm. Page V verso of the sketchbook violet moiré. Pencil. Verso: some handwritten notations.

Drawing full of force but difficult to interpret. A rock juts out on the left like the wing of a stage, and the ground at its foot spreads out toward a flat space. Swirling strokes indicate a tree in the background. The sunlit mass at the foot of the tree represents a smooth-surfaced rock, often seen by the artist both in Fontainebleau Forest and the Aix countryside. For this detail, cf. Venturi Nos. 404, 673, 674, 786, 929, 971, 1050, 1053, and our Nos. 1152, 1154.

BIBLIOGRAPHY: *Carnet violet moiré*, 1955 (reproduced). Berthold, p. 159 (not reproduced). W. V. Andersen, Cézanne's Carnet violet moiré, *BurlM*, June 1965, p. 313 (reproduced fig. 46).

COLLECTIONS: Cézanne *fils*, Paris. Jean-Pierre Cézanne, Paris. Mlle Edmée Maus, Geneva.

1156. MAN IN A LANDSCAPE, 1889–92

$4\frac{1}{4} \times 2\frac{11}{16}$ inches—$10,9 \times 6,8$ cm. Page VIII verso of the sketchbook violet moiré. Pencil. Verso: handwritten notations.

A scene rapidly sketched; the whole is difficult to interpret. W. V. Andersen sees the "sketch of a standing male figure in a landscape; to the right, the trunk of a great tree (compare to page V verso)." I personally wonder whether it is not a first rough draft for a watercolor *Portrait of Vallier,* cf. Venturi Nos. 1090, 1092, 1524. The objection will be raised that the legs of Vallier and of many other seated men painted by the artist are crossed in a different way; this is true, although No. 413 (Venturi No. 1403) shows them as in our drawing. In any case, the argument is of only minor importance.

BIBLIOGRAPHY: *Carnet violet moiré*, 1955 (reproduced). Berthold, p. 159 (not reproduced): "landscape with tree." W. V. Andersen, Cézanne's Carnet violet moiré, *BurlM,* June 1965, p. 313 (reproduced fig. 43).

COLLECTIONS: Cézanne *fils*, Paris. Jean-Pierre Cézanne, Paris. Mlle Edmée Maus, Geneva.

1157. THE VILLAGE OF L'ESTAQUE, 1890–95

$11\frac{7}{16} \times 18\frac{1}{8}$ inches—29×46 cm. Pencil. Verso: the watercolor Venturi No. 1047.

Pencil lay-in of a vast panorama, showing the houses of L'Estaque in front of a horizon of hills, a factory smokestack rising straight up on the right. The perspective is established in this striking though unfinished drawing.

BIBLIOGRAPHY: Venturi, No. 1503. A. Neumeyer, 1958, No. 71 (reproduced). Yvon Taillandier, *Paul Cézanne,* 1965 (reproduced p. 34); confusion between Rhode Island and Rhodesia.

EXHIBITIONS: Art Institute of Chicago, and Metropolitan Museum, New York, 1952, No. 48.

COLLECTION: Museum of Art, Providence, R.I.

1158. MONT SAINTE-VICTOIRE, SEEN FROM BELLEVUE, 1892–95

$12 \times 17\frac{3}{4}$ inches—$30,5 \times 45,1$ cm. Pencil on laid paper. Verso: blank page.

Preparatory study for the painting Venturi No. 457. The planes and accents are noted with sobriety—I am tempted to say with humility—producing an admirably orchestrated page.

COLLECTIONS: Arthur B. Davies, Washington. F. Delius, New York.

1159. LANDSCAPE WITH HOUSES IN THE FOREGROUND, 1892–95

$12\frac{7}{16} \times 21\frac{3}{8}$ inches—$31,6 \times 54,2$ cm. Pencil, paper torn upper left, rectangular collection stamp lower right, watermark in the lower margin. Verso: blank page.

The side of a wooded hill surrounding a sloping meadow, with two or three houses in the foreground. Vigorous contours, dense hatching, diagonal movement down to the right.

BIBLIOGRAPHY: Frantisek Rachlik, *Cézanne,* Prague, 1948 (reproduced pl. 4). *Dessins français de Prague*, Prague, and Cercle d'Art, Paris, 1968 (reproduced pl. 43).

COLLECTION: National Gallery, Prague (Inv. K 13924).

1160. TREES, 1892–95

$12\frac{3}{8} \times 16\frac{3}{4}$ inches—$31,4 \times 42,5$ cm. Pencil on gray laid paper. Verso: blank page.

Similar motif to that of No. 918, but lengthwise on the page and of far superior quality. A few lightly sketched trees in front of horizontal lines indicating a walled enclosure; other trees are seen above the wall and a group of houses is suggested.

BIBLIOGRAPHY: Venturi, Vol. I, recorded as verso of No. 1500 (our No. 918); No. 918 had been framed on the reverse side of our No. 1160.

COLLECTIONS: Bernheim-Jeune, Paris. Thannhauser, Lucerne. Dudensing, New York. Knoedler & Co., New York. Sale, Klipstein & Kornfeld, Bern, June 5-6, 1959, No. 97 (not reproduced). James Lord, New York.

1161. BARE TREE, 1892–95
$8\frac{15}{16} \times 10\frac{11}{16}$ inches—21,1 × 27,2 cm. Page IX from the sketchbook CP IV. Pencil. Verso: No. 1214.

The bare branches of a tree spreading out in fan shape, the whole leaning slightly to the left. Cf. Nos. 932, 1179, and Venturi Nos. 1024, 1494.

BIBLIOGRAPHY: Venturi, Vol. I, under No. 1315 (not reproduced); Venturi sees this tree as a pine, but one could take it as another species of tree stripped of its leaves. *Dessins*, 1938, No. 43 (reproduced). *Dessins*, 1957, No. 24 (reproduced). C. F. Ramuz, *L'exemple de Cézanne*, Lausanne, 1951 (reproduced).

COLLECTIONS: Cézanne *fils*, Paris. Paul Guillaume, Paris. A. Chappuis, Tresserve.

1162. TREES, 1892–95
$19\frac{1}{8} \times 11\frac{13}{16}$ inches—48,5 × 30 cm. Pencil on laid paper, small stain at the top. Verso: blank page.

Lightly drawn on a large sheet of paper and probably intended by Cézanne as a preparatory study for a watercolor. On the right is a large tree with a branch spreading out to the left, where it crosses a slender, sinuous sapling. In the lower right is an object which is difficult to define.

EXHIBITIONS: Lyons, 1939, No. 74. Rétrospective, Paris, 1939, No. 52.

COLLECTION: John Wyeth, New York.

1163. TREES, 1892–95
$12\frac{5}{8} \times 19\frac{1}{2}$ inches—32,1 × 49,5 cm. Pencil, paper yellowed with age. Verso: blank page.

Study showing an open area with a few trees, notably one on the left and another on the right, their branches meeting in an almost horizontal movement.

EXHIBITIONS: Cézanne, Aquarelle und Zeichnungen, Galerie Alfred Flechtheim, Berlin, 1927, No. 44. The Hague, 1956, No. 107. Zurich, 1956, No. 162. Munich, 1956, No. 123 (the dimensions 31 × 38 cm. relate to the frame).

COLLECTIONS: Alfred Flechtheim, Berlin. Purrmann, Zurich. H. Vollmoeller, Zurich.

1164. TREES CROSSING OVER A STRETCH OF WATER, 1892–95
$10\frac{11}{16} \times 8\frac{5}{16}$ inches—27,2 × 21,1 cm. Page LI from the sketchbook CP IV. Pencil. Verso: a watercolored drawing, "*Lit défait*," paginated LII.

A light, sensitive drawing. Cf. the similar motifs of Venturi Nos. 937, 938, 993, 1001.

BIBLIOGRAPHY: Venturi, Vol. I, under No. 1316 (not reproduced).

COLLECTIONS: Cézanne *fils*, Paris. Paul Guillaume, Paris. A. Chappuis, Tresserve. Private collection, Paris.

1165. LANDSCAPE WITH TREES, 1892–95
$8\frac{5}{16} \times 10\frac{1}{4}$ inches—21,1 × 26,1 cm. Page XIX from the sketchbook CP IV. Pencil. Verso: No. 1220.

Trees in the foreground and between them a flat area crossed by an enclosure. A mountain stretches out to the right in the background.

BIBLIOGRAPHY: Venturi, Vol. I, under No. 1315 (not reproduced). *Dessins*, 1957 (partially reproduced on the cover).

COLLECTIONS: Cézanne *fils*, Paris. Paul Guillaume, Paris. A. Chappuis, Tresserve. Private collection, Paris.

1165bis. A STEEPLE AMID TREES, 1892–96
$13\frac{1}{2} \times 12\frac{1}{2}$ inches—34,3 × 31,7 cm. Pencil. Verso: blank page.

By the side of a road, surrounded by trees, is a square steeple with a cupola and lantern. It has twinned, round-headed windows. The main body of the building seems to be hidden by the foliage, yet the sketchiness of that area leaves this open to doubt. To the right in the foreground: the projecting angle of a roof.

COLLECTIONS: Helene Taeubler, Berlin. Private collection, Chicago.

1166. HOUSES AND SLENDER TREES, 1892–96
$8\frac{5}{16} \times 10\frac{3}{4}$ inches—21,1 × 27,3 cm. Page LXXV from the sketchbook CP IV. Pencil, touches of watercolor top right. Verso: No. 589.

The landscape covers the right side of the page. Near the center, an enclosure wall runs back at right angles to the wing of a house, the wing seen from the front. The roof of a building is visible further back to the right, between some bare trees.

BIBLIOGRAPHY: Venturi, Vol. I, under No. 1318 (not reproduced). *Dessins*, 1938, No. 13 (reproduced).

EXHIBITION: Orangerie, 1936, No. 166.

COLLECTIONS: Cézanne *fils*, Paris. Paul Guillaume, Paris. A. Chappuis, Tresserve. Private collection, Paris. Private collection, New York.

1167. HOUSE AND AQUEDUCT, 1892–96
$10\frac{5}{8} \times 13\frac{3}{4}$ inches—27 × 35 cm. Pencil, stains. Verso: unknown.

Façade of a house, seen from roof level, and further back the arches of an aqueduct; other roofs rise higher still in the background. The aqueduct is not continued on the left, its arches disappearing behind a turret with a triangular roof. The planes of this drawing are distinctive and the relation between the gable on the left and the other surfaces particularly noteworthy.

EXHIBITION: Quatre Chemins, Paris, 1936.

COLLECTIONS: Cézanne *fils*, Paris. Present owner unknown.

1168. SKETCH OF BUILDINGS, 1892–96

$2\frac{11}{16} \times 4\frac{1}{4}$ inches—6,8 × 10,9 cm. Page X verso of the sketchbook violet moiré. Pencil. Verso: notation of a few numbers.

Unfinished sketch partly covered by handwriting. On the left a fir tree rises beside a group of large buildings with roofs forming triangular surfaces. A little tower can be seen to the right, and some trees.

BIBLIOGRAPHY: *Carnet violet moiré*, 1955 (reproduced). Berthold, p. 159 (not reproduced). W. V. Andersen, Cézanne's Carnet violet moiré, *BurlM*, June 1965, p. 313 (reproduced fig. 41).

COLLECTIONS: Cézanne *fils*, Paris. Jean-Pierre Cézanne, Paris. Mlle Edmée Maus, Geneva.

1169. SKETCH OF MONT SAINTE-VICTOIRE, 1892–96

$8\frac{5}{16} \times 10\frac{11}{16}$ inches—21,1 × 27,2 cm. Page LIX from the sketchbook CP IV. Pencil. Verso: No. 690.

A cluster of bushes and rocks surmounted by a tree, its crown dividing the line of a distant ridge which is crossed by a smaller crest jutting out from the side of the mountain. Cf. the paintings Venturi Nos. 664, 763.

BIBLIOGRAPHY: Venturi, Vol. I, under No. 1316 (not reproduced).

COLLECTIONS: Cézanne *fils*, Paris. Paul Guillaume, Paris. A. Chappuis, Tresserve. Private collection, Paris.

1170. LANDSCAPE WITH TREES, A ROAD, AND HOUSES, 1892–96

$12\frac{1}{2} \times 18\frac{3}{4}$ inches—31,8 × 47,6 cm. Pencil on laid paper. Verso: blank page.

The foreground opens onto a road with a few trees to the left; on the right is a rock in front of some bigger trees. A group of houses in the background, surrounded by vegetation, cuts off the horizon. A vigorous, intensely rhythmic drawing.

COLLECTION: National Gallery, Prague (Inv. K 13922).

1171. SMALL HOUSE SURROUNDED BY TREES, 1892–96

$11 \times 17\frac{1}{8}$ inches—28 × 43,5 cm. Pencil on laid paper with the watermark: MONTGOLFIER VIDALON-LES-ANNONAY Anc^e Manuf^re Ca... Verso: blank page.

This drawing, which covers only part of the page, represents the heart of a landscape. In the middleground there is a little house at the foot of a cluster of big trees. Through an open space the slope of a mountain is seen, its crest cutting off the horizon, then leading down to the right.

COLLECTIONS: Mouradian & Vallotton, Paris. Private collection, Paris.

1172. LANDSCAPE AND NOTATIONS, circa 1896

$2\frac{11}{16} \times 4\frac{1}{4}$ inches—6,8 × 10,9 cm. Page VII verso of the sketchbook violet moiré. Pencil. Verso: No. 1070.

Unfinished landscape seen from above: a mountain rising up behind a tract of land with a rectangular area.— Notations written across the drawing: 12114 *Bleu de cobalt/Chrome clair*.

BIBLIOGRAPHY: *Carnet violet moiré*, 1955 (reproduced). Berthold, p. 159 (not reproduced). W. V. Andersen, Cézanne's Carnet violet moiré, *BurlM*, June 1965, p. 313 (reproduced fig. 44).

COLLECTIONS: Cézanne *fils*, Paris. Jean-Pierre Cézanne, Paris. Mlle Edmée Maus, Geneva.

1173. STUDIES, INCLUDING A BOAT AND FIGURES, circa 1896

$10\frac{1}{16} \times 16\frac{1}{8}$ inches—25,5 × 41 cm. Pencil on laid paper, traces of pencil rubbings. Verso: the watercolor Venturi No. 964.

The various drawings on this page are all related to the watercolors done by Cézanne during his stay in Talloires in 1896, and especially to the watercolor Venturi No. 964 on the reverse side of our sheet.—(a) Left: sketch of a boat, with two figures and a rocky landscape.—(b) Center: two studies of a man in a straw hat, picking up something.—(c) Right: standing man.—(d) Flat-bottomed boat.—(e) Above the boat: rough sketch of a round object.—(f) Man in a hat.

COLLECTIONS: Georges Bernheim, Paris. Sale, Georges Bernheim, Paris, June 7, 1935, No. 2 (reproduced). Galerie Motte, Geneva. Sale, Galerie Motte, Geneva, Dec. 1954 (reproduced). M. Knoedler & Co., New York.

1174. LANDSCAPE WITH CROSSES, 1890–94

$2\frac{11}{16} \times 4\frac{1}{4}$ inches—6,8 × 10,9 cm. Page IX of the Page IX of the sketchbook violet moiré. Pencil. Verso: No. 1072.

A fine little sketch, done during a trip. In the foreground are some graves in a dry-stone enclosure with a cross on the right, and another cross on the left cut in half by the edge of the paper. The building behind the trees seems to have Gothic-style openings. It is not easy to interpret the diagonal rising to the right or the shadowed parts of the wall. W. V. Andersen dates this landscape 1896, since he believes it to represent the north façade of the Chapel of Notre-Dame-de-la-Salette, adjacent to the Monastery of the Grande Chartreuse (Isère). In the carnet violet moiré the artist noted down the itinerary leading to the Grande Chartreuse from Chambéry, where he is known to have stayed in 1896 (the name of the monastery, however, is not mentioned). Andersen recognized the motif from a photograph taken at the monastery by L. Chavand, of Saint-Pierre-de-Chartreuse; in his opinion the drawing can therefore be dated by exterior evidence, without any need for comparisons in style. I, on the other hand, after comparing this sketch with many others, find it nearer in treatment to the drawings attributed to the years 1889–94 than to those dating from the artist's stay at Talloires in 1896. On October 29, 1970, I visited the Grande Chartreuse to look for this motif but was not successful in identifying it as represented in the carnet violet moiré. Monsieur L. Chevand was good enough to make a sketch of the locality, marking the site, but unfortunately he was unable to show me the photograph mentioned by W. V. Andersen. A priest from the monastery bursary, a calm, intelligent man who holds M. Chavand in high esteem, accompanied me to the precincts of the Chapel of Notre-Dame-de-la-Salette. Reproduction of the drawing in hand, he was at first inclined to recognize the site, but after examining the details he came to the conclusion, as did I, that even with allowances made for a road under construction, the very evident discrepancies invalidated a positive identification of the motif. The building, for example, has no ogives. Also the priest maintained that there had never been an outdoor cemetery on this side, between the chapel and the principal entrance to the monastery. Andersen too sees a churchyard in the drawing. It may be remarked that the crosses are not similar to the characteristic Carthusian cross comprising two straight bars. In conclusion, therefore, the date of this sketch cannot be established with certainty by exterior evidence, and to me at present 1890–94 seems the most probable date.

BIBLIOGRAPHY: *Carnet violet moiré*, 1955 (reproduced). Berthold, p. 159 (not reproduced). W. V. Andersen, Cézanne's Carnet violet moiré, *BurlM*, June 1965, pp. 313-14 (reproduced fig. 49).

COLLECTIONS: Cézanne *fils*, Paris. Jean-Pierre Cézanne, Paris. Mlle Edmée Maus, Geneva.

1175. TREES AND A RUSTIC HOUSE, 1888–92
   $4\frac{5}{8} \times 9\frac{5}{8}$ inches—11,8 × 19,4 cm. Page XIV from the sketchbook CP I. Pencil. Verso: No. 756.

Study of the same motif as the painting Venturi No. 646. The gable with a narrow window on the right is seen in non-classical perspective. On the left a little wall turns at right angles and leads toward the background; trees in leaf rise up above the house on this side.

BIBLIOGRAPHY: Venturi, Vol. I, under No. 1270 (not reproduced). *Dessins*, 1938, No. 5 (reproduced).

EXHIBITION: Aix-en-Provence, 1961, No. 57.

COLLECTIONS: Cézanne *fils*, Paris. Paul Guillaume, Paris. A. Chappuis, Tresserve.

1176. STRAW HAT, 1890–94
   $2\frac{11}{16} \times 4\frac{1}{4}$ inches—6,8 × 10,9 cm. Page I verso of the sketchbook violet moiré. Pencil. Verso: a few hand-written notations.

Sketch of a straw hat on a flat surface. Partly covering the drawing, some notations: *St. Laurent/Brignoud*. Lower down: 450, 420.

BIBLIOGRAPHY: *Carnet violet moiré*, 1955 (reproduced). Berthold, p. 159 (not reproduced). W. V. Andersen, Cézanne's Carnet violet moiré, *BurlM*, June 1965, p. 313 (reproduced fig. 50).

COLLECTIONS: Cézanne *fils*, Paris. Jean-Pierre Cézanne, Paris. Mlle Edmée Maus, Geneva.

1177. LANDSCAPE WITH TREES, 1895–98
   $9\frac{5}{16} \times 6$ inches—23,7 × 15,2 cm. Page VI of the Album, Paul Mellon Collection. Pencil. Verso: No. 1141.

A meadow stretching back in three successive planes to a row of trees, their foliage forming a screen. Behind them there seems to be another horizontal strip, perhaps a stretch of water, with a small house to the right. A few trees are indicated rather symmetrically in the foreground.

BIBLIOGRAPHY: Venturi, Vol. I, under No. 1302 (not reproduced). *Dessins*, 1938 (reproduced pl. 10). *Album*, 1966 (reproduced).

COLLECTIONS: Cézanne *fils*, Paris. Paul Guillaume, Paris. A. Chappuis, Tresserve. Mr. and Mrs. Paul Mellon, Upperville, Va.

1178. TREES AND ROCKS, 1895–98
   $18\frac{1}{8} \times 12\frac{3}{16}$ inches—46 × 31 cm. Pencil on gray paper. Verso: blank page.

Compositional study that remains no more than a rough sketch. It may be compared with the paintings Venturi Nos. 779, 788.

BIBLIOGRAPHY: Venturi No. 1498.

COLLECTIONS: Ambroise Vollard, Paris. Pierre Loeb, Paris. Present owner unknown.

1179. STUDY OF A TREE, 1896–99
   $12\frac{5}{16} \times 18\frac{3}{4}$ inches—31,3 × 47,5 cm. Pencil on laid paper. Verso: page blank except for a rectangular collection stamp.

A harmonious, powerful drawing: a tree with its numerous bare branches spread out, standing solitary in front of a leafy forest. Cf. No. 1161.

BIBLIOGRAPHY: Frantisek Rachlik, *Cézanne*, Prague, 1948 (reproduced pl. 5). *Dessins français à Prague*, Prague and Cercle d'Art Paris, 1968 (reproduced pl. 41).

COLLECTION: National Gallery, Prague (Inv. K. 13925).

1180. STUDY OF TREES, 1896–99
   $18\frac{1}{2} \times 12\frac{3}{16}$ inches—47 × 31 cm. Pencil. Verso: the watercolor Venturi No. 1633.

Three tree trunks in the form of a partly-open fan in the left foreground and behind them a receding row of trees with bare branches. A very fine study.

BIBLIOGRAPHY: Venturi No. 1632.

COLLECTIONS: Ambroise Vollard, Paris. Present owner unknown.

1181. SLOPING TREES, 1896–99
   $12 \times 18\frac{1}{2}$ inches—30,6 × 47 cm. Pencil on gray laid paper. Verso: blank page.

Trees rising in a powerful diagonal toward the right with others crossing them in the opposite direction, and a central horizontal plane. An agitated, imposing, and melancholy drawing.

BIBLIOGRAPHY: Venturi No. 1499. *Dessins*, 1957, No. 44-45 (reproduced).

EXHIBITIONS: Kunsthalle, Basel, 1936, No. 145. De Watteau à Cézanne, Geneva, 1951, No. 89.

COLLECTIONS: Thannhauser, Berlin. L. Lichtenhan, Basel. A. Deuber, Basel.

1182. MONT SAINTE-VICTOIRE, 1897–1900
   $12\frac{3}{16} \times 18\frac{7}{8}$ inches—31 × 48 cm. Pencil. Verso: blank page.

Summary but impressive study of the mountain seen from the entrance to the grounds of the Château Noir. Project for the canvas Venturi No. 663.

BIBLIOGRAPHY: F. Novotny, *Cézanne und das Ende der*

wissenschaftlichen Perspektive, Vienna, 1938, p. 202, No. 79 (not reproduced). J. Rewald, *Cézanne*, Paris, 1939 (reproduced fig. 76). Idem, *Paul Cézanne*, New York, 1948, No. 100 (reproduced). *Art News*, Nov. 1948 (reproduced). J. Rewald, *The Ordeal of Paul Cézanne*, London, 1950 (reproduced fig. 76). Idem, *Paul Cézanne*, Spring Books, London, 1959 and 1965 (reproduced fig. 76).

EXHIBITIONS: Quatre-Chemins, Paris, 1936. Rétrospective, Paris, 1939, No. 54. Lyons, 1939, No. 75. Wildenstein Gallery, London, 1939, No. 92. Fine Arts Associates, New York, 1952, No. 9.

COLLECTIONS: Cézanne *fils*, Paris. Paul Guillaume, Paris. Alfred Flechtheim, Berlin. Private collection, Paris. Mouradian & Vallotton, Paris. J. R., Paris. Private collection, New York.

1183. FRAGMENT OF A LANDSCAPE, 1897–1900

$18\frac{1}{2} \times 12\frac{3}{16}$ inches—47×31 cm. Margins trimmed. Pencil. Verso: No. 613.

This drawing has been little worked on and appears to be a pencil study for an intended watercolor. Cf. No. 1184, seen from a point farther to the right, and the watercolor Venturi No. 1613.

COLLECTION: Private collection, Paris.

1184. IN BIBÉMUS QUARRY, circa 1900

$8\frac{5}{16} \times 10\frac{1}{8}$ inches—$21,1 \times 25,7$ cm. Page XI from the sketchbook CP IV. Pencil. Verso: blank page.

Study of detail: a pine tree on the left separated by a deep gully from a square-cut rock to the right. The same motif figures in the oils Venturi Nos. 773, 777, and especially in the watercolor Venturi No. 1613. Cf. also our No. 714 (b).

BIBLIOGRAPHY: Venturi, Vol. I, under No. 1315 (not reproduced).

COLLECTIONS: Cézanne *fils*, Paris. Paul Guillaume, Paris. A. Chappuis, Tresserve.

1185. LANDSCAPE WITH A LOW WALL, 1900–1904

$20\frac{1}{2} \times 12\frac{11}{16}$ inches—$52 \times 32,3$ cm. Pencil on laid paper. Verso: blank page.

Large, leafy, fan-shaped bush in a garden with other shrubs and several vertical trees. Lower down, in the foreground, a little horizontal stone wall.—This is perhaps a preparatory study for a watercolor; cf. for example the foreground of Venturi Nos. 1030, 1036.

BIBLIOGRAPHY: *Dessins français de Prague*, Prague and Cercle d'Art, Paris, 1968 (reproduced pl. 42).

COLLECTION: National Gallery, Prague (Inv. K 13923).

1186. TREES AND A CHAIR, 1900 or later

$8\frac{1}{2} \times 5$ inches—$21,6 \times 12,7$ cm. Page XXIIII from the second sketchbook Mrs. Enid A. Haupt. Pencil. Verso: blank page.

The curve of a garden bench, with an iron chair to the right. A tree, static in feeling, on the left, and another, dynamic, on the right. From its form the latter would seem to be haunted by an image of the crucifixion.

BIBLIOGRAPHY: Rewald, *Carnets*: C IV, p. XXIIII (not reproduced). *Dessins*, 1957, No. 11 (reproduced).

COLLECTIONS: Cézanne *fils*, Paris. M. Renou, Paris. Poyet, Lyons. M. Renou, Paris. Sam Salz, New York. Mrs. Enid A. Haupt, New York.

1187. HEAD OF MME CÉZANNE, 1897–1900

$5\frac{3}{8} \times 7\frac{3}{8}$ inches—$13,7 \times 18,7$ cm. Page XXXIV from the sketchbook CP IV, trimmed down by a bookbinder and inserted in a copy of Léo Larguier's book, *Cézanne, ou la lutte avec l'ange de la peinture* (Julliard, 1947). Pencil, numerous trial touches of watercolor in no relation to the sketch, paper browned with age. Verso: No. 1147.

Head of Mme Cézanne against a pillow. Daubs of watercolor, varied and harmonious, were tried out on the page during work on a watercolor.

BIBLIOGRAPHY: Venturi, Vol. I, under No. 1316 (not reproduced): "Mme Cézanne regardant en bas. Quelques touches d'aquarelle."

COLLECTIONS: Cézanne *fils*, Paris. Paul Guillaume, Paris. A. Chappuis, Tresserve.

1188. MME CÉZANNE *(La Dormeuse)*, 1897–1900

$9\frac{3}{16} \times 12\frac{3}{16}$ inches—$23,4 \times 31$ cm. (dimensions of the half-page bearing the drawing). Pencil on laid paper, traces of framing; on half of the same page, folded back: branch of a tree, in watercolor. Verso: blank page. Watermark: PL BAS.

Bust-length study of Mme Cézanne asleep, her head leaning on her hand against a pillow. She is wearing a garment flounced at the wrist. Age, and perhaps sickness, are manifest in this most human and remarkably fine drawing.

EXHIBITION: Hauptwerke der Sammlung Hahnloser, Winterthur, Lucerne, 1940, No. 164.

COLLECTIONS: Simon Meller, Budapest. Arthur Hahnloser, Winterthur. Hans R. Hahnloser, Bern.

1189. HEAD OF MME CÉZANNE, 1897–1900

$9\frac{5}{16} \times 6$ inches—$23,7 \times 15,2$ cm. Page XIII of the Album, Paul Mellon Collection. Pencil. Verso: No. 595.

One side of the head, exposed to a brilliant light coming from the right, is left white. A photograph of Mme Cézanne taken around 1900 helps us to date this sketch.

BIBLIOGRAPHY: Venturi, Vol. I, under No. 1304 (not reproduced): "Tête de Mme Cézanne; inachevée." *Dessins*, 1938 (reproduced pl. 30). *Album*, 1966 (reproduced). Th. Reff, *BurlM*, Nov. 1967, No. 776, Vol. CIX, p. 653; the author doubts that the photograph furnishes a clue to the date of the drawing.

COLLECTIONS: Cézanne *fils*, Paris. Paul Guillaume, Paris. A. Chappuis, Tresserve. Mr. and Mrs. Paul Mellon, Upperville, Va.

1190. AMBROISE VOLLARD, SEEN FROM THE BACK, 1896–99

$8\frac{9}{16} \times 5$ inches—$21,7 \times 12,7$ cm. Page XXIII verso from the second sketchbook Mrs. Enid A. Haupt. Verso: blank page.

Ambroise Vollard, seated, a hat on his head, seen in left lost profile; cf. No. 1191. Vollard tells us that he met Cézanne in 1896, after organizing an exhibition of the artist's paintings in his gallery, Rue Laffitte, in 1895. (Vollard, 1914, p. 73 and p. 55.)

BIBLIOGRAPHY: Rewald, *Carnets:* C IV, p. XXIII verso (not reproduced). *Dessins,* 1957, No. 13 (reproduced); error: confusion with C I, p. 43, of the Rewald Carnets, our No. 439.

COLLECTIONS: Cézanne *fils,* Paris. M. Renou, Paris. Poyet, Lyons. M. Renou, Paris. Sam Salz, New York. Mrs. Enid A. Haupt, New York.

1191. PORTRAIT OF AMBROISE VOLLARD, 1896–99

$7\frac{3}{16} \times 4\frac{9}{16}$ inches—18,2 × 11,6 cm. Page 31 from the first sketchbook Mrs. Enid A. Haupt. Pencil. Verso: No. 1191A.

Ambroise Vollard, in his book on Cézanne (1914), relates (p. 73) that he met the painter for the first time in 1896. The sitter's gaze is directed straight at the viewer, his head and shoulders turned slightly to the left. He is wearing a jacket similar to the one of the oil portrait Venturi No. 696, in the Petit Palais, Paris. Cf. Nos. 1190–1194.

BIBLIOGRAPHY: Rewald, *Carnets:* C I, p. 31 (reproduced pl. 34). *Dessins,* 1957, No. 10 (reproduced).

COLLECTIONS: Cézanne *fils,* Paris. M. Renou, Paris. Poyet, Lyons. M. Renou, Paris. Sam Salz, New York. Mrs. Enid A. Haupt, New York.

1191A. ANGEL HOLDING A FRAME

Pencil. Inaccessible reverse side of No. 1191. (Not reproduced.)

BIBLIOGRAPHY: Rewald, *Carnets:* C I, p. 31 verso (not reproduced): "Croquis d'un ange volant, tenant un tableau (?) et d'un personnage agenouillé à droite (peut-être pour *L'Apothéose de Delacroix,* Venturi No. 245)." Berthold, cat. No. 283 (not reproduced); the author thinks that the subject copied could be that of our No. 1025. The presence of a kneeling figure makes me feel that Rewald's supposition is more likely.

1192. THE DINNER, 1896–99

$7\frac{1}{16} \times 4\frac{1}{2}$ inches—18 × 11,5 cm. Pencil. Verso: the watercolor Venturi No. 900.

Five figures sitting around a circular table, each in front of his plate. A mantel clock ornamented by a female figure is seen behind the head of the bearded man presiding at the table. Floorboards are indicated in perspective in the foreground.—Venturi mentions an inscription, hidden by the framing, not written by Cézanne but by a frame maker. Date: at first view this drawing seems to resemble those of the period 1876–1880, but on examining it more closely it is evident from the masterly handling of planes that it must be dated 1895–1900. The floor, back wall, and table together create a spatial effect which is accurate while remaining free, a characteristic quality of the artist's later years. The central figure resembles Vollard, or Geffroy; cf. No. 1194, particularly the *shirtfront* and jacket.

BIBLIOGRAPHY: Venturi No. 1219, dated 1875–82.

COLLECTIONS: Wildenstein, New York. Private collection, California. Sale, Christie's, London, July 25, 1952 (the watercolor verso). Mr. Ruddock, London.

1193. AMBROISE VOLLARD, 1896–99

$10\frac{11}{16} \times 8\frac{5}{16}$ inches—27,2 × 21,1 cm. Page XLII from the sketchbook CP IV. Pencil, two touches of watercolor not related to the subject. Verso: No. 1102.

At first glance this seems to be a study for *The Card Players,* but the attitude and profile indicate that it is a sketch of Ambroise Vollard.

BIBLIOGRAPHY: Venturi, Vol. I, under No. 1316 (not reproduced: "homme barbu."

COLLECTIONS: Cézanne *fils,* Paris. Paul Guillaume, Paris. A. Chappuis, Tresserve.

1194. AMBROISE VOLLARD, 1899

20 × 18 inches—51,1 × 45,9 cm. (sheet); $18\frac{7}{8} \times 15\frac{3}{8}$ inches—45,7 × 39,7 cm. (sight). Pencil. Verso: blank page.

Portrait of Ambroise Vollard, seen in not quite front view. The strokes of the drawing are very light, and the style appears to be characteristic for the period. Vollard said that the drawing was done in the year 1899.—Compare the portrait Venturi No. 696 and the drawings Nos. 1190, 1191.

BIBLIOGRAPHY: Venturi No. 1480. Vollard 1914 (reproduced p. 103); see also text p. 93. Berthold (reproduced Abb. 154). Neumeyer 1958, No. 46 (reproduced). *Art Journal,* XXII 2, 1962–63, p. 100 (reproduced).

COLLECTIONS: Ambroise Vollard, Paris. Mr. and Mrs. F. Deknatel, Cambridge, Massachusetts. Fogg Art Museum, Cambridge, Massachusetts.

1195. AFTER COYSEVOX: *Marie Serre,* circa 1900

$8\frac{1}{4} \times 4\frac{13}{16}$ inches—20,9 × 12,2 cm. Page XLIX from the sketchbook BS II. Pencil. Verso: No. 1216.

After Charles-Antoine Coysevox's bust of *Marie Serre,* mother of the painter Hyacinthe Rigaud, her head draped with a kerchief falling down over the nape of the neck to the left; marble (1706) in the Louvre. See fig. 159.

BIBLIOGRAPHY: Venturi No. 1390. Berthold, cat. No. 182 (reproduced Abb. 155). Basel catalog, No. 203 (reproduced); in the text, Table I, opposite Venturi 1390 the number 103 should read 203).

COLLECTIONS: Cézanne *fils,* Paris. Paul Guillaume, Paris. W. Feuz, Bern. Kunstmuseum, Basel.

1196. AFTER PUGET: *Hercules resting,* 1894–97

$10\frac{5}{8} \times 8\frac{5}{16}$ inches—27 × 21,1 cm. Page LXX from the sketchbook CP IV. Pencil. Verso: No. 1036.

Unfinished study of Pierre Puget's marble *Hercule au repos* in the Louvre, seen from the back. (See fig. 141.) Although incomplete, this sketch communicates a feeling of great serenity. Among the 17 sketches of the same subject by Cézanne, cf. especially Nos. 1059, 1060.

BIBLIOGRAPHY: Venturi No. 1318. Berthold, cat. No. 121 (reproduced).

COLLECTIONS: Cézanne *fils,* Paris. Paul Guillaume, Paris. A. Chappuis, Tresserve.

FIG. 159. Charles-Antoine Coysevox (1640–1720): bust of *Marie Serre*, mother of the painter Hyacinthe Rigaud (1659–1743), marble dated 1706 and signed, in the Louvre; height 41 cm. Musée National du Louvre, *Catalogue des Sculptures* II, 1922, No. 1108. *(Photograph: R. W. Ratcliffe)*

1197. AFTER N. COUSTOU: *Adonis*, 1894–97

$16\frac{9}{16} \times 10\frac{5}{8}$ inches—42 × 27 cm. Pencil on laid paper. Verso: blank page.

This fine drawing was done after Nicolas Coustou's marble *Adonis se reposant de la chasse* in the Louvre. See fig. 160. Its execution is mainly confined to contours.

BIBLIOGRAPHY: *Review Shirakaba*, Tokyo, Shirakaba-ha, Feb. 1921 (reproduced pl. 6). *Masterpieces of the Orient and the Occident* (edited by the Municipal Museum of Osaka), Kyoto, Benri-dô, 1936 (reproduced pl. 80). Chuji Ikegami, The Drawings of Paul Cézanne, *Bijutsushi* No. 76, Tokyo 1970 (reproduced p. 136).

EXHIBITIONS: Shirakaba-ha Collection, Hoshi-Seiyaku Gallery, March 1921. Masterpieces of the Orient and the Occident, Municipal Museum of Osaka, Osaka, Sept. 1936.

COLLECTIONS: Bought in Paris and sent to Japan in 1920 by Masanosuke Sôma for the literary society Shirakaba-ha. Destroyed by bombing, Aug. 6, 1945, in the house of K. Yamamoto at Ashiya.

1198. AFTER N. COUSTOU: *Adonis*, 1894–97

$10\frac{3}{4} \times 8\frac{5}{16}$ inches—27,3 × 21,1 cm. Page LXXX verso from the sketchbook CP IV. Pencil, numerous stains of oil color. Verso: No. 975. This leaf, unlike the others, is numbered only on recto.

After Nicolas Coustou's marble *Adonis se reposant de la chasse* in the Louvre. See fig. 160. A fine drawing, but disfigured by stains. Cf. No. 1199.

BIBLIOGRAPHY: Venturi No. 1322. Berthold, cat. No. 152 (reproduced).

COLLECTIONS: Cézanne *fils*, Paris. Paul Guillaume, Paris. A. Chappuis, Tresserve. Private collection, Paris.

1199. AFTER N. COUSTOU: *Adonis*, 1897–1900

$8\frac{3}{16} \times 5\frac{1}{8}$ inches—20,8 × 13 cm. Page XII from the sketchbook BS I. Pencil. Verso: blank page.

After Nicolas Coustou's marble *Adonis se reposant de la chasse* in the Louvre. See fig. 160. Cf. the two other copies of this same subject, Nos. 1197, 1198.

BIBLIOGRAPHY: Venturi No. 1336. Berthold, cat. No. 153 (reproduced). Basel catalog, No. 164 (reproduced).

EXHIBITIONS: The Hague, 1956, No. 127. Zurich, 1956, No. 191.

COLLECTIONS: Cézanne *fils*, Paris. Paul Guillaume, Paris. W. Feuz, Bern. Kunstmuseum, Basel.

1200. AFTER PUGET: *Milo of Crotona*, 1897–1900

$8\frac{1}{2} \times 5\frac{3}{16}$ inches—21,5 × 13,1 cm. Page XXV from the sketchbook BS III. Pencil. Verso: blank page.

FIG. 160. Nicolas Coustou (1658–1733): *Adonis se reposant de la chasse* (1710), marble formerly at Marly, then in the Tuileries Gardens, now in the Louvre; height 1,76 m. Musée National du Louvre, *Catalogue des Sculptures* II, 1922, No. 1098. *(Photograph: R. W. Ratcliffe)*

After Pierre Puget's marble representing *Milo of Crotona* attacked by a lion, in the Louvre. See fig. 30. Cf. No. 977, earlier in date.

BIBLIOGRAPHY: Venturi No. 1431. Berthold, cat. No. 105 (reproduced Abb. 7 and 161). Basel catalog, No. 196 (reproduced).

COLLECTIONS: Cézanne *fils*, Paris. Paul Guillaume, Paris. W. Feuz, Bern. Kunstmuseum, Basel.

1201. AFTER PUGET: *Milo of Crotona*, 1897–1900

$8\frac{3}{8} \times 5\frac{3}{16}$ inches—21,2 × 13,1 cm. Page XX from the sketchbook BS I. Pencil. Verso: blank page.

Study after Pierre Puget's marble representing *Milo of Crotona* attacked by a lion, in the Louvre. See fig. 30.

BIBLIOGRAPHY: Venturi No. 1345. Berthold, cat. No. 103 (reproduced). Basel catalog, No. 197 (reproduced).

COLLECTIONS: Cézanne *fils*, Paris. Paul Guillaume, Paris. W. Feuz, Bern. Kunstmuseum, Basel.

1202. AFTER J. CHINARD: *Bust of a man*, 1897–1900

$8\frac{1}{4} \times 5\frac{1}{8}$ inches—21 × 13 cm. Page XXII from the sketchbook BS I. Pencil. Verso: blank page.

After the bust of an unknown man by Joseph Chinard, a sculptor from Lyons. Terra cotta in the Louvre since 1898. See fig. 161.

FIG. 162. Antique bust of the Roman emperor *Titus* Flavius Sabinus Vespasianus (41–81), marble in the Louvre. Musée National du Louvre, *Catalogue sommaire des Marbres antiques*, 1922, No. 1032. (*Photograph: R. W. Ratcliffe*)

BIBLIOGRAPHY: Venturi No. 1347. Berthold, cat. No. 198, as bust of Alexis Pirou by J.-J. Caffieri (reproduced Abb. 153). Basel catalog, No. 191 (reproduced). Th. Reff, *AB*, June 1960, p. 147; original model identified.

COLLECTIONS: Cézanne *fils*, Paris. Paul Guillaume, Paris. W. Feuz, Bern. Kunstmuseum, Basel.

1203. AFTER THE ANTIQUE: *Bust of Caracalla*, 1894–98

$7\frac{3}{16} \times 4\frac{9}{16}$ inches—18,2 × 11,6 cm. Page 26 verso from the first sketchbook Mrs. Enid A. Haupt. Pencil. Verso: drawing heightened with watercolor of this same bust, but seen in right profile (Berthold, cat. No. 56, reproduced).

The right side is unfinished. After a bust of the Roman emperor *Caracalla*, marble in the Louvre. See fig. 126.

BIBLIOGRAPHY: Rewald, *Carnets*: C I, p. 26 verso (not reproduced): étude d'après le buste d'un empereur romain." Berthold, cat. No. 52 (reproduced): "after the bust of Septimius Severus." Th. Reff, *AB*, June 1960, p. 147: identification of the bust of Caracalla.

COLLECTIONS: Cézanne *fils*, Paris. M. Renou, Paris. Poyet, Lyons. M. Renou, Paris. Sam Salz, New York. Mrs. Enid A. Haupt, New York.

1204. AFTER THE ANTIQUE: *Bust of Caracalla*, about 1900

$8\frac{1}{4} \times 4\frac{13}{16}$ inches—21 × 12,2 cm. Page XLIV from the sketchbook BS II. Pencil. Verso: No. 686.

FIG. 161. Joseph Chinard (1756–1813): *Buste d'homme*, terra cotta in the Louvre. This bust was acquired in 1898 and is at present in the Museum reserve (Inv. RF 1062). (*Photograph: Giraudon*)

A garment envelops the figure's shoulders in a circular movement. After the bust of the emperor *Caracalla*, marble in the Louvre. See fig. 126.

BIBLIOGRAPHY: Venturi No. 1382. Berthold, cat. No. 55 (reproduced). Basel catalog, No. 204 (reproduced).

COLLECTIONS: Cézanne *fils*, Paris. Paul Guillaume, Paris. W. Feuz, Bern. Kunstmuseum, Basel.

1205. AFTER THE ANTIQUE: *Titus,* about 1900

$8\frac{1}{4} \times 5\frac{3}{16}$ inches—21 × 13,1 cm. Page XVIII from the sketchbook BS I. Pencil. Verso: blank page.

After the bust of the Roman emperor *Titus* Flavius Sabinus Vespasianus, marble in the Louvre. See fig. 162. The shadow under the nose is stressed to render the density of the marble, while the white parts on the left fuse with the surface of the paper. Magnificent drawing.

BIBLIOGRAPHY: Venturi No. 1343. Berthold, cat. No. 57 (reproduced Abb. 158). Basel catalog, No. 205 (reproduced).

COLLECTIONS: Cézanne *fils*, Paris. Paul Guillaume, Paris. W. Feuz, Bern. Kunstmuseum, Basel.

1206. AFTER J.-J. CAFFIERI: *Nivelle de la Chaussée,* circa 1900

$8 \times 5\frac{3}{16}$ inches—20,3 × 13,1 cm. Page X from the sketchbook BS I. Pencil. Verso: blank page.

FIG. 164. Jean-Louis Lemoyne (1665–1755): bust of the architect *Jules Hardouin-Mansart* (1646–1708). Marble, dated 1703 and signed, height 1,10 m., in the Louvre. Musée National du Louvre, *Catalogue des Sculptures* II, 1922, No. 1409. *(Photograph: R. W. Ratcliffe)*

After the terra cotta bust of Pierre-Claude *Nivelle de la Chaussée* by Jean-Jacques Caffieri, in the Louvre. See fig. 163.

BIBLIOGRAPHY: Venturi No. 1335. Berthold, cat. No. 197 (reproduced Abb. 152). Basel catalog, No. 194 (reproduced). Th. Reff, in *AB,* June 1960, p. 146, rightly maintains, in contradiction to Berthold and the Basel catalog, that Cézanne drew from the terra cotta, and not from the marble in the Comédie Française.

COLLECTIONS: Cézanne *fils*, Paris. Paul Guillaume, Paris. W. Feuz, Bern. Kunstmuseum, Basel.

1207. AFTER J. L. LEMOYNE: THE ARCHITECT *J. Hardouin Mansart,* about 1900

$7\frac{7}{8} \times 4\frac{13}{16}$ inches—20 × 12,2 cm. Page LI from the sketchbook BS II. Pencil, small stain at lower edge. Verso: No. 1117.

The face wears a smiling expression. After a bust of the architect *Jules Hardouin Mansart,* marble in the Louvre. See fig. 164.

BIBLIOGRAPHY: Venturi No. 1394. Berthold, cat. No. 188 (reproduced Abb. 157). Basel catalog, No. 193 (reproduced).

COLLECTIONS: Cézanne *fils*, Paris. Paul Guillaume, Paris. W. Feuz, Bern. Kunstmuseum, Basel.

FIG. 163. Jean-Jacques Caffieri (1712–92): bust of the poet *Pierre-Claude Nivelle de la Chaussée* (1692–1754), terra cotta in the Louvre. Musée National du Louvre, *Catalogue des Sculptures* II, 1922, No. 986.

1208. AFTER MICHELANGELO: YOUNG SLAVE, towards 1900

$8\frac{1}{2} \times 5$ inches—21,6 × 12,7 cm. Page XXVI bis, not paginated, from the second sketchbook Mrs. Enid A. Haupt. Pencil. Verso: No. 1208A.

After *The Young Slave*, or *The Dying Slave*, by Michelangelo, marble in the Louvre. See fig. 54. Retouches in the drawing of the head.

BIBLIOGRAPHY: Rewald, *Carnets*: C IV, p. XXVI bis (reproduced pl. 125). Berthold, cat. No. 62 (reproduced Abb. 160); dated circa 1900.

COLLECTIONS: Cézanne *fils*, Paris. M. Renou, Paris. Poyet, Lyons. M. Renou, Paris. Sam Salz, New York. Mrs. Enid A. Haupt, New York.

1208A. AFTER PUGET: *Hercules resting*

Inaccessible reverse side of No. 1208. (Not reproduced.)

BIBLIOGRAPHY: Rewald, *Carnets*: C IV, p. XXVI bis verso (not reproduced); "Etude d'après Puget: *Hercule* (la tête seulement), au Louvre (voir Carnet I, p. 28 verso)"; this note refers to our No. 1006. Berthold, cat. No. 124 (not reproduced).

FIG. 166. Antoine-Louis Barye (1796–1875): *Lion au serpent*, bronze in the Louvre; prior to 1911 it was in the Tuileries Gardens. Musée National du Louvre, *Catalogue des Sculptures* II, 1922, No. 907. Our photograph was taken from a plaster cast exhibited in the Musée des Monuments français. Various versions of the work exist, and some smaller bronzes; the one that in Cézanne's time was in the Tuileries is 1,35 m. high.

(Photograph: Chappuis)

1209. AFTER RUBENS: A HORSE, about 1900

$8\frac{1}{2} \times 5$ inches—21,6 × 12,7 cm. Page XXVII from the second sketchbook Mrs. Enid A. Haupt. Pencil. Verso: blank page.

Head and chest of a horse seen from a lower level as it advances toward the viewer. After Rubens' painting *The Capture of Jülich*, in the Louvre. See fig. 165. (There seems to be no justification for the title *Voyage de la Reine à Pont-de-Cé*.)

BIBLIOGRAPHY: Rewald, *Carnets*: C IV, p. XXVII (reproduced pl. 153). Berthold, cat. No. 224 (reproduced Abb. 156).

COLLECTIONS: Cézanne *fils*, Paris. M. Renou, Paris. Poyet, Lyons. M. Renou, Paris. Sam Salz, New York. Mrs. Enid A. Haupt, New York.

1210. AFTER BARYE: *Lion and serpent*, about 1900

$8\frac{1}{2} \times 5$ inches—21,6 × 12,7 cm. Page XL verso from the second sketchbook Mrs. Enid A. Haupt. Pencil. Verso: blank page.

After Antoine-Louis Barye's bronze *Lion and Serpent* formerly in the Tuileries Gardens; in the Louvre since 1911. Possibly drawn from a plaster cast or a smaller bronze of the same subject. See fig. 166.

BIBLIOGRAPHY: Rewald, *Carnets*: C IV, p. XL verso (reproduced pl. 143). Berthold, cat. No. 171 (reproduced).

COLLECTIONS: Cézanne *fils*, Paris. M. Renou, Paris. Poyet, Lyons. M. Renou, Paris. Sam Salz, New York. Mrs. Enid A. Haupt, New York.

FIG. 165. Peter Paul Rubens (1577–1640): detail from the painting *The Capture of Jülich* (1610) in the Medici series in the Louvre. (There seems to be no justification for the title *Voyage de la Reine à Pont-de-Cé*.) Musée National du Louvre, *Catalogue des Peintures* III, 1922, No. 2097.

(Photograph: Giraudon)

1211. AFTER AN OLD MASTER: KNIGHTS ON HORSE-BACK, circa 1900

Measurements not known. Pencil. Verso: blank page.

Unfinished study after an unidentified work representing a skirmish between knights on horseback. A fine drawing, but difficult to decipher. In the right background: an ogive.

COLLECTIONS: Arthur B. Davies, London. Hugh Walpole, London. O. T. Falk, Oxford.

1212. AFTER GIRARDON: *Boileau-Despréaux*, circa 1900

$8\frac{1}{8} \times 5\frac{1}{8}$ inches—20,6 × 12,9 cm. Page XXIX from the sketchbook BS I. Pencil. Verso: blank page.

After François Girardon's marble bust of the poet *Nicolas Boileau-Despréaux*, in the Louvre. See fig. 136. A fine study, in the noble style of the artist's maturity. Cf. No. 1036, drawn from the same bust.

BIBLIOGRAPHY: Venturi No. 1355. Berthold, cat. No. 185, text p. 26 (reproduced Abb. 18). Basel catalog, No. 206 (reproduced).

COLLECTIONS: Cézanne *fils*, Paris. Paul Guillaume, Paris. W. Feuz, Bern. Kunstmuseum, Basel.

1213. AFTER J.-F. MILLET: *The Reaper*, circa 1900

$8\frac{1}{2} \times 5$ inches—21,6 × 12,7 cm. Page XVII from the second sketchbook Mrs. Enid A. Haupt. Pencil. Verso: blank page.

After Jean-François Millet's drawing *Le Faucheur* in the Cabinet des Dessins of the Louvre. See fig. 167. There is

also an etching of this subject by Millet and different versions in pencil.

BIBLIOGRAPHY: Rewald, *Carnets*: C IV, p. XVII (reproduced pl. 36). Berthold, cat. No. 246 (reproduced); Model suggested: etching. J. Gasquet, p. 16: "Sur ses albums, vingt fois je le vis copier le faucheur, le semeur de Millet." (No other copy of the reaper is known. and none of the sower.) Th. Rousseau, Jr., *Paul Cézanne*, Paris, 1953 (reproduced pl. 29). Idem, Amsterdam, 1954 (reproduced pl. 29). Franz Erpel, *Paul Cézanne*, Berlin, 1960 (reproduced p. 35).

COLLECTIONS: Cézanne *fils*, Paris. M. Renou, Paris. Poyet, Lyons. M. Renou, Paris. Sam Salz, New York. Mrs. Enid A. Haupt, New York.

1214. SKULL ON A TABLE, 1900 or later

$8\frac{5}{16} \times 10\frac{11}{16}$ inches—21,1 × 27,2 cm. Page X from the sketchbook CP IV. Pencil. Verso: No. 1161.

Facing to the left, the skull is placed on a table or on some kind of studio furniture. A curtain is indicated in the background.

BIBLIOGRAPHY: Venturi, Vol. I, under No. 1315 (not reproduced): "Très près du No. 1130." *Dessins*, 1938, No. 46 (reproduced).

EXHIBITIONS: Orangerie, Paris, 1936, No. 166. Lyons, 1939, No. 73 "crâne sur une bible." Wildenstein, London, 1939, No. 91 "skull on a Bible."

COLLECTIONS: Cézanne *fils*, Paris. Paul Guillaume, Paris. A. Chappuis, Tresserve.

1215. PAGE OF STUDIES, INCLUDING A SKULL, circa 1900

$7\frac{11}{16} \times 4\frac{3}{4}$ inches—19,5 × 12,1 cm. Page VII from the sketchbook BS II. Pencil. Verso: blank page.

(a) Human skull, seen in right three-quarter view; unfinished.—(b) Above: head and elbow, after the allegorical figure of Bellona in Rubens' painting *The Apotheosis of Henri IV*, in the Louvre. See fig. 9.

BIBLIOGRAPHY: Venturi No. 1366. Berthold, cat. No. 210 (reproduced). Basel catalog, No. 207 (reproduced).

EXHIBITION: Kunstverein, Hamburg, 1963, No. 34 (reproduced).

COLLECTIONS: Cézanne *fils*, Paris. Paul Guillaume, Paris. W. Feuz, Bern. Kunstmuseum, Basel.

1216. AFTER DESJARDINS: THE PAINTER *Pierre Mignard*, circa 1900

$8\frac{1}{4} \times 4\frac{13}{16}$ inches—20,9 × 12,2 cm. Page XLIX verso from the sketchbook BS II. Pencil. Verso: No. 1195.

Numerous retouches, especially to the eyes. From the marble bust of *Pierre Mignard*, painter of historical subjects and portraits, by Martin van den Bogaert, known as Desjardins, in the Louvre. See fig. 130. Cf. Nos. 1027, 1028.

BIBLIOGRAPHY: Venturi No. 1391. Berthold, cat. No. 323 (reproduced). Basel catalog, No. 183 (reproduced).

COLLECTIONS: Cézanne *fils*, Paris. Paul Guillaume, Paris. W. Feuz, Bern. Kunstmuseum, Basel.

FIG. 167. Jean-François Millet (1814–75): *Faucheur*, black chalk drawing. There is an etching of this subject and a number of very similar drawings, of which one, 28,3 cm. × 10,1 cm., is in the Cabinet des Dessins of the Louvre (RF 5800).

1217. BATHER CROSSING HIS ARMS BEHIND HIS NECK, circa 1900

$8\frac{1}{16} \times 5$ inches—20,4 × 12,6 cm. Leaf (not paginated) removed from the sketchbook BS III in 1923 by Georges Rivière, for a reproduction of the reverse side. Pencil heightened with white, brown stain on the right. Verso: No. 945.

Man walking to the left, his torso turned toward the viewer and his arms crossed behind his head. Touches of white heightening on the calves (lower right) and elbow (upper left). Cf. Nos. 437, 440 (a). This type of bather figures in many of the paintings, with differing degrees of modification.

BIBLIOGRAPHY: Berthold (reproduced Abb. 53). Basel catalog, No. 210 (reproduced).

COLLECTIONS: Cézanne *fils*, Paris. W. Feuz, Bern. Kunstmuseum, Basel.

1218. BATHERS, 1897–1900

$4\frac{7}{8} \times 7\frac{5}{8}$ inches—12,4 × 19,3 cm. Page XI (but erroneously numbered XII, like the following page) from the sketchbook BS III. Pencil, with little touches of violet watercolor. Verso: blank page.

(a) Two bathers facing each other, both with open arms. Together, with the head of a third bather emerging from the water between them, they form a rhythmic composition. Various renderings of the right bather's rear leg. Some of the shadows are heightened with violet watercolor.—(b) Right: sketch of a bather going down into the water.—These same figures appear in the paintings Venturi Nos. 727, 729.

BIBLIOGRAPHY: Venturi No. 1413 (as page XII). Vollard, 1914 ((a) reproduced p. 111). Basel catalog, No. 211 (as page XII), (reproduced). *La Vie*, Nov. 29, 1913 (reproduced as frontispiece). Meier-Graefe, *Cézanne und sein Kreis* ((a) reproduced p. 11). Charles Sterling, *Cézanne et les Maîtres d'autrefois*, *La Renaissance*, May 1936 ((a) reproduced). Rewald, *The Ordeal of Paul Cézanne*, London, 1950 (reproduced p. 73). Idem, Spring Books, London, 1959 and 1965 (reproduced p. 73). Yvon Taillandier, Paul Cézanne, Paris, New York, Munich, 1961 and 1965 (reproduced p. 21). Douglas Cooper, in *Master Drawings*, Vol. 1, No. 4, 1963, p. 56; date suggested: 1897–1900.

COLLECTIONS: Cézanne *fils*, Paris. Paul Guillaume, Paris. W. Feuz, Bern. Kunstmuseum, Basel.

1219. SKETCH OF A BATHER, circa 1900

$8\frac{5}{16} \times 10\frac{11}{16}$ inches—21,1 × 27,2 cm. Page VIII from the sketchbook CP IV. Pencil. Verso: No. 795.

Stretching out his right arm parallel to his thigh, the figure is leaning forward to touch the head of another bather, summarily indicated, half emerging from the water; another bather, with his back turned and also in the water, is seen between the legs of the first bather. There are different versions of the contours, in a search for an accurate rendering. Cf. Nos. 965, 1218, and Venturi Nos. 1215, 1615.

BIBLIOGRAPHY: Venturi, Vol. I, under No. 1315 (not reproduced).

COLLECTIONS: Cézanne *fils*, Paris. Paul Guillaume, Paris. A. Chappuis, Tresserve. Private collection, Paris.

FIG. 168. Desiderio da Settignano (about 1430–64): *Bust of a Child*. Also attributed to Donatello. Our photograph was taken from a plaster cast in the Victoria and Albert Museum, London. The original marble, height 27 cm., formerly in the Dreyfus Collection, is now in the National Gallery of Art, Washington, D.C. (Mellon Collection).

(Photograph: R. W. Ratcliffe)

1220. SKETCHES OF FEMALE NUDES, 1900 or later

$8\frac{1}{4} \times 10\frac{1}{4}$ inches—21 × 26 cm. Page XX from the sketchbook CP IV. Pencil. Verso: No. 1165.

(a) Left: woman bather lying face down, seen in left lost profile. Study for the canvas *Les Grandes Baigneuses*, Venturi No. 719. Cf. No. 461 (b).—(b) Upside down: woman bather walking toward the right background and indications of vegetation; drawing little developed.

BIBLIOGRAPHY: Venturi, Vol. I, under No. 1315 (not reproduced).

COLLECTIONS: Cézanne *fils*, Paris. Paul Guillaume, Paris. A. Chappuis, Tresserve.

1221. AFTER DESIDERIO DA SETTIGNANO: *Bust of a child*, circa 1895

$9\frac{5}{16} \times 6$ inches—23,7 × 15,2 cm. Page XL verso of the Album, Paul Mellon Collection. Pencil. Verso: blank page.

After a plaster cast exhibited in 1894 and the years following in the Musée de Sculpture Comparée of the Trocadéro. Cf. No. 1222. The original marble by Desiderio da Settignano is in the National Gallery of Art, Washington, D.C. See fig. 168.

BIBLIOGRAPHY: Venturi No. 1313; the word "verso" omitted. Berthold, cat. No. 90 (reproduced Abb. 137). *Album*, 1966 (reproduced).

COLLECTIONS: Cézanne *fils*, Paris. Paul Guillaume, Paris. A. Chappuis, Tresserve. Mr. and Mrs. Paul Mellon, Upperville, Va.

1222. AFTER DESIDERIO DA SETTIGNANO: *Bust of a child*, after 1900

$7\frac{15}{16} \times 4\frac{7}{8}$ inches—20,1 × 12,4 cm. Page IV verso from the sketchbook BS II. Pencil. Verso: No. 1137.

A plaster cast of this bust was exhibited in the Musée de Sculpture Comparée of the Trocadéro in 1894 and the years following. See fig. 168. Also after the same bust: No. 1221.

BIBLIOGRAPHY: Venturi No. 1363. Berthold, cat. No. 91 (reproduced). Basel catalog, No. 208 (reproduced).

COLLECTIONS: Cézanne *fils*, Paris. Paul Guillaume, Paris. W. Feuz, Bern. Kunstmuseum, Basel.

1223. ROCOCO CLOCK, after 1900

$8\frac{7}{16} \times 5\frac{3}{16}$ inches—21,4 × 13,1 cm. Page VI verso from the sketchbook BS I. Pencil. Verso: No. 685.

Study after a rococo-style clock. The original model, no doubt in gilded bronze, has not been traced.

BIBLIOGRAPHY: Venturi No. 1330. Berthold, cat. No. 334 (reproduced). Neumeyer, 1958, No. 52 (reproduced); see text of No. 53: "... the artist is applying his search for the underlying geometry of nature to the higher organism of an expressive Baroque style. The synthesis of the two is unique in the nineteenth century." Basel catalog, No. 209 (reproduced). Th. Reff, *AB*, June 1960, note 35, indicates a clock that might be the original model, but the comparison seems to me doubtful. Yvon Taillandier, *Paul Cézanne*, Paris, New York, Munich, 1961 and 1965 (reproduced p. 13).

COLLECTIONS: Cézanne *fils*, Paris. Paul Guillaume, Paris. W. Feuz, Bern. Kunstmuseum, Basel.

ABBREVIATIONS

(See also Selected Bibliography for full citations)

AA	*L'Amour de l'Art*
AB	*The Art Bulletin*
A.I.C.	Art Institute of Chicago
Album 1966	Chappuis, *Album de Paul Cézanne*, Paris, 1966
Andersen, *Sk.*	Wayne V. Andersen, "Cézanne's Sketchbook in the Art Institute of Chicago," *Burlington Magazine*, May 1962
BS	Basel, official seal
Berthold	Gertrude Berthold, *Cézanne und die alten Meister*, Stuttgart, 1958
YurlM	*The Burlington Magazine*
Carnet violet moiré	Facsimile reproduction of this carnet made by Daniel Jacomet, Paris, 1955
Cat. Basel	Chappuis, *Die Zeichnungen von Paul Cézanne*, Kupferstchkabinett der Oeffentlichen Kunstsammlungen Basel, Katalog, 1962
Cézanne dessinateur	Chappuis, "Cézanne dessinateur: copies et illustrations," *GBA*, Nov. 1965.
CP	Chappuis family collection mark
Dessins 1938	Chappuis, *Dessins de Paul Cézanne*, Paris, 1938
Dessins 1957	Chappuis, *Dessins de Cézanne*, Lausanne, 1957
GBA	*Gazette des Beaux-Arts*
Longstreet 1964	Stephen Longstreet, *The Drawings of Cézanne*, Los Angeles, 1964
Neumeyer 1958	Alfred Neumeyer, *Cézanne Drawings*, New York, 1958
Reff, *Bather*	Theodore Reff, "Cézanne's Bather with outstretched arms," *Gazette des Beaux-Arts*, March 1962
Rewald, *Carnets*	John Rewald, *Paul Cézanne, Carnets de Dessins*, Paris, 1951
Schniewind	Carl O. Schniewind, *Paul Cézanne, Sketchbook owned by the Art Institute of Chicago*, New York, 1951
Venturi	Lionello Venturi, *Cézanne, son Art, son Oeuvre*, Paris, 1936
Vollard 1914	Ambroise Vollard, *Paul Cézanne*, Paris 1914/15

SELECTED BIBLIOGRAPHY

Publications of interest to students of Cézanne's drawings

Asterisk indicates that no reference to this work is made in the present catalogue.

ANDERSEN, WAYNE V. "Cézanne's Sketchbook in the Art Institute of Chicago," *Burlington Magazine*, CIV (1962), p. 196.
———. "A Cézanne Copy after Couture," *Master Drawings*, I, No. 4 (1963), p. 44.
———. "A Cézanne Self-Portrait reidentified," *Burlington Magazine*, CVI (1964), p. 284.
———. "Cézanne's Carnet violet-moiré," *Burlington Magazine*, CVII (1965), p. 313.
———. "Cézanne's Portrait Drawings from the 1860's," *Master Drawings*, V, No. 3 (1967), p. 265.
———. "Cézanne, Tanguy, Chocquet," *Art Bulletin*, XLIX (1967), p. 137.
*———. *Cézanne's Portrait Drawings*. Cambridge, Mass., and London, England: M.I.T. Press, 1970.
BADT, KURT. *Die Kunst Cézannes*. Munich: Prestel-Verlag, 1956.
BERNARD, EMILE. "Le Dessin de Cézanne," *L'Amour de l'Art*, January 1924, p. 37.
BERTHOLD, GERTRUDE. *Cézanne und die alten Meister*. Stuttgart: Kohlhammer, 1958.
BOUCHOT-SAUPIQUE, JACQUELINE. "Un Carnet de croquis de Cézanne," *Revue des Arts*, I (1951), p. 243.
CHAPPUIS, ADRIEN. *Dessins de Paul Cézanne*. Paris: Chroniques du Jour, 1938.
———. *Dessins de Cézanne*. Lausanne: Mermod, 1957.
———. *Die Zeichnungen von Paul Cézanne*. Kupferstichkabinett der Oeffentlichen Kunstsammlung Basel, Katalog. Olten and Lausanne: Urs Graf-Verlag, 1962. Also edition in French.
———. "Cézanne Dessinateur: copies et illustrations," *Gazette des Beaux-Arts*, November 1965, p. 293.
———. *Album de Paul Cézanne*. Paris: Berggruen, 1966.
COOPER, DOUGLAS. Review of Basel catalogue, in *Master Drawings*, I, No. 4 (1963), p. 54.
CLARK, KENNETH (Lord Clark). Introduction to catalogue, "An Exhibition of Watercolours," The Arts Council of Great Britain, London, 1946.
DELLIS, MAX. "Notes relatives à quelques dessins de Cézanne," *Gazette des Beaux-Arts*, March 1971, p. 189.
DENIS, MAURICE. "Le Dessin de Cézanne," *L'Amour de l'Art*, February 1924, p. 37.
GASQUET, JOACHIM. *Cézanne*. Paris: Bernheim-Jeune, 1921 and 1926.
HOETINK, H. R. *Franse Tekeningen uit de 19e Eeuw*. Museum Boymans-van Beuningen, Rotterdam, 1968.
IKEGAMI, CHÛJI. "The Drawings of Paul Cézanne" (in Japanese), *Bijutsushi* (Tokyo), No. 76, 1970.
*LEM, F. H. *Paul Cézanne*. Paris: Le Prieuré, 1969.
LONGSTREET, STEPHEN. *Paul Cézanne, Drawings*. Los Angeles: Borden, 1964.
MEIER-GRAEFE, J. *Cézanne und sein Kreis*. Munich: Piper, 1922.
SCHAPIRO, MEYER. "The Apples of Cézanne," *Art News Annual*, XXXIV (1968), p. 35.

NOVOTNY, FRITZ. *Cézanne und das Ende der wissenschaftlichen Perspektive*. Vienna, 1938. Reprinted in: *Ueber das Elementare in der Kunstgeschichte, und andere Aufsätze*. Vienna, 1968.
———. "Cézanne als Zeichner," *Wiener Jahrbuch für Kunstgeschichte*, XIV (1950), p. 250. Reprinted in same place as article cited above.
NEUMEYER, ALFRED. *Cézanne Drawings*. New York: Yoseloff, 1958.
———. Review of Kurt Badt, *The Art of Cézanne*, in *Art Bulletin*, XLIX (1967), p. 271.
*NICODEMI, GIORGIO. *Cézanne, Disegni*. Milan, 1944.
PROVENCE, MARCEL. "Cézanne et ses amis. Numa Coste," *Mercure de France*, III (1926), p. 54.
RACHLÌK, FRANTIŠEK. *Cézanne*. Prague, 1948.
REFF, THEODORE. "Cézanne's Drawings 1875–1885," *Burlington Magazine*, CI (1959), p. 171.
———. Review of Gertrude Berthold, *Cézanne und die alten Meister*, in *Art Bulletin*, XLII (June 1960), p. 145.
———. "Reproductions and Books in Cézanne's Studio," *Gazette des Beaux-Arts*, November 1960, p. 303.
———. "Cézanne's Bather with outstretched arms," *Gazette des Beaux-Arts*, March 1962, p. 173.
———. "Cézanne, Flaubert, St. Anthony, and the Queen of Sheba," *Art Bulletin*, XLIV (June 1962), p. 113.
———. "Cézanne and Hercules," *Art Bulletin*, XLVIII (1966), p. 35.
REWALD, JOHN. "Cézanne au Louvre," *L'Amour de l'Art*, 1935, p. 283.
———. "The Louvre, Cézanne's Book to consult: Models and Sketches," *The Illustrated London News*, May 9, 1956.
———. *Cézanne et Zola*, Paris, 1936. (Thesis).
———. *Cézanne, Correspondance*. Paris: Grasset, 1937.
———. *Cézanne, sa vie, son oeuvre, son amitié pour Zola*. Paris, 1939. (English edition: *Paul Cézanne*, New York, 1948).
———. *Carnets de Dessins, Catalogue raisonné*. Paris: Quatre Chemins-Editart, 1951.
———. *Cézanne, Geffroy et Gasquet, suivi de Souvenirs sur Cézanne de Louis Aurenche*. Paris: Quatre Chemins-Editart, 1959.
———, and Marchutz, Léo. "Cézanne et la Provence," *Le Point* (Colmar), August 1936.
RIVIERE, GEORGES. *Le Maître Paul Cézanne*. Paris: Floury, 1923.
SALMON, ANDRÉ. "Dessins inédits de Cézanne," *Cahiers d'Art*, 1926, p. 263.
SCHNIEWIND, CARL O. *Paul Cézanne, Sketchbook owned by the Art Institute of Chicago*. 2 vols. New York: Curt Valentin, 1951.
TAILLANDIER, YVON. *Paul Cézanne*. Paris, New York and Munich, 1961 and 1965.
VENTURI, LIONELLO. *Cézanne, son Art, son Oeuvre*. 2 vols. Paris: Paul Rosenberg, 1936.
VOLLARD, AMBROISE. *Paul Cézanne*, Paris: Ed. Vollard, 1914.

CONCORDANCES

1. Catalogue numbers in Lionello Venturi, *Cézanne* (Paris, 1936),
and corresponding numbers in the present catalogue

VENTURI	CHAPPUIS	VENTURI	CHAPPUIS	VENTURI	CHAPPUIS
1162	76	1201	318	1240	398, verso 701 bis
1163	103	1202	266	1241	394
1164	95	1203	317	1242	713
1165	101	1204	256	1243	777
1166	106	1205	120	1244	701, verso 887
1167	81	1206	watercolor, not cat.	1245	909
1168	94	1207	258	1246	718
1169	113	1208	250	1247	882
1170	79	1209	234	1248	365
1171	204	1210	253	1249	650
1172	203	1211	259	1250	513
1173	202	1212	252	1251	373
1174	201	1213	260	1252	946
1175	205	1214	448	1253	469
1176	285	1215	watercolor, not cat.	1254	518
1177	86	1216	323	1255	649
1178	275	1217	354	1256	440, verso 306
1179	277	1218	353	1257	441
1180	48	1219	1192	1258	366
1181	279	1220	311	1259	971
1182	323	1221	271	1260	385
1183	283	1222	692	1261	386
1184	135	1223	159	1262	388
1185	206	1224	351	1263	431
1186	235	1225	356	1264	514
1187	watercolor, not cat.	1226	301	1265	352
1188	151	1227	82	1266	116
1189	323, verso 119	1228	319, verso 702	I	533
1190	224	1229	945	I verso	829
1191	132	1230	321	II	639
1192	watercolor, not cat.	1231	378	1267	472
1193	109	1232	239	1268	578
1194	229	1233	watercolor, not cat.	IV verso	540
1195	230	1234	412	1269	606
1196	233	1235	300	1270	497
1197	143	1236	157	VII verso	547
1198	221	1237	611, verso 789	VIII	261
1199	220	1238	403	VIII bis	466
1200	294	1239	396	IX	845

VENTURI	CHAPPUIS	VENTURI	CHAPPUIS	VENTURI	CHAPPUIS
IX verso	1079	XIV	519	1303	1068
XII	verso 885, not cat.	XIV verso	537	VIII	1081
XII verso	885	1287	616	VIII verso	343
XIII verso	832	1288	364	IX	870
XIV	1175	1289	1120	1304	1064
XIV verso	756	XXVIII verso	424	X	1124
1271	604	1290	862	X verso	1152
XV verso	967	XXX	727	XI verso	609
1272	602	XXX verso	534	XII	827
1273	603	XXXI	767	XII verso	538
XVI bis	452	XXXIII	840	XIII	1189
XVII	793	XXXIII verso	776	XIII verso	595
XXVII	465	XXXIV	800	XIV	1016
1274	962	XXXIV verso	662	XIV verso	1015
XXXIII verso	961	XXXV	886	XV	1069
1275	1098	XXXV verso	832	XV verso	953
XLIII	664	XXXVI	831	XVI	954
XLIII verso	873	XXXVI verso	484	XVI verso	859
XLIIII	1010	1291	470	XVII	1073
1276	1062	XXXVII verso	851	1305	867
1277	505	1292	307	1306	864
1278	473	XXXVIII verso	877	XVIII verso	872
1279	590	XXXIX	747	XIX	948
1280	665	XXXIX verso	542	XIX verso	936
L verso	449	1293	614	XXI	1014
LI verso	861	XL verso	411	XXI verso	871
1281	674	XLI	536	XXII	923
LIII	360	XLI verso	720	XXII verso	892
1282	675	1294	654	XXIII	651
unnumbered	433	XLIV	655	XXIII verso	847
verso of the binding	539 A	1295	520	XXIV	1071
III	267	XLV verso	952	XXV	576
III verso	807	XLVI	907	1307	490
IV	838	XLVI verso	1083	1308	596
IV verso	833	1296	308	1309	1024
V	1020	XLVII verso	888	XXVII verso	1143
1283	482	1297	359	XXVIII	658
VII	482 A	1298	358	XXVIII verso	657
VII verso	482 B	XLIX	389	XXIX	659
1284	480	1299	481	XXIX verso	watercolor, not cat.
IX	794	L	348	XXX	1023
IX verso	630	L verso	631	XXX verso	479
X	622	on back of cover	734	XXXI	1082
X verso	732	1300	835	XXXI verso	488
XI	621 A	I verso	1149	XXXI bis	841
XI verso	621	1301	1131	XXXI bis verso	530
1285	309	III	866	XXXII	865
XII verso	541	1302	768	XXXII verso	1146
1286	310	V	808	XXXIII	875
XIII bis	535	VI	1177	XXXIII verso	891
XIII bis verso	523	VI verso	1141	XXXIV verso	640

VENTURI	CHAPPUIS	VENTURI	CHAPPUIS	VENTURI	CHAPPUIS
1310	1130	on back of cover	1101	1373	1046
1311	503	1323	601	1374	1059
1312	1121	1324	1005	1375	1004
1313	1221	1325	529	1376	673
XLIX	889	1326	1118	1377	1138
XLIX verso	599	1327	559	1378	1009
1314	598	1328	1137	1379	588
LI verso	666	1329	685	1380	1027
LII	546	1330	1223	1381	687
1315	635	1331	1119	1382	1204
LIII	unnumbered	1332	942	1383	993
LIII verso	890	1333	671	1384	1128
LIV verso	684	1334	501	1385	958
VII	795	1335	1206	1386	1052
VIII	1219	1336	1199	1387	1012
IX	1161	1337	1115	1388	1013
X	1214	1338	681	1389	605
XI	1184	1339	1106	1390	1195
XIX	1165	1340	1056	1391	1216
XX	1220	1341	943	1392	1140
XXV	watercolor, not cat.	1342	682	1393	1011
1316	1044	1343	1205	1394	1207
XXVII	watercolor, not cat.	1344	1018	1395	1117
XXVIII	1078	1345	1201	1396	584
XXXIII	1147	1346	560	1397	667
XXXIV	1187	1347	1202	1398	345
XLI	1102	1348	504	1399	552
XLII	1193	1349	1039	1400	1104
XLIII	watercolor, not cat.	1350	1034	1401	454
XLIV	691	1351	1113	1402	527
XLV	778	1352	1114	1403	413
XLVI	watercolor, not cat.	1353	1054	1404	964
LI	1164	1354	680	1405	1150
LII	watercolor, not cat.	1355	1212	1406	1103
LIX	1169	1356	1049	1407	467
LX	690	1357	922	1408	970
LXIII	watercolor, not cat.	1358	506	1409	1021
1317	1087	1359	1003	1410	watercolor, not cat.
LXV	959	1360	1002	1411	1066
LXVI	928 A	1361	1055	1412	526
LXIX	1036	1362	1136	1413	1218
1318	1196	1363	1222	1414	1135
LXXV	1166	1364	1105	1415	678
1319	589	1365	1033	1416	1142
1320	1036	1366	1215	1417	371
LXXVII	1090	1367	1099	1418	1148
1321	975	1368	554	1419	553
1322	1198	1369	1026	1420	429
LXXXIII	1075	1370	498	1421	926
LXXXIII verso	1154	1371	652	1422	928
LXXXIV	watercolor, not cat.	1372	555	1423	watercolor, not cat.

VENTURI	CHAPPUIS	VENTURI	CHAPPUIS	VENTURI	CHAPPUIS
1424	watercolor, not cat.	1463	985	1502	897
1425	1060	1464	981	1503	1157
1426	watercolor, not cat.	1465	982	1504	898
1427	1144	1466	729	1505	902
1428	475	1467	1065	1506	899
1429	925	1468	853	1507	880
1430	974	1469	850	1508	124
1431	1200	1470	849	1570	122
1432	894	1471	710	1571	931
1433	428	1472	697 verso 697 A	1572	820
1434	963	1473	938	1573	940
1435	965	1474	405 verso 821	1574	211, verso 188
1436	629	1475	715 recto 731	1575	128, verso 187
1437	1000	1476	1125	1576	177
1438	999	1477	728	1577	240, verso 191
1439	688	1478	610 verso 350	1578	168, verso 248
1440	493	1479	363	1579	212, verso 232
1441	950	1480	1194	1580	184, verso 170
1442	487	1481	717	1581	165, verso 241
1443	679	1482	1095	1582	249
1444	1025	1483	1094	1583	477, verso 757
1445	499	1484	not catalogued	1584	104, verso 227
1446	976	1485	1085	1585	186
1447	502	1486	941	1586	980
1448	207	1487	935	1587	1061, verso 1153
1449	457	1488	937	1588	787
1450	85	1489	969	1589	105, verso 112
1451	305	1490	517	1590	823, verso 798
1452	1111	1491	632	1622	939
1453	1086	1492	646	1623	619
and study mentioned	1089	1493	957	1624	272
1454	973	1494	watercolor, not cat.	1625	455
1455	489	1495	916	1626	1109
1456	1129	1496	878	1627	78
1457	990	1497	919	1631	815
1458	983	1498	1178	1632	1180
1459	987	1499	1181		
1460	989	1500	918, verso 1160, pages separated		
1461	986				
1462	988	1501	watercolor, not cat.		

2. Numbers in Gertrude Berthold, *Cézanne und die alten Meister* (Stuttgart, 1958), and corresponding numbers in the present catalogue

BERTHOLD	CHAPPUIS	BERTHOLD	CHAPPUIS	BERTHOLD	CHAPPUIS
1	1053	4	1051	7	586
2	1055	5	1056	8	587
3	1052	6	588	9	1054

BERTHOLD	CHAPPUIS	BERTHOLD	CHAPPUIS	BERTHOLD	CHAPPUIS
10	307	61	375	111	577
11	635	62	1208	112	1005
12	308	63	473	113	1057
13	310	64	678	114	1003
14	637	65	not catalogued	115	1004
15	636	66	980	116	1001
16	634	67	566	117	1006
17	306	68	570	118	576
18	309	69	569	119	578
19	1097	70	567	120	1060
20	1096	71	858	121	1196
21	1098	72	1087	122	1059
22	1099	73	1089	123	1002
23	1100	74	1086	124	1208A
24	1041	75	568	125	83
25	1043	76	565	126	499
26	1042	77	1088	127	1132
27	604	78	573	128	689
28	602	79	572	129	391
29	603	80	574	130	689A
30	599	81	232	131	986
31	993	82	418	132	not catalogued
32	1050	82	verso 372	133	990
33	687	83	558	134	988
34	688	84	559	135	981
35	562	85	556	136	982
36	561	86	557	137	984
37	1049	87	555	138	983
38	683	88	601	139	987
39	1029	89	680	140	989
40	685	90	1221	141	980 bis
41	1108	91	1222	142	985
42	1129	92	1126	143	682
43	584	93	671	144	1112
44	1115	94	560	145	1113
45	1048	95	1105	146	672
46	607	96	502	147	950
47	563	97	505	148	493
48	1121	98	976	149	592
49	487	99	207	150	591
50	1136	100	504	151	1107
51	1137	101	503	152	1198
52	1203	102	506	153	1199
53	1062	103	1201	154	974
54	1063	104	977	155	975
55	1204	105	1200	156	973
56	watercolor, not cat.	106	1131	157	305
57	1205	107	978	158	1047
58	679	108	1000	159	501
59	590	109	1058	160	1046
60	589	110	999	161	1044

BERTHOLD	CHAPPUIS	BERTHOLD	CHAPPUIS	BERTHOLD	CHAPPUIS
162	1045	213	489 bis	264	480
163	363	214	455	265	85
164	not catalogued	215	457	266	272
165	605	216	1128	267	1032
166	1110	217	369	268	170
167	1111	218	1130	269	168
168	1109	219	594	270	468
169	681	220	593	271	640
170	482	221	595	272	232
171	1210	222	596	273	524
172	497	223	597	274	606
173	498	224	1209	275	405
174	471	225	312A	276	351
175	472	226	677	277	469
176	470	227	1025	278	474
177	1035	228	311	279	997
178	1033	229	1024	280	996
179	1034	230	1114	281	998
180	1030	231	1113	282	not catalogued
181	1026	232	1011	283	1191A
182	1195	233	1012	284	165
183	1027	234	958	285	214
184	1028	235	991	286	232
185	1212	236	676	287	74
186	1036	237	50	288	240
187	1040	238	619	289	821
188	1207	239	156	290	500
189	669	240	494	291	142
190	668	241	195	292	392
191	1117	242	141	293	1039
192	1119	243	186	294	1037
193	1118	244	325	295	1017
194	1116	245	326	296	1127
195	670	246	1213	297	1019
196	1120	247	184	298	313
197	1206	248	183	299	58
198	1202	249	675	300	484
199	1038	250	488	301	483
200	1031	251	182	302	262
201	1018	252	171	303	370
202	600	253	994	304	995
203	1106	254	172	305	626
204	489	255	358	306	206
205	598	256	359	307	652
206	490	257	351	308	330
207	627	258	354	309	169
208	1007	259	not catalogued	310	241
209	1139	260	356	311	726
210	1215	261	87	312	10
211	1138	262	481	313	2
212	1140	263	715	314	32

BERTHOLD	CHAPPUIS	BERTHOLD	CHAPPUIS	BERTHOLD	CHAPPUIS
315	64	327	579	337 verso	721
316	55	328	821	338	89A
317	126	329	581	339	89
318	625	330	583	340	194 bis
319	832	331	1123	340 recto	224 bis
320	664	332	1123	341	459
321	639	333	550	342	not identified
322	620	334	1223	343 verso	543
323	1216	335	538	344	not identified
324	943	336	731	345	304
325	457	336 verso	715	346	not identified
326	580	337	458		(perhaps No. 1211)

3. Catalogue numbers in Adrien Chappuis, *Die Zeichnungen von Paul Cézanne*,
catalogue of the Kupferstichkabinett, Oeffentlichen Kunst sammlung Basel, 1962, and
corresponding numbers in the present catalogue

BASEL	CHAPPUIS	BASEL	CHAPPUIS	BASEL	CHAPPUIS
1	3	32	195	63	211
2	41	33	191	64	316
3	179	34	165	65	315
4	162	35	178	66	350
5	153	36	177	67	320
6	199	37	176	68	328
7	91	38	175	69	291
8	154	39	174	70	284
9	160	40	236	71	285
10	92	41	188	72	286
11	161	42	198	73	283
12	139	43	444	74	269
13	156	44	197	75	187
14	137	45	254	76	268
15	135	46	190	77	129
16	136	47	118	78	128
17	138	48	247	79	258
18	104	49	228	80	264
19	105	50	229	81	293
20	245	51	227	82	376
21	171	52	232	83	361
22	184	53	223	84	119
23	173	54	222	85	741
24	212	55	248	86	798?
25	240	56	249	87	787
26	165	57	362	88	755
27	170	58	255	89	392
28	168	59	256	90	726
29	169	60	447	91	852
30	142	61	393	92	725
31	186	62	323	93	610

BASEL	CHAPPUIS	BASEL	CHAPPUIS	BASEL	CHAPPUIS
94	518	134	529	174	1135
95	477	135	251	175	1150
96	699	136	945	176	463
97	431	137	1008	177	462
98	373	138	1009	178	970
99	820	139	946	179	1103
100	735	140	965	180	1137
101	823	141	467	181	1136
102	773	142	652	182	1027
103	345	143	681	183	1216
104	553	144	687	184	1105
105	552	145	686	185	1033
106	554	146	993	186	1018
107	584	147	1005	187	1117
108	605	148	1004	188	1118
109	667	149	1003	189	1119
110	105	150	1002	190	1039
111	428	151	1060	191	1202
112	429	152	1059	192	1106
113	555	153	980	193	1207
114	560	154	940	194	1206
115	559	155	680	195	506
116	498	156	1061	196	1200
117	222	157	1115	197	1201
118	928	158	1049	198	1113
119	894	159	588	199	1114
120	475	160	1054	200	1138
121	671	161	1052	201	1140
122	685	162	1055	202	1128
123	958	163	1056	203	1195
124	937	164	1199	204	1204
125	673	165	handwriting, not cat.	205	1205
126	1099	166	handwriting, not cat.	206	1212
127	1011	167	handwriting, not cat.	207	1215
128	1012	168	1148	208	1222
129	1013	169	1144	209	1223
130	963	170	1021	210	1217
131	964	171	926	211	1218
132	watercolor, not cat.	172	watercolor, not cat.		
133	629	173	1153		

INDEX OF SUBJECTS

after *L'Ecorché* attributed to Michelangelo: 185, 418, 565–574, 980, 1086–1089

after Spanish paintings and engravings: 169(c), 173, 244, 351, 405, 524, 606, 726, 731, 789

after Rubens: 102, 311, 369, 455–457, 489–490, 593–598, 627, 677, 721, 832, 1007, 1024, 1025, 1114, 1128, 1130, 1138–1140, 1209, 1211

after Greco-roman sculpture: 34, 58, 73, 74, 304, 306–310, 330, 500, 561–563, 584, 586–588, 599, 602–604, 607, 634–637, 683, 685–688, 993, 1019, 1029, 1041–1043, 1048–1056, 1062, 1063, 1096–1100, 1108, 1115, 1121, 1129, 1131, 1136, 1137, 1203–1205

after paintings, drawings and engravings of various schools: 1–5, 10, 28–31, 36, 52, 59, 63, 65, 130, 140, 148, 191–194, 206, 211, 237, 313, 360, 392, 469, 628, 942, 972, 1017